Guide to FREE CAMPSITES 2026

Thirteenth Edition

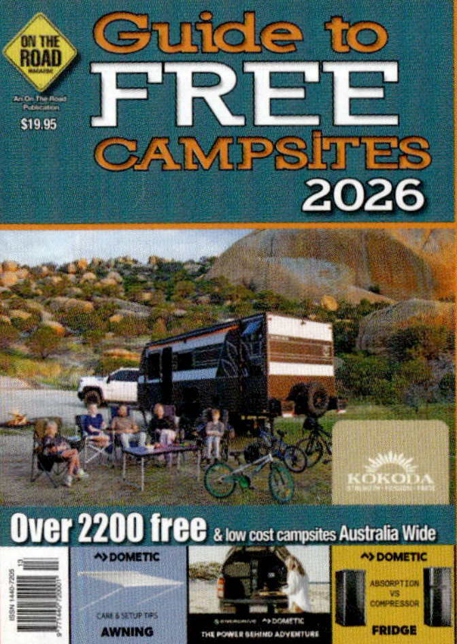

Front Cover:
Stunning overnight stop in the Pyramid Hills region, central northern Victoria.
Photo : Anthony Kilner

Contents

An On The Road Publication

Campsite Listings

Other Features

Good Gear Tips & Advice

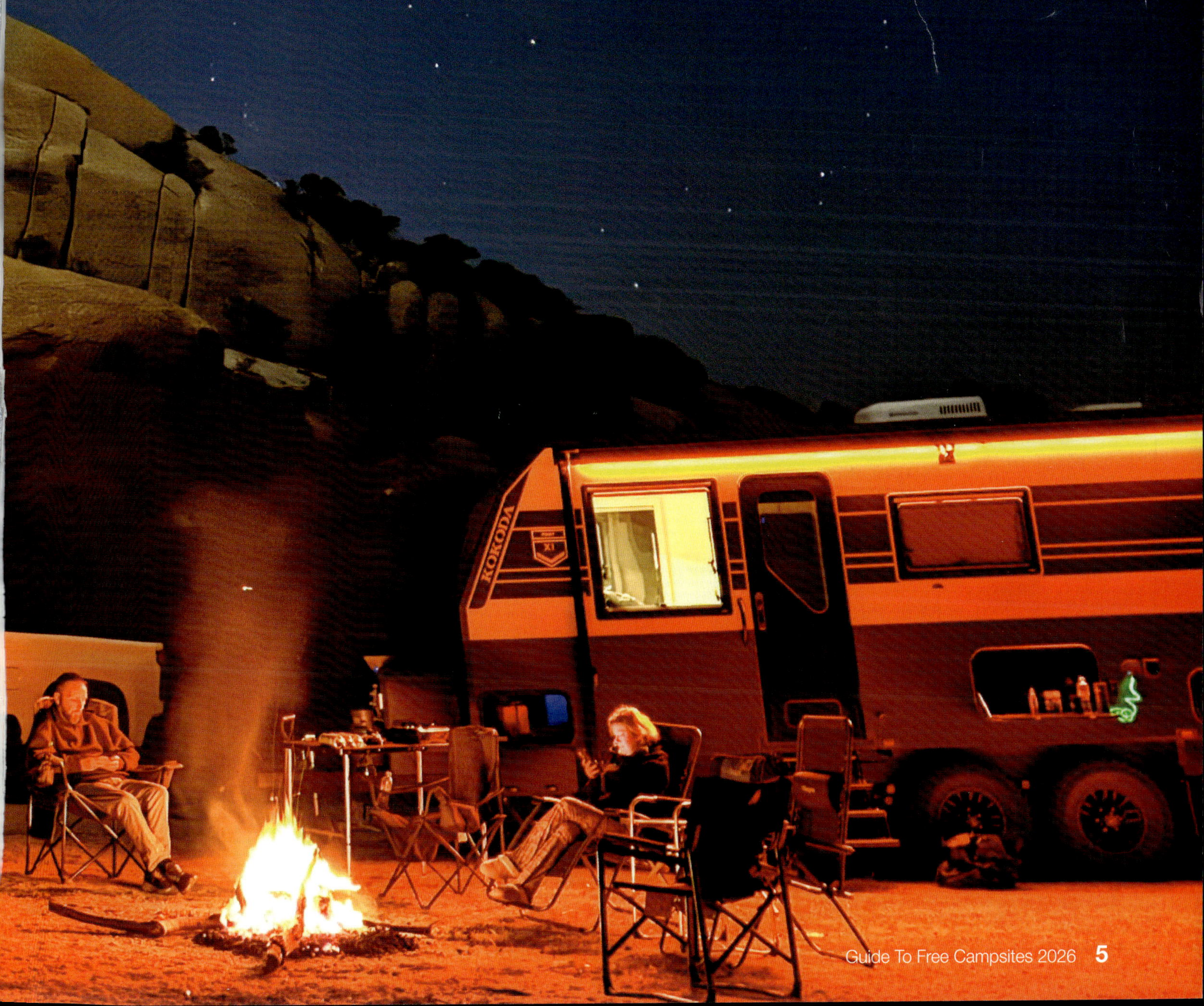

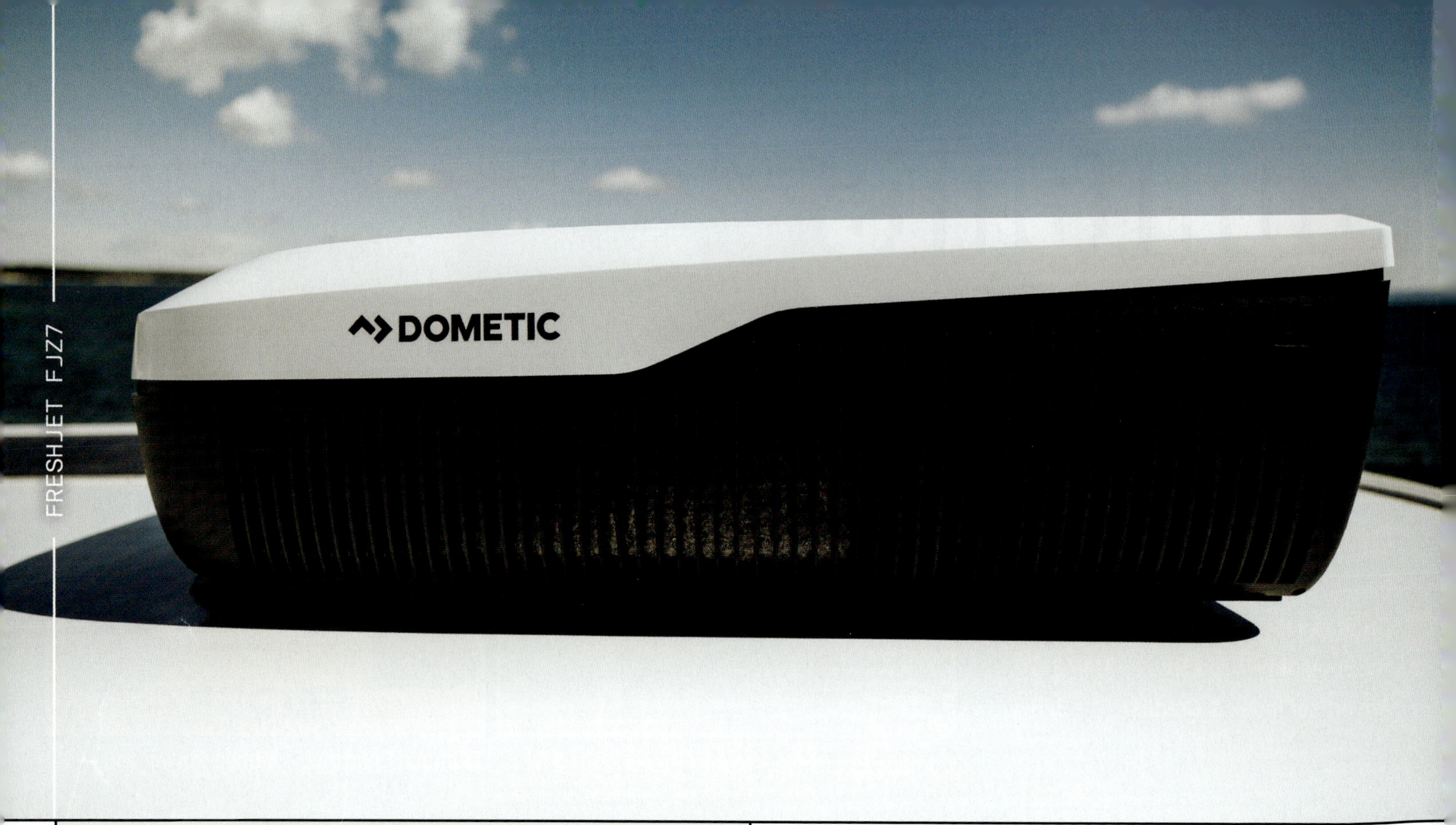

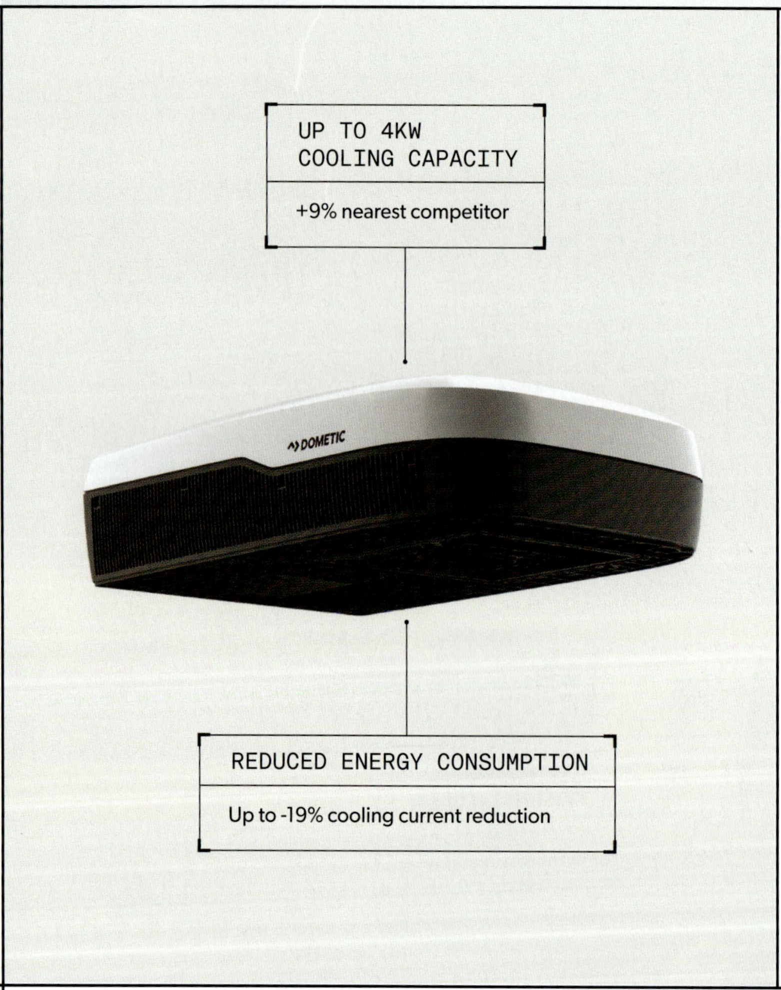

NEW BOX AWNING HAS ARRIVED.

DOMETIC BAW3000

Box awning

Upgrade your RV experience with the Dometic BAW3000 — a premium box awning built for long-term reliability, effortless single-person operation, and seamless compatibility with your existing setup. Featuring European components and UV-protected fabric, it's the perfect fit for Australian adventurers.

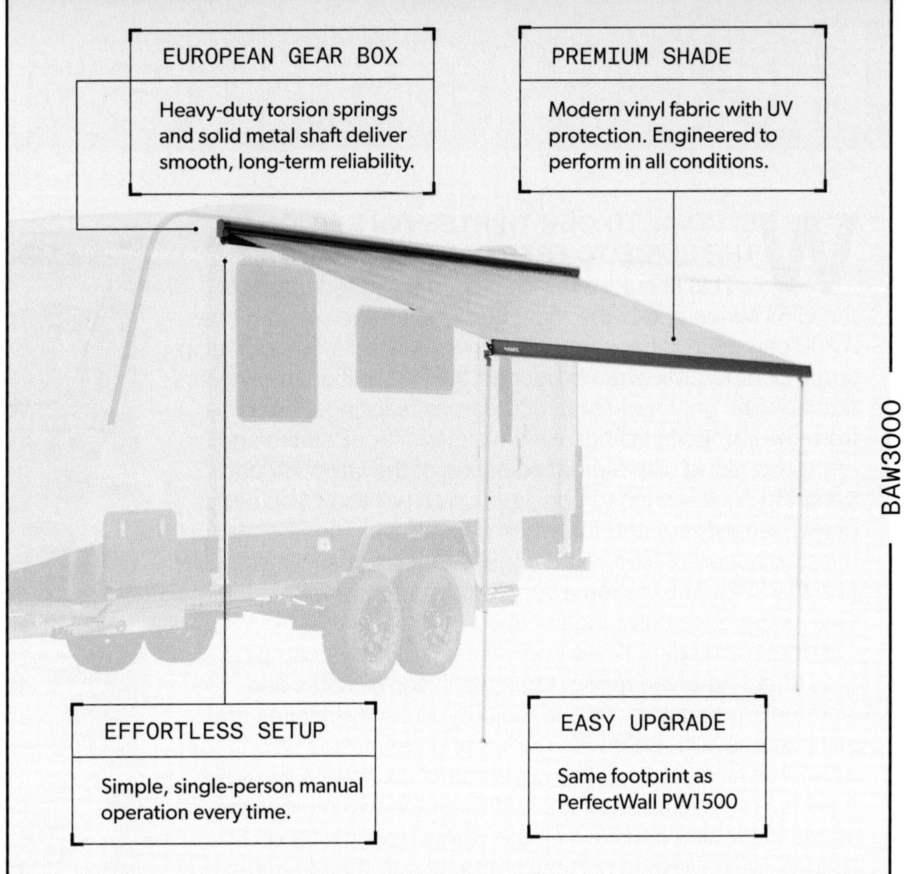

DOUBLE HINGE REFRIGERATOR

DOMETIC RUA / RUC

Absorption / Compressor refrigerator

Available in both absorption and compressor variations, the Dometic RUA and RUC refrigerators provide the reliable refrigeration performance that the RV market has come to expect from Dometic refrigerators. The T-rated cooling systems ensure excellent performance in both high and low ambient temperatures, making these refrigerators an excellent choice for all conditions. The built-in control panel is intuitive and easy to use, allowing users to select a temperature range and a variety of preset modes. Each model features double hinge opening giving you the convenience to open from either left or right at any time.

Free Campsites Intro

WELCOME TO OUR THIRTEENTH EDITION OF THE GUIDE TO FREE CAMPSITES 2026

This is our thirteenth edition as stated above of the GFC series and is the most comprehensive yet with over 2,200 campsite listings from all across Australia, to put that in some perspective when produced the first edition many years ago now we only had some 800 campsite listings. Apart from the campsite listings we have maps for all states and territories along with a great selection of the latest RV and camping accessories to consider which will allow you even greater enjoyment and fun when going bush. Together with a top selection of featured campsite reports I believe you will find the 2026 publication a very handy guide when planning your going bush camping escape.

In these changing times some listings do have camping fees attached given recent changes in some states and National Parks but by far the majority of our campsites are still free and you are free to camp for an enjoyable stay in the great Aussie outdoors. The coverage of campsites by states has also been expanded and although the two big eastern states in Victoria and New South Wales have plenty of listings, we have paid particular attention to the other states and looked hard for more free camping options. Camping sites do change due to various factors (bush fires, flood damage, environmental reasons etc) and at the discretion of the relevant authority. All efforts have been made to ensure that at the time of going to press all listings are up to-date and accurate. Each state now also has its own dedicated campsite index at the end of each of the state listings and just before the state maps.

The maps are another area we have looked to further improve with new and better maps covering all states and territories. Also, the total number of maps has increased to 16 giving far better coverage of campsite locations. We still include GPS details to further assist you when looking for that free campsite escape.

As well as the campsite listings totalling over 2,200 across Australia, we have also provided detailed info via our featured campsite reports on a wide selection of campsites. These are some of the best and most attractive sites open to travellers and give you a snapshot of what they have to offer as well as more details re facilities and activities at each site.

We trust you find this our latest edition **Guide to Free Campsites** a handy reference source and that it helps you get to spend many days away camping and enjoying the great Australian bush experience.

We have used the following icons on the campsite listings :

Toilets : This icon is self-explanatory and in nearly all cases these are drop toilets.

Water : This icon represents the availability of water at the campsite in normal conditions (not drought conditions). We recommend you still carry emergency water and boil any water that is to be consumed.

Fireplace : This icon indicates the availability of designated fireplaces or that a camp fire can be used - again subject to fire restrictions.

4WD : Indicates that this particular site should be accessed by a 4WD vehicle given the likely conditions of the roads.

$: These sites require payment of a fee, generally under $20 per night, however the amount can vary according to the relevant authority's charging policies.

Camper Trailer : Indicates that this particular campsite has sufficient space for camper trailers and that the access to the campground is appropriate.

Caravan : Indicates that this particular campsite has sufficient space and road access for caravans and motorhomes and that the access to the campground is appropriate.

Dog : Indicates that this particular campsite allows pets with a reminder to consider other campers and also the local wildlife. If in doubt keep dogs on leads.

Fish : Indicates that this camp area has either fresh or saltwater fishing options available, it does not guarantee that you will catch fish......

MAPS

At the end of each state section, we have included reference maps with the campsites number located on the map in its approximate position. The campsite number then links back to the appropriate state listing for further details and information.

These maps are designed as a planning tool as some of the campsite names and regions may be unfamiliar to many people. Utilisation of GPS and good quality maps such as Hema are highly recommended..

HOW TO USE THIS GUIDE

Each Australian state has its own section within the magazine listing free and low-cost sites. These site listings provide the following information:

First Line – Campsite Number, Campsite Name, Region within the state where located. If the Campsite name and number is printed in RED then that indicates that a featured campsite report is offered either on the opposite page or the preceding page.

Second Line - Map Reference and GPS co-ordinates.

Third-Fourth line - Basic directions to the campsite. Plus, the phone number or email if available.

Then **BELOW** the listing info on each campsite is a series of icons depicting what facilities or features are available at the listed site.

The phone number typically would be one of the following, either the local shire, Tourism, Forestry or National Park office, and should be utilised as to checking the status of the site or sites you are interested in and the access available to said site.

Given that most campsites are reached by non-sealed roads local weather conditions are a real determining factor in successful entry and exit from the various sites. Hence, we strongly recommend you check with the local authority prior to arrival.

The GPS co-ordinates in most cases reference the site or camp entrance, however given many camping sites cover a significant length or area the GPS location is an aid to locating the general campsite area.

FEATURED CAMPSITES

A large selection of featured campsite reports are included for each state in the Guide. These reports are located throughout the listings. The campsite number on the featured sites refers back to the listings and also the map. The campsite reports are compiled by our team of contributors and give a great first-hand account of the site that we believe you will find valuable.

Our aim with the featured campsite reports is to give you a far more comprehensive understanding of the campsite itself and the region that it's located within. In particular to the attractions it has to offer and activities that one may partake in.

GOOD GEAR, TIPS ADVICE AND INFO AND RV SPOTLIGHT

Within this section we highlight some of the latest camping accessories to help make your travel experience that much more enjoyable. Together with an RV Spotlight on the latest Vista Crossover XLE camper trailer.

CAMPSITE INDEX

The campsite index is another quick reference guide and located at the completion of the state listings before the maps. The page number refers to the listing page that has that particular campsite's details.

CORRECTIONS & UPDATES

Given that it is our intention to make this Guide an on-going annual publication we would welcome any observations, corrections or updates on the listed campsites, please email the details to editor@ontheroad.com.au. As stated earlier this edition has a number of low-cost campsites listed, some previously free sites in Victoria now have charges attached, most of which are paid prior to arrival (online) with the relevant authorities. These changes in Victoria are on-going and our recommendation is that it is best to check the relevant websites for the latest information or status changes.

This guide was compiled in October/November'2025 and whilst all care and diligence was taken some inaccuracies may have occurred for which we apologise. Equally some sites may have closed or their facilities altered. Checking with the listed contact number prior to travel is as stated earlier highly recommended.

AUSTRALIAN MADE

FOR COLD BEER.

AND MORE GEAR.

WE DO THE THINKING FOR YOU

All-in-one solution that takes the guesswork out of 12V power. No complex decisions, no complicated setup, just a simple, ready-to-go solution that lets you spend less time planning and more time exploring.

FAST AND EASY INSTALL

Plug'n'play, pre-wired and simple to mount. Installs in half the time of individual components and get powered up faster with a true set-and-forget solution.

SPACE SAVING FOOTPRINT

A complete off-grid power solution without the clutter. Compact by design, with no wasted space, Redworks leaves you with more space to pack the essentials.

AUSTRALIAN MADE

Each tough, powder-coated panel is designed, built and tested in Australia and backed by market leading technical support and Australia wide after sales service.

REDARCELECTRONICS.COM/REDWORKS

Victoria

Free Camps Guide – Useful Resources & Contacts – VIC

Parks Victoria
Ph: 131 963 (8am -6pm weekdays and 9am-6pm weekends)
Web: www.parkweb.vic.gov.au

Department of Sustainability & Environment Customer Service Centre
Ph: 136 186
Web: www.dse.vic.gov.au

Fisheries: Department of Primary Industries – Fisheries & Aquaculture
Ph: 136 186
Web: www.dpi.gov.au

Country Fire Authority Headquarters – Burwood
Ph: 03 9262 8444
Bushfire Information Hotline
Phn: 1800 240 667
Web: www.cfa.vic.gov.au

RACV
Roadside Assistance
Ph: 131 111
Memberships Phn: 137 228
Web: www.racv.com.au

Vic Roads
Traffic Management Centre/Road Conditions
Ph: 03 9854 2666
Web: www.vicroads.vic.gov.au

Weather Information
Bureau of Meteorology
Ph: 1900 926 102
Web: www.bom.gov.au

Victorian Tourism Information Service
Ph: 132 842
Web: www.visitvictoria.com

Free Campsites in Victoria

1. The Kurrajongs Camping - High Country
Map Ref: MAP 1 C3   GPS: 35 57 22 S   147 25 11 E
Located in Mount Lawson SP 40kms W of Walwa or 16kms NE of Bungil Junction via Murray Rd. Small vehicles only. Ph: 13 19 63

2. Kurrajongs Camping Area - High Country
Map Ref: MAP 1 C3   GPS: 35 57 35 S   147 25 20 E
Within the Mt Lawson State Park opposite Lake Hume. Access along Murray River Rd then Talgarno Rd. Ph: 13 19 63

3. Burrowye Reserve - High Country
Map Ref: MAP 1 C3   GPS: 35 59 15 S   147 31 37 E
Camp Area beside Murray River 25km W of Walwa off Murray River Rd. Ph: 13 19 63

4. Gadds Bend
Map Ref: MAP 1 C3   GPS: 35 56 45 S   147 40 24 E
Located in Murray River Reserve 8.5km E of Walwa via Murray River Rd.

5. Jingellic Reserve
Map Ref: MAP 1 D3   GPS: 35 55 47 S   147 42 33 E
Small bush campsite on banks of Murray River along the Murray River Rd, 700m E of Jingellic Rd. Ph: 13 19 63

6. Neils Reserve - High Country
Map Ref: MAP 1 D3   GPS: 35 58 25 S   147 48 39 E
Beside the Murray River 7km E of Walwa along the Murray River Rd. Dry weather only Ph: 13 19 63

7. Clarke Lagoon Reserve - High Country
Map Ref: MAP 1 D3   GPS: 36 01 27 S   147 54 36 E
Within the Murray River Reserve 6km N of Tintaldra off Murray River Rd. Camping beside the Murray River. Dry weather only Ph: 13 19 63

8. Cottontree Camping Area
Map Ref: MAP 1 B4   GPS: 36 06 53 S   147 18 18 E
From the Village of Granya take the signposted Webb Lane to the signposted access to the camping area. Ph: 13 19 63

9. Koetong Creek Camping Area - Murray
Map Ref: MAP 1 C4   GPS: 36 06 10 S   147 27 05 E
Located in the Mt Lawson State Park near Koetong Creek. From the Murray Valley Hwy take the signposted Firebrace Track then the Mt Lawson Road. Dry weather only Ph: 13 19 63

10. Hinces Creek Camping Area - High Country
Map Ref: MAP 1 D4   GPS: 36 05 15 S   147 46 08 E
Located on Hinces Creek Track which is signposted off Cudgewa North Road. Ph: 13 19 63

11. Blue Gum Camping Area - High Country
Map Ref: MAP 1 D4   GPS: 36 07 50 S   147 46 19 E
Located in Burrowa-Pine Mountain NP. Off Bluff Falls Rd past Bluff Creek. Ph: 13 19 63

12. Bluff Creek Camping Area - High Country
Map Ref: MAP 1 D4   GPS: 36 07 21 S   147 46 40 E
Situated within the Burrowa-Pine NP. Take the Cudgewa North Rd to the signposted Bluff Falls Rd. Ph: 13 19 63

13. Lighthouse Crossing Reserve
Map Ref: MAP 1 D4   GPS: 36 05 40 S   147 59 18 E
Camp spot 6km N of Towong on Murray River Rd.

14. Towong Reserve Camping Area - High Country
Map Ref: MAP 1 D4   GPS: 36 07 40 S   147 59 39 E
Towong Reserve is 13kms NE of Corryong on Towong Hill Rd. Ph: 13 19 63

15. Corryong Recreations Reserve
Map Ref: MAP 1 D4   GPS: 36 11 34 S   147 54 06 E
Camping area on Showgrounds Rd Corryong via Strzelecki Way. Must be self contained. Limited stay. Ph: 02 6076 2277

16. Indi Bridge Reserve - High Country
Map Ref: MAP 1 D4   GPS: 36 14 10 S   148 02 00 E
On the Murray River SE of Corryong via Upper Murray Rd off Corryong-Khancoban Rd. Ph: 02 6076 2277

Towong Reserve Camping Area No 14

Towong, Vic

12km north-east of Corryong

Stephanie Jackson

Camping on the grass next to the Murray River.

At the settlement of Towong, 12kms north-east of the Victorian town of Corryong, there's little more than a few scattered houses and farms, but the area has one ancient claim to fame. It's here that the mighty Murray River has been cutting a swathe across the landscape since the distant days of the dreamtime, and with a camping reserve on the banks of this iconic waterway, travellers can set up home in this picturesque location for up to four weeks without parting with a single cent for the privilege.

The Towong Reserve is accessible to every vehicle and rig, however colossal it might be, and with a large flat expanse of grass on the riverbank, campers don't need to be stepping on each others' toes. There are open areas that offer the welcome sunshine of a winter's day, and plenty of shade in summer, thanks to the avenue of large deciduous trees that line the track that slices through the reserve.

It was the heart of winter when we arrived at the reserve, and as the river's dark and icy waters rushed past on their long journey to the sea, the thought of swimming was as appealing as emulating a lemming and leaping off a cliff. At other times of the year, it's a pleasant spot for aquatic activities, including fishing for the trout that thrive in this section of Australia's longest river.

A subtle breeze tossed ragged strands of clouds across the azure sky, but as the sun slithered down beyond the horizon, Nature threw one of her tantrums, and as a gale battered the landscape, we lashed our tent down firmly in anticipation of worse to come, and retreated into our campervan.

As the wind intensified, there was one excursion into the wild night that was unavoidable, and guided by the beam from my headlight, with its batteries failing, I made my way cautiously to the pit toilet that is the only facility provided at the camping area. One false step along the riverbank and it would be goodbye for eternity, for if I didn't drown in the swirling water, hypothermia would certainly get me. I eventually stumbled across the gravel track that slices through the reserve, and discovered the loo, a curious structure with thick steel walls and a heavy steel door that opened with a gigantic sliding bolt before clanging shut behind me like the portal of a grim prison cell.

Although the reserve is adjacent to a bitumen road, it's never a route that's congested with traffic, and with few vehicles passing by during the night, it was only the grumbling of the wind and the repetitive calls of a boobook owl, resting in the willow trees that grasp the riverbank with contorted roots, which momentarily kept sleep at bay.

The screeching chorus of corellas heralded the arrival of dawn, and with the wind have died to a whisper, I lit a small fire to chase away the icy fingers of winter. A solitary wood duck, swept along by the river's raging current, passed by at breakneck speed, then fluttered into the sky before settling on a sunlit fragment of the grassy bank. I'd had enough of the fast pace of life too, and the Towong Reserve proved to be the perfect place to escape from the mayhem of an urban existence.

The Murray River.

Just The Facts

Towong Reserve Camping Area

Getting there: The Towong Reserve is 13kms north-east of the Victorian town of Corryong on Towong Hill Road. The camping area is accessible to all vehicles and rigs.

Facilities: There are no facilities here other than a pit toilet.

Pets: Pets are permitted.

Charges: There is no charge for camping here for a maximum of four weeks.

Contact: For additional information, contact the Corryong Visitor Information Centre by phoning 02 6076 2277.

Indi Bridge Campsite

No 16

Towong, Vic

13km north of Corryong, Vic

John Mainwaring

About 13 kms past Corryong in Victoria's north east you come to a little place called Towong. And just past that you come to the upper reaches of the Murray River where it is a clear and vibrant mountain river. The old bridge over the river at this point leads to a nice little camping area set aside by the Tumbarumba Shire Council for travellers to enjoy. Since it is essentially a large roadside pull-over on a quiet country road, this is suitable for any rig including heavies such as large motor homes. It is 2WD accessible with positions directly overlooking the fast flowing Murray.

There are a few points of interest around this area. Corryong is where Tom Riley, the Man From Snowy River was laid to rest. Towong has a historic racecourse that was the scene of an interesting robbery many years ago. Another claim to fame, its historic buildings made it perfect for use in the movie Pharlap. Just up the road is Khancoban and just beyond that you can visit a couple of the power stations that make up part of the Snowy Hydro and learn about one of the mega projects that helped build a modern Australia. There are a number of loop trips in the local area which you can explore and check out the local Murray Valley farming scenes or some nearby walks.

Also of interest is the bridge. At 61 metres in length and built in 1938, it is starting to look a little shabby but as you will find when you camp at this spot, this is a quiet road so the dollars for new bridges would go elsewhere. This one is hanging in there and adds to the rustic feel of the whole area.

A couple of features of the camp area are also worth a mention. There are enormous 100 year old elm trees lining the roadside and providing shade across the camp area. The local shire is happy for travellers to park up for several weeks, so you are welcome to sit back and enjoy the locality. A toilet is provided at the site. You can have your dogs with you and if fishing is your thing, you can hurl in a line from your campsite. Supplies are available in the local towns, most conveniently over the border in Victoria with Corryong being the local big smoke. You will need to bring your own firewood unless you are happy with a few elm twigs.

As the name suggests the campsite sits by the old bridge crossing the upper reaches of the Murray.

Always beware of council restrictions here they allow you to stay 4 weeks.

Over the farm fields you have views of the snow capped Australian Alps.

Just The Facts

Indi Bridge Camping Area

Location: On the Murray River south-east of Corryong via Upper Murray Rd off Coorying-Khancoban Rd
Facilities: Toilets, fireplace
Charges: Free
Contact: (02) 6076 2277

Free Campsites in Victoria

17. Pigs Point Reserve Camping Area - High Country
Map Ref: MAP 1 B4 GPS: 36 16 49 S 147 14 15 E
On the Mitta Mitta river 9km S of Tallangatta. Ph: 13 19 63

18. Katie Peters Reserve
Map Ref: MAP 1 B5 GPS: 36 27 22 S 147 18 54 E
Located 8km E of Eskdale via Omeo Hwy & Mitta North Rd. Travel 6.5kms from turnoff.

19. The Mill
Map Ref: MAP 1 B5 GPS: 36 31 53 S 147 21 49 E
Camping area 18km SE of Eskdale or 1.5km N of Mitta Mitta on E side of the road. Track to bush camp spots.

20. Snowy Creek Campground - High Country
Map Ref: MAP 1 C5 GPS: 36 35 49 S 147 26 13 E
Beside Snowy Creek S of Mitta Mitta. Take the signposted Holloway Log Rd. Dry weather only Ph: 02 6072 3410

21. The Walnuts
Map Ref: MAP 1 C6 GPS: 36 36 54 S 147 25 33 E
Camping area 14kms S of Mitta Mitta beside Snowy Creek. Ph: 02 6072 3410

22. Staceys Bridge - High Country
Map Ref: MAP 1 D5 GPS: 36 26 34 S 147 49 45 E
Camp Area 46km S of Corryong at Nariel. Ph: 02 6076 2277

23. Bunroy Junction Camping Area - High Country
Map Ref: MAP 1 D5 GPS: 36 22 06 S 148 02 14 E
Within the Biggara Valley S of the Indi Bridge Reserve. Access off Bunroy Creek Track. Located on edge of Alpine National Park. Ph: 02 6076 2277

24. Hairpin Bend Camping Area - High Country
Map Ref: MAP 1 D5 GPS: 36 22 47 S 148 02 14 E
Located on Murray River SE of Corryong, access along the Indi River track off Bunroy Creek track. Ph: 02 6076 2277

25. Wheelers Creek Hut Camp Area - Corryong District Forest - High Country
Map Ref: MAP 1 D5 GPS: 36 32 48 S 147 52 41 E
Camping in vicinity of hut along the Benambra-Corryong Rd, 67km N of Benambra. Ph: 02 6076 3100

26. Dogman Hut Camping Area - High Country
Map Ref: MAP 1 E5 GPS: 36 32 16 S 148 07 58 E
Within the Davies High Plain area NE of Omeo beside the Murray River. Access along Tom Groggin Track. Alternatively use the Alpine Way in NSW. Ph: 13 19 63

27. Buckwong Creek Camping Area - Alpine NP - High Country
Map Ref: MAP 1 E5 GPS: 36 34 29 S 148 08 10 E
Located 2.9km S of the Murray River crossing to NSW along Davies Plain Track. Ph: 13 19 63

28. Mountain Creek Camping Area
Map Ref: MAP 1 B6 GPS: 36 42 01 S 147 15 07 E
Camping area 11km along Mountain Creek Road off Kiewa Valley Hwy, E of Tawonga Ph: 13 19 63

29. Lightning Creek Campground - High Country
Map Ref: MAP 1 C6 GPS: 36 39 38 S 147 25 52 E
Off the Omeo Hwy 20km S of Mitta Mitta. Beside Lightning Creek. Ph: 13 19 63

30. Eustace Creek Camping Area - High Country
Map Ref: MAP 1 C6 GPS: 36 37 46 S 147 38 27 E
On the shores of Lake Dartmouth. Access from Benambra-Corryong Rd and then along the Eustace Gap track at Sassafras Gap. Ph: 13 19 63

31. Diamantina Horseyards Camping Area - High Country
Map Ref: MAP 1 B7 GPS: 36 54 44 S 147 10 07 E
From Mt Beauty take Simmonds Creek Rd for 8.5kms to join Pyramid Hill Track. Continue south for 3.6kms to meet Dungey Track and south for 10kms to meet West Kiewa Logging Rd. Continue south for 9.5km crossing river many times to large area. Ph: 13 19 63

32. Pretty Valley
Map Ref: MAP 1 B6 GPS: 36 53 37 S 147 15 05 E
Within Alpine NP 7km SW Falls Creek. Dispersed camping except within 200m of Bogong High Plains or Pretty Valley Rd historic huts & horse yards. Overlooks pondage.

Staceys Bridge Camping Reserve

No 22

Nyah, VIC

25kms north west of Swan Hill

Grassy campsites in Staceys Bridge Camping Reserve

Colin and Prue Kerr

Nestled beside Nariel Creek in Victoria's high country less than an hour's drive south of Corryong, the lovely, quiet campsite at Staceys Bridge is a real delight.

Separated by the roadway running between Benambra and Corryong, the two campsite sections here are all grassy, some with shade, and are large enough for all size rigs.

With the cool, clear water of the creek flowing within metres of most sites, this is a splendid place on a hot day to loll about in the water or sit on the edge, dangle your feet and watch the kids splash and play. During our recent stay we watched several fisho's trying their luck for trout in a quiet section of the creek, but we didn't hear of any being caught. I'm sure they were enjoying the experience anyway!

Back in 2003 the whole area around here was the site of massive bushfires which devastated this beautiful bushland as they spread out over a million hectares of national park, state forest and private land. The fires are believed to have been the largest in terms of extent and severity in Victoria in over 60 years. Today, the countryside here has recovered magnificently with little evidence of the fire blackened scene that would have confronted visitors just a few short years ago.

With bushwalking and bike trails leading in various directions from the campsite along the valley, this is a splendid base from which many visitors come to explore and get close to the best nature can offer. For further bush walking and bike trail information phone 131963.

Toilets are provided at the camping reserve

Facilities at the campsite include toilets in a clean modern block with a handwashing tap and basin also provided. There are a number of fire places and tables and chairs scattered around the campground and unlike in many campsites, there are rubbish bins available.

A sign at the campsite talks about the Nariel Valley being the home of Australia's first folk festival. This is held over the Christmas/New Year period every year at the nearby Nariel Creek Camping and Picnic Reserve. It is hard to imagine a more delightful valley setting for such an event and have made a note to return to the area for what is sure to be a colourful, entertaining event.

Just The Facts

Staceys Bridge Camping Reserve

GETTING THERE: Staceys Bridge Camping Reserve on the banks of Nariel Creek is 40 kms south of Corryong on the Corryong-Benambra Road in Victoria's north east high country. This is an all-sealed road from Corryong with quite a few bends. If travelling north from Benambra there is a 67 km section of windy, gravel road to negotiate before reaching the campsite.

FACILITIES: A reasonably large, grassy camping area either side of the road. There are toilets with hand washing basin and tap, bins, fire places and a few scattered tables and chairs. Generators, used responsibly, are permitted.

RATES: Free.

DISABLED: Handrails in toilet, mostly flat camping area.

PETS: Allowed on leash.

CONTACT: Visitor Information – Towong Shire – Phone (02)6076.2277; web: www.towong.com

Nariel Creek flows past the camping reserve

Free Campsites in Victoria

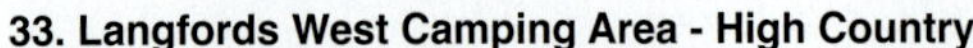

33. Langfords West Camping Area - High Country
Map Ref: MAP 1 B7 GPS: 36 55 43 S 147 18 16 E
South of Falls Creek. Signposted access along Bogong High Plains Road, within the Alpine NP. Ph: 13 19 63

34. Raspberry Hill Campground - High Country
Map Ref: MAP 1 B7 GPS: 36 56 34 S 147 19 10 E
Located in Alpine NP 16km S of Falls Creek off the Bogong High Plains Rd. Ph: 13 19 63

35. Buckety Plain Camping Area - Alpine NP - High Country
Map Ref: MAP 1 B7 GPS: 36 56 36 S 147 20 04 E
Located 19km S of Falls Creek, signposted access along Bogong High Plains Road. Ph: 13 19 63

36. McNamaras Hut Bush Camp - High Country
Map Ref: MAP 1 B7 GPS: 36 59 20 S 147 18 53 E
From Omeo Hwy at Anglers Rest take Callaghans Rd and follow west for 8lms to signposted McCoys Track. Stay on track and leave gates as found. Travel 4kms to T-intersection with signposted Grays Hill Track. Turn right and continue 11kms to hut. Ph: 13 19 63

37. Big River Bridge Camping Area - High Country
Map Ref: MAP 1 C6 GPS: 36 53 35 S 147 27 49 E
Located beside the Mitta Mitta River with access on the Omeo Hwy, 63km S of Mitta Mitta and 45km N Of Omeo. Ph: 13 19 63

38. Jokers Flat Campground
Map Ref: MAP 1 C7 GPS: 36 55 18 S 147 27 52 E
Off the Omeo Hwy 40km N of Omeo camping beside Mitta Mitta River. Ph: 13 19 63

39. Anglers Rest - High Country
Map Ref: MAP 1 C7 GPS: 36 59 22 S 147 29 20 E
Located in Alpine NP 30k N of Omeo off the Omeo Hwy beside the Cobungra River. Ph: 13 19 63

40. CRB Campground
Map Ref: MAP 1 C7 GPS: 36 59 16 S 147 29 41 E
Within Alpine NP 77kms S of Mitta Mitta or 28kms N of Omeo beside the river. Ph: 13 19 63

41. CRB Campground No 2
Map Ref: MAP 1 C7 GPS: 36 59 16 S 147 29 41 E
Located in Alpine NP. Camping are 28km N of Omeo by river. Ph: 13 19 63

42. Hinnomunjie Bridge Reserve Camping Area - High Country
Map Ref: MAP 1 C7 GPS: 36 56 44 S 147 36 29 E
From the Omeo Hwy 7km north of Omea take signposted Omeo Valley Rd and travel for 11.8km to large reserve beside the road and river. Ph: 03 5159 1455

43. Ferny Flat Campground - High Country
Map Ref: MAP 1 C7 GPS: 36 53 36 S 147 37 51 E
Within the Alpine NP access along Kelly's Rd from Omeo Valley Rd. Ph: 13 19 63

44. Taylors Crossing Riverside Camping Area - High Country
Map Ref: MAP 1 C6 GPS: 36 49 58 S 147 39 56 E
Access via Table Lands Rd 11km N of Benambra along the Corryong Rd. Ph: 13 19 63

45. Kennedys Hut Camping Area - High Country
Map Ref: MAP 1 C6 GPS: 36 48 58 S 147 39 30 E
Situated in Lake Dartmouth area on the banks of the Mitta Mitta River via Wombat Track and then Four Mile Creek Track. Ph: 13 19 63

46. Wombat PO Hut Camping Area - High Country
Map Ref: MAP 1 C6 GPS: 36 46 19 S 147 35 41 E
Within the Alpine NP at the junction of Wombat Creek track and Four Mile Creek track which are accessed by Kelly's Creek Rd. Ph: 13 19 63

47. Gibbo River Bush Camping - High Country
Map Ref: MAP 1 C6 GPS: 36 45 26 S 147 42 16 E
34km N of Omeo along the Corryong-Benambra Rd. Camping in open area beside river. Dry weather only Ph: 13 19 63

48. Ah Sye's Camping Area - High Country
Map Ref: MAP 1 C6 GPS: 36 43 43 S 147 43 51 E
Located in the Omeo area 30km N of Benambra. Access along the Benambra-Corryong Rd S of Expedition Creek. Dry weather only Ph. 13 19 63

49. Buenba Flat Camping Area - High Country
Map Ref: MAP 1 D6 GPS: 36 42 10 S 147 55 28 E
Located 45km NE of Benambra. From Benambra take Limestone Rd then Beloka Rd then Buenba Rd to the bridge. Ph: 13 19 63

50. Davies Plain Hut Camping Area - High Country
Map Ref: MAP 1 E6 GPS: 36 39 10 S 148 07 53 E
Signposted access along Davies Plain Track, 16km S of the Murray River crossing to NSW. Ph: 13 19 63

51. Charlies Creek Plain Camping Area - High Country
Map Ref: MAP 1 D6 GPS: 36 44 04 S 148 04 10 E
Located along Davies Plain Track, 13km S of Davies Plain Hut and 2.5km N of the junction of Davies Plain Track and McCarthy Track. Ph: 13 19 63

52. The Poplars/McCarthys Camping Area - High Country
Map Ref: MAP 1 E6 GPS: 36 46 36 S 148 06 28 E
On the banks of the Murray River within the Davies High Plain area. Located along McCarthys Track, E of the junction of Limestone Creek track. Ph: 13 19 63

53. Limestone Creek Camping Area - High Country
Map Ref: MAP 1 D6 GPS: 36 51 32 S 148 03 31 E
Signposted access on Limestone Creek Track. 2.5km N of Black Mountain Road. Ph: 13 19 63

54. Native Dog Flat Camping Area - High Country
Map Ref: MAP 1 D7 GPS: 36 53 45 S 148 05 24 E
Beside the Buchan River along Black Mountain Rd. Located 50km E of Benambra. Ph: 13 19 63

55. Suggan Buggan Campground - East Gippsland
Map Ref: MAP 1 E7 GPS: 36 57 15 S 148 19 42 E
Camp Area 75km N of Buchan along the Snowy River Rd 23km N of McKillops Rd beside the river. Many sites along the river. Ph: 13 19 63

56. Willis Campground - High Country
Map Ref: MAP 1 E7 GPS: 36 53 40 S 148 25 21 E
74km south from Jindabyne in NSW or 90km from Buchan in VIC.
Ph: 13 19 63

57. Victoria River Track Camping Area - High Country
Map Ref: MAP 1 B7 GPS: 37 06 00 S 147 18 25 E
Bush campsite beside dam, 8km along Victoria River Track off the Great Alpine Road, 24km W of Omeo. Ph: 13 19 63

58. Victoria Falls Camping Area - High Country
Map Ref: MAP 1 B7 GPS: 37 05 37 S 147 25 30 E
Within the Victoria Falls historic area along the Great Alpine Rd 21km W of Omeo. Dry weather only Ph: 13 19 63

59. Dogs Grave Campground - High Country
Map Ref: MAP 1 B8 GPS: 37 14 01 S 147 22 48 E
SW of Omeo from Upper Livingstone Rd into Birregun Rd. Ph: 13 61 86

60. Cassilis Recreation Reserve Camping Area - High Country
Map Ref: MAP 1 C8 GPS: 37 13 49 S 147 36 52 E
From Swifts Creek proceed west along Cassilis Rd 11.5km to signposted access track which leads in 1kms to reserve. Ph: 03 5159 1455

61. Moscow Villa Hut - East Gippsland
Map Ref: MAP 1 D8 GPS: 37 13 58 S 147 55 32 E
Within the Nunniong SF along Bentley Plain Rd off Nunniong Rd. Ph: 03 5159 5100

62. Bentleys Plain Reserve Camping Area - East Gippsland
Map Ref: MAP 1 D8 GPS: 37 13 39 S 147 55 24 E
Within the Nunniong State Forest 35km E of Swifts Creek on the Bentley Plain Rd. Ph: 03 5159 5100

63. Haunted Stream bush Camping Area - High Country
Map Ref: MAP 1 C8 GPS: 37 23 25 S 147 37 10 E
25km S of Swifts Creek. Numerous sites beside Haunted Stream and the old mining site called Dawson City. Ph: 13 61 86

64. Tambo River Reserves Bush Camp - East Gippsland
Map Ref: MAP 1 C8 GPS: 37 22 01 S 147 46 38 E
Bush campsites along the Tambo River accessed off Ensay-Doctors Flat Rd. Bring firewood and gas/fuel stove preferred. Ph: 03 5157 3311

Featured Campsite

Brought to you by

kokodacaravans.com.au

Willis Camping Area

No 56

NSW and Victorian Border, Qld

74km south of Jindabyne

John Mainwaring

The back country drive between Jindabyne and Buchan follows the Snowy River for much of the route and one of the nicest riverside campsites is the Willis Camping Area. It is 90 kms north of Buchan and 74kms south of Jindabyne, and the curious thing is that people seem to claim it for either state. It was the former site of a border customs office prior to Federation, and unless there's a surveyor's post that I missed I am really not sure which state it is in. There are around 20 large campsites so let's just say there's 10 in Victoria and 10 in NSW and be done with it.

The camping area is on a sweeping bend of the Snowy River where there's a large sandy beach and frankly, that is the main point of difference and quite an attraction. The camp area has toilets, picnic tables and fireplaces and is on a gentle slope down to the river. The most obvious local inhabitants are the roos and emus with brumbies making fairly noisy excursions down to the river for a drink. But being sandwiched between Kosciuszko and the Alpine and Snowy National Parks, this is a wilderness area with plenty of interesting flora and fauna all around.

Apart from the attraction of a white sand beach next to a beautiful river in a bush clad valley, this can also be a very nice canoeing destination. The Barry Way follows the river for many kilometers, and in fact along a 20 kilometer stretch heading north you will find numerous smaller camp areas including Scotchies Yard, Pinch River, No Name and Jacob's River. What this gives you is the opportunity to be dropped off upstream with your canoe or lilo so you can float along the Mighty Snowy and return to your campsite. Political deals to return a half decent "environmental flow" back to the Snowy have meant this is now a bit of fun with some exciting fast water sections.

The Snowy River meanering through the alpine hills.

Now for those thinking that this area is well within the Kosciuszko National Park and therefore subject to parks fees, fear not. Either it is too hard to collect or the bureaucracy has been generous. There are no fees required to be paid in the Barry Way section of the Kosciuszko National Park. It is all 2WD accessible and I have seen some folks taking caravans along it, but bear in mind there are numerous narrow sections, particularly down the Victorian end.

Camping amongst the gum trees.

Discover our **280SL** and **2802SL** motorhomes - built for everyday comfort with premium interiors, and a powerful electrical system for off-grid adventures. Enjoy user-friendly design, effortless power, and true freedom on every journey. Contact us today.

WIRR-AWAY MOTORHOMES

Phone: (03) 5023 0230
Email: info@wirraway.com.au
Location: Mildura VIC 3500
Website: www.wirraway.com.au

Free Campsites in Victoria

65. Timbarra bush Camping Area - East Gippsland
Map Ref: MAP 1 D8 GPS: 37 20 55 S 148 04 10 E
23km NW of Buchan beside the Timbarra River off Timbarra Rd. Many campsites beside the river. Ph: 03 5162 1900

66. Timbarra Central
Map Ref: MAP 1 D8 GPS: 37 22 02 S 148 05 01 E
Camp area 30km NW of Buchan, turn to Timbarra Rd 4kms S of Buchan for 26kms. Riverside location. 7km dirt road. GPS at entry, follow track to site. Ph: 13 61 86

67. Timbarra Bridge Camping Area
Map Ref: MAP 1 D8 GPS: 37 22 52 S 148 05 47 E
23km NW of Buchan, take Buchan Rd towards Bruthen. After 4.1kms turn into Timbarra Rd and continue for 24km to bridge over Timbarra River and camping area. Ph: 03 5162 1900

68. Little River Falls - Snowy River NP
Map Ref: MAP 1 E7 GPS: 37 03 40 S 148 18 35 E
Located in Snowy River NP on McKillops Rd, Wulgulmerang 65kms N of Buchan via Gelantipy Rd. Veer right at Wulgulmerang East, site on left, 21 day limit. Ph: 13 19 63

69. McKillops Bridge Campground - East Gippsland
Map Ref: MAP 1 E7 GPS: 37 05 30 S 148 24 40 E
From Bruthen take C608 then right into Bonang-Gelantipy Rd. Dry weather only. Ph: 13 19 63

70. Snowy River Camping Area
Map Ref: MAP 1 E7 GPS: 37 05 28 S 148 24 46 E
Signposted access along McKillops Rd, 500m W of McKillops Bridge. Access with care from Bonang and check conditions first. Ph: 13 19 63

71. Little River Junction Camping Area - East Gippsland
Map Ref: MAP 1 E8 GPS: 37 07 30 S 148 22 36 E
This camping ground found at the junction of the Little and Snowy Rivers along Little River track which is signposted off McKillops Rd. Ph: 13 19 63

72. Waratah Flat Camping Area - East Gippsland
Map Ref: MAP 1 F8 GPS: 37 17 19 S 148 34 34 E
Within the snowy River NP on the banks of the Rodger River via Waratah Flat Rd. Ph: 13 19 63

73. Goongerah Camping Area - East Gippsland
Map Ref: MAP 1 F8 GPS: 37 20 36 S 148 42 06 E
Signposted access along the Bonang-Orbost Road at Goongerah, 24km S of Bonang and 78km N of Orbost. Ph: 13 19 63

74. Delegate River Campground - East Gippsland
Map Ref: MAP 1 F8 GPS: 37 11 36 S 148 49 30 E
8km from the small border town of Bendoc. Follow Gap Rd to camping spot on Delegate River. Dry weather only Ph: 02 6458 1456

75. Wilsons Hut Camping Area - East Gippsland
Map Ref: MAP 1 G8 GPS: 37 10 57 S 148 53 32 E
Located in Bendoc State Forest south of Bendoc. Follow Clarkeville Rd south for 4km to signposted track then 1.4km east to hut. Bring drinking water & firewood. Ph: 13 61 86

76. Ada River Campground - East Gippsland
Map Ref: MAP 1 G9 GPS: 37 24 20 S 148 53 54 E
Camp Area 22km N of Club Tce. Turn NW off the Club Tce-Combienbar Rd 10km onto Errinundra Valley Rd. Beside Ada River. Ph: 13 19 63

77. Frosty Hollow Camping Area - East Gippsland
Map Ref: MAP 1 G8 GPS: 37 17 55 S 148 57 48 E
Located within Errinundra NP 70km NE of Orbost. Signposted off Coast Range Road or Back Creek Rd from Bendoc. Dry weather only Ph: 13 19 63

78. Tennyson Campground - East Gippsland
Map Ref: MAP 1 G8 GPS: 37 14 31 S 149 07 01 E
Located in Buldah State Forest SE of Bendoc. Access is from the Monaro Hwy at Chandlers Creek, follow signage to Buldah for 15km to Tennyson Track then 4.4km to site. Bring water & firewood. Ph: 13 61 86

79. Coopracambra bush camping - East Gippsland
Map Ref: MAP 1 H8 GPS: 37 20 19 S 149 13 49 E
30km N of Cann River main access via Monaro Hwy. Dispersed bush camping, no facilities, for self-sufficient campers. Walk-in or 4WD access only. Ph: 13 19 63

80. Genoa Point - East Gippsland
Map Ref: MAP 1 J9 GPS: 37 28 09 S 149 35 15 E
On the Princes Hwy Genoa is 23kms NW of Mallacoota.

McKillop's Bridge Snowy River Campground No 69

Snowy River National Park, Vic
10 km west of Deddick

John Mainwaring

McKillop's Bridge is a bit of an iconic scene in Victoria's eastern Gippsland. A long way from anywhere, it is a sort of "bridge to nowhere" having been built as an infrastructure project to open up the area to settlement. Fortunately it did not work out, leaving the entire area as a camper's playground. Nowadays its massive welded steel truss span provides access from the Buchan-Jindabyne Road to Bonang and Delegate in the east of Gippsland making some explorations into this remote area possible for 2WD and 4WD alike, including some interesting loops.

The main campsite is on the western bank of the Snowy River, well elevated from the river's high flood mark, in a sparse woodland setting. In fact the whole area can be described as sparse woodland, being notably drier than the general vicinity as it is within the rain shadow of a nearby mountain. This area is on a gentle slope of a few degrees with large sites well separated from one another. There is caravan access but personally I would come in from the eastern side via Bonang as the road in from the Buchan-Jindabyne road is excitingly narrow in numerous places, although amazingly scenic.

There is a couple of interesting walks nearby however it is the sandy river beaches that attract people in the summer. Canoeing is very popular, including 3-4 day excursions with a pick up downstream near Buchan. But it is the bridge that is perhaps the greatest attraction. The story of it being built, then being knocked down a couple of days before its official opening in 1934 and then all the effort put into re-building it is really pretty interesting. These were Great Depression times too so it was quite a blow to lose such a large piece of community infrastructure. Twisted steel struts downstream show the powerful forces that this usually placid river can bring to bear. The rebuilt version was 5 metres higher and it has passed the test of time. At 250 metres long it is the longest welded steel truss bridge in the world, so visit this place and there is one less thing on the bucket list. The panoramic backdrop of bush clad hills that make up the nearly 100,000 hectares of Snowy River National Park are part of the attraction but this big old bridge and a nicely situated camp area on the banks of the Snowy make this one well worth a visit.

Challenging bush walking is just one of the activities available at this campsite.

This point of the river is ideal for kayaking through some tough sections of stream.

Just The Facts

McKillop's Bridge Snowy River Campground

Location: From Bruthen take C608 then right turn into Bonang-Gelantipy Rd.
Facilities: There are toilets, a fireplace and picnic table, water, space for caravans.
Rates: Free.
Pets: No dogs.
Contact: www.australianalps.environment.gov.au/parks/snowy.html

Free Campsites in Victoria

81. Deptford Camping Area - East Gippsland
Map Ref: MAP 1 C9 GPS: 37 35 31 S 147 41 50 E
Located along Deptford Rd accessed from Bruthen. Take Deep Creek Rd off the Great Alpine Rd 2.4km W of Bruthen then turn into Nicholson Creek Rd. Turn left for 1.6km to Deptford Rd then left for 5km to camping area located 200m above the river. Bring water & firewood. Ph: 13 61 86

82. Buchan Caves Campground - East Gippsland
Map Ref: MAP 1 D9 GPS: 37 29 43 S 148 09 50 E
Located at Buchan Caves in Buchan. Signposted access via Caves Road off Buchan Road. Ph: 13 19 63

83. Jacksons Crossing Camping Area - East Gippsland
Map Ref: MAP 1 E8 GPS: 37 23 36 S 148 20 06 E
Located within Snowy River NP on banks of Snowy River via Varney's Track off Yalmy Rd. Ph: 13 19 63

84. Hicks Camping Area - East Gippsland
Map Ref: MAP 1 E9 GPS: 37 24 48 S 148 21 36 E
Located beside Yalmy River N of Orbost in the Snowy River NP. Accessed off Varney's track which runs off Yalmy Rd. Ph: 13 19 63

85. West Track Bush Camp - East Gippsland
Map Ref: MAP 1 E9 GPS: 37 26 34 S 148 22 21 E
Located in Snowy River NP. Accessed along Yalmy Rd via West Track 5.3km north of Moresford Rd. Continue further 12.5km via 4WD track which can have overgrown sections to open area above bend in the river. Bring firewood.

86. Raymond Falls Camping Area - East Gippsland
Map Ref: MAP 1 E9 GPS: 37 29 12 S 148 18 46 E
Located in Snowy River NP beside Raymond Creek N of Orbost. Accessed off Yalmy Rd and then on to Moresford track. Ph: 13 19 63

87. Balley Hooley Camping Area - East Gippsland
Map Ref: MAP 1 E9 GPS: 37 31 04 S 148 15 50 E
From Buchan proceed towards Orbost for 4.5km to signposted Basin Rd then continue to Balley Hooley for 11km to camping area at junction of Snowy & Buchan Rivers. Only two vehicle sites. Ph: 13 19 63

88. Long Point Camping Ground - East Gippsland
Map Ref: MAP 1 E9 GPS: 37 36 20 S 148 20 48 E
At Orbost take the signposted Buchan-Orbost Rd and follow NE for 21kms to signposted Long Point Track. Then 7.6kms to grassed camping area. Bring firewood. Ph: 13 61 86

89. Woods Point Camping Ground - East Gippsland
Map Ref: MAP 1 E9 GPS: 37 38 50 S 148 19 22 E
From Orbost take McLeod Street, which becomes "B" road and then the Garnett Track to the camping ground on the banks of the Snowy River. Ph: 03 5161 1222

90. Orbost Club Hotel
Map Ref: MAP 1 E10 GPS: 37 42 26 S 148 27 16 E
Parking area behind pub at 63 Nicholson St, Orbost. Register at bar on arrival, fee for showers. Patrons only. Ph: 03 5154 1003

91. Snowy Riverside
Map Ref: MAP 1 E10 GPS: 37 45 08 S 148 31 08 E
Camp area E off Princes Hwy to Lochend Rd on S side of river at Orbost.

92. Manto's Landing
Map Ref: MAP 1 E10 GPS: 37 44 57 S 148 30 55 E
Camp area 10km S of Orbost. Turn E off Princes Hwy to 722 Lochend Rd.

93. Banksia Bluff Camping Area - East Gippsland
Map Ref: MAP 1 F10 GPS: 37 47 44 S 148 44 56 E
Access from Marlo along the Cape Conran Road, or from the Princes Hwy via the Cabbage Tree Creek-Cape Conran Road. Ph: 03 5154 8438

94. Binns Beach Campground - East Gippsland
Map Ref: MAP 1 G10 GPS: 37 46 47 S 148 55 20 E
Within Cape Conran Coastal Park. From Bemm River go SW along signposted rd to Pearl Point. After 5.5km access campground. Bring water and gas/fuel stove preferred. Ph: 13 19 63

95. Choof Choof Campsite - East Gippsland
Map Ref: MAP 1 G10 GPS: 37 42 57 S 149 07 42 E
Located in Tamboon SF south of Cann River, follow Tamboon Rd south for 16km then turn west into Furnell Landing Rd, then 5km to signposted Choof Choof Track. 460m to small camping suitable for 2 campsites. Ph: 13 61 86

96. Tostaree Cottages - Gippsland
Map Ref: MAP 1 D10 GPS: 37 44 51 S 148 11 03 E
Camp area at Tostaree on Jonsons Rd. Check with office before parking. Ph: 0408 031 668

Free Campsites in Victoria

97. Camerons Arm Camping Area - East Gippsland
Map Ref: MAP 1 D10 GPS: 37 46 48 S 148 08 09 E
Situated in the Lake Tyers Forest Park on Cameron's Arm No1 track, off Lake Tyers Road from the Princes Hwy E of Nowa Nowa. Ph: 13 19 63

98. Trident Arm Camping Area - East Gippsland
Map Ref: MAP 1 D10 GPS: 37 49 44 S 148 08 13 E
2km along Trident Arm Track, which is signposted off Tyers House Road. Ph: 13 19 63

99. Pettmans Beach Camping Area
Map Ref: MAP 1 D10 GPS: 37 49 45 S 148 11 08 E
At the end of Pettman Rd off Tyers House Road within the Lake Tyers Forest Park. Ph: 13 19 63

100. The Glasshouse Camping Area - East Gippsland
Map Ref: MAP 1 D10 GPS: 37 50 50 S 148 06 34 E
Located 45km W of Orbost. Turn onto Lake Tyers Rd, and follow to end. Dry weather only Ph: 13 19 63

101. Waterwheel Beach Tavern
Map Ref: MAP 1 D10 GPS: 37 51 26 S 148 05 08 E
Located at 577 Lake Tyers Rd, Lake Tyers. Parking area on left at end of road. Check in at bar for parking instructions First 2 nights free. Limited sites. Ph: 03 5156 5855

102. Wyanga Park Winery
Map Ref: MAP 1 D10 GPS: 37 51 18 S 147 59 06 E
Camp area 10kms N of Lakes Entrance at 248 Baades Rd, Lakes Entrance. Register at bar and patronise winery. Ph: 03 5155 1508

103. Log Crossing
Map Ref: MAP 1 D10 GPS: 37 49 36 S 147 56 29 E
Camp area N of Kalimna on Log Crossing Rd. Turn off Hwy to Uncle Rd then E to Log Crossing Rd. Ph: 13 61 86

104. Blond Bay Nature Reserve - Gippsland
Map Ref: MAP 1 C10 GPS: 37 50 00 S 147 40 00 E
Located between Sales and Bairnsdale off the Forge Creek Rd just out of Bairnsdale.

105. Avon River Streamside
Map Ref: MAP 1 B11 GPS: 38 01 49 S 147 14 54 E
Camp spot 4km S of Perry Bridge via Springberg Lne, 3km dirt road. Ph: 13 19 63

106. Marlay Point - East Gippsland
Map Ref: MAP 1 B11 GPS: 38 03 40 S 147 14 59 E
18kms from Sale located on the Marlay Point Rd. Ph: 1300 366 244

107. Emu Bright Camping Area -Gippsland
Map Ref: MAP 1 C10 GPS: 37 59 44 S 147 39 10 E
Located 5km E of Loch Sport on shores of Lake Victoria. Access via Lake Victoria track. Ph: 13 19 63

108. Waddy Point Bush Camp - Gippsland
Map Ref: MAP 1 C10 GPS: 37 59 56 S 147 36 06 E
Travel east along Stratford-Bengworden Rd for 42km to Lower Goon Nure Rd. Turn south and after 8.5km at T-junction turn south. Continue for 800m and turn into Waddy Point Rd for 2kms to information bay then 550m to Waddy Point Rd then 1.6kms to camp. Ph: 13 19 63

109. Storm Point Bush Camp - Gippsland
Map Ref: MAP 1 C11 GPS: 38 01 27 S 147 33 20 E
Located in Blond Bay Wildlife Reserve on Lake Victoria. Access is from Stratford-Bengworden Rd. From park information bay continue west passing Waddy Point Rd keep right at Y-junction to signposted Boundary Track then 4km keep left to Storm Point Fire Break. Continue 6.5kms to T-intersection to Storm Point then 2.8km to dispersed camping. Bring own fire drum & firewood. Ph: 13 19 63

110. Red Bluff Camping Area
Map Ref: MAP 1 B11 GPS: 38 03 19 S 147 31 29 E
Site beside Lake Victoria via Lakeside Track off Lochsport Road. Ph: 13 19 63

111. Thalia Point Camping Area - Gippsland
Map Ref: MAP 1 B11 GPS: 38 04 23 S 147 30 08 E
Located within Gippsland Lakes Coastal Park 4kms north of Spoon Bay along Lake Side Track. Ph: 13 19 63

112. Spoon Bay Camping Area
Map Ref: MAP 1 B11 GPS: 38 04 42 S 147 27 37 E
Located beside Lake Victoria at Spoon Bay via Lakeside Track off the Lochsport Road Ph: 13 19 63

Marlay Point No 106

Near Sale, Vic
3km north of Sale

Stephanie Jackson

Campsites are right on the banks of Lake Wellington.

Marlay Point is a location due east of Sale on the shore of Lake Wellington. It is a large, open and grassed area around 18 kms east of Sale on Marlay Point Road which is accessed off Bengworden Road. Bengworden Road is north of Sale off Princes Highway and is a popular alternative route between Sale and Bairnsdale if you are just a little tired of highway driving. It passes through some pleasant but unremarkable farming country and provides you with the country back road alternative.

Marley Point is home to a yacht club and very little else. It is next to the large reserve known as the Clydebank Morass State Game Reserve where the Avon enters Lake Wellington, one of the largest lakes in the Gippsland Lakes system. As a result you will have about a million frogs as croaking neighbours, which surprisingly is quite a relaxing background noise which eases you into a very relaxed state.

The facilities in this free camp area are actually pretty good. There are clean, modern flush toilets, an electric BBQ within a covered picnic shelter, a boat ramp and some very nice waterside campsites, plus space for another dozen or so caravans on an elevated area overlooking the lake. The only downside I have heard is that occasionally the mossie numbers get a bit extreme but that can be said of just about anywhere on the Gippsland Lakes system and it has never managed to put me off. This is a completely free site so some of the money you save staying here can be spent on one of the more potent insect repellents.

Fishing, swimming, relaxing and gazing at the lake are popular pursuits and if you have a boat there is a boat ramp right on the point. The access is good with sealed bitumen all the way in from the Princes Highway so your 2WD, caravan and motorhome set up will all get in without any problems.

The diversion off the main highway between Sale and Bairnsdale via Bengworden Road is not a bad idea with attractive countryside and practically no traffic. The side road down to Marlay Point is even quieter. An overnighter or even a dalliance of a couple of days makes this Bengworden route even more attractive and a handy spot to know about when you are making your way through the Gippsland Lakes region.

Just The Facts

Marlay Point

Getting There : This site is around 18 kms from Sale. About 3 kms north of Sale is a right hand turn to Bengworden Road, very well sign-posted as this is a popular alternative route to Bairnsdale. About 12 kms along this road you will come to Clydebank Road and then Marlay Point Road but all the way along there are signs indicating you are on the way to Marlay Point. From the other direction the Bengworden Road route is signposted about 5 kms west of Bairnsdale.

Facilities : Clean and very modern flush toilets, an electric BBQ (in the large shelter building which also has an enclosed fireplace), a large grassed area for camping and several picnic tables. There is also a concrete boat ramp.

Charges : Free

Contact : Wellington Shire Council on 1300 366 244 or Sale Visitor Centre on (03) 5144 1108

Pets : Pets OK under control.

There is a great BBQ shelter next to the water.

NEXT LEVEL JOURNEYS BEGIN HERE

Future Caravans is changing the way Australia explores.
Designed and built for our harsh conditions, every van delivers true off-road capability, modern luxury, and the freedom to go further.
Semi off-road models are also available for those who want comfort and flexibility on a range of terrains.
From couple's vans to premium toy haulers, we customise layouts to suit your lifestyle. More storage for your bikes, more comfort for long trips, more power to stay off-grid longer.
It is your adventure. We build it around you.
Enjoy complete peace of mind with our nationwide warranty
Wherever your journey takes you, Future Caravans support is always within reach.
Proudly Australian made.
Proudly supporting Australian adventures.

Visit our showroom and let's design your Future Caravan today.
Future Caravans 12 Fleet St, Somerton VIC Phone: 0411 899 353 info@futurecaravans.com.au **www.futurecaravans.com.au**

Free Campsites in Victoria

113. Golden Beach - East Gippsland
Map Ref: MAP 1 B11 GPS: 38 11 40 S 147 25 21 E
Access is on a sealed road from Sale on the Princes Hwy via Longford 250kms E of Melbourne.

114. Paradise Beach Campground - East Gippsland
Map Ref: MAP 1 B11 GPS: 38 11 40 S 147 25 21 E
Access via Shoreline Drive 3km N of Golden Beach, one of many camping sites in this area. Ph: 13 19 63

115. Shoreline Drive Bush Camping Area - Gippsland
Map Ref: MAP 1 B11 GPS: 38 13 02 S 147 23 36 E
From Longford take the Longford-Loch Sport Rd for 29km to Golden Beach then south along Shoreline Drive. Ph: 13 19 63

116. Molesworth Camping Ground - Close to Melbourne
Map Ref: MAP 2 B2 GPS: 37 09 49 S 145 32 24 E
In the village of Molesworth on the Goulburn Valley Hwy 14km NE of Yea. Ph: 03 5797 6278

117. Brookes River Reserve - High Country
Map Ref: MAP 2 C2 GPS: 37 11 40 S 145 40 31 E
Beside the Goulburn River W of Alexandra. From the Maroondah Hwy take Swan Rd then in to Brookes Cutting Rd. Ph: 13 19 63

118. Narrows Flat
Map Ref: MAP 2 D1 GPS: 37 07 29 S 145 56 20 E
Camp area N from Lake Eildon on Delatite Plantation Rd then into Walsh Rd.

119. Blue Gum Flat
Map Ref: MAP 2 D2 GPS: 37 10 29 S 145 59 54 E
Within Delatite Arm Reserve, camping area 8km N of Goughs Bay via Howes Creek Rd. Dirt rd. Ph: 13 19 63

120. Newtons Campground
Map Ref: MAP 2 D2 GPS: 37 10 51 S 146 00 20 E
Camp area 7.5km N of Goughs Bay via Howes Creek Rd & Walshs Rd. Dirt road. Ph: 13 19 63

121. The Orchard
Map Ref: MAP 2 E2 GPS: 37 10 52 S 146 00 34 E
Camp area 8km N of Goughs Bay via Howes Creek Rd & Walshs Rd. Dirt road. Ph: 13 19 63

122. Delatite Arm Reserve Camping Area - High Country
Map Ref: MAP 2 E2 GPS: 37 10 52 S 146 00 33 E
Located on the S shore of the Delatite Arm of Lake Eildon via Walshes Road from Goughs Bay off the Mansfield-Jamieson Rd. 14km S of Mansfield and 21km N of Jamieson. Ph: 03 5733 1200

123. Buttercup Creek Camping Areas - High Country
Map Ref: MAP 2 F1 GPS: 37 04 54 S 146 20 24 E
A number of sites in the Buttercup Creek Reserve 24km E of Mansfield off the Buttercup Rd. Ph: 13 61 86

124. Carters Road Campground
Map Ref: MAP 2 F1 GPS: 37 06 11 S 146 22 02 E
Camping area 10km E of Merrijig. Turn N along Carters Rd and travel for 500m. Ph: 13 61 86

125. Carters Mill Camping & Picnic Area
Map Ref: MAP 2 F2 GPS: 37 06 11 S 146 22 02 E
Camp area 10km E of Merrijig or 3km W of Mirimbah. Turn N along Carters Rd for 400m, unlevel area and small vehicles only. Ph: 13 61 86

126. Carters Road Campground - High Country
Map Ref: MAP 2 F2 GPS: 37 06 18 S 146 22 04 E
Within the Mt Stirling area 13km E of Merrijig via the Mansfield-Mt Bulla Rd and then Carters Rd. Ph: 13 61 86

127. Klingsporn Bridal Track - Alpine NP
Map Ref: MAP 2 F2 GPS: 37 06 39 S 146 24 00 E
Located in Mount Buller State Forest via Mt Buller Rd, Mirimbah. Camp area at Mirimbah S of Mt Buller Rd on S side opposite Mt Sterling Rd. 16kms NW of Mt Buller. Often closed in winter. Ph: 03 5775 7000

128. Razorback Hut Camping Area - High Country
Map Ref: MAP 2 F1 GPS: 37 06 24 S 146 28 04 E
Accessed via Circuit Road from Mt Bulla Rd, take the track just before the No 3 Rd intersection. Ph: 13 61 86

There is plenty of space and shade at the camp ground.

Brookes River Reserve No 117

Alexandra, Vic
142 km north east of Melbourne

The Alexandra Railway Museum.

On The Road magazine is full of the exotic and far-flung 'must sees' destinations and great camping options in this wondrous land we call Oz. .

One camping option, for those in Victoria, especially Melbourne, I want to let you in on is a secret location just outside a postcard country town – Brooks River Reserve 4klm from Alexandra. , it's just over an hour from Lilydale and no more than two hours from just about anywhere in Melbourne.

Brooks River Reserve tucks neatly into that folder of "we could be anywhere but five minutes to town", especially loved by the female cohort and the weekend RV warriors. You only have to navigate 1klm of good dirt to arrive at your destination, two van parking areas divided by a gully. Each area would comfortably accommodate 3-4 vans. Set in dairy country, the reserve is bordered by rolling green hills and pastures on one side and the Goulbourn River on the other. The area is flat and an easy in-and-out for the larger vans. There is one drop toilet and plenty of sunshine for the solar savvy.

But wait, there's more! One hundred metres of access road will walk you down to the river. Resist the temptation to send your kids into the sinkhole areas either side of the track. Some are over three metres deep, and if they attempt it anyway, just mention the "drop bears". Once at the bottom you will see over 200 metres of river frontage, ideal for picnics, overnight camping and serious partying. Easy access to the water is limited and the river travels at some speed, but on a hot summers' day, I guess you'd take the chance of a long walk back.

Signs indicate that campfires are not permitted. However there is a number of ad-hoc campfire sites scattered around the reserve. Phone and internet are reasonable. Hot showers are available in town adjacent to the Alexandra Cricket Club in Vickery Street.

Wildlife can be seen on walks near the river like this wombat.

Alexandra is a great little town and hub to places like Lake Eildon and Cathedral Mountain. There's a Railway Museum for the buffs (alexandratramway.org.au/),a golf course (www.alexandragolfclub.com.au), several cafes, clubs and a supermarket. So, if your desperate for a change of scenery and a chance to re-boot, you won't be disappointed with Brooks River Reserve.

129. Pineapple Flat Camping Area - High Country
Map Ref: MAP 2 G1 GPS: 37 03 58 S 146 29 57 E
Access via King Basin Rd off Circuit Rd. Camping beside the King River. Ph: 13 19 63

130. Craigs Hut Camping Area - High Country
Map Ref: MAP 2 G2 GPS: 37 06 36 S 146 31 54 E
From Mansfield via Stirling Rd then Circuit Rd on to Clear Hills Track. Ph: 13 61 86

131. King Hut Camping Area - High Country
Map Ref: MAP 2 G1 GPS: 37 05 30 S 146 34 35 E
Found in the Whitfield region. Off King Basin Rd via Speculation Rd which is signposted off Circuit Rd. Ph: 13 19 63

132. Lake Cobbler Camping Area - High Country
Map Ref: MAP 2 G1 GPS: 37 02 58 S 146 37 34 E
47km S of Whitfield beside Lake Cobbler. Access via Cobbler Lake Road, off Whitfield-Myrtleford Road. Ph: 13 19 63

133. Pickerings Flat Camping Area - High Country
Map Ref: MAP 2 F2 GPS: 37 11 23 S 146 21 20 E
Access along Howqua Track, 400m E of Davons. Ph: 13 19 63

134. Blackbird Flat Camping Area
Map Ref: MAP 2 F2 GPS: 37 11 40 S 146 20 43 E
Bush campsites by the Howqua River along Howqua Track 16kms S of Mansfield-Mount Buller Rd. Ph: 13 19 63

135. Sheepyard Flat - High Country
Map Ref: MAP 2 E2 GPS: 37 11 25 S 146 20 41 E
Within the Howqua historic area 34lm SE of Mansfield. Access via Howqua Track. Camping beside river. Ph: 13 19 63

136. Davons Camping Area - High Country
Map Ref: MAP 2 F2 GPS: 37 11 20 S 146 20 58 E
Within the Howqua Hills historic area off Howqua track via Sheepyard Flat. Ph: 13 19 63

137. Howqua Hills Flats - Alpine NP
Map Ref: MAP 2 F2 GPS: 37 11 41 S 146 20 42 E
Numerous camp areas 19km SE of Merrijig via Howqua Track. Turn S off C320 2km E of Merrijig to Howqua Track for 17km, windy dirt road. GPS at entry before bridge. Riverside. 21 day limit. Ph: 03 5775 7000

138. Noonans Flat Camping Area - High Country
Map Ref: MAP 2 F2 GPS: 37 11 13 S 146 21 39 E
Within the Howqua Hills historic area along the Howqua Track E of Pickerings Flat. Ph: 13 19 63

139. Tobacco Flat Camping Area - High Country
Map Ref: MAP 2 F2 GPS: 37 13 00 S 146 18 54 E
Located in Howqua Hills Historic Area and access is via Howqua Hills Track. Proceed south through Sheepyard Flat for 2kms to Howqua Hills Track and continue for 3.8kms to signposted access camping area beside river. Ph: 13 19 63

140. Frys Flat Camping Area - High Country
Map Ref: MAP 2 F2 GPS: 37 12 02 S 146 20 10 E
Within the Howqua Hills historic area 35km SE of Mansfield, along the Howqua Track. Ph: 13 19 63

141. Seven Mile Flat Camping Area - High Country
Map Ref: MAP 2 F2 GPS: 37 11 40 S 146 25 20 E
In the Alpine NP 45km E of Mansfield via the Howqua Track and Brocks Rd. Ph: 13 19 63

142. Howqua River Flats - Alpine NP
Map Ref: MAP 2 F2 GPS: 37 11 54 S 146 25 44 E
Numerous camp areas 29km SW of Merrijig via Brocks Rd Merrijig. Turn S off C320 2km E of Merrijig to Howqua Track, 27km dirt road and steep in places. Small vehicles only. 21 day limit. Ph: 03 5775 7000

143. Eight Mile Flat Camping Area - High Country
Map Ref: MAP 2 F2 GPS: 37 11 53 S 146 25 45 E
Within the Alpine NP signposted access along Brocks Road, on the banks of the Howqua River. Ph: 13 19 63

144. Upper Jamieson Hut Camping Area
Map Ref: MAP 2 F2 GPS: 37 15 28 S 146 26 52 E
Camping in hut vicinity but after rain the river crossing may be impassable. 6.7kms S of Eight Mile Gap and 1.2km W of signpost to Low Saddle Rd on Brocks Rd. Across river 800m to site. Dry weather only. Ph: 13 19 63

Sheepyard Flat No 135

Howqua, Vic

30kms south of Jamieson

By Colin and Prue Kerr

Victoria's high country is brilliant for horse riding.

Looking For a beaut, out-of-the-way free campsite in the Victorian High Country? Well, Sheepyard Flat has to be one of the best you'll find.

Located within the Howqua Hills historic area, this quite extensive campsite along the banks of the Howqua River is suitable for all size rigs. Bear in mind however, the access road from Merrijig is partly gravel and has many bends.

The area here is not only quite scenic with some lovely tall timber lining the valley and adjacent range, this is also an area where there is to be found quite a few relics from the old gold mining days dating back to the 1870s.

From the campsite, there is a pleasant walk of around one kilometre beside/overlooking the river (with information signs along the way) to a tall brick chimney and remains of a gold smelting furnace built in 1884. It is quite an impressive structure which these days, looks totally out of character on this delightful section of riverside trail. A little further on, the trail came to Fry's Hut. Fred Fly, a master bushman, prospector and fisherman, built his home here in the 1930s using split timber with his own personal style of workmanship. He lived a solitary existence in this area for many years. Allow around 1½ to 2 hours return for this walk from your Sheepyard Flat Campsite. Camping is also allowed in a cleared area around Fry's Hut.

A few kilometres upstream from Sheepyard Flat Campsite, further old mining relics can be found at Tunnel Bend, named after the 100 metre tunnel built into the hillside connecting to a 4 km long water race, the remains of which can still be seen above the roadway.

Back at the campsite, the clear, clean waters of the Howqua River flowing past is an ideal spot to cool off on a hot day or just sit beside with a good book. You could also try your luck trout fishing in a quiet section of the river.

There are toilets provided here, a few scattered fixed tables and chairs, an information shelter and a number of fire places – campfires only allowed at these locations. There are no bins provided here and all rubbish must be taken away with you.

As a service to campers at peak times (long weekends, etc) the 'Ice Truck' calls by daily – with ice, drinks, snacks, papers and other basics. During our recent stay we enjoyed the delightful sight of horse riders coming through the campsite. There are horse riding trails along the river bank and through nearby hills with horse yard facilities located at several nearby campsites.

Back at Merrijig, the Merrijig Pub, or 'The Jig', is a popular local watering-hole with a great reputation for good food including their famous homemade pizzas, chicken parma, 500 gram rib-eye steaks and tasty lamb shanks.

Just The Facts

Sheepyard Flat Campsite

Getting There: Sheepyard Flat Campsite is located approx. 18 km south east of Merrijig (east of Mansfield). After passing through Merrijig on the Mount Buller Road, there is 2 km of seal and then turn south on the unsealed Howqua Track (many windy bends) for 16 kms to the campsite.

Facilities: Large open campsites (mostly grassy sites) beside the Howqua River – suitable for all rigs. Toilets, a few scattered tables and chairs, fire places and information shelter. No bins – take all rubbish with you. Generators allowed. Nearest main supplies and services – Mansfield, approx. 40 Km (1 hour). There are 4WD, bike riding, horse riding and bush walking trails throughout the Howqua Hills area.

Dogs: Allowed on lead.

Rates: Free.

Disabled: Nothing specific.Flat open campground.

Nearby: Walk and drive trails to nearby huts and historical gold mining relics.

FURTHER INFORMATION:

Parks Victoria – phone 13 1963; web:www.parks.vic.gov.au; or Mansfield Visitor Information Centre – phone 1800 039 049

Frys Hut was home to master bushman, prospector and fisherman Fred Fly.

145. Bindaree Hut Camping Area - High Country
Map Ref: MAP 2 G2 GPS: 37 10 06 S 146 32 36 E
Beside the Howqua River signposted off Bindaree Rd. Located in Alpine NP. Ph: 13 19 63

146. Pikes Flat Camping Area - Alpine NP - High Country
Map Ref: MAP 2 G2 GPS: 37 10 49 S 146 30 44 E
On the Howqua River via the Bluff Link Rd. 12km N of Bindaree Rd. Dispersed bush camping beside the Howqua River. Ph: 13 19 63

147. Upper Howqua Camping Area - High Country
Map Ref: MAP 2 G2 GPS: 37 10 24 S 146 33 44 E
Access along Bindaree Rd which is signposted off Circuit Rd, only 2 sites. Ph: 13 19 63

148. Bluff Hut Camping Area - Alpine NP - High Country
Map Ref: MAP 2 G2 GPS: 37 13 10 S 146 31 44 E
Numerous campsites, accessed 12.5km along Bluff Link Road, which is signposted off Brocks Road at Eight Mile Gap. Ph: 13 19 63

149. Lovicks Camping Area - High country
Map Ref: MAP 2 G2 GPS: 37 12 42 S 146 34 58 E
Access via Bluff Track off Brocks Track. Located in Alpine NP. Ph: 13 19 63

150. Howitt Hut Camping Area - High Country
Map Ref: MAP 2 G2 GPS: 37 13 54 S 146 41 53 E
Within the Alpine NP signposted off Howitt Road, 30km N of Arbuckle Junction. Located beside Calendonia River. Ph: 13 19 63

151. Wonnangatta Valley Camping Area - High Country
Map Ref: MAP 2 H2 GPS: 37 12 25 S 146 40 57 E
Located in a large secluded valley beside the Wonnangatta River with numerous riverside campsites. Best way in from Myrtleford via Abbeyards Rd. Ph: 13 19 63

152. Lankey Plain Hut Bush Camping Area - High Country
Map Ref: MAP 2 J2 GPS: 37 06 41 S 147 10 01 E
Located 200m along King Spur Track signposted off the Dargo High Plains Rd 20kms south of the Great Alpine Rd. Ph: 13 19 63

153. Thirty Mile Creek Camping Area - High Country
Map Ref: MAP 2 J2 GPS: 37 10 51 S 147 08 01 E
Small site beside creek on Ritchie Road, 12km W of 25 Mile Creek camping area N of Dargo. Dry weather only Ph: 03 5140 1243

154. Twenty-five Mile Creek Camping Area - High Country
Map Ref: MAP 2 J2 GPS: 37 11 33 S 147 10 49 E
Situated on Ritchie Road. 10km W of Dargo High Plains Road, 45km N of Dargo. Dry weather only Ph: 03 5140 1243

155. The Gums Camping Area - Close to Melbourne
Map Ref: MAP 2 B3 GPS: 37 28 08 S 145 23 40 E
Camping area 10km N of Kinglake within Kinglake NP. Access via Eucalyptus Rd (Glenburn Rd). Ph: 13 19 63

156. Ferns Camping Area - Close to Melbourne
Map Ref: MAP 2 C3 GPS: 37 25 34 S 145 34 07 E
Within the Murrindindi State Forest. Access via Murrindindi Rd off the Melba Hwy S of Yea. Ph: 13 61 86

157. Bull Creek Camping Area - Close to Melbourne
Map Ref: MAP 2 C3 GPS: 37 25 52 S 145 34 29 E
Located S of Yea via Murrindindi Rd off the Melba Hwy. Numerous sites. Ph: 13 61 86

158. Cooks Mill campinga area - Close to Melbourne
Map Ref: MAP 2 C3 GPS: 37 22 46 S 145 45 38 E
Within the Cathedral Range State Park. 10km SE of Taggerty via Cathedral Lane and Little River Rd. Ph: 13 19 63

159. Rubicon Valley - Close to Melbourne
Map Ref: MAP 2 D2 GPS: 37 18 38 S 145 51 05 E
Access is via the Maroondah Hwy at Taggerty, taking a right towards Eildon and turning up Rubicon Rd. 150kms NE of Melbourne. Ph: 13 61 86

160. Kendall's Camping Area - High Country
Map Ref: MAP 2 D2 GPS: 37 18 36 S 145 51 09 E
Within the Rubicon SF access via Rubicon Rd signposted 3km S of Thornton. Ph: 13 61 86

The Rubicon Valley

No 159

Rubicon Valley, VIC

24km south east of Eildon

John Mainwaring

Not too far from Eildon and off the side road from Taggerty in Victoria's north east there is a pleasant and easily accessed valley called Rubicon. It is historically interesting as the site of the first hydro project in Victoria, and you can camp within walking distance of most of the bits and pieces of this facility, with diversion aqueducts, a power house at the foot of the main water drop and some river flats with the remnants of the old support village from the days when this was a manned facility. Although just a tiny contributor to the grid nowadays, it is automated and still doing its thing as it has for over 100 years.

This is one of the wettest spots in Victoria and the steepness of the river's fall made hydro power an attractive option. The campsites are on a couple of large river flats where the support village used to be, before it was all automated. There is still evidence of some of the old homes, with occasional chimneys poking out of the undergrowth and in spring, bunches of daffodils and blue bells pop up where the cottage gardens once were. There are a few old fruit trees too, no doubt greatly appreciated by the rosellas and possums in the vicinity.

In a way this is a mini Snowy River project. The river beside the campsites is often a little bereft of water supplies as the hydro water races divert the flow for turbine turning duty at several points down the hill a ways. But upstream from the main powerhouse this river is a sensational, steep, rocky cascading water course. You can easily see why this spot was chosen for power generation.

The camp areas have toilets and fireplaces but nothing else so this is bush camping with just a few comforts. There is tall mountain ash forest surrounding the area. There are a few walks in the area, with one up around the powerhouse and if you are keen you can walk up the pipeline that brings the water down to the generators. Spectacular views of the valley are the reward for your efforts. A loop drive also takes you past the sets of aqueducts that supply the water to the feed pipe prior to its drop down into the valley.

Rubicon is about 150 kms north east of Melbourne near the town of Taggerty. Supplies are available from Eildon. It is a beaut little campsite in a historically interesting location with excellent 2WD access for large caravans so a good one to check out on your travels

The joy of swimming in a mountain pool.

The aqueduct pipeline and walking path.

A monument to power generation.

Camping amongst giant trees.

Just The Facts

The Rubicon Valley

Getting there: Access is via the Maroondah Highway at Taggerty, taking a right towards Eildon and turning up the Rubicon Road. This area is 150 kms north east of Melbourne not far from Eildon.
Facilities: Pit toilets, fireplaces.
Charges: Free.
Contact: DSE Ph 13 6186
Pets: Permitted

Free Campsites in Victoria

161. The Boy's Camping Area - Close to Melbourne
Map Ref: MAP 2 D3 GPS: 37 19 15 S 145 51 38 E
Within the Rubicon State Forest. S of Thornton, access via Rubicon Rd. Ph: 13 61 86

162. Barnewall Plains Camping Area - High Country
Map Ref: MAP 2 D3 GPS: 37 21 36 S 145 55 31 E
Located within the Mt Torbreck scenic reserve 14km S of Eildon via the Barnewall Plains Rd. Ph: 13 61 86

163. Running Creek Camping Area
Map Ref: MAP 2 D3 GPS: 37 21 09 S 145 59 08 E
Beside the track off the Jamieson-Eildon Road, 8.9km west of Taponga camping area in Big River SF. Small area. Ph: 13 61 86

164. Running Creek Camping Area
Map Ref: MAP 2 D3 GPS: 37 21 09 S 145 59 07 E
Located off the Jamieson-Eildon Rd, 8.9km W of Taponga camping area then in 400m to site. Ph: 13 61 86

165. Burnt Bridge Camping Ground - Yarra & Dandenong
Map Ref: MAP 2 E3 GPS: 37 20 55 S 146 03 38 E
24km from Jamieson along the Jamieson-Eildon Rd within the Big River State Forest. Ph: 13 61 86

166. The Pines Camping Area - Close to Melbourne
Map Ref: MAP 2 E3 GPS: 37 21 26 S 146 03 40 E
S of Bulldog Flat Jamieson-Eildon Road close to Newman's Track. Ph: 13 61 86

167. Bulldog Flat Camping Area - Yarra & Dandenongs
Map Ref: MAP 2 E3 GPS: 37 21 11 S 146 03 46 E
Within the Big River State Forest numerous sites accessed along Jamieson-Eildon Rd. Ph: 13 61 86

168. Horseshoe Camping Area
Map Ref: MAP 2 E3 GPS: 37 22 00 S 146 03 20 E
Located in Lower Big River SF south of Jamieson. 1.3kms S of The Pines camping area on the northern end of the Bridge over Big River. Ph: 13 61 86

169. Taponga Camping Area - Big River State Forest - Yarra & Dandenongs
Map Ref: MAP 2 E3 GPS: 37 22 11 S 146 03 29 E
Access is on the E side of Eildon-Jamieson Rd, 100m S of Jim Bullock camping area Ph: 13 61 86

170. Jim Bullock Camping Area - Yarra & Dandenongs
Map Ref: MAP 2 E3 GPS: 37 22 09 S 146 03 46 E
Signposted access from Jamieson-Eildon Road within the Big River State Forest Ph: 13 61 86

171. Old Coach Camping Area - Yarra & Dandenongs
Map Ref: MAP 2 E3 GPS: 37 23 17 S 146 04 22 E
Along Big River Rd, signposted along Jamieson-Eildon Rd. Ph: 13 61 86

172. Chaffe Creek Camping Area - Yarra & Dandenongs
Map Ref: MAP 2 E3 GPS: 37 23 44 S 146 04 38 E
Also in the Big River State Forest signposted access along Big River Rd S of the Old Coach camping area. Ph: 13 61 86

173. Grannys Flat Camping Ground - High Country
Map Ref: MAP 2 E2 GPS: 37 17 25 S 146 12 54 E
Within the Mansfield SF 8km E of Jamieson along the Jamieson-Licola Rd. Ph: 13 61 86

174. Doctors Creek Reserve - Upper Goulburn Historic Area
Map Ref: MAP 2 E3 GPS: 37 19 56 S 146 07 50 E
Camp area 5km S of Jamieson via Mansfield Woods Point Rd, Jamieson. Riverside. Ph: 13 61 86

175. Skipworth Reserve
Map Ref: MAP 2 E3 GPS: 37 20 46 S 146 08 34 E
Camping area 7km S of Jamieson beside River. Ph: 13 61 86

176. Kevington Hotel
Map Ref: MAP 2 E3 GPS: 37 21 30 S 146 09 41 E
Camping area next to hotel. Check with hotel first. Ph: 03 5777 0543

Free Campsites in Victoria

177. Tunnel Bend Reserve - High Country
Map Ref: MAP 2 E3 GPS: 37 23 01 S 146 12 54 E
Located near Jamieson 37kms S of Mansfield. Access via the Mansfield-Woods Point Rd. Ph: 13 19 63

178. Twelve Mile Reserve - High Country
Map Ref: MAP 2 E3 GPS: 37 23 05 S 146 13 43 E
Camping area 21km S of Jamieson. Ph: 13 19 63

179. Flour Bag Creek Reserve - High Country
Map Ref: MAP 2 E3 GPS: 37 22 54 S 146 13 00 E
8km S of Kevington Hotel along the Mansfield-Woods Point Rd. Ph: 13 19 63

180. Blue Hole Reserve - High Country
Map Ref: MAP 2 E3 GPS: 37 23 19 S 146 14 51 E
Within the Upper Goulburn historic area along the Mansfield-Woods Point Rd. Ph: 13 19 63

181. Snakes Reserve - High Country
Map Ref: MAP 2 E3 GPS: 37 25 01 S 146 14 40 E
Camp Area 27km S of Jamieson off the Mansfield-Woods Point Rd. Dirt Road. Ph: 13 19 63

182. Picnic Point Reserve - High Country
Map Ref: MAP 2 F3 GPS: 37 24 41 S 146 14 52 E
Along the Mansfield-Woods Point Rd. Accessed 2.5km S of Blue Hole Reserve. Ph: 13 19 63

183. Knockwood Reserve - High Country
Map Ref: MAP 2 E3 GPS: 37 26 05 S 146 13 45 E
Located on the Mansfield-Woods Point Rd 24km N of Woods Point General Store. Ph: 13 19 63

184. Gaffneys Creek - High Country
Map Ref: MAP 2 E3 GPS: 37 28 40 S 146 11 33 E
Camp area 17km N of Woods Point or 39km S of Jamieson. Ph: 13 19 63

185. Mitchells Flat Camping Area - High Country
Map Ref: MAP 2 F3 GPS: 37 18 14 S 146 21 56 E
In the Mansfield region on the edge of the Alpine NP. Access via Mitchells track off Jamieson-Licola Rd. Ph: 13 19 63

186. Wrens Flat camping reserve - High Country
Map Ref: MAP 2 F3 GPS: 37 20 36 S 146 22 20 E
Within the Mansfield State Forest. Located on Mt Sunday Rd off the Jamieson-Licola Rd. Ph: 13 61 86

187. Horse Paddock Camping Area - High Country
Map Ref: MAP 2 H3 GPS: 37 23 59 S 146 45 11 E
Signposted access along Kellys Lane 700m south of Howitt Rd or 4.6kms north-west of Arbuckle Junction. Ph: 13 19 63

188. Talbotville Camping Area - High Country
Map Ref: MAP 2 J3 GPS: 37 20 10 S 147 04 06 E
Within the Grant historic area beside Crooked River along McMillan track along Dargo-High Plains Rd. Ph: 13 19 63

189. Eaglevale Camping Area - High Country
Map Ref: MAP 2 J3 GPS: 37 22 13 S 147 00 45 E
50km NW of Dargo beside Wonnangatta River. Signposted access along the Wonnangatta Road at the junction of the Eaglevale Track. Ph: 13 19 63

190. Bullock Flat Camping Area - High Country
Map Ref: MAP 2 J3 GPS: 37 22 48 S 147 03 41 E
Next to the Wonnangatta River 43km NW of Dargo off the Crooked River Rd. Ph: 13 19 63

191. Grant Camping Area - High Country
Map Ref: MAP 2 J3 GPS: 37 20 38 S 147 09 21 E
Within the Grant historic area. From the Dargo High Plains Road, signposted on to McMillan Track. Ph: 13 19 63

192. Collins Flat Camping Area - High Country
Map Ref: MAP 2 K3 GPS: 37 20 36 S 147 18 10 E
Signposted access 16km along Upper Dargo Road off Dargo High Plains Rd. Ph: 03 5140 1243

Featured Campsite

Brought to you by

Tunnel Bend Reseserve No 177

High Country, Vic

About 50km from Mansfield

John Mainwaring

Camping in the thick forest is really getting away from it all.

Usually when you talk about fishing Victoria's Goulburn River, people will assume you are talking about the lower reaches, downstream of Lake Eildon where it flows slowly, cold and deep through farmland all the way down past Alexandra, Seymour, Nagambie, Shepparton and on to the confluence with the Murray near Echuca. But then there is the Upper Goulburn, above where it flows into Lake Eildon where it is a true High Country river, fed by dozens of little tributaries flowing down from the well-wooded foothills of the Great Dividing Range.

This is one easy river to fish, and yet there never seem to be too many taking advantage of such a magnificent area so easily accessed. Although a portion of the road is unsealed, it is a high quality gravel road and 2WD-accessible in practically all weathers. Caravan access is easy if you have a long and comfortable stay in mind. River access is very, very easy, with the road running next to the water for much of the trip up the valley. All the way from Jamieson to the old gold mining settlement of Knockwood on the Mansfield-Woods Point Road, access to the river is no more than about 10 to 20 metres from the road, with numerous campsites practically at the water's edge. A couple of these in between Jamieson and Kevington have a small fee, namely Doctor's Reserve and Skipworth Reserve.

But if it is free bush camping you want then head further in towards Knockwood where you will find Tunnel Bend Reserve, 12 Mile Reserve, Blue Hole, Picnic Point and Snake Reserve. These can have a few clientele at Christmas and Easter, but generally you will have one of these areas entirely to yourself, all for free.

Most parts of this section of the river are fairly easily walked in a decent set of waders. Access further up the Goulburn is possible for walkers, or you can follow Army Track, which follows the river's path a little further. Gaffney's Creek is a feeder into the Goulburn and that is the tributary that the road follows further upstream towards Gaffney's Creek settlement. The road continues up to Woods Point where the road once again crosses the Goulburn. The river's source is in the bush about 10km from Woods Point. Up here there is a couple more camping reserves (Scott's Reserve and Comet Flat) but payment of a small fee is required for each of these. Personally I would not take a bulky caravan any further in towards Woods Point than Knockwood Reserve camping area as the roads get a bit narrow and opposing traffic would be a challenge.

This is a fairly densely forested area and all the campsites are well treed (handy for the hammock) with plenty of shade and shelter. Each of the campsites has a long drop toilet. If complete solitude is your aim, keep your eyes peeled for some tight and small "unofficial" spots along the way where there is room for a vehicle and a small camper trailer, or a couple of spots which would be nice with a swag and a tight camp. Being so close to the river, the occasional flood can give these sites a bit of a freshen up.

The Goulburn has plentiful brown trout and redfin and some pretty large eels. I have not seen carp but you would have to assume the odd one is about, and there may be a few Murray cod that have made their way up from Eildon.

Just The Facts

Tunnel Bend Reserve

Getting there: The gateway to the area is Jamieson, 37km south of Mansfield and 200km northeast of Melbourne via Eildon. The Mansfield Shire has paved this road so it is a smooth and scenic run through bushland.

Facilities: Long drop toilets and a few campfire hot plates.

Rates: No charge.

What to catch: Target fish in the Upper Goulburn are mainly brown trout and redfin.

Pets: Dogs allowed. Most of the area is state forest.

Contact: Department of Sustainability & Environment Customer Service Centre on 13 61 86, Mansfield office (03) 5733 1200, www.dse.vic.gov.au/forests

Free Campsites in Victoria

193. Black Flat Camping Area - East Gippsland
Map Ref: MAP 2 K3 GPS: 37 22 04 S 147 17 58 E
Signposted access 11km along Upper Dargo Road N of Dargo off the Dargo High Plains Rd. Ph: 03 5140 1243

194. Ollies Jumpup Campground - East Gippsland
Map Ref: MAP 2 K3 GPS: 37 23 11 S 147 16 52 E
12km N of Dargo along Upper Dargo Rd. Dry weather only Ph: 13 61 86

195. Jimmy Iversons Campground - High Country
Map Ref: MAP 2 K3 GPS: 37 23 56 S 147 16 28 E
Signposted camp area 63km SW of Omeo or 10km N of Dargo. 5.5km N of Dargo turn NE onto Upper Dargo Rd. Dry weather only Ph: 13 61 86

196. Two Mile Creek - High Country
Map Ref: MAP 2 K3 GPS: 37 24 43 S 147 15 45 E
Camp area 7km N of Dargo along the Upper Dargo Rd. Dry weather only Ph: 13 61 86

197. Italian Flat Campground - East Gippsland
Map Ref: MAP 2 K3 GPS: 37 24 25 S 147 15 42 E
8km N of Dargo. From the High Plains Rd turn into Upper Dargo Rd. Situated on the Dargo River. Dry weather only Ph: 13 61 86

198. Toolangi Recreation Area
Map Ref: MAP 2 B4 GPS: 37 32 07 S 145 28 28 E
Camp area near Toolangi Streamside Reserve at 68 Cherrys Lane, Toolangi. Exit Healesville-Kinglake Rd at primary school. Camp located at creekside. Gold coin donation. Ph: 03 5772 0333

199. Anderson Mill Camping Area - Close to Melbourne
Map Ref: MAP 2 C4 GPS: 37 32 34 S 145 44 12 E
From Marysville proceed west towards Melbourne along C512 for 4.2km to signposted Anderson Mill Rd. Then 3.4km to track signposted to camping area then 260m to camp area. Bring water and firewood. Ph: 13 61 86

200. Upper Yarra Reservoir Park Camping Area - Close to Melbourne
Map Ref: MAP 2 D4 GPS: 37 40 10 S 145 53 24 E
24km NE of Warburton via Woods Point Rd. Ph: 13 19 63

201. McCelland Camping Area - Big River State Forest - Yarra & Dandenongs
Map Ref: MAP 2 D3 GPS: 37 31 02 S 146 01 17 E
1km E of Dairy Flat camping area access track. 2WD access only in dry weather Ph: 13 61 86

202. Married Mens Camping Area - Big River State Forest - Yarra & Dandenongs
Map Ref: MAP 2 D4 GPS: 37 31 45 S 145 56 34 E
Access Track is located to the W of the Big River Road and the Eildon-Warburton Rd junction, 5.8km NE of the Marysville-Woods Point Road. 2wd access in dry weather only Ph: 13 61 86

203. Big River Camp Camping Area - Big River State Forest
Map Ref: MAP 2 D4 GPS: 37 31 43 S 145 56 41 E
Large camping area on Big River Road at its junction with the Eildon-Warburton road, 5.8km NE of the Marysville-Woods Point Road. Ph: 13 61 86

204. Dairy Flat Camping Area - Big River State Forest - Yarra & Dandenongs
Map Ref: MAP 2 D4 GPS: 37 31 13 S 146 00 44 E
4WD access only, 100m N of Miners Flat access track. Ph: 13 61 86

205. Gang Gang Gully Camping Area
Map Ref: MAP 2 D4 GPS: 37 31 10 S 146 01 53 E
1km E of McClelland Camping area access track then 400m to site. Only 2wd access in dry weather. Ph: 13 61 86

206. Bobuck Ridge Camping Area
Map Ref: MAP 2 E4 GPS: 37 31 07 S 146 02 13 E
Access 700 m E of Gang Gang Gully camping area, then in 800m to camping area. Ph: 13 61 86

207. Specimen Creek Camping Area - Close to Melbourne
Map Ref: MAP 2 E4 GPS: 37 31 14 S 146 02 39 E
800m E of Bobuck Ridge camping area access track, then in 500m m to camping area. Ph: 13 61 86

208. Fishbone Flat Camping Area - Close to Melbourne
Map Ref: MAP 2 D4 GPS: 37 31 38 S 145 59 47 E
3.1km E of Petroffs Road. 4WD access only Ph: 13 61 86

209. Stockmans Reward Camping Area - Yarra & Dandenongs
Map Ref: MAP 2 D4 GPS: 37 31 33 S 146 00 42 E
Signposted access off Big River Road E of Big River Camp in Big River State Forest. Ph: 13 61 86

210. Frenchmans Creek Camping Area - Yarra & Dandenongs
Map Ref: MAP 2 E4 GPS: 37 31 32 S 146 03 52 E
Found in the Upper Big River State Forest E of Marysville. Access via Big River Rd. Ph: 13 61 86

211. Vennelles Campground
Map Ref: MAP 2 E4 GPS: 37 31 14 S 146 04 44 E
From Marysville turn right onto Cumberland Rd, signs to Lake Mountain lookout, turn onto Big River Rd to campsites. Ph: 13 61 86

212. Snowy Road Bush Camping Area - Yarra & Dandenongs
Map Ref: MAP 2 D4 GPS: 37 32 31 S 146 00 58 E
Within the Upper Big River State Forest along Snowy Rd S of Big River Rd. Ph: 13 61 86

213. Jack Scott's Reserve Camping Area - High Country
Map Ref: MAP 2 E4 GPS: 37 33 34 S 146 14 22 E
Located in Upper Goulburn SF 2kms north-west of Woods Point along the Mansfield-Woods Point Rd. Open area on bend in river. Ph: 03 5775 7000

214. Scotts Reserve Camping Area
Map Ref: MAP 2 E4 GPS: 37 33 34 S 146 14 24 E
Located 2km from Woods Point General Store along the Mansfield-Woods Point Rd on bend of river. Ph: 1800 039 049

215. Comet Flat camping reserve - Gippsland
Map Ref: MAP 2 E4 GPS: 37 34 39 S 146 16 03 E
4km SE of Woods Point along the river bank. Take the Johnson Hill track. Ph: 03 5777 8220

216. Rumpff's Flat Camping Area - High Country
Map Ref: MAP 2 F4 GPS: 37 30 29 S 146 29 32 E
From Licola follow Jamieson-Licola Rd north-west for 8.6kms then take signposted Link Rd for 1.8km to signposted Glencairn Rd and follow north for 13.5kms. At junction proceed west along signposted Middle Ridge Rd for Ph: 13 61 86

217. Connor Plain Campsite - High Country
Map Ref: MAP 2 F4 GPS: 37 33 21 S 146 29 39 E
From Licola follow Jamieson-Licola Rd north-west for 21kms to camping area beside road on the western side. Ph: 13 61 86

218. Platypus Campground
Map Ref: MAP 2 G4 GPS: 37 30 43 S 146 38 40 E
Located in Alpine NP. Camping area 23km N of Licola on Tamboritha Rd beside Wellington River. Ph: 13 19 63

219. Wellington River Camping Area
Map Ref: MAP 2 G4 GPS: 37 31 03 S 146 36 55 E
Beside the Wellington River along Tamboritha Rd. Campsites start 9.4km N of Licola. Ph: 13 19 63

220. Red Box Campground
Map Ref: MAP 2 G4 GPS: 37 31 07 S 146 37 22 E
Located in Alpine NP. Camping area 19km N of Licola on Tamboritha Rd beside Wellington River. Ph: 13 19 63

221. Cockatoo Camping Area - High Country
Map Ref: MAP 2 G4 GPS: 37 31 21 S 146 36 50 E
Located in Alpine NP. Camping area 16km N of Licola on Tamboritha Rd beside Wellington River. Access 1.3km from Muttonwood CA. Ph: 13 19 63

222. Manna Gums Campground
Map Ref: MAP 2 G4 GPS: 37 31 58 S 146 36 30 E
Located in Alpine NP. Camping are 14km N of Licola on Tamboritha Rd beside Wellington River. Ph: 13 19 63

223. Muttonwood Campground
Map Ref: MAP 2 G4 GPS: 37 31 49 S 146 36 52 E
Located in Alpine NP. Camping are 16km N of Licola on Tamboritha Rd beside Wellington River. Ph: 13 19 63

224. Boobook Camping Area - High Country
Map Ref: MAP 2 G4 GPS: 37 33 08 S 146 37 01 E
Located along Tamboritha Rd on Wellington River south of Licola in Alpine NP. Access 300m north of Wild Cherry CA, then 120m to well shaded area beside the river. Ph: 13 19 63

Featured Campsite

Brought to you by

Comet Flat Campground No 215

High Country / Gippsland, Vic

3 to 5kms from Woods Point

Anthony Kilner

Nestled along the Goulburn River, Comet Flat Campground offers a serene escape with the soothing sounds of water flowing over rocks, birdcalls, and crackling campfires in winter. Surrounded by tree-lined mountains, it's a peaceful spot for nature lovers.

Located about 180kms (3.5–4 hours' drive) from Melbourne, near Woods Point in Victoria's Central High Country, the campground provides ample spaces for camping along the river. A pit toilet is available at the far end of the site.

The road from Woods Point to Comet Flat is narrow in places, requiring careful driving. There are several creek crossings that need a 4WD with decent ground clearance. These rocky-bottomed crossings can be challenging when the water is high and fast-flowing, so caution is advised.

Given the access conditions, the area is best suited for tent, swag, camper trailers or small off-road, single-axle caravans. The track can be overgrown, and low-hanging branches might damage larger caravans.

Woods Point, once a bustling mining hub during the Victorian gold rush, still reflects its heritage with relics scattered around the region. The town offers essentials, including the Commercial Hotel with good food, cold drinks, and limited accommodation. The general store also stocks the basics including maps and books. There is no fuel available in town, so be prepared.

There's a lot to explore at Woods Point with a Museum, walks and some awesome 4WDriving in the surrounding hills. The quaint little town is popular with motorbikes and 4WD enthusiasts, especially on weekends, so the area can get busy.

Comet Flat is an ideal base for 4WD, biking, or bushwalking adventures across the surrounding mountains.

Lighting a campfire and staying by the Goulburne River.

Just The Facts

Comet Flat Camping Ground

Getting There: From central Melbourne it's approximately 3.5 Hours to Woods Point travelling via Lilydale through to Marysville then following the Marysville-Woods Point Road through Cambarville and Matlock to Woods Point. It's mostly dirt roads from Cambarville to Woods Point.

Another pleasant drive is to head from Lilydale to Warburton then follow the Warburton-Woods Point Road to Big River then the Marysville-Woods Point Road to Woods Point. It's mostly dirt roads from Cambarville to Woods Point.

A third option that takes approximately 4 hours, is to head to Yarra Glen on the Melba Highway and follow the highway to Yea then to Mansfield. From Mansfield head to the Mt Buller Road and turn off onto the Mansfield-Woods Point road. After Kevington it's mostly dirt road, narrow at times until Woods Point. There are quite a few free camps with toilets along this road.

Facilities: Pit toilet, fire pits

Pets: Allowed

Charges: Free

Contact: DELWP - 136186

There are several creek crossings requiring good ground clearance.

Free Campsites in Victoria

225. Wild Cherry Camping Area - High Country
Map Ref: MAP 2 G4 GPS: 37 33 17 S 146 37 07 E
Located along Tamboritha Rd on Wellington River south of Licola in Alpine NP. Access 1.7km north of park information board, then 300m to well shaded area beside the river. Ph: 13 19 63

226. Barkly River Camping Area - High Country
Map Ref: MAP 2 G4 GPS: 37 33 52 S 146 34 10 E
Situated in Alpine NP 15km from Licola. Take Target Creek Rd into Glencairn Rd . Camping on Barkly River. Ph: 13 19 63

227. Currawong Campground
Map Ref: MAP 2 G4 GPS: 37 33 07 S 146 36 44 E
Located in Alpine NP. Camping are 11km N of Licola on Tamboritha Rd beside Wellington River. Ph: 13 19 63

228. Millers Hut Camping Area - High Country
Map Ref: MAP 2 H4 GPS: 37 32 40 S 146 49 34 E
Access via Mt Wellington Track which is signposted off Moroka Road. Ph: 13 19 63

229. Moroka Bridge Camping Area
Map Ref: MAP 2 H4 GPS: 37 30 04 S 146 57 19 E
Small bush campsite beside the road at Bridge over the Moroka River on the W side of the river, 26km E of Arbuckle Junction along Moroka Road. Ph: 13 19 63

230. Horseyard Flat Camping Area - High Country
Map Ref: MAP 2 H4 GPS: 37 28 58 S 146 58 54 E
Located 65km NE of Licola. Access is by 2WD road via Arbuckle Junction up from Licola or via Marathon Rd from Briagolong near Maffra. Coming in one way and exiting the other is a good option. Ph: 13 19 63

231. Black Snake Creek Camping Area - High Country
Map Ref: MAP 2 J3 GPS: 37 26 48 S 147 08 24 E
Located in Dargo region 20km W of town beside Wonnangatta River. Access off the crooked River Rd. Ph: 03 5140 1243

232. Dargo Hotel
Map Ref: MAP 2 K4 GPS: 37 27 42 S 147 15 06 E
Camp area in paddock behind pub via Lind Ave & Omeo Rd, Dargo. Register at bar. Ph: 03 5140 1231

233. Orrs Creek campsite
Map Ref: MAP 2 J4 GPS: 37 29 39 S 147 12 05 E
Located in Dargo area 7kms S of Dargo on the western side along Dargo-Bairnsdale Rd. Ph: 03 5140 1243

234. Meyers Flat campsite
Map Ref: MAP 2 K4 GPS: 37 30 36 S 147 13 32 E
Located in Dargo area 12kms S of Dargo between the road and river along Dargo-Bairnsdale Rd. Ph: 03 5140 1243

235. Castleburn Creek Camping Area - High Country
Map Ref: MAP 2 J4 GPS: 37 32 29 S 147 12 14 E
Signposted along Dargo-Bairnsdale Rd 67km north of Princes Hwy and 18km south of Dargo. Grassed area beside Castleburn Creek. Ph: 13 61 86

236. Rock Creek Track Camping Area - Gippsland
Map Ref: MAP 2 K4 GPS: 37 36 08 S 147 20 20 E
From Dargo Rd 46kms north of the Princes Hwy take signposted road to Angusvale. Travel 7kms north-east to signposted Mitchell Rd then 1.4kms to signposted Angusvale Track then 3.3km to camping area. Ph: 13 19 63

237. Scout Loop Track Campground - Close to Melbourne
Map Ref: MAP 2 B5 GPS: 37 53 59 S 145 34 42 E
Within Kurth Kiln Regional Park signposted access 100m east of Magazine Track Campground. Large area in natural bush with 30 site. Horseyards located here. Bring water & firewood. Ph: 13 19 63

238. Kurth Kiln Camping - Yarra & Dandenongs
Map Ref: MAP 2 B6 GPS: 37 53 59 S 145 34 42 E
Kurth Kiln Regional Park is about 8kms from Gembrook 60kms E of Melbourne. Signposted access to the east of the historic site and picnic area. Ph: 13 19 63

239. Nash Creek Campground - Close to Melbourne
Map Ref: MAP 2 C6 GPS: 37 56 48 S 145 41 18 E
In the Bunyip State Park from Gembrook via Beenak East Rd & Black Snake Creek Rd. Dry weather only Ph: 13 19 63

240. Starlings Gap Camping Area - Yarra State Forest - Yarra & Dandenongs
Map Ref: MAP 2 C5 GPS: 37 48 55 S 145 48 10 E
Located on Big Creek Road via Black Sands Road off the Yarra Junction-Noojee Road, turn off is just SE of Gladysdale. Ph: 13 61 86

241. Latrobe River Camping Area - West Gippsland
Map Ref: MAP 2 D5 GPS: 37 52 52 S 145 53 36 E
Camp Area 15km W of Noojee. Located on the Ada River Rd off the Noojee-Powelltown Rd. Ph: 13 61 86

242. Poplars Reserve
Map Ref: MAP 2 D5 GPS: 37 49 08 S 145 59 38 E
Camp area 9km N of Noojee via Loch Valley Rd & Loch Valley Ext Rd. Narrow road. Beside river and steep access. Ph: 03 5624 8100

243. Loch Valley Campground - West Gippsland
Map Ref: MAP 2 D5 GPS: 37 49 10 S 145 59 41 E
7km N from Noojee, via Loch Valley Rd & Loch Valley Ext Rd. Camping beside river. Dry weather only. Ph: 13 61 86

244. Noojee Camping Area - West Gippsland
Map Ref: MAP 2 D5 GPS: 37 51 20 S 146 02 25 E
Outside the town of Noojee via Mt Baw Baw tourist road. Ph: 13 61 86

245. Toorongo Falls Camping Area - Gippsland
Map Ref: MAP 2 D5 GPS: 37 51 18 S 146 02 28 E
Signposted along the Baw Baw Tourist Rd 3.9kms east of Noojee. Proceed north for 5/5kms to large open camping area, close to Toorongo River. Ph: 13 61 86

246. Andersons Campground - Gippsland
Map Ref: MAP 2 F5 GPS: 37 43 26 S 146 23 23 E
Beside the Aberfeldy River 27km S of Woods Point along the Walhalla Rd. Ph: 03 5165 2200

247. Junction Campground
Map Ref: MAP 2 F5 GPS: 37 45 31 S 146 24 04 E
Situated beside the Aberfeldy River with access along Junction Track. Ph: 13 61 86

248. Jorgenson Flat Camping Area - Gippsland
Map Ref: MAP 2 F5 GPS: 37 44 54 S 146 24 44 E
Within the Thomson SF located beside Donnelly Creek along Donnelly Creek track. 40km N of Walhalla. Ph: 03 5165 2200

249. Little O'Tooles Camping Area - Gippsland
Map Ref: MAP 2 F5 GPS: 37 45 02 S 146 26 42 E
Located beside Donnelly Creek in Thomson State Forest, with signposted access along Donnelly Creek Track which is signposted of Walhalla Rd Ph: 03 5165 2200

250. O'Tooles Camping Area - Gippsland
Map Ref: MAP 2 F5 GPS: 37 45 02 S 146 26 57 E
Located beside Donnelly Creek, with access signposted along Donnelly Creek Track, which is signposted off the Walhalla Rd. Ph: 03 5165 2200

251. Merringtons Camping Area - Gippsland
Map Ref: MAP 2 F5 GPS: 37 45 39 S 146 24 06 E
Within the Thomson SF reached via Merrington's Track off Walhalla Rd. Ph: 03 5165 2200

252. Aberfeldy Bridge - Gippsland
Map Ref: MAP 2 F5 GPS: 37 51 14 S 146 25 51 E
From Princes Hwy at Moe turn north and head 50kms to Walhalla. Ph: 13 19 63

253. Cheynes Bridge - Gippsland
Map Ref: MAP 2 G5 GPS: 37 45 50 S 146 40 10 E
In the MacAllister SF along the Licola-Heyfield Rd at the bridge crossing at the MacAllister River. Ph: 13 61 86

254. Huggetts Crossing Camping Area - Gippsland
Map Ref: MAP 2 H5 GPS: 37 48 41 S 146 51 12 E
From the Upper Maffra Rd turn into signposted Horstmans Rd for 2km to Kentucky Rd and continue for 7.8kms to junction, track on left to Huggetts Crossing. The follow northerly for 4km to the large scenic camping area Ph: 13 61 86

255. Dermodys Camp Camping Area - West Gippsland
Map Ref: MAP 2 H5 GPS: 37 48 15 S 146 54 55 E
20km NW from Maffra on the Avon River, located at end of Dermody Rd. Dry weather only Ph: 03 5139 7777

256. Wombat Crossing Camping Area - Gippsland
Map Ref: MAP 2 H5 GPS: 37 48 02 S 146 55 46 E
From Valencia Creek, 8km west of Briagolong and 17km north from Maffra, follow signposted Wombat Rd for 6.5kms then turn into Wombat Track. At 500m keep left at Y-junction and continue for 1.5kma to circular camping a Ph: 13 61 86

Featured Campsite

Brought to you by

kokodacaravans.com.au

Aberfeldy Bridge Camping Area No 252

Mt Baw Baw National Park, VIC
50 km north of Moe

John Mainwaring

Dense bush, gold mining history and cheeky water dragons greet you at this delightful camping area on the Aberfeldy River.

Just 13 kms north of Walhalla on the road towards Aberfeldy is a location known as Aberfeldy Bridge. This bridge is close to a large horse shoe bend in the Aberfeldy River where there are some elevated flat areas that provide a very nice camp area in a deep valley setting surrounded by inviting, bush clad hills. This is part of the Mt Baw Baw National Park although it is a fair distance from Mt Baw Baw itself and really it is more naturally aligned with Walhalla and the Donnelly Creek camping areas just up the road near the old gold mining town of Aberfeldy.

Anyway there are 2 access routes to Aberfeldy Bridge, one being up a good quality dirt road from Walhalla. This is not recommended for caravans because it gets windy and hugs the hillside a little and there are sections where you would have a tight situation if you ran into opposing traffic. If you have a van that you love to take bush camping, your better bet would be to take the second access which takes you over the Thompson Dam (Melbourne's largest water storage) which then joins up with the Walhalla-Aberfeldy Road and you can head back south around 4 or 5 kms to get to Aberfeldy Bridge. Occasional corners are narrow but nothing too concerning, and apart from a few corrugations it is all good 2WD stuff.

Sitting by the campfire next to the Alberfeldy Bridge.

You really get the feeling of being away from it all.

Bushwalking high into the hills.

The Aberfeldy River valley has a fairly extensive catchment with some steep sides so when it rains that river can really pump some water through the countryside. The campsite can get a bit of a flush periodically if flood waters rise a bit, and on those occasions it can be closed but this is usually a mid-winter or early spring event with closures lasting a few weeks. During winter 2012 it had a brief sabbatical like this but it cleans things up, deposits some fairly convenient mats of fire wood and everything recovers pretty quickly. All part of the cycle in these parts. Even the bridge was swept away a few years ago but the solid concrete thing they have put in now looks good for another 100 years or so.

There is room for perhaps a dozen campsites in the main camping area and there are several more private little alcoves on the few hundred metres of track along the river frontage from the bridge itself. Although it can get busy at peak times, the times I have stayed here it has been a pleasantly solitary activity. I would assume there is some gold mining history to this site but I don't know any specifics. Certainly the area was a gold mining powerhouse with Walhalla just to the south and Aberfeldy and the Donnelly Creek workings just to the north being really big gold areas over a long period. The entire area has now reverted to very attractive wilderness just beckoning campers wanting a bit of pristine countryside.

For those not familiar with the area, Walhalla is one of Gippsland's better known gold mining towns and it has a raft of attractions, not the least its scenic setting in a similar steep sided valley surrounded by dense bush. It is around 120 kms east of Melbourne and around 50 kms north of Moe on the Princes Highway, so easily accessed.

Just The Facts

Aberfeldy Bridge Camping Area

Getting there: From Princes Highway at Moe in Gippsland, turn north and head the 50 kms to Walhalla for the main route in or via Erica and up to the Thompson Dam for the secondary route, more advisable for vans.

Facilities: Pit toilets and fireplaces.

Charges: Free

Pets: Not permitted (National Park)

Contact: Parks Victoria 13 1913

257. Avon River - Gippsland
Map Ref: MAP 2 H5 GPS: 37 48 22 S 146 55 01 E
The Avon-Mt Hedrick Scenic Reserve approx 15kms N of Maffra with simple access via Green Hill Rd.

258. Valencia Creek picnic and Camping Area - East Gippsland
Map Ref: MAP 2 H5 GPS: 37 45 48 S 146 59 34 E
Located 8km N of small hamlet of Valencia Creek via Valencia Creek-Morgan Rd in Briagolong SF. Ph: 03 5145 5215

259. Alistair Fieldings Camping Area - East Gippsland
Map Ref: MAP 2 J5 GPS: 37 39 38 S 147 08 30 E
Accessed via Lee Creek track from the Lee Creek camping area within the Briagolong State Forest 15km N of Stratford. Ph: 03 5145 5215

260. Lee Creek Camping Area - Gippsland
Map Ref: MAP 2 J5 GPS: 37 40 53 S 147 09 56 E
Located at the junction of Freestone Creek Road and Lees Creek Track. Ph: 03 5145 5215

261. Shadey's Place Camping Area - Gippsland
Map Ref: MAP 2 J5 GPS: 37 42 51 S 147 06 48 E
Signposted access along Freestone Creek Road, 6km N of Carneys campsite. Ph: 03 5145 5215

262. Johnston's Flat Camping Area - East Gippsland
Map Ref: MAP 2 J5 GPS: 37 42 38 S 147 08 52 E
Located within Briagolong State Forest. Signposted access along Freestone Creek Road, 2km N of Shadey's Place. Ph: 03 5145 5215

263. Lloyds Knob Camping Area - Gippsland
Map Ref: MAP 2 J5 GPS: 37 42 21 S 147 08 59 E
Signposted access along Freestone Creek Road, 1.5km N of Johnston's Flat. Ph: 03 5145 5215

264. Carneys campsite - East Gippsland
Map Ref: MAP 2 J5 GPS: 37 45 10 S 147 07 12 E
Located in Briagolong State Forest. Signposted access along Freestone Creek Road, 2.5km N of McKinnons Point. Ph: 03 5145 5215

265. McKinnons Point Camping Area - East Gippsland
Map Ref: MAP 2 J5 GPS: 37 46 02 S 147 06 40 E
Access along Freestone Creek Road. 14km N of Briagolong. Ph: 03 5145 5215

266. Blue Pools Campground - East Gippsland
Map Ref: MAP 2 J5 GPS: 37 46 55 S 147 06 48 E
Access The Blue Pool water hole 10km north of Briagolong on the Freestone Creek. Ph: 13 61 86

267. Froam picnic and Camping Areas - East Gippsland
Map Ref: MAP 2 J5 GPS: 37 46 53 S 147 07 10 E
Within the Briagolong State Forest 15km N of Stratford. Access along Freestone Creek Road. Ph: 03 5145 5215

268. Seninis Campground - Gippsland
Map Ref: MAP 2 F6 GPS: 38 01 22 S 146 20 22 E
Within the Moondarra State Park signposted of the Moe-Erica Rd along the Seninis Track. Dry weather only Ph: 13 19 63

269. Walhalla North Gardens Campground
Map Ref: MAP 2 F6 GPS: 37 55 57 S 146 26 55 E
Camp area at Walhalla, 1km N of PO. Other campsites & big rigs at S entrance to town Ph: 13 19 63

270. North Gardens Campground - Gippsland
Map Ref: MAP 2 F6 GPS: 37 55 51 S 146 26 42 E
Located in Walhalla township off Walhalla Rd. Ph: 13 19 63

271. Thomson Bridge
Map Ref: MAP 2 F6 GPS: 37 57 26 S 146 25 12 E
Located in Erica State Forest 8km E of Rawson or 5km SW of Walhalla on Old Depot Rd, Rawson. Ph: 13 61 86

272. Coopers Creek Camping Area - Gippsland
Map Ref: MAP 2 F6 GPS: 37 58 52 S 146 25 30 E
Within Boola Boola State Forest. Located SE of Rawson via Coopers Creek Track off Walhalla Rd. Ph: 03 5165 2200

Free Campsites in Victoria

273. Bruntons Bridge Camping Area - Gippsland
Map Ref: MAP 2 F6 GPS: 37 59 54 S 146 28 21 E
Located beside Thomson River within the Boola Boola SF signposted from Walhalla Ph: 03 5165 2200

274. Cowwarr Weir
Map Ref: MAP 2 G6 GPS: 37 59 49 S 146 39 34 E
Camping area 5km W of Cowwarr at weir. Turn N from Toongabbie-Cowwarr Rd on to Weir Rd and follow signs. Ph: 03 5139 3100

275. Heyfield RV Stop
Map Ref: MAP 2 H6 GPS: 37 59 06 S 146 47 15 E
Camping area 700m SE of Post Office at corner MacFarlane & Clarke sts. Limited Stay. Ph: 0418 108 691

276. Newry Recreation Reserve
Map Ref: MAP 2 H6 GPS: 37 54 20 S 146 54 28 E
Camping area 2km N of Newry via Newry-Boisdale & Three Chain Rds, next to golf course. Donation appreciated & limited stay.

277. Nambrok Hall
Map Ref: MAP 2 H7 GPS: 38 04 13 S 146 51 12 E
Camp area 173 Nambrok Hall Rd, 13kms NW of Rosedale. N off Princes Hwy to Nambrok Rd. Ph: 0429 422 207

278. Willow RV Park
Map Ref: MAP 2 H7 GPS: 38 08 31 S 146 47 28 E
Camp spot 1km N of Rosedale. Signposted as Wellington RV Park beside La Trobe River.

279. The Aussie Pub Rosedale
Map Ref: MAP 2 H7 GPS: 38 09 07 S 146 47 24 E
Camping area at hotel. Check in with hotel. Ph: 03 5199 2504

280. Harriers Swamp Campground - East Gippsland
Map Ref: MAP 2 H7 GPS: 38 12 24 S 146 50 37 E
Camp Area 9km SE of Rosedale within the Holey Plains State Park. Turn E 3.5km S of Rosedale off the Willung Rd onto Rosedale-Stradbroke Rd.
Ph: 13 19 63

Featured Campsite

Brought to you by

The Avon Campsites No 257

Gippsland, VIC

15 kms north of Maffra

John Mainwaring

The Avon is one of the most interesting of the rivers flowing out of the High Country into Gippsland's lowlands and lakes system. This one is a shingle river, made up predominantly of pebble banks heaped onto a solid bed rock.

The nice camp sites for the Avon are up nearer the headwaters in the shadow of the Mt Wellington Plateau, accessed just north of Maffra in the Avon-Mt Hedrick Scenic Reserve. There are several areas set up as camping zones, including Wombat Crossing, Dermody Camp and Huggetts Crossing. These sites hark back to the times when low country farmers used to drive some cattle up to the high plains around Mt Howitt and Mt Wellington to make use of the spring and summer growth up there, and these locations were pause points and crossings of the river on the way up and down.

Tranquil river camping

To my mind, Wombat Crossing and Dermodys Camp are pretty nice, both being accessible by 2WD next to pleasant sections of the Avon River. But the pick of the lot is Huggetts Crossing with spacious camp areas with room for 20-30 camping parties and a magnificent water hole. All 3 camps lack any facilities other than fire-places and toilets plus a couple of picnic tables. Dogs are permitted at all of these camp areas as well, so it can be a destination for the entire family. Huggetts and Dermodys are within the 5700 hectare Avon-Mt Hedric Scenic Reserve. They are linked by a 9 kilometre walking track called the "Avon River Walking Trail" which is pretty spectacular, particularly where it passes "The Channel" which is an area where the passage of the river was confronted by a thick layer of granite bedrock. The river carved its way through, creating a gorge like a narrow Roman aqueduct with smooth sides. You can also access this by the road and there is a car park with a lookout. Rocky escarpments along the river give this a very "Northern Territory" feel.

281. Holey Hill Camping Area - East Gippsland
Map Ref: MAP 2 H8 GPS: 38 13 54 S 146 56 21 E
Within the Holey Plains NP off the Rosedale-Stradbroke Rd. Follow directions from Rosedale as for Harriers Swamp CA to West Boundary Track. Continue on the Rosedale-Stradbroke Road to the signposted Holey Hill Track. Ph: 13 19 63

282. Loch Recreation Reserve
Map Ref: MAP 2 C8 GPS: 38 22 03 S 145 42 44 E
Camping area 1km NE of Loch off Loch-Poowong Rd. Ph: 03 5659 4360

283. Boolarra Club Hotel
Map Ref: MAP 2 E8 GPS: 38 22 48 S 146 16 36 E
Camping area at hotel on Monash Way Boolarra. Check with hotel. Ph: 03 5169 6420

284. Boolarra Apex Park
Map Ref: MAP 2 E8 GPS: 38 25 45 S 146 18 32 E
Camping area 8km SE of Boolarra. Turn W at Boolarra South sign then after 30m turn S on to Morwell River Rd.

285. Morwell River Camping Areas - Gippsland
Map Ref: MAP 2 E9 GPS: 38 25 39 S 146 18 33 E
From the town of Boolarra take the C456 to Churchill & Morwell and then on to the Morwell River Rd. Campsites beside the river. Ph: 03 5683 9000

286. Gormandale Recreation Reserve
Map Ref: MAP 2 G8 GPS: 38 17 32 S 146 42 03 E
Camping area on Hyland Hwy, Gormandale. Ph: 03 5197 7200

287. Bass Valley Camping Ground
Map Ref: MAP 2 G8 GPS: 38 21 38 S 146 45 52 E
Camping area 8km N of Bena on Bass Valley Rd beside river.

288. Gippsland Coastal Park
Map Ref: MAP 2 J8 GPS: 38 20 07 S 147 14 36 E
Camp area between Seaspray & Golden Beach via Longford-Loch Sport Rd, Loch Sport. Ph: 13 19 63

289. Turtons Creek Camping Area - Gippsland
Map Ref: MAP 2 E9 GPS: 38 32 10 S 146 15 08 E
Within Turtons Creek Reserve N of Foster. From Sth Gippsland Hwy take the signposted Boolarra Rd to Turtons Creek Rd. Camping along the creek. Ph: 03 5683 9000

290. Dingo Creek
Map Ref: MAP 2 F9 GPS: 38 34 34 S 146 23 11 E
Camp area 20km N of Port Welshpool. Head N off South Gippsland Hwy to Woorarra Rd to Dingo Creek Rd.

291. Minnie Ha Ha Falls Camping Reserve
Map Ref: MAP 2 F9 GPS: 38 31 11 S 146 27 53 E
Located on Albert River Rd via Jack River & Staceys Creek Rd. 20 mins from Yarram. Ph: 03 5182 6553

292. White Woman's Waterhole - Gippsland
Map Ref: MAP 2 G9 GPS: 38 28 56 S 146 46 20 E
Approx 15kms N of Yarram and between Wron Wron and Woodside on the Napier Rd with very good signage. Ph: 13 19 63

293. McGaurans Beach Camping Area
Map Ref: MAP 2 J9 GPS: 38 26 52 S 147 06 04 E
21km NE of Woodside via Giffard Road then into McGaurans Beach Road. Camping site at end of road. Ph: 13 19 63

294. Byrnes Road Bush Camping Area - Gippsland
Map Ref: MAP 2 H9 GPS: 38 31 16 S 147 00 24 E
From South Gippsland Hwy at Woodside take Woodside Beach Rd for 10kms to signposted Byrnes Rd. Continue north for 4.5kms and turn right for 160m to large bush camp. Ph: 13 19 63

295. Reeves Beach Coastal Reserve - Gippsland
Map Ref: MAP 2 H9 GPS: 38 34 22 S 146 57 10 E
Head from Woodside towards Woodside Beach turning right at Balloong Rd, continue several kms then left into Reeve's Beach Rd to the end. Ph: 13 19 63

296. Racecourse Recreation & Camping Reserve
Map Ref: MAP 2 G10 GPS: 38 39 06 S 146 41 36 E
1.2kms out of Port Albert on the Port Albert/Tarraville Rd. Ph: 1300 366 244

White Woman's Waterhole No 292

Near Woodside, VIC

15 kms north of Yarram

John Mainwaring

Sometimes a place name will make you pause and take notice, and all sorts of preconceived notions fill your head. So it was for me with White Woman's Waterhole. I visualised an idyllic rocky water hole surrounded by towering mountain ash and lush ferns. There was even a romanticised version of how it came by such a name, perhaps the favourite spot of a local settler. As usual with preconceived ideas, I was way wide of the mark.

In fact the name may be a complete furphy. The story goes that an English woman survived a wreck on the nearby 90 Mile Beach back in the 1840s. She was taken in or taken prisoner (depends on the point of view) by a local Aboriginal clan but she is said to have engraved a message on a tree near this waterhole. A passing stockman saw it, arranged a search party, rescued her and she returned to England. All very sweet in that version. There is the other version that this was a story started by McMillan, an early explorer in the area, based on some dodgy observations. Numerous searches failed to find her but did result in a few massacres of the local Aboriginal groups which suited many settlers at the time. So a happy ending or a mystery about whether she ever existed at all and a shabby part of our settler heritage were brought to the fore. I have no idea so take your pick. The waterhole has retained the name in memory of these happenings.

The waterhole is a very quiet, peaceful place to camp.

The campsite has concrete fireplaces.

What is important though is that this is a pleasant and easily accessed camp area right down in the South Eastern corner of this great continent. There are around 40 individual sites with a very gentle slope, nice grassy covering and shade provided by open forest Yellow Stringybark. If you are exploring this area around Yarram and The Prom this is a spot to call into perhaps as a pleasant base camp. It is a sandy and nicely treed area overlooking the waterhole. The ground is firm so all fine for 2WDs and large units, there are toilet facilities and you are allowed fires in the concrete fireplaces. Very important for the dog lovers, this is a state forest where pooches are permitted. It is practically in the middle of the 6700 hectare Won Wron State Forest with all sorts of interesting critters in the vicinity. That may be an attraction, or the handy location, or the dubious history. Whatever takes you there, it is a quiet and very peaceful spot that needs highlighting on your free camp spots list.

Just The Facts

White Woman's Waterhole

Getting there: This site is 210 kms east of Melbourne and about 15 kms north of Yarram. It is in between Won Wron and Woodside on the Napier Road (5 kms east of Won Wron) with very good signage pointing you there on a good road suitable for 2WD and caravans.

Facilities: Concrete fireplaces, toilets and a few picnic tables.

Charges: Free

Pets: Pets OK under control.

Contact: Parks Victoria 13 1963 or www.parks.vic.gov.au

Brought to you by

Racecourse Recreation And Camping Reserve

No 296

South Gippsland, Vic

1.2kms northeast of Port Albert

By Miriam Blaker

It's been a long time since this place has seen a thoroughbred, let alone hosted a horse racing event. The first race was held here in 1851, on a sandy course of 1400 metres. In 1934, during the Depression, the racecourse was abandoned. Restoration of the grounds and reserve began in 1956 and in Easter 1980 the Racecourse was reborn as a recreation and camping reserve.

The Port Albert Racecourse Recreation and Camping Reserve was once a bustling hub for horse lovers, today this historic area is a quiet and delightful surprise for those looking to stop along the South Gippsland Highway. It's barely a minute from the picturesque fishing village of Port Albert in East Gippsland.

Enter the campground through a gate off the Port Albert Tarraville Road and continue down a long drive and you'll find a grassed and spacious area where you can set up and relax. Buildings dot the area, including various shelter sheds and horse yards nearby. The old racing tower is a stand-out feature. Years ago the community opened this up as a campground and today the Friends of Port Albert are active in maintaining the grounds for passing visitors. On a regular basis they rally together to mow grassed areas, cut branches off the driveway, repair toilets or fix the spouting. This amazing community of volunteers is slowly but surely making the oldest Sand Race Track in Victoria beautiful again.

Welcome to a shady grassed park of beautiful trees and wildlife.

Remnants of the racing times.

A Visitors Book is housed in the small Information shelter. Camping is free with gold coin donations welcomed and going towards the upkeep of the buildings and grounds. You can camp anywhere amongst the trees, in the paddocks or near the old racecourse buildings. There are flushing toilets, shelter against the elements, a "wet bar" and a sense of peace and fun from golden racing days. Wildlife is prevalent and at night you'll likely spot kangaroos.

Take a drive around the sandy racecourse track and imagine how it must have been in its heyday. Although the interior is overgrown it's not hard to imagine the hustle and bustle from those rich racing days.

Nearby, in the picturesque village of Port Albert, there's 48 hours free camping on the car park near the boat ramp with a dump point and toilets close by. Explore the historic buildings and at The Wharf you can enjoy some of the best fish and chips on the coast.

Boats at the jetty in Port Albert.

Just The Facts

Racecourse Recreation Camping Reserve

Getting there: The Racecourse and Camping Reserve is 1.2kms out of Port Albert, on the Port Albert-Tarraville Road in Langsborough.

Facilities: Flushing toilets, water (untreated), old racecourse buildings and shelter.

Pets: Allowed.

Charges: Free. Gold coin donations welcomed.

Contact: Wellington Shire Council on 1300 366 244 or Marnie on 0407 297 546.

297. Foster Station Park
Map Ref: MAP 2 E10 GPS: 38 39 42 S 146 12 42 E
Camping area at old railway station site via Station Rd & Lower Franklin Rd. Self contained vehicles only.

298. Fish Creek Hotel
Map Ref: MAP 2 D10 GPS: 38 41 41 S 146 04 58 E
Located at 7 Old Waratah Rd, Fish Creek 13kms SW of Foster. From Meeniyan exit Hwy A440 S to Meeniyan-Promontory Rd for 17kms then S to Fish Creek. Toilets open during pub hours, free for patrons. Ph: 03 5683 2404

299. Shallow Inlet Campground
Map Ref: MAP 2 E11 GPS: 38 49 16 S 146 10 18 E
Bush camping. Turn W 19km S of Foster on to Lester Rd. Travel 4km dirt road to area adjacent to beach. Open Nov-April. Ph: 03 5687 1365

300. Bear Gully Reserve - Gippsland
Map Ref: MAP 2 D11 GPS: 38 53 24 S 145 59 12 E
35km SW of Fish Creek within the Cape Liptrap NP, via Walkerville-Fish Creek Rd. Ph: 13 19 63

301. Ulupna Beach Campsite - Murray
Map Ref: MAP 3 A2 GPS: 35 49 48 S 145 26 10 E
Island is located near Strathmerton which is just 10km west of Cobram on the Murray Valley Highway. Ph: 13 19 63

302. Carters Beach Camping Area
Map Ref: MAP 3 A2 GPS: 35 49 18 S 145 27 13 E
From Strathmerton follow Bourchiers Rd north then turn left onto signposted Ulupna Island to Bridge Rd then 1.5km to river after park entrance. Ph: 13 19 63

303. Doctors Bend Camping Area - Central Murray
Map Ref: MAP 3 A2 GPS: 35 49 02 S 145 28 10 E
Riverside camping within Barmah NP. North of Strathmerton via Ulupna Bridge Rd. Ph: 13 19 63

304. Apex Beach - Murray
Map Ref: MAP 3 B2 GPS: 35 48 48 S 145 32 48 E
Within the Tocumwal Regional Park. Located on the W side of Goulburn Valley Hwy. Take Bridge St to park entrance. Camping beside river. Dry weather only Ph: 13 19 63

305. Pebbly Beach Camping Area - Murray
Map Ref: MAP 3 B2 GPS: 35 49 04 S 145 34 10 E
Located on the opposite side of Tocumwal township. Ph: 13 19 63

306. Finley Beach - Murray
Map Ref: MAP 3 B2 GPS: 35 49 30 S 145 33 42 E
Located in Tocumwal Regional Park S of Tocumwal. 2km upstream of the bridge. Access via Finley Track. Camping beside river. Dry weather only Ph: 13 19 63

307. Tocumwal Regional Park Camps
Map Ref: MAP 3 B2 GPS: 35 49 20 S 145 33 32 E
Numerous camp areas 2.5kms S of Tocumwal via Goulburn Valley Hwy, turn E off A39 and travel 2km S along Finley Track, riverside. Ph: 13 19 63

308. Guilmartins Beach Camping Area - Central Murray
Map Ref: MAP 3 B2 GPS: 35 49 37 S 145 34 00 E
Within Tocumwal Regional Park, access off the Goulburn Valley Hwy and then by road signposted State Forest/Guilmartins Bend. Ph: 13 19 63

309. Bouchiers Beach Camping Area - Central Murray
Map Ref: MAP 3 B2 GPS: 35 50 21 S 145 34 31 E
Beach camp within Cobram SF access via Green Lane at northern forest entrance. Ph: 13 19 63

310. Boomagong Beach Camping Area - Central Murray
Map Ref: MAP 3 B2 GPS: 35 50 03 S 145 34 07 E
In Cobram SF between Cobram and Tocumwal access via Green Lane at the northern forest end. Ph: 13 19 63

311. Green Beach Camping Area
Map Ref: MAP 3 B2 GPS: 35 50 56 S 145 35 06 E
Located west of Brentnalls Beach, turn west at junction 300m south and follow 900m to track which leads north 200m to beach. Ph: 03 5872 2132

312. Weiss Beach Camping Area
Map Ref: MAP 3 B3 GPS: 35 51 40 S 145 35 47 E
On Cobram Track from Stewarts turn-off continue west for 1.7kms to track on right. This leads to camping area after 900m. Ph: 03 5872 2132

Brought to you by

Ulupna Beach campsite No 301

Strathmerton, Vic

10 km west of Cobram.

John Mainwaring.

Pleasant riverside camping is available pretty much anywhere along the Murray if you take a back road and explore a little. One particularly nice spot is Ulupna Island, near the small town of Strathmerton which is on one of the major migratory routes for north-south travelers, the Goulburn Valley Highway which becomes the Newell Highway.

Technically it is an island because a minor branch of the Murray loops around a large section of land so in wet times it is certainly an island in the stream (well bridged of course), but the rest of the time you would hardly notice. This is a particular favourite as a Murray destination as it has some considerable depth of red gum forest on both sides of the river giving it a "middle of nowhere" quality. There are also sandy beaches in a couple of areas, with easy access for conventional vehicles although mind those puddles. There is sufficient space for 50-100 campers without crowding and the open areas are adequate to permit camping away from those overhanging red gum boughs that look great but should never be camped under.

Sunrise with an early morning mist over the water.

There are some spectacular old trees by the river.

The camping area is nicely elevated above the river and some of the camping spots are on the bank edge several meters above the water. Many of these sites have convenient steps excavated into the bank for water access and I have seen many a fisherman sitting back with a line in the water without them having to move from their fireside chair.You will find Strathmerton around 10 kms from Cobram in Victoria's central north.

Free Campsites in Victoria

313. Stewarts No 1 Beach Camping Area
Map Ref: MAP 3 B3 GPS: 35 51 46 S 145 37 26 E
From Wilsons Beach turn off and follow main track towards Stewarts for 1.8kms to a track on left. Follow N for 300m to No.1 beach. Ph: 03 5872 2132

314. Wilsons Beach Camping Area
Map Ref: MAP 3 B3 GPS: 35 52 09 S 145 36 06 E
Along Cobram Track 1.1km to intersection with signposted Stewarts. Turn right for 100m to track on left another 900m to camping area. Ph: 03 5872 2132

315. Brentnalls Beach Camping Area
Map Ref: MAP 3 B3 GPS: 35 52 01 S 145 37 44 E
Located north of Weiss Beach. Continue along Cobram Track for 1.7km to track on right which leads to track junction then go north for 300m to camping area. Ph: 03 5872 2132

316. The Big Strawberry
Map Ref: MAP 3 B3 GPS: 35 53 17 S 145 34 28 E
Camping spot at Koonoomoo. Check in at caf, with power available for a fee. Limited stay. Ph: 03 5871 1300

317. Stewarts No 2 Beach Camping Area
Map Ref: MAP 3 B3 GPS: 35 52 01 S 145 37 44 E
Located S our Stewarts No 1 Beach. From the turn-off continue east for 500m to No. 2 beach. Ph: 03 5872 2132

318. Davies Beach Camping Area
Map Ref: MAP 3 B3 GPS: 35 52 32 S 145 37 40 E
Within Cobram SF along the Murray River NW of Cobram. From Dead River beach follow track W to meet with Cobram Track then NW for 400m to Davies Beach track then 1km to camping area. Ph: 03 5872 2132

319. Dead River Beach - Murray
Map Ref: MAP 3 C3 GPS: 35 52 49 S 145 37 50 E
Located in Cobram State Forest. Camp Area 6km NW of Cobram. Turn N off Cobram-Koonoomoo Rd. 1.7km W of Cobram onto Racecourse Rd, then along Dead River Track. Camping beside river. Dry weather only Ph: 13 19 63

320. Cobram West Camps - Cobram Regional Park
Map Ref: MAP 3 GPS: 35 53 37 S 145 38 48 E
Numerous camp areas 3km NW of Cobram via Wondah St Cobram. Turn N from C370 and take track over levee. After grid follow middle dirt track for 2km, riverside. Ph: 13 19 63

321. Big Toms Beach - Murray
Map Ref: MAP 3 B3 GPS: 35 53 34 S 145 38 47 E
Within the Cobram Regional Park off Wondah St on the banks of the Murray. Dry weather only Ph: 13 19 63

322. Little Toms Beach Camping Area - Murray
Map Ref: MAP 3 B3 GPS: 35 54 08 S 145 39 32 E
Within the Cobram Regional Park beside the Murray River. From park entrance via Wondah St to the camp ground. Ph: 13 19 63

323. Scotts Beach - Murray
Map Ref: MAP 3 B3 GPS: 35 55 36 S 145 40 25 E
Located in the Cobram Regional Park. A couple km E of Cobram via River Rd. Dry weather only Ph: 13 19 63

324. Horseshoe Lagoon
Map Ref: MAP 3 C3 GPS: 35 55 41 S 145 41 45 E
Camp area 7km E of Cobram. Turn S off Barooga Rd onto River Rd for 5km then N onto Horseshoe Track. Camping along river.

325. Horseshoe Beach
Map Ref: MAP 3 C3 GPS: 35 55 42 S 145 41 48 E
Camp Area 6.8km E of Cobram. Turn S off Barooga Rd onto River Rd for 4.8km, then N onto Horseshoe Track. Camping beside river. Dry weather only Ph: 13 19 63

326. Seppels Beach Camping Area - Central Murray
Map Ref: MAP 3 C3 GPS: 35 56 06 S 145 43 10 E
Located in Cobram Regional Park. From the park entrance along Pye Rd proceed north for 950m to Main Track then east along Main Track for 1.4km to signposted Seppels Track then 750m to river. 4WD beach boat launch. Ph: 13 19 63

327. McKays Beach Camping Area - Central Murray
Map Ref: MAP 3 C3 GPS: 35 56 45 S 145 43 35 E
Located in Cobram Regional Park. Access off Murray Valley Hwy 6km south east of Cobram via signposted Pye Rd. Continue to park entrance then north for 950m to Main Track then east for 3.2km to beach area. 4WD beach boat launch. Ph: 13 19 63

328. Dicks Bend State Forect Bush Camping - Central Murray
Map Ref: MAP 3 C4 GPS: 35 57 06 S 145 42 50 E
Cobrawonga State Forest is located 28km north west of Yarrawonga along Murray River and access via signposted Cemetery Rd from the Hwy. From entrance tracks lead to various parts of forest and river. Ph: 13 19 63

329. Cobram East Camps - Cobram Regional Park
Map Ref: MAP 3 C4 GPS: 35 55 41 S 145 41 45 E
Numerous camp areas 7km E of Cobram via Cobram River Rd. Turn S off Barooga Rd for 5km then N to Horseshoe Track. Riverside. Ph: 13 19 63

330. Cobrawonga No 1 Beach Camping Area - Murray
Map Ref: MAP 3 C3 GPS: 35 58 40 S 145 47 51 E
Within the Cobrawonga SF 16km SE of Cobram. Ph: 13 19 63

331. Bourkes No 2 Beach Camping Area
Map Ref: MAP 3 C3 GPS: 35 58 33 S 145 49 39 E
Camping along the Murray River SE of Cobram or NE of Yarrawonga off Murray Valley Hwy. From the park entrance proceed north for 2kms to track on left then follow 600m then turn tight for 300m. Ph: 03 5872 2132

332. Bourkes No 1 Beach campinr area
Map Ref: MAP 3 C3 GPS: 35 58 37 S 145 50 05 E
Camping along the Murray River SE of Cobram off Murray Valley Hwy. From the park entrance proceed north for 3kms to the river. Ph: 03 5872 2132

333. Bourkes Bend No 3
Map Ref: MAP 3 C4 GPS: 35 58 39 S 145 49 25 E
Within Bourke's Bend State Forest. From park entrance along Bourke's Bend Track a number of camping areas within this stretch of the river. Dry weather only. Ph: 13 19 63

334. Bourke Bend State Forest bush camping
Map Ref: MAP 3 C4 GPS: 35 59 49 S 145 49 31 E
Camping along the Murray River throughout the forest. Various tracks lead to river. Self sufficient campers Ph: 03 5872 2132

335. Percys Beach Camping Area - Central Murray
Map Ref: MAP 3 C3 GPS: 35 57 31 S 145 51 48 E
On the Murray River within Nevins Bend SF. 12km NW of Yarrawonga access via Harris Track. Ph: 13 19 63

336. Nevins Bend State Forest bush camping - Murray
Map Ref: MAP 3 D3 GPS: 35 58 20 S 145 52 53 E
Within the Nevins Bend State Forest, access via Thoms Rd off the Murray Valley Hwy. Located some 12km NW of Yarrawonga. Bush camping on banks of Murray River throughout forest. Ph: 13 19 63

337. Bruces Beach No 2 - Murray
Map Ref: MAP 3 D3 GPS: 35 57 48 S 145 54 51 E
Within the Yarrawonga Regional Park Access via Bruces Rd to the park entrance. Camping beside river. Dry weather only Ph: 13 19 63

338. Forges Beach No2 - Murray
Map Ref: MAP 3 D4 GPS: 35 59 56 S 145 57 31 E
Within the Yarrawonga Regional Park. Access via Forges Pump Rd 7km NW of Yarrawonga. Camping on the Murray. Dry weather only Ph: 13 19 63

339. Forges Beach No1 - Murray
Map Ref: MAP 3 D4 GPS: 35 59 46 S 145 57 46 E
Camp area 10km NW of Yarrawonga via Murray Valley Hwy, Forges Pump Lane & Forges Bend track.

340. Chinamans Bend
Map Ref: MAP 3 D4 GPS: 36 00 30 S 145 58 20 E
In the Yarrawonga Regional Park 7km W of Yarrawonga accessed via Brears Rd. Camping beside river. Dry weather only Ph: 13 19 63

341. Green Bank
Map Ref: MAP 3 D4 GPS: 36 00 35 S 145 58 38 E
Within Murray River Reserve5km W of Yarrawonga. Travel N off highway 3km W of Yarrawonga on to Cullens Rd and take L fork at Information Board. Camping beside river. Ph: 13 19 63

342. Yarrawonga River Camp
Map Ref: MAP 3 D4 GPS: 36 00 43 S 145 58 51 E
Camp area 5km W of Yarrawonga, turn N off Murray Valley Hwy to Cullen Rd on loop near river.

343. Lower Ovens bush camping - Murray
Map Ref: MAP 3 E4 GPS: 36 02 54 S 146 11 51 E
Lower Ovens Regional Park at the junction of Ovens & Murray Rivers. Signposted off the Murray Valley Hwy 3km E of Bundalong. Ph: 13 19 63

344. Parolas Bend
Map Ref: MAP 3 E4 GPS: 36 04 03 S 146 12 10 E
Camp area 24km W of Rutherglen. Turn N off B400 E of Ovens River opposite Riverside CP, travel along Parolas Track. Camping beside Ovens River. Ph: 13 19 63

Brought to you by

Bourkes Bend No 333

24kms east of Cobram

By Miriam Blaker

Bourkes Bend Campground is in the middle of Bourkes Bend State Forest, half-way between the Victorian town of Cobram and Yarrawonga in NSW. With 104 river beaches between Yarrawonga and Barmah there is no shortage of places to camp but there's also another tantalising reason to visit this district.

From Cobram it's about 20kms north east of the township to the forest that takes you to the campgrounds. There are three distinct camping areas at Bourkes Bend. Number 1 beach is a roomy spot beside the river with level shady and sunny campsites. Number 2 is an intimate beach, close to the water and number 3 is a large, open flat grassy area, on a low embankment. Careful where you set up as dead branches are notorious for falling off old Red River Gums with little warning. There are no toilet facilities here.

This is a top spot to launch a boat and enjoy a spot of fishing. Just be aware that the Murray River has NSW regulations and requires a NSW licence. Its wide-open spaces and riverbank beach is a great place to laze about or enjoy walks around the long shoreline. The camping area is dog-friendly and the surrounding state forest has plenty of firewood for the evening campfire so you can use your chainsaw to your heart's content.

Plenty of open space and shady trees.

Cobram isn't too far away from Bourkes Bend, a quiet sleepy town on the Murray River border with its twin town of Barooga on the other side. Surrounding the town are rich pastoral, dairy and fruit farms, thanks to the irrigated water supplied by the Murray River and the warm Mediterranean-like climate. Cobram's diverse agricultural district produces citrus fruits, vegetables, wheat, oats, barley, canola, sunflowers, wool and beef cattle and it's here travellers can enjoy a different side of the Murray.

Dubbed the heart of Victoria's food bowl, there's plenty of foodie adventures here. Take a self-guided tour of the Farm Gate Trail and sample everything from farm fresh fruit to artisan chocolates, gourmet cheeses and craft beers. Be sure to try some of the famous exports of the region, including Murray River Salt, Mallee lamb and fresh grapes. Hit the backroads and roadside stalls and you'll likely return to your campsite with some delicious additions to the camp meal: citrus fruits, olives, cheeses and an array of local wines. There's even true free-range pork, salt-bush fed lamb and, for the truly adventurous, some edible cacti.

The campground is right on the bank of the beautiful Murray River.

Just The Facts

Bourkes Bend

GPS: 35 58 47 S 145 49 34 E

Getting there: Turn north off the Murray Valley Highway, 19km west of Yarrawonga onto Bourkes Bend Track.

No facilities at this campground.

Pets: Allowed.

Charges: Free.

Contact: Parks Victoria 13 1963 or the Cobram/Barooga Visitor Information Centre on (03) 5872 2132.

345. Camerons Track bush Camping Area - Murray
Map Ref: MAP 3 E4 GPS: 36 04 32 S 146 12 02 E
Camerons Track is signposted off the Murray Valley Hwy on the western side of bridge over Lower Ovens River. Ph: 13 19 63

346. Taylors Bend Camping Area - Murray
Map Ref: MAP 3 F4 GPS: 36 02 15 S 146 17 49 E
Within Murray River Reserve, access via Brimin Rd off the Murray Valley Hwy 18km W of Rutherglen. Ph: 13 19 63

347. Lumbys Bend Bush Camping Area - Murray
Map Ref: MAP 3 F4 GPS: 36 02 24 S 146 18 10 E
Accessed via Raitts Road off Murray Valley Hwy 14km W of Rutherglen. Ph: 13 19 63

348. Wahgunyah East Camps - Murray River Reserve
Map Ref: MAP 3 F4 GPS: 36 02 26 S 146 21 21 E
Camp area 11km W of Rutherglen. N off Murray Valley Hwy to Moodemere Rd. Located in Stantons Bend Rd, Rutherglen. Ph: 13 19 63

349. Stantons Bend Camping Area - Murray
Map Ref: MAP 3 F4 GPS: 36 03 02 S 146 21 46 E
Accessed via Moodemere Road which is signposted off the Murray Valley Hwy 9km E of Raitts Road and 5km W of Rutherglen. Ph: 13 19 63

350. Hiskins Bend Camping Area
Map Ref: MAP 3 F4 GPS: 36 03 06 S 146 22 02 E
Off the Murray Valley Hwy 5.4km W of Rutherglen via Moodemere Rd to Hiskins Rd leading to river then a further 800 m to camping area. Ph: 13 19 63

351. Willows Camping & Recreation Reserve
Map Ref: MAP 3 F4 GPS: 36 01 10 S 146 22 53 E
Located in Wahgunyah across the river from Corowa. Reserve is at the end of Short Street 200m to hotel. No fees but donations welcome. Ph: 02 6033 1186

352. Granthams Bend Camping Area - Murray
Map Ref: MAP 3 G4 GPS: 35 59 07 S 146 24 51 E
From Rutherglen take the C376 road N towards Corowa. Signposted to Granthams Bend Reserve. Ph: 13 19 63

353. Shaws Flat Camping Area - Murray
Map Ref: MAP 3 G4 GPS: 35 59 05 S 146 29 03 E
Located N of Rutherglen off Up River Road which is off C376 road. Ph: 13 19 63

354. Police Paddocks - Murray
Map Ref: MAP 3 G4 GPS: 35 58 55 S 146 30 54 E
Within the Gooramadda State Forest N of Rutherglen via Gooramadda Rd & Police Paddocks Rd. Beside Murray River. Ph: 13 19 63

355. Doolans Bend Camping Area - Murray
Map Ref: MAP 3 H4 GPS: 36 01 48 S 146 39 09 E
Within the Murray River Reserves access off the Barnawartha-Howlong Rd. Natural boat launch. Dry Weather Only Ph: 13 19 63

356. Richardson Bend Camping Area - Murray
Map Ref: MAP 3 H4 GPS: 36 03 25 S 146 44 52 E
Within the Murray River Reserve. Accessed off the Old Barnawartha Road, from the Murray Valley Hwy. Ph: 13 19 63

357. The Forest Camp Camping Area
Map Ref: MAP 3 E5 GPS: 36 13 18 S 146 10 44 E
From Wangaratta take Booths Rd, Wangaratta-Yarrawonga Rd then the road signposted Boweya 13. After 5.9km take signposted Killawarra Forest to the park entrance,then 2.3km to the site. Ph: 13 19 63

358. Wilsons Bend - Warby Ovens NP
Map Ref: MAP 3 F5 GPS: 36 14 40 S 146 16 01 E
Dispersed camping 14km NW of Wangaratta via Francis Rd, Peechelba. Turn 14km NW of Wangaratta along Francis Rd and follow to sites on Ovens River. Water crossings and watch overhead. Ph: 13 19 63

359. Frosts Reserve
Map Ref: MAP 3 F5 GPS: 36 14 40 S 146 16 01 E
Located within Warby-Ovens NP 14kms NW of Wangaratta. Turn E 14km NW of Wangaratta or 8kms S of Peechelba along Francis Rd, follow to river and sites on Ovens River.

360. Tuan Campground
Map Ref: MAP 3 G5 GPS: 36 07 42 S 146 35 23 E
Camp area off Hume Hwy to C377 Main St then W to Chiltern-Rutherglen Rd then NE to Depot Rd.

Free Campsites in Victoria

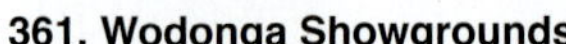

361. Wodonga Showgrounds
Map Ref: MAP 3 J5 GPS: 36 08 16 S 146 53 37 E
Camping area at showgrounds in Victoria Cross Parade, Wodonga. Limited stay. Ph: 02 6024 1872

362. Wenhams Camp Camping Area
Map Ref: MAP 3 E6 GPS: 36 20 28 S 146 12 14 E
Access from Wangaratta via Booths Road, then Wangaratta-Yarrawonga Rd to Wangandary Rd then Gerret Road/Wenham signposted Wenhams Campsite. Ph: 13 19 63

363. Ovens Billabongs - High Country
Map Ref: MAP 3 F6 GPS: 36 22 47 S 146 21 54 E
Beside the Ovens River SE of Wangaratta via Faithful St to a track signposted Ovens Billabong. Ph: 1800 801 065

364. Tarrawingee Bushland Reserve - Goldfields
Map Ref: MAP 3 F7 GPS: 36 24 50 S 146 27 22 E
Bush campsites beside the Ovens River south-east of Wangaratta. From the Great Alpine Rd 12kms from Wangaratta take signposted River Road, follow south for 2.4kms to access track on south side of bridge and follow it into bush camping beside the river. Ph: 1800 801 065

365. River Road Reserve
Map Ref: MAP 3 G7 GPS: 36 24 51 S 146 27 23 E
Campsites beside the Ovens River SE of Wangaratta. From Great Alpine Rd east of Tarrawingee take signposted River Rd 2kms to signposted access over the bridge. Ph: 1800 801 065

366. Pioneer Bridges - High Country
Map Ref: MAP 3 G7 GPS: 36 26 30 S 146 31 31 E
On the Ovens River via the Great Alpine Rd E of Everton. Take the signpost marked Everton Rd. Ph: 1800 801 065

367. Reedy Creek Camping Area - High Country
Map Ref: MAP 3 G6 GPS: 36 19 16 S 146 32 57 E
Within the Chiltern-Mt Pilot NP numerous campsites along Woolshed Rd off Beechworth-Chiltern Rd. 6km N of Beechworth. Ph: 13 19 63

368. Kangaroo Crossing - Beechworth - Goldfields
Map Ref: MAP 3 G6 GPS: 36 18 47 S 146 35 58 E
16km from Beechworth via Woolshed Falls Rd. Ph: 1300 366 321

369. Yackandandah Creek - Murray
Map Ref: MAP 3 J6 GPS: 36 16 32 S 146 48 16 E
Located 4kms S of Yackandandah via Bells Flat Rd and Yack Gate Rd. Final section is narrow gravel road. Ph: 02 6027 1988

370. Stanley Forest Camping Area - High Country
Map Ref: MAP 3 J6 GPS: 36 20 32 S 146 48 42 E
4km s of Yackandandah in the Stanley State Forest. Via Bells Flat Rd then Yack Gate Rd. A number of campsites found in this area. Ph: 13 61 86

371. Boyds Camping Area - High Country
Map Ref: MAP 3 K7 GPS: 36 25 38 S 147 02 47 E
Situated on the eastern banks of the Kiewa River at Gundowring. From the Kiewa Valley Rd take Boyd Rd for 1km to access track on east side of bridge over the river then 150m to open grassed area. Ph: 13 61 86

372. Dederang Hotel
Map Ref: MAP 3 K7 GPS: 36 27 58 S 147 00 46 E
Camping area behind hotel on Kiewa Valley Hwy. Check in with hotel. Limited stay. Ph: 02 6028 9325

373. Edi Cutting Camping Area - High Country
Map Ref: MAP 3 F8 GPS: 36 39 22 S 146 25 16 E
On the King River via the Wangaratta-Whitfield Rd. Ph: 13 19 63

374. Nug Nug camping reserve - High Country
Map Ref: MAP 3 H8 GPS: 36 39 42 S 146 42 20 E
Beside the Buffalo River 15km S of Myrtleford along Nug Nug Road off the Buffalo River Road. Ph: 03 9786 1672

375. Nug Nug Reserve
Map Ref: MAP 3 H8 GPS: 36 39 42 S 146 42 20 E
Camping area 14km S of Myrtleford. Turn 13km S of Myrtleford on to Nug Nug Rd. Ph: 0418 336 272

376. Lake Catani campground - High Country
Map Ref: MAP 3 H9 GPS: 36 44 07 S 146 48 43 E
Located in Mt Buffalo NP. Access via Mt Buffalo Tourist Rd. Camp area beside Lake Catani. Open summer only. Ph: 13 19 63

Free Campsites in Victoria

377. White Gum Bush Camping - High Country
Map Ref: MAP 3 C9 GPS: 36 47 48 S 145 53 47 E
From the Midland Hwy 18kms south of Benalla and 45km north of Mansfield take signposted road Lima 5. Follow for 3.9kms then Ethell Rd for 8.5kms to signposted A Rd. Follow A Rd for 11kms to signposted A11 Rd, turn left for 2.8kms to bush camp. Ph: 13 61 86

378. James Camping Reserve
Map Ref: MAP 3 D9 GPS: 36 50 12 S 145 56 50 E
Located in Strathbogie Ranges State Forest 13km SW of Swanpool. Access from Swanpool-Lima Rd, then into Lima East Rd. Camp beside Black Charlies Creek. Ph: 13 61 86

379. Samaria Well Camping Area - High Country
Map Ref: MAP 3 D9 GPS: 36 49 28 S 146 03 47 E
Within Mt Samaria State Park 14km N of Mansfield. Access along Browns Rd off the Mt Samaria Rd at the parks entrance. Ph: 13 19 63

380. Jones Campground - High Country
Map Ref: MAP 3 E9 GPS: 36 50 30 S 146 08 37 E
In the Toombullup Ranges 18km S of Tatong take the road from Tatong to Tolmie and then Jones Rd. Ph: 13 61 86

381. Spring Creek Sawmill Camping Area - High Country
Map Ref: MAP 3 D10 GPS: 36 52 28 S 146 05 10 E
Within the Mt Samaria State Park. 15km N of Mansfield. Ph: 13 19 63

382. Stringybark Creek camping reserve - High Country
Map Ref: MAP 3 E10 GPS: 36 52 41 S 146 12 12 E
Toombullup State Forest is located about 39kms from Mansfield via Tolmie. Last 11kms on the Tatong-Tolmie Rd is gravel though narrow in places. Ph: 03 5733 1200

383. Toombullup School Site - High Country
Map Ref: MAP 3 E10 GPS: 36 53 20 S 146 14 10 E
6km NW of Tolmie along the Tolmie-Tatong Rd. Dirt road. Ph: 13 61 86

384. Blue Range Creek Campground - High Country
Map Ref: MAP 3 D10 GPS: 36 56 11 S 146 05 42 E
Camp area 14km N of Mansfield. Access via the Blue Range Rd Ph: 13 61 86

385. Sandy Flat Camping Area
Map Ref: MAP 3 F10 GPS: 36 56 07 S 146 25 20 E
Beside the King River 9km SE of Lake William Hovell picnic area beside Sandy Flat track. Ph: 13 19 63

386. Top Crossing Hut - Alpine NP
Map Ref: MAP 3 F10 GPS: 36 57 48 S 146 26 29 E
Camp area 81kms S of Wangaratta or 97km NE of Mansfield in Alpine NP. From Whitfield travel S on King Valley Rd for 5km then S to Upper King River Rd then 22km to Top Crossing Track then 5km to camp. 21 day limit. Ph: 13 19 63

387. Bennies Camping Area - Alpine NP - High Country
Map Ref: MAP 3 G10 GPS: 36 57 18 S 146 32 03 E
Located 29km S of Whitfield beside the Rose River. Access on the Upper Rose River Rd. Ph: 13 19 63

388. Blades Camping Area
Map Ref: MAP 3 H9 GPS: 36 49 17 S 146 39 41 E
Camp area 36kms S of Myrtleford via Buffalo River Rd, then take Abbeyards Rd. Ph: 1800 111 885

389. Tea Tree Camping Area
Map Ref: MAP 3 H10 GPS: 36 50 21 S 146 39 53 E
Camp area 39kms S of Myrtleford via Buffalo River Rd, then Abbeyards Rd by riverside. Ph: 1800 111 885

390. Buffalo River State Forest - High Country
Map Ref: MAP 3 H10 GPS: 36 55 59 S 146 43 10 E
Numerous camping sites. With access to most from Abbeyards Road. Ph: 13 61 86

391. Ah Youngs Camping Area
Map Ref: MAP 3 J9 GPS: 36 50 30 S 146 51 04 E
Camping area 18km S of Porepunkah. From Porepunkah roundabout turn S on to Buckland Valley Rd. Dirt rd. Ph: 13 61 86

392. Maguire Point Camping Area - High Country
Map Ref: MAP 3 J10 GPS: 36 50 36 S 146 51 04 E
Within the Buckland Valley State Forest SW of Bright. Access along Buckland Valley Rd. Ph: 13 61 86

393. Camp Flat
Map Ref: MAP 3 J10 GPS: 36 51 13 S 146 51 32 E
Camp area 23km S of Porepunkah. From Porepunkah roundabout turn S onto Buckland Valley Rd and follow for 23km to camp beside river. 7km dirt road. Ph: 13 61 86

394. Buckland Valley Camping Areas - High Country
Map Ref: MAP 3 J10 GPS: 36 51 12 S 146 51 36 E
Access from Porepunkah on the Great Alpine Rd via the Buckland Valley Rd. Ph: 13 61 86

395. Smoko Camping Area
Map Ref: MAP 3 K10 GPS: 36 49 39 S 147 04 36 E
Camping area 15km S of Bright. Turn E off Great Alpine Rd and follow track for 700m to campsite by river. Ph: 13 61 86

396. Shippens Flat
Map Ref: MAP 3 J10 GPS: 36 55 23 S 146 54 15 E
Camp area 30km S of Porepunkah. From Porepunkah roundabout turn S onto Buckland Valley Rd and follow for 30km to camp beside river. 15km dirt road. Ph: 1800 111 885

397. Leinster Flat
Map Ref: MAP 3 J10 GPS: 36 55 48 S 146 55 32 E
Camp area 31km S of Porepunkah. From Porepunkah roundabout turn S onto Buckland Valley Rd and follow for 31km to camp beside river. 17km dirt road. Ph: 1800 111 885

398. Good Hope Flat
Map Ref: MAP 3 J10 GPS: 36 56 00 S 146 55 32 E
Camp area 32km S of Porepunkah. From Porepunkah roundabout turn S onto Buckland Valley Rd and follow for 32km to camp beside river. 18km dirt road. Ph: 1800 111 885

399. Headrace Flat
Map Ref: MAP 3 J10 GPS: 36 56 48 S 146 55 50 E
Camp area 33km S of Porepunkah. From Porepunkah roundabout turn S onto Buckland Valley Rd and follow for 33km to camp beside river. 20km dirt road. Ph: 1800 111 885

400. The Bend
Map Ref: MAP 3 J11 GPS: 36 57 48 S 146 55 55 E
Camp area 36km S of Porepunkah. From Porepunkah roundabout turn S onto Buckland Valley Rd and follow for 36km to camp beside river. 21km dirt road. Ph: 1800 111 885

401. Beveridges Station Camping Area - High Country
Map Ref: MAP 3 J11 GPS: 36 59 13 S 146 57 40 E
Beside Buckland River 40km S of Porepunkah. Signposted access along Buckland Valley Road. Ph: 13 19 63

402. Evans Creek Hut Camping Area - High Country
Map Ref: MAP 3 F11 GPS: 37 00 22 S 146 22 43 E
Located east of Mansfield along Evans Creek Track, 23kms south-east of Tolmie by taking signposted Cambatong Rd for 22kms to Evans Creek Track, turn right for 1.2kms to hut. Ph: 13 61 86

403. Merton Racecourse Reserve
Map Ref: MAP 3 B10 GPS: 36 58 21 S 145 42 32 E
Camp area at 3138 Merton-Euroa Rd, Merton N of town. Gold coin donation.

404. Lindsay Island Camping Area - Murray
Map Ref: MAP 4 B1 GPS: 34 09 04 S 141 08 26 E
Access via Lindsay Island Road signposted off the Old Mail Route/Old River Road 70km W of the Calder Hwy from Merbein. Ph: 13 19 63

405. Lock 9
Map Ref: MAP 4 C1 GPS: 34 11 30 S 141 35 39 E
Camping 9km N of Cullulleraine. 8km dirt rd. Turn W at boat ramp sign and follow track.

406. Wallpolla Island - Murray
Map Ref: MAP 4 C1 GPS: 34 09 12 S 141 46 42 E
Within the Wallpolla SF 25kms W of Merbein via the Old Mail Rd. Dry weather only

407. Lock 10 Bush Camping Area - Mallee
Map Ref: MAP 4 C1 GPS: 34 06 40 S 141 54 06 E
Dispersed bush camping along the banks of the Murray River either side of the weir at Lock 10. Access road is signposted off the Old Mail Route, 8km west of Calder Hwy from Merbein, then drive north for 5.9km to the lock and bush camping. Ph: 13 19 63

408. Abbotsford Bend Bush Camping - Mallee
Map Ref: MAP 4 C1 GPS: 34 06 47 S 141 59 04 E
Located north west of Merbein. Access via a track off Hoyles Rd which is signposted off the Calder Hwy on south side of bridge crossing river to Curlwaa. After accessing through gate between hwy and private property travel 200m to forested area and boat ramp. Numerous sites along access track. Ph: 13 19 63

409. Merbein Common - Murray
Map Ref: MAP 4 C1 GPS: 34 09 04 S 142 03 02 E
West of Mildura Merbein Common is accessed via 3 different entrances along Old Wentworth Rd. Ph: 13 19 63

410. Horseshoe Bend Bush Camping - Murray
Map Ref: MAP 4 D1 GPS: 34 09 22 S 142 04 28 E
On the banks of the Murray River 10km NW of Mildura via Old Wentworth Rd off River Ave. Dry weather only Ph: 13 19 63

411. Marina Campground
Map Ref: MAP 4 D1 GPS: 34 12 30 S 142 14 01 E
Camp area 15km E of Mildura off Billabong Rd at Nichols Point.

412. McDougall Wines
Map Ref: MAP 4 D1 GPS: 34 13 50 S 142 12 24 E
Camp area 3km from Calder Hwy at cnr Eleventh St and Ginquam Ave, Mildura. 7 day limit, free for patrons. Ph: 0417 104 065

413. Kings Billabong Reserve - Murray
Map Ref: MAP 4 D1 GPS: 34 14 14 S 142 13 54 E
10km SE of Mildura on the banks of the Murray. From Mildura use Eleventh St. Signposted of the Hwy. Dry weather only Ph: 13 19 63

414. Red Cliffs Scenic Reserve - Mallee
Map Ref: MAP 4 D2 GPS: 34 18 47 S 142 13 56 E
Located east of Red Cliffs. From the Hwy in Red Cliffs take the road east signposted Indi Avenue/Red Cliffs Tourist Drive. Continue east for 4.4km to Woomera Ave turn right for 800m then left into road no signpost,continue for 1km between vineyard to enter reserve. Numerous tracks lead to river and camps. Ph: 13 19 63

415. Echo Point Bush Camping Area - Mallee
Map Ref: MAP 4 D2 GPS: 34 18 17 S 142 17 54 E
From the Hwy in Red Cliffs take the road east signposted Indi Avenue/Red Cliffs Tourist Drive. Continue east for 4.4km to Woomera Ave turn right for 800m then left into road no signpost, continue for 1km between vineyard to enter reserve. Continue for 1.5km to signposted track to Echo Point then 4.4km to camp area. Gas/Fuel stove preferred. Ph: 13 19 63

416. Karadoc Sandbar Camping Area - Mallee
Map Ref: MAP 4 D2 GPS: 34 19 26 S 142 17 38 E
Located south east of Red Cliffs. From Calder Hwy 3km south of Red Cliffs take Kulkyne Way (C253) and follow for 7.5km to Edey Rd/Karadoc. Continue for 2.1km to large bend and then turn left and continue on no through road for 1.7km to camping. Ph: 13 19 63

417. The Shearers' Quarters Camping Area - Mallee
Map Ref: MAP 4 B2 GPS: 34 33 46 S 141 04 35 E
Located 46km west of Cullulleraine. From the Stuart Hwy take signposted West Settlement Rd/Shearers' Quarters and proceed south for 31km to signposted access to the Shearers' Quarters then 2.5km to quarters and camp area. Ph: 13 19 63

418. Rocket Lake - Mallee
Map Ref: MAP 4 C2 GPS: 34 38 17 S 141 49 54 E
Access via Rocket Lake track from the Nowingi Line track from Nowingi on the Calder Hwy.

419. Johnsons Bend - Murray River Reserve
Map Ref: MAP 4 D2 GPS: 34 25 25 S 142 21 53 E
Camp area 8.5km N of Nangiloc on Blake Rd, Iraak. Turn N on Kulkyne Way for 4km, turn W to Rudds Rd for 2km, N on Barko Rd for 400m then W for 1.8km. Dirt & gravel tracks, low hanging branches. Riverside. Ph: 13 19 63

420. Spences Bend - Murray
Map Ref: MAP 4 D2 GPS: 34 27 48 S 142 21 15 E
Camp Spot 2km N of Nangiloc off the Kulkyne Way which is signposted off the Calder Hwy. Camping beside river. Ph: 13 19 63

421. Police Bend - Murray River Reserve
Map Ref: MAP 4 D2 GPS: 34 28 43 S 142 23 00 E
Camp area 2.7km W of Nangiloc via Kulkyne Way, Nangiloc. Entry S of Recreation Reserve, dirt track to riverside. 4WD only. Ph: 13 19 63

422. Watts Bend - Murray
Map Ref: MAP 4 D2 GPS: 34 32 12 S 142 22 15 E
From Red Cliff take the Red Cliff-Colignan Rd. Dry weather only.
Ph: 13 19 63

423. Emmerts Bend - Murray
Map Ref: MAP 4 D2 GPS: 34 34 12 S 142 24 40 E
Camp Spot 7km S of Colignan off Kulkyne Way. Camping beside river. Dry weather only Ph: 13 19 63

424. Britt Bend Camping Area - Murray
Map Ref: MAP 4 D2 GPS: 34 35 21 S 142 27 32 E
Signposted access along River Track 4.2km S of park entrance. Then 3.1km to next signposted access track which leads to the river. Ph: 13 19 63

Watt's Bend No 422

Colignan, VIC

7km south of Nangiloc

John Mainwaring

Heading south out of Mildura there are quite a few very nice free camp areas along the Murray near the small settlements of Nangiloc and Colignan. These are easily accessed via the Red Cliffs-Colignan Road that branches off the Calder Highway just south of Red Cliffs. They are fine for 2WD although you may be able to find a few private spots where high clearance and 4WD is needed. Some are sufficiently treed in to make them best for tents and swags and others are very open so motorhomes and caravans don't have any difficulties.

The ones I visited recently were Watt's Bend, Police Bend and Spence's Bend: all handy to the tarmac road. At the time the river was running magnificently high; the rains in the south east have been good and it is fantastic seeing the areas around our big brown rivers getting a refresh. Some of those ancient red gums were starting to despair I reckon. But with such high water there were extensive areas that I could not reach as many of the access tracks had been flooded, creating islands of many of the riverside areas that have some excellent campsites. But no problem, there were still literally hundreds of spots available to campers along this stretch of the Murray either side of Colignan. You may have a favourite spot deep into some section of the forest but around here, there will always be Back Up Sites 1 through to 100 you can select from.

Being just 15 to 20 minutes from Red Cliffs you can easily nip out for supplies if you would like to park up for a while but want to keep a few fresh items on the menu. The main activities riverside seem to be fishing, relaxing, reading and a bit of walking.

In this area there are some very old red gums and the customary caution is made about parking under these trees. Not a good idea. While I was there we heard a massive crack and turned in time to see a huge bough splash into the river on the NSW side, so always look up and make your assessments before selecting your site. There are plenty to choose from so you should be able to avoid the big widow makers. These sites can be a very handy base to explore the local area, including Mildura & Red Cliffs, Hattah-Kulkyne National Park or the Murray Sunset National Park.

There is space for large motorhomes.

Take notice of the warning signs.

Boat access for fishing.

Just The Facts

Watt's Bend

Getting there: Heading south out of Red Cliffs, take the Red Cliffs-Colignan Road and note the sign-posted camping areas indicated to the left where the road runs adjacent to the river in several areas both north and south of Colignan. Colignan access points are well indicated on the Calder Highway too.

Facilities: There are no amenities in these areas with dispersed camping along the river only. You need to be self-contained and independent.

Charges: Free

Pets: Pets OK under control.

Contact: Parks Victoria 13 1963 or parkweb.vic.gov.au or email for information at info@parks.vic.gov.au

Free Campsites in Victoria

425. Deep Bend Camping Area - Murray
Map Ref: MAP 4 D2 GPS: 34 38 25 S 142 28 18 E
Signposted access along River Track 6.5km S of Tarpaulin and Britt Bend access track. Ph: 13 19 63

426. Firemans Bend Camping Area - Murray
Map Ref: MAP 4 D2 GPS: 34 40 57 S 142 30 04 E
Signposted access along river track 1.3km N of Jinkers Bend access track. Ph: 13 19 63

427. Jinkers Bend Camping Area - Murray
Map Ref: MAP 4 E2 GPS: 34 41 55 S 142 29 59 E
Signposted access along River Track 500m N of the Northern access track to Ki Bend, then in 200m to the river. Ph: 13 19 63

428. Ki Bend Camping Area - Murray
Map Ref: MAP 4 D3 GPS: 34 43 57 S 142 30 04 E
3 access tracks signposted along River Track at 6.3km, 8.3km and 9.5km marks. Ph: 13 19 63

429. The Boiler Camping Area - Murray
Map Ref: MAP 4 D3 GPS: 34 44 58 S 142 30 28 E
Signposted access along River Track, 8km S of Firemans Bend access track and 3.4km N of S entrance. Ph: 13 19 63

430. Pound Bend Bush Camping - Mallee
Map Ref: MAP 4 E3 GPS: 34 46 19 S 142 38 45 E
Located along the Murray River opposite the village of Wemen via a signposted track to boat ramp 500m east of Wemen Fuel Stop. Then drive 250m to bush camping beside river. Ph: 13 19 63

431. Wemen Camping - Murray
Map Ref: MAP 4 E3 GPS: 34 46 55 S 142 38 12 E
From Robinvale travel 4kms south on the Sea Lake Rd, turn right on Happy Valley Rd for 5.5kms left on to Hocking Rd for 3.5kms then right on to Happy Valley Landing Rd to the river. Ph: 13 19 63

432. Carina Bend Bush Camping - Mallee
Map Ref: MAP 4 E2 GPS: 34 40 32 S 142 41 43 E
Located south west of Robinvale in SF. Proceed south along Murray Valley Hwy and take C251 to Sea Lake for 2.5km to signposted Happy Valley Rd. Continue for 6kmto Hocking Rd then south for 3.6km to Happy Valley Landing Rd. Numerous tracks lead to bush campsites beside river. Ph: 13 19 63

433. Gadsens Bend State Forest - Mallee
Map Ref: MAP 4 E2 GPS: 34 38 57 S 142 43 03 E
Located south west of Robinvale via Centre Rd which is signposted off Happy Valley Rd 5.6kms west of the Robinvale-Sea Lake Rd. Once inside forest numerous tracks lead to bush campsites beside the river. Ph: 13 19 63

434. Pump Road Camp
Map Ref: MAP 4 E2 GPS: 34 36 25 S 142 48 10 E
Camp spot 2km E of Robinvale. Turn N into Pump Rd for 500m. Bridge has a 2T weight limit. Turn E over water pipes and follow tracks to spots on river.

435. Walshs Bend Camp
Map Ref: MAP 4 E2 GPS: 34 37 16 S 142 48 45 E
Camp spot 5km E of Robinvale. Turn N into Tol Tol Rd for 600m then turn N onto track, signposted. Dirt track 2kms to camping area.

436. Begg's Bend - Murray
Map Ref: MAP 4 E2 GPS: 34 38 20 S 142 51 02 E
4km S of Robinvale is Tol Tol Rd. Campsites along the river. Ph: 13 19 63

437. Invincible Bend State Forest - Mallee
Map Ref: MAP 4 E2 GPS: 34 38 52 S 142 51 38 E
Located south east of Robinvale along Murray Valley Hwy take signposted Tol Tol Rd then travel 3.2kms to Invincible Bend Lane, travel east for 700m to entrance of SF then numerous tracks lead to bush campsites. Ph: 13 19 63

438. Belsar Island State Forest - Mallee
Map Ref: MAP 4 E2 GPS: 34 41 58 S 142 54 51 E
Located south east of Robinvale off Murray Valley Hwy take signposted Belsar Rd then travel north 1.4kms to entrance of SF then River Track for 5km to river. Numerous tracks lead to bush campsites. Ph: 13 19 63

439. Two Pumps Camp - Murray River Reserve
Map Ref: MAP 4 E3 GPS: 34 36 25 S 142 48 10 E
Camp area 2km SE of Robinvale on Pump Rd, Robinvale E of cemetery turn N for 500m. Bridge has 2 tonne limit. Turn E over water pipes and follow dirt tracks to riverside. Ph: 13 19 63

440. Pile Bend State Forest - Mallee
Map Ref: MAP 4 F3 GPS: 34 42 42 S 143 08 28 E
Access is signposted off the Murray Valley Hwy 500m west of Boundary Bend via signposted track River Access which leads in 440m to forest entry. Numerous tracks lead to bush & river camps. Ph: 13 19 63

Begg's Bend State Forest Camping Area No 436

Robinvale, VIC
4 km south of Robinvale

John Mainwaring

The bush by the river provides a great habitat for the endangered Regent Parrot.

This is a handy spot just off the Murray Valley Highway a few kilometres south of Robinvale. There are dozens of nice campsites, most of them on elevated banks overlooking the river but with a number of beach areas if you want a swimming spot or an easy canoe launching spot.

Robinvale is an interesting town, being established in 1924 but boosted after WWII with a Soldier Resettlement Scheme. They must have been keen to remind the blokes of this with sensitively named roads in the area such as Tobruk Rd, Benghazi Rd and Crete Rd - very nice. Unlike some of the poorly thought out soldier settlements, this one did pretty well with a bit of hard work and careful planning of the irrigation activities.

Big crops around this area now are almonds, olives and table grapes and you will see the extensive irrigated lands that make all this possible. There are some rich soils in the area but a lot of these crops are effectively massive hydroponic operations sitting in a sandy support substrate. The highly efficient drip feed irrigation systems feed and water all at the same time.

Another feature of this area is the beautiful Regent parrot, a species that was not doing so well a few years ago. I think they are still on the Threatened List but there seems to be good numbers of them around Robinvale especially after the last 2 good breeding seasons, so if you like a bit of bird spotting that is one you will be able to scratch onto the "seen list".

Begg's Bend is a convenient overnighter site or a stopover for several nights, taking in the local attractions. Being so handy to Robinvale is a plus for supplies (good supermarket in town) and this camping area is only 2 or 3 kms from the Murray Valley Highway with very good dirt roads in this small state forest area. A word of caution that the most southerly section of Begg's Bend (upstream) is less than ordinary due to a collection of irrigation water uptakes, so you will want to stay well away from them. They are ugly and noisy if they are turned on. The downstream section of the park in between Margooya Lagoon and the river is much nicer along there.

The cleared camping area makes it an easy stopover.

Just The Facts

Begg's Bend

Getting there: About 4 kms south of Robinvale is Tol Tol Road. A couple of kms along this road you will come to the entrance to Begg's Bend State Forest which takes you in behind Margooya Lagoon to some really nice spots overlooking the river.

Facilities: Nil.

Charges: Free.

Pets: Permitted.

Contact: Parks Victoria on 13 1963 or speak to the folks in the Robinvale Euston Visitor Information Centre in Robinvale, phone (03) 5026 1388.

441. Passage Camp - Murray
Map Ref: MAP 4 F3 GPS: 34 43 08 S 143 11 59 E
Murray River based access from Boundary Bend. Dry weather only Ph: 13 19 63

442. Narrung State Forest - Mallee
Map Ref: MAP 4 F3 GPS: 34 45 39 S 143 13 48 E
Located south east of Boundary Bend. From the hwy travel 11km south east and take track signposted Narrung State Forest/Centre Track and follow 700m to junction with Loop Track then 1.6km to river. Ph: 13 19 63

443. Wakool Junction - Murray
Map Ref: MAP 4 F3 GPS: 34 51 42 S 143 20 50 E
Camp Area 7km E of Piambie. From the Murray Valley Hwy follow Coghill Rd to Wakool Junction and then 4km to campground. Dry weather only Ph: 13 19 63

444. Kenley Camping Area - Murray River Reserve
Map Ref: MAP 4 F3 GPS: 34 50 18 S 143 21 04 E
Camp area 8km E of Hwy on River Track, Kenley. Turn E off B4000 and travel 27km N of B400.B12 junction to Coghill Rd. 1.5km dirt road, small vehicles only. Riverside. Ph: 13 19 63

445. Murray River Reserve - Mallee
Map Ref: MAP 4 F3 GPS: 34 53 16 S 143 18 30 E
Located south east of Piambie. From the hwy take signposted Angle Rd and follow for 3.6km to track on right not signposted which leads to the river. 4WD recommended. Ph: 13 19 63

446. Major Mitchell Lagoons - Mallee
Map Ref: MAP 4 F3 GPS: 34 51 57 S 143 20 23 E
Located south east of Piambie. From the hwy take signposted Angle Rd and follow for 6km to junction with Kenley Rd. Take Kenley Rd east for 1.9km to track on right signposted Major Mitchell Lagoons then 300m to river. Ph: 13 19 63

447. Mopoke Hut Camping Area - Mallee
Map Ref: MAP 4 C3 GPS: 34 48 38 S 141 45 34 E
Located off Mopoke Hut Track off Last Hope Track Ph: 13 19 63

448. Mount Crozier Camping Area - Mallee
Map Ref: MAP 4 C3 GPS: 34 54 34 S 141 42 19 E
Located 23km N of Lake Becking. Ph: 13 19 63

449. Mt Crozier Camping Area - Mallee
Map Ref: MAP 4 C3 GPS: 34 54 33 S 141 42 20 E
Within Murray-Sunset NP signposted access along Mt Crozier Track which is accessed from Pioneer Drive from Lake Becking, 23km north of Lake Becking. 4WD recommended. Ph: 13 19 63

450. Lake Becking Camping Area - Mallee
Map Ref: MAP 4 C3 GPS: 35 02 21 S 141 42 56 E
16km N of Mallee Hwy on E side of Lake Becking, 2km N of Lake Crosbie Ph: 13 19 63

451. Lake Crosbie Camping Area - Mallee
Map Ref: MAP 4 C3 GPS: 35 03 20 S 141 43 49 E
Camping area 13km N of Mallee Hwy on S side of Pink Lakes, 10km W of Underbool Via Pink Lakes Rd. Ph: 13 19 63

452. Manangatang Travellers Rest
Map Ref: MAP 4 E3 GPS: 35 03 10 S 142 53 00 E
Camping area on Wattle St, Manangatang, opposite hotel. Donation appreciated. Limited stay.

453. Ngallo Park Camping Area - Mallee
Map Ref: MAP 4 B4 GPS: 35 16 21 S 141 04 11 E
This site is 15km SW of Murrayville and 2.6km S of the Mallee Hwy on E side of Ngallo South Road. Ph: 13 19 63

454. Blue Gums Camping Area
Map Ref: MAP 4 B4 GPS: 35 21 47 S 141 08 14 E
Located in Big Desert SF 300m S of Firebreak Track along Blue Gums Track. Dry weather only. Ph: 13 61 86

455. Coburns Pines Camping Area - Mallee
Map Ref: MAP 4 B4 GPS: 35 23 51 S 141 04 16 E
Located in the Western section of the forest, N of Big Desert Wilderness Park. Signposted access at the junction of Firebreak Track and Coburns Track, 12.4km W of Murrayville Track Ph: 13 61 86

456. Yellow Gums Camping Area - Mallee
Map Ref: MAP 4 B4 GPS: 35 24 30 S 141 09 27 E
Located in Big Desert SF. 4WD recommended. Along Cactus Bore Track, 6.7km south of Firebreak Track which is signposted along Murrayville Track,10kms south of Mallee Hwy. Travel west for 4.2kms to signposted Cactus Bore Track. Ph: 13 61 86

457. Red Gums Camping Area - Mallee
Map Ref: MAP 4 B4 GPS: 35 25 06 S 141 06 13 E
Signposted access along Coburn's Track S of Firebreak Track. Within the Big Desert State Forest. Dry weather only Ph: 13 61 86

458. Big Billy Bore Camping Area - Mallee
Map Ref: MAP 4 B4 GPS: 35 30 59 S 141 19 40 E
Signposted access along Murrayville Track, 33.3km S of Murrayville, then 650m to camping area. Dry weather only Ph: 13 19 63

459. Underbool Recreation Area
Map Ref: MAP 4 C4 GPS: 35 10 08 S 141 48 47 E
Camping area at Gnarr Rd Underbool, N of railway line. Registration box at toilet block.

460. Walpeup Lake Camping Area - Mallee
Map Ref: MAP 4 D4 GPS: 35 11 51 S 142 08 12 E
From Ouyen take B12 and then south onto Patchewollock Rd, follow for 15.3km to unsealed road signposted Walpeup, then 3km to signposted Lake Walpeup. Continue for 340m then turn into McIvena Rd then 4km to lake. Ph: 13 19 63

461. Lake Walpeup Reserve
Map Ref: MAP 4 D4 GPS: 35 11 53 S 142 08 18 E
Camping 14km SE of Walpeup. Turn off Walpeup-Patchewallock Rd on to Walpeup Lake Rd then E on to McLivena Rd. 5km dirt rd.

462. Snowdrift Picnic & Camping Area - Mallee
Map Ref: MAP 4 C4 GPS: 35 25 54 S 141 54 40 E
Located in Wyperfeld NP. Follow main park road from the entrance for 10km to signposted Wirrengren Plain Track. Large camping area at base of sand dune. Ph: 13 19 63

463. Casuarina Campground - Mallee
Map Ref: MAP 4 C4 GPS: 35 26 42 S 141 59 41 E
Located in the Wyperfeld NP off the Meridian Rd W of Patchewollock. Dry weather only Ph: 13 19 63

464. Nyah State Forest - Murray
Map Ref: MAP 4 F4 GPS: 35 09 20 S 143 22 58 E
On the Murray River adjacent to Nyah township signposted off Murray Valley Hwy. Dry weather only Ph: 13 19 63

465. Vinifera State Forest - Murray
Map Ref: MAP 4 F4 GPS: 35 11 41 S 143 25 10 E
10km NW of Beverford. Signpost access off the Murray Valley Hwy. Riverside camping Dry weather only Ph: 13 19 63

466. Speewa Ferry Crossing
Map Ref: MAP 4 F4 GPS: 35 12 50 S 143 30 31 E
Camp area 16km N of Swan Hill. Turn W off Murray Valley Hwy to Speewa Punt Rd. Check weight & size of vehicle for ferry recommendation

467. Loddon Floodway - Murray
Map Ref: MAP 4 G4 GPS: 35 22 42 S 143 41 28 E
Camp Spot 20km SE of Swan Hill via Pental Island Rd then Caelli Lane. Dry weather only Ph: 13 19 63

468. The Springs Camping Area - Mallee
Map Ref: MAP 4 B5 GPS: 35 38 31 S 141 18 32 E
Located along Murrayville track, 14.8km S of Big Billy Bore camping area Ph: 13 19 63

469. Broken Bucket Camping Area - Mallee
Map Ref: MAP 4 B5 GPS: 35 58 10 S 141 24 05 E
Signposted access along Murrayville Track, 30km S of The Springs CA. Located 54km N of Nhill. Dry weather only Ph: 13 19 63

470. Wonga Camping Area - Mallee
Map Ref: MAP 4 D5 GPS: 35 35 12 S 142 03 02 E
Within the Wyperfeld NP 25km N of Yaapeet, located on Part Entrance Rd. Ph: 13 19 63

471. Round Swamp Camp - Mallee
Map Ref: MAP 4 C5 GPS: 35 42 36 S 141 43 08 E
Located in Wyperfeld NP, access via Kurnbrunin Rd from Albacutya. Follow this road west for 14km to Bullygall Rd which leads north for 1.5km, turn into Milmed Rock/4WD only track for 4.5km to signposted Murrayville Track, then 17km to camp area. Ph: 13 19 63

472. OTIT Campground Lake Albacutya Regional Park - Mallee
Map Ref: MAP 4 C5 GPS: 35 43 41 S 141 59 30 E
8km NW of Yaapeet on the Yaapeet-Hopetoun Rd. Dry weather only Ph: 13 19 63

Nyah Sports Ground Free Campsite No 464

Nyah, VIC
25kms north west of Swan Hill

Jim Foster

There are free campsites then there are free campsites. Some have smelly long drop toilets but are beside great fishing spots or very scenic places. Some have no shade and are bare and dusty while others have tall grass with rubbish tangled all through it. Some have great amenities but no other reason to camp there so it's great to find a free campsite that seems to have almost everything for those seeking a free night or two with all the necessities.

The free campsite at Nyah 25kms further downstream along the Murray River from Swan Hill is such an area.

Nyah (not Nyah West) has a wonderful sports ground area that includes their first class harness racing track. The campsites roughly surround this track. There are numerous campsites scattered throughout the park with some areas large enough to accommodate a fleet of big rigs.

When you enter the main gates of the park the largest area is off to your left. This is a nice level area surrounded by lots of shady trees with a large open area in the middle for those relying on solar panels for their power supply. This spot is favoured by bigger rigs for its ease of entry and exit. It is also favoured by those who need the toilet block to be reasonably close.

Camping in the large grassy space of Nyah Sports Ground.

Continuing past the first camping area you will come across another large open area also offering shade or clear sky. This spot is still OK for larger rigs it's just a bit further to the amenities.

The next section is best accessed by the second gate into the sports park just along the street a little from the main gate. This leads you into another large area but one that narrows a little as you continue along the track. The sites here are probably the best for those using solar power during the winter months as they take the sun all day long ensuring plenty of power in your batteries. But these sites are also close to the river while being large enough for most rigs to manoeuvre in. This spot is also closest to the boat ramp.

Nyah is a very good base for those wishing to visit Swan Hill which is only 25kms away to the south, or Tooleybuc 25kms to the north. The old-style little country town of Nyah West, only a few kms away is also worth a look.

Nyah campsite has a black water dump site, several flush toilets and drinking water, plenty of shady sites and green grass. It is only a short walk up to a shop that sells almost everything and a little further to other shops and businesses.

The campsite is free but as it is maintained by the local Lions Club I would ask all who use this wonderful campsite to please place a donation in the donation box on the rear wall of the toilet block next to the dump site.

Where: Nyah can be found 25kms north of Swan Hill. Coming in from the south the turn off to the campsite is just past the last shop at the bottom of a small slope. The turn off is signposted both for the harness track and the campsite also with a Dump Site sign.

Fishing on the bank of the Murray River .

Free Campsites in Victoria

473. Western Beach Campground - Mallee
Map Ref: MAP 4 C5 GPS: 35 46 48 S 141 56 10 E
Within Lake Albacutya Park 14km N of Rainbow. Access via Western Beach Rd off Albacutya Rd. Ph: 13 19 63

474. Yaapeet Beach Campground - Mallee
Map Ref: MAP 4 D5 GPS: 35 46 04 S 142 00 22 E
Eastern side of Lake Albacutya access via Yaapeet. Dry weather only Ph: 13 19 63

475. Williamsons Beach Camping Area - Mallee
Map Ref: MAP 4 C5 GPS: 35 57 14 S 141 51 13 E
Located on the N shores of Lake Hindmarsh off Nhill-Rainbow Road, E of the Amy Johnson Hwy. Ph: 13 19 63

476. The Wattles Camping Area - Mallee
Map Ref: MAP 4 C5 GPS: 35 56 59 S 141 52 30 E
Located on the northern shores of Lake Hindmarsh. 12km N of Jeparit. Dry weather only Ph: 13 19 63

477. Schulzes Beach Camping Area - Mallee
Map Ref: MAP 4 C6 GPS: 36 03 41 S 141 50 57 E
Located on western shores on Lake Hindmarsh. NW of Jeparit. Ph: 13 19 63

478. Lake Lascelles
Map Ref: MAP 4 D5 GPS: 35 43 31 S 142 22 29 E
Located near Hopetoun. Turn N at E end of Austin St and follow track to eastern foreshore. 2km dirt rd. Limited stay.

479. Mallee Bush Retreat
Map Ref: MAP 4 D5 GPS: 35 43 39 S 142 22 15 E
Camp area on the W foreshore of Lake Lascelles via Strachan St, Hopetoun E end of Austin St. Fee for power, pay online or honesty box. Ph: 0439 529 973

480. Beulah - Luna Park
Map Ref: MAP 4 D5 GPS: 35 56 29 S 142 24 53 E
Camp area 38km N or Warracknabeal at 56 Luna Park Rd, Beulah, opposite caravan park. 28 day limit. Ph: 03 5390 2200

481. The Marshes Camping Area - Murray
Map Ref: MAP 4 G5 GPS: 35 39 23 S 143 43 09 E
Located W of Lake Charm, via Bael Bael-Boga Road within the Heathcote-Graytown NP. Ph: 13 19 63

482. First Marsh, Second Marsh & Third Marsh Bush Camping Areas - Central Murray
Map Ref: MAP 4 G5 GPS: 35 40 17 S 143 44 15 E
From the Murray Valley Hwy 1.5km south of Lake Charm take the signposted Kangaroo Lake Rd and follow it west for 800m. Proceed south along the Lake Charm-Quambatook Rd for 9.3kms to the entrance on the north of the road. Dry weather only. Ph: 13 19 63

483. Lake Bael Bael Camping Ground - Murray
Map Ref: MAP 4 G5 GPS: 35 40 31 S 143 44 05 E
Located approx 12W of Kerang. Dispersed camping on NW side of lake. Access via Fairley Road off Murray Valley Hwy. Ph: 03 5452 1266

484. Middle Reedy Lake Camping Area - Murray
Map Ref: MAP 4 G5 GPS: 35 40 17 S 143 52 23 E
Located on Middle Reedy Lake N of Kerang via Pratt Road off Murray Valley Hwy Ph: 13 19 63

485. Lake Meran picnic and camping - Murray
Map Ref: MAP 4 G5 GPS: 35 53 27 S 143 48 24 E
Within the Leaghur State Park 25km SW of Kerang. Access via Vallance Track off Lake Meran Track. Ph: 13 19 63

486. Park Entrance Picnic & Camping Area - Central Murray
Map Ref: MAP 4 G5 GPS: 35 55 38 S 143 47 12 E
Within the Leaghur SF 28km south of Kerang and 23km north of Boort. Access track is 200m east of the Kerang-Boort Rd then 50m to camp area. Dry weather only. Ph: 13 19 63

487. Leaghur State Park
Map Ref: MAP 4 G5 GPS: 35 55 43 S 143 47 02 E
Camping area 28km S of Kerang off Boort-Kerang Rd. Two areas within the park. Ph: 03 5452 1266

488. Benwell State Forest bush camping - Murray
Map Ref: MAP 4 G5 GPS: 35 34 17 S 144 02 10 E
Located within the Benwell State Forest NW of Koondrook and access via Watson Lane and Hall Rd. Ph: 03 5450 3951

Free Campsites in Victoria

489. Guttram State Forest - Murray
Map Ref: MAP 4 G5 GPS: 35 36 42 S 144 06 55 E
Within Murray River Reserve, access to camps via river track off Cassidy's Lane from Koondrook. Dry weather only Ph: 13 19 63

490. Twin Bridges - Gunbower State Forest
Map Ref: MAP 4 G5 GPS: 35 39 47 S 144 07 47 E
Dispersed camping 3km SE of Koondrook via Kerang-Koondrook Rd, Koondrook. Travel along Canoe Trail via weir. Riverside. Ph: 13 61 86

491. Gunbower Island bush camping - Murray
Map Ref: MAP 4 H5 GPS: 35 39 02 S 144 08 10 E
Island located within Gunbower State Forest. Numerous sites with access from various points along the Murray Valley Hwy. Ph: 03 5456 2266

492. Gunbower National Park bush camping
Map Ref: MAP 4 H5 GPS: 35 44 46 S 144 16 29 E
Numerous camp sites along the Murray River and Gunbower Creek. Ph: 03 5841 2500

493. Terrick Terrick Campground
Map Ref: MAP 4 H6 GPS: 36 10 07 S 144 14 33 E
Within Terrick Terrick NP. Camping area 5km N of Mitiamo. Take Mitiamo-Forest Rd and trave N for 4km then turn E on to Cemetery Track. Signposted. Ph: 13 19 63

494. Mt Terrick Terrick Camping Area - Central Murray
Map Ref: MAP 4 H6 GPS: 36 10 07 S 144 14 32 E
Camping area in the Terrick Terrick NP 60km N of Bendigo. From the small town of Mitiamo take Haig St to the signposted Cemetery Track to campground. Ph: 13 19 63

495. Masters Landing - Gunbower NP
Map Ref: MAP 4 H5 GPS: 35 55 21 S 144 25 59 E
Camp area 8.5km NE of Gunbower via River Track, Gunbower. Take Gunbower Island Rd NE 4.5km then E to Brereton Rd for 3.8km then S to unsealed track for 700m to riverside. 21 day limit. Ph: 13 19 63

496. Turner Bend - Murray River Reserve
Map Ref: MAP 4 H6 GPS: 35 58 50 S 144 30 57 E
Camp area 3km E of Torrumbarry at 565 Headworks Rd, Torrumbarry. Turn N off Hwy. Ph: 13 19 63

497. Arnold Bend - Murray River Reserve
Map Ref: MAP 4 H6 GPS: 36 02 18 S 144 35 19 E
Dispersed camping 26km SE of Gunbower via Fraser Rd, Torrumbarry. Turn N off Hwy, riverside. Ph: 13 19 63

498. Betha Bend - Murray River Reserve
Map Ref: MAP 4 H6 GPS: 36 02 33 S 144 36 11 E
Camp area 6km NW of Wharparilla via Glyn Rd. Turn N off Hwy to Farley Rd for 3.6km then E via Glyn Rd to campsite. Ph: 13 19 63

499. Farley Bend Bush Camping - Central Murray
Map Ref: MAP 4 H6 GPS: 36 02 35 S 144 36 41 E
Situated within Murray River Parklands 15km west of Echuca. From Murray Valley Hwy take signposted Farley Rd north for 2km then take signposted Moorabinda Rd for 1.9km to Glyn Rd. Turn right and after 400m enter park entrance. Track leads 300m to river and then 1.2 to river bend. Ph: 13 19 63

500. Wills Bend - Murray River Reserve
Map Ref: MAP 4 H6 GPS: 36 03 14 S 144 38 22 E
Dispersed camping 5km NW of Wharparilla via O'Sullivan Rd, Wharparilla. GPS at entry. Ph: 13 19 63

501. Pianta Bend Bush Camping - Central Murray
Map Ref: MAP 4 J6 GPS: 36 04 23 S 144 40 45 E
Situated within Murray River Parklands 7km west of Echuca. Access is signposted 2.7km along Pianta Rd which is signposted off the Murray Valley Hwy. From entrance travel 1.5km to river and sites. Ph: 13 19 63

502. Christies Beach Campground - Murray
Map Ref: MAP 4 J6 GPS: 36 06 12 S 144 48 37 E
In the Echuca Regional Park 9km E of Echuca. Signposted off Simmie Rd. Ph: 13 19 63

503. Betts Bend Campground - Echuca Regional Park
Map Ref: MAP 4 J6 GPS: 36 06 47 S 144 48 28 E
Camp area 9km E Echuca via Simmie Rd via Goulburn Rd. Ph: 13 19 63

504. Rivers Edgee Campground
Map Ref: MAP 4 J6 GPS: 36 06 47 S 144 48 28 E
Camp area E from Echuca on Goulburn Rd then N on Simmie Rd.

Free Campsites in Victoria

505. Barmah Lakes Camping Area
Map Ref: MAP 4 J6 GPS: 35 57 23 S 144 57 34 E
Within Barmah NP beside the river. Access via signposted Rd Maloney St/ Dharnya Centre 14km E of Cobb Hwy. Camping is signposted 6kms along this road. Ph: 13 19 63

506. Barmah Forest - Murray
Map Ref: MAP 4 J6 GPS: 35 57 34 S 144 57 50 E
Close to township of Barmah off the Murray Valley Hwy. Dry weather only. Ph: 13 19 63

507. The Gulf Camping Area
Map Ref: MAP 4 J5 GPS: 35 50 31 S 145 09 08 E
Access via Gulf Rd signposted off Picola North Rd as Gulf Rd/Murray Mills Rd. 11km to camping area. Bush camping beside the river. Ph: 13 19 63

508. Serviceton Reservoir
Map Ref: MAP 4 A6 GPS: 36 20 35 S 140 58 54 E
Camp are 3.5km NE of Serviceton via Serviceton North-Telopea Downs Rd. Turn R onto Kings and Madderns Rd. Spot on L. Self contained vehicles only.

509. Serviceton Recreation Reserve
Map Ref: MAP 4 A6 GPS: 36 23 16 S 140 58 56 E
Camping area S of township on Baldocks-Grosser Rd. Ph: 0419 032 418

510. Green Swamps Wildlife Reservie bush camp - Goldfields
Map Ref: MAP 4 A7 GPS: 36 26 53 S 141 02 13 E
Signposted access along Lillimur South Rd 20.5 south west of Kaniva. Camping around the swamp's shores. Bring firewood, gas/fuel stove preferred. Ph: 03 5393 2893

511. Mooree Reserve
Map Ref: MAP 4 B7 GPS: 36 27 25 S 141 03 26 E
Camp area 26km SW of Kaniva via S Lillimur Rd & L onto Leeor Rd. 4WD only

512. Broughtons Waterhole Campground - Goldfields
Map Ref: MAP 4 B7 GPS: 36 34 07 S 141 20 12 E
Located in Little Desert NP near Kaniva. Signposted access along McDonald Hwy 9.1km east of Kaniva-Edenhope Rd. Drive 100m to site. Ph: 13 19 63

513. Lake Charlegrark Camping and Cottages - Goldfields & Grampians
Map Ref: MAP 4 B7 GPS: 36 46 32 S 141 14 25 E
35km NE of Edenhope. Signposted access along Kaniva-Edenhope Road. Lakeside location. Ph: 03 5386 6281

514. Lake Bringalbert
Map Ref: MAP 4 B8 GPS: 36 50 05 S 141 09 22 E
Camping area 5km N of Bringalbert. Donation appreciated.

515. Lake Ratzcastle Camp Area
Map Ref: MAP 4 B7 GPS: 36 48 38 S 141 27 58 E
Camping area 11km S of Goroke, 2km off Goroke-Harrow Rd.

516. Jane Duff Highway Paark
Map Ref: MAP 4 C7 GPS: 36 43 58 S 141 43 21 E
Camp area 21km W of Natimuk on Natimuk-Frances Rd, Duffholme. Ph: 13 19 63

517. Kiata Campground
Map Ref: MAP 4 C7 GPS: 36 26 51 S 141 47 53 E
Located in Little Desert NP. Camping area 12km S of Kiata via Kiata South Rd. Signposted. 4km dirt rd. Ph: 13 19 63

518. Dimboola Recreation Reserve
Map Ref: MAP 4 C7 GPS: 36 27 30 S 142 01 43 E
Camping area at Lloyd St, Dimboola. Limited stay.

519. Ackle Bend
Map Ref: MAP 4 C7 GPS: 36 30 10 S 142 01 11 E
Within Little Desert National Park camping area 6km S of Dimboola. Via Riverside and Horseshoe Bend Rds. 2km of dirt rd. Ph: 13 19 63

520. Walker Lake
Map Ref: MAP 4 E7 GPS: 36 32 20 S 142 55 19 E
Camp area 23km S of Donald via Donald-Avon Plains Rd.

Free Campsites in Victoria

521. Browns Lake Campground
Map Ref: MAP 4 E7 GPS: 36 27 44 S 143 01 56 E
Camp area at Camerera Rd, turn W off Sunraysia Hwy at Cope Cope.

522. Mount Jeffcott Campground - Mount Jeffcot Flora & Fauna Reserve
Map Ref: MAP 4 F6 GPS: 36 18 30 S 143 08 18 E
Camp are 4km S of town via Camerons Mail Rd, Jeffcott. Turn S off Borung Hwy. Ph: 13 19 63

523. Mt Jeffcott Campground
Map Ref: MAP 4 F6 GPS: 36 18 30 S 143 08 18 E
Camp area S of Jeffcott, turn S off Borung Hwy at Jeffcott to Cameron's Mail Rd.

524. Skinner Flat Reservoir
Map Ref: MAP 4 F6 GPS: 36 21 58 S 143 35 09 E
Camping spot 27km SE of Charlton, turn E 25km SE of Charlton along 1km dirt road.

525. Hard Hill Tourist Reserve
Map Ref: MAP 4 F7 GPS: 36 24 52 S 143 36 22 E
Camping area at Wedderburn. 600m N of Information Centre in Wilson St. Limited Stay. Ph: 03 5494 3489

526. Kooreh Hall
Map Ref: MAP 4 F7 GPS: 36 38 26 S 143 23 08 E
Limited stay at Koreh 12km E of St. Arnaud.

527. Logan Pub - Goldfields
Map Ref: MAP 4 F7 GPS: 36 37 20 S 143 29 37 E
Camp Spot at Logan at rear of hotel. Ask landlord permission. Ph: 03 5496 2220

528. Teddington Camping Area -St Arnaud Range NP - Goldfields
Map Ref: MAP 4 F8 GPS: 36 50 35 S 143 15 43 E
Located above the Upper Teddington Reservoir along Teddington Road, 6.2km W of Sunraysia Hwy at Stuart Mill Ph: 13 19 63

529. Glenalbyn Campground - Goldfields & Grampians
Map Ref: MAP 4 G7 GPS: 36 32 05 S 143 44 35 E
Within the Kooyoora State Park 15km W of Inglewood. Access via Brennah-Glenalbyn Road off the Calder Hwy. Ph: 13 19 63

530. Melville Caves Campground - Goldfields
Map Ref: MAP 4 G7 GPS: 36 36 04 S 143 41 54 E
Within the Kooyoora State Park. Signposted off the Wedderburn-Dunolly Rd. Ph: 13 19 63

531. Butchers Campsite - Goldfields
Map Ref: MAP 4 G7 GPS: 36 37 12 S 143 47 02 E
Located in Kingower SF 11km along Rheola-Inglewood Rd south west of Inglewood. At signposted Kingower-Arnold Rd follow for 2.7kms to signposted Ironbark Ext Rd. Access is just north of this road. Ph: 13 61 86

532. Bridgewater Recreation Reserve
Map Ref: MAP 4 G7 GPS: 36 36 23 S 143 56 41 E
Camping area at Bridgewater off Bridgewater-Maldon Rd. Limited stay.

533. Longbush State Forest Camp
Map Ref: MAP 4 G7 GPS: 36 41 53 S 143 41 34 E
Camp area 4km SE of McIntyre, N off Wimmera Hwy to Wedderburn-Dunolly Rd then S to Longbush Rd and Cains Rd.

534. Orchid Dam Camping Area - Goldfields
Map Ref: MAP 4 G7 GPS: 36 38 58 S 143 45 46 E
Located in Kingower SF 11km along Rheola-Inglewood Rd south west of Inglewood. At signposted Kingower-Arnold Rd follow for 3.6kms to signposted McIntyre-Inglewood Rd. Access is just north of this road. Follow this south for 3kms to signposted Gap Rd for 850m to camp area around dam. Ph: 13 61 86

535. Moliagul Campground
Map Ref: MAP 4 G7 GPS: 36 45 02 S 143 39 50 E
Located via Dunolly-Moliagul Rd, Moliagul 14kms N of Dunolly. Limited stay.

536. Newbridge Recreation Reserve Camping Area - Goldfields & Grampians
Map Ref: MAP 4 G7 GPS: 36 44 18 S 143 54 09 E
Signposted access along the Maldon-St Arnaud Hwy in Newbridge, on the eastern side of bridge over Loddon River. Shady, grassed sites on the river bank. Ph: 03 5438 7469

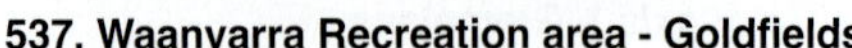

537. Waanyarra Recreation area - Goldfields
Map Ref: MAP 4 G8 GPS: 36 49 10 S 143 48 05 E
Camp Area 10km NE of Dunolly or 33km S of Bridgewater in Dunolly State Forest. Turn E onto Waanyarra Cemetery Rd. Ph: 13 11 86

538. Laanecoorie River Reserve
Map Ref: MAP 4 G8 GPS: 36 49 32 S 143 53 55 E
Camping at Laanecoorie beside the Loddon River.

539. Bullock Picnic Camp
Map Ref: MAP 4 G7 GPS: 36 47 06 S 144 09 11 E
Camp area 7km S of Maron via Bullock Rd, Marong. Ph: 13 61 86

540. Rush Dam picnic and Camping Area - Goldfields
Map Ref: MAP 4 H7 GPS: 36 30 02 S 144 21 01 E
Within the Greater Bendigo NP. Situated on Camp Rd which is off Millwood Rd which is off the Raywood Rd. Ph: 13 19 63

541. Mulga Dam picnic and Camping Area - Goldfields
Map Ref: MAP 4 H7 GPS: 36 29 55 S 144 22 22 E
Located in Greater Bendigo NP. Located on Camp Road from Bendigo-Tennyson Rd Ph: 13 19 63

542. Loeser bush Camping Area - Goldfields
Map Ref: MAP 4 H7 GPS: 36 37 41 S 144 17 56 E
Within the Greater Bendigo NP at junction of Loeser & Black Rock Rd Ph: 13 19 63

543. Notleys Picnic Area - Goldfields
Map Ref: MAP 4 H7 GPS: 36 38 54 S 144 15 30 E
Located in Greater Bendigo NP 20km N of Eaglehawk. Signpost access along Eaglehawk-Neilborough Rd off the C336 (Bendigo-Pyramid Rd) Ph: 13 19 63

544. English's Bridge - Goldfields
Map Ref: MAP 4 H7 GPS: 36 37 24 S 144 33 39 E
Beside Campaspe River NE of Bendigo take Comer Lane from the Midland Hwy. Dry weather only Ph: 03 5430 4444

545. Aysons Reserve
Map Ref: MAP 4 J7 GPS: 36 27 34 S 144 40 08 E
Camping area 8km NE of Elmore. Turn N off Midland Hwy. Travel 5km NE along Burnewang Rd for 3km to site beside Campaspe River.

546. Green's Lake - Goldfields
Map Ref: MAP 4 J7 GPS: 36 26 18 S 144 49 42 E
Greens Lake is located 15km W of Stanhope via the Midlands Hwy.

547. Cooma Bend Camping Area - Central Murray
Map Ref: MAP 4 K6 GPS: 36 18 49 S 145 20 51 E
From the Midland Hwy west of Shepparton proceed north west along Mooroopna-Echuca Rd for 6km. Take signposted Alexander Rd go north for 3.7km to signposted Meaklim Road. Continue east for 930m to park entrance. Numerous tracks lead to river and bush camps. Ph: 13 19 63

548. Reedy Swamp Road Camping Area - Central Murray
Map Ref: MAP 4 K6 GPS: 36 19 27 S 145 21 43 E
From Shepparton take C358 for 6.6km to signposted Daldy Rd which leads west for 2.9km to a junction. Take sandy track on left for 150m to signposted Reedy Swamp Track. Numerous tracks lead to river and bush camps. Ph: 13 19 63

549. Goulburn River Bush Camping - Central Murray
Map Ref: MAP 4 K6 GPS: 36 22 49 S 145 23 30 E
From the Midland Hwy west of Shepparton take the track on the northern side of the road at the western side of Daintons Bridge over the river. Track is at the 80km sign west or 60km sign east. Numerous access tracks lead to sites. Ph: 03 5831 4400

550. Cemetary Bend - Cemetary Bend State Forest
Map Ref: MAP 4 K7 GPS: 36 31 32 S 145 19 56 E
Located on Wattle Track, Toolamba. Dispersed camping 21km SW of Shepparton via Toolamba Rd. Entry 1.8km W of Toolamba Rd. High clearance, off road caravans only. 4WD required during wet weather. Ph: 13 61 86

551. Arcadia Streamside Reserve
Map Ref: MAP 4 J7 GPS: 36 35 54 S 145 13 37 E
Dispersed camping 5km NE of Murchison via High Rd (C245) for 1km them N to Donegans Rd then 2km to camping on river. High clearance, off road caravans only. 4WD required in wet weather. Ph: 13 61 86

552. Greens Camp Ground
Map Ref: MAP 4 J7 GPS: 36 38 45 S 145 01 41 E
Camp area 8km S of Rushworth via Rushworth-Nagambie Rd and Reedy Creek Rd. 1km dirt road beyond Balaclava Hill Info Centre. Ph: 13 19 63

The Greens Lake campsite has room for any size rig and plenty of trees.

Greens Lake Free Campsite No 546

Robinvale, VIC
15 km west of Stanhope

Jim and Cheryl Foster

Greens Lake is a shallow lake in open country twenty four km east of Elmore just off the Midlands Highway in Northern Victoria. Together with Cooper Lake it forms the Corop Lakes. These lakes contain abundant carp and redfin, generally to 1.3 kg and occasionally to 2.7 kg, also some goldfish and tench. A boat is required for best results. The best time to fish these lakes is from spring to autumn.

We didn't fish the lake as when we were there the weather was less than clement. The main reason we stopped was because the wind was blowing from the west, a head wind for us, at a speed of at least 50km an hour with squally showers every ten minutes or so; not ideal weather for caravanning.

What we did find however, was that the lake is only two km off the highway to the north. The first km is sealed but the second is not, although it was in reasonably good condition when we visited.

There are numerous campsites along the lake shore both under shady gum trees and in the open. You can actually camp right by the water and throw a line out from under your awning if you so wish. There is a boat ramp if you are into boat fishing but if you like to toss a line in from the shore, you will be better served if you do so after dark when the fish come in close to the shallower water.

The tiny hamlet of Corop is just 3.2km west of the turnoff to Greens Lake and you can buy basic foodstuffs and fuel at the one shop the town boasts or you can head east for 15km to the slightly larger town of Stanhope for the supermarket there.

Just The Facts

Greens Lake

Getting there: Greens Lake can be found on the Greens Lake Recreational Reserve two km north of the Midlands Highway and 15km west of Stanhope. Or at: Lat. 36. 26. 18. 34. S. Long. 144. 49. 42. 06. E. You can have a good look at the lake and camping area on Google Earth as the immediate area is shown in high resolution

Facilities: The Reserve has a boat ramp, shady trees, fireplaces and good flush toilets.

Cost: Free.

553. Whroo Reserve - Rushworth - Goldfields
Map Ref: MAP 4 J7 GPS: 36 38 50 S 145 01 41 E
7kms from the town of Rushworth. Camping area along Green's Rd. Ph: 03 5856 1561

554. Greens Campground - Goldfields
Map Ref: MAP 4 J7 GPS: 36 38 48 S 145 01 56 E
Within the Whroo Historic Reserve from Rushworth follow the Rushworth-Nagambie Rd and then turn on to Greens Rd. Ph: 13 19 63

555. Baileys Rocks Campground - Goldfields
Map Ref: MAP 4 B9 GPS: 37 17 20 S 141 10 40 E
In the Dergholm State Park NW of Casterton via Baileys Rocks Rd off Casterton-Naracoorte Rd. Ph: 13 19 63

556. Parsons (Collins) Lake - Parsons Lake Reserve
Map Ref: MAP 4 B8 GPS: 37 00 05 S 141 21 05 E
Area 63km SW of Natimuk via Sullivan Rd, Edenhope. Limited stay. Ph: 13 19 63

557. Fulham Streamside Reserve Camping Area - Grampians
Map Ref: MAP 4 C8 GPS: 37 09 12 S 141 50 50 E
On the Glenelg River 10km N of town of Balmoral. Access off Natimuk-Hamilton Road. Ph: 13 19 63

558. Rocklands Reservoir Bush Camp - Goldfields
Map Ref: MAP 4 C8 GPS: 37 13 44 S 141 58 24 E
Situated on western shores of reservoir 15kms east of Balmoral. Access via signposted Rocklands Rd or to the east via Hynes Rd off the Henty Hwy. Ph: 1800 807 056

559. Cherrypool Highway Park - Goldfields
Map Ref: MAP 4 D8 GPS: 37 06 33 S 142 11 10 E
Located 50km south of Horsham along the Henty Highway. Signposted access on the eastern side of the highway beside the Glenelg River. Ph: 13 19 63

560. Brookes Road Camping Area
Map Ref: MAP 4 D8 GPS: 37 11 48 S 142 08 22 E
Camping on northern end of the Eastern foreshore of Rocklands Reservoir via Brookes Road off the Henty Hwy Ph: 13 61 86

561. Brodies Camping Area - Rocklands SF - Grampians
Map Ref: MAP 4 C8 GPS: 37 14 58 S 141 59 38 E
Camping on the N Shore of Rocklands Reservoir via Rockland-Cherrypool Road within the Rockland SF. Ph: 13 61 86

562. Mountain Dam Campground - Goldfields
Map Ref: MAP 4 C8 GPS: 37 13 40 S 142 05 17 E
Within the Rocklands State Forest on the shores of Rocklands Reservoir. Access via Rockland-Cherrypool Rd. Dry weather only Ph: 13 11 86

563. Hynes Reserve Camping Ground - Goldfields & Grampians
Map Ref: MAP 4 D8 GPS: 37 13 29 S 142 06 17 E
Camp area 9km W of Glenisla. Access via Hynes Rd off Henty Hwy. Within the Rocklands Reservoir park. Ph: 13 19 63

564. Glendinning Campground - Grampians
Map Ref: MAP 4 C9 GPS: 37 17 50 S 141 59 51 E
Camp Area 20km SE of Balmoral, via Yarramyljup or Glendinning Rds. Ph: 13 11 86

565. Fergusons Campground - Goldfields
Map Ref: MAP 4 C9 GPS: 37 17 42 S 142 03 40 E
In Rocklands State Forest on the shores of Rocklands Reservoir. Access via Fergusons Rd off Gartons Rd off the Henty Hwy. Dry weather only Ph: 13 61 86

566. Plantation Campground
Map Ref: MAP 4 D8 GPS: 37 03 34 S 142 30 53 E
10km N of Halls Gap Information Centre. Turn N off C216 on to Mt Zero Rd and travel for 9km on dirt road. Ph: 03 5361 4000

567. Lake Lonsdale Camping Area - Grampians
Map Ref: MAP 4 E8 GPS: 37 00 53 S 142 38 32 E
12km W of Stawell. Signposted access via Sandbar Road off the Western Hwy. Ph: 1300 659 961

568. Campbells Bridge Bushland Reserve - Goldfields
Map Ref: MAP 4 E8 GPS: 36 55 33 S 142 47 00 E
Located 15kms north of Stawell on C238 Stawell-Donald Road beside the road at bridge over the Wimmera River. Ph: 13 19 63

Whroo Historic Camping Area No 553

Rushworth, VIC

170 km north of Melbourne

Stephanie Jackson

A series of steps leads down to the base of the old mine

The main streets of the picturesque Victorian town of Rushworth, with their weatherboard cottages, old pubs, shops, and churches, are recognised as a National Trust Urban Conservation Area, but this town with its population of around 1,000 is rarely a hive of activity.

To the south lies the 33,000 hectare Rushworth State Forest, the largest ironbark forest in the world, but it wasn't timber that brought wealth to the town in past years. It was gold. Its discovery in 1853 brought thousands of optimistic men flocking to the area, but it was two seamen who struck it rich in a big way. In 1854, they stumbled across a large nugget of gold lying in the grass on the top of a hill, and the following year, their Balaclava mine, was opened. It became the richest mine in the north-eastern region of the state, and produced more than one million pounds worth of gold.

In the language of the local indigenous people 'Wooroo' meant 'mouth', and as gaping holes appeared across the landscape, business boomed in the settlement of Whroo that sprung up some 7kms south of Rushworth. Stores and hotels were constructed, but the town wasn't destined for long-term glory. By the 1890s, the glitter of gold had been replaced by the gloom of poverty, and Whroo slid into oblivion.

You won't find great riches here today, but what you will find, if you drive along the unsealed road that leads into the forest, is the 500 hectare Whroo Historic Reserve that encompasses the site of the old township and the goldfields. And here there's a secluded area where you can camp without spending a cent.

A track leads through a long tunnel into the heart of the open cut mine.

There's no sign of the old settlement, but it's hard to miss the conspicuous evidence of past mining activities. You might see a swamp wallaby dart across a landscape where weathered mullock heaps lie scattered among the forest; crimson rosellas feeding on the seeds of a peppercorn tree that sprouted where once a miner's hut had perhaps stood; and kangaroos grazing beneath the gnarled branches of fruit trees that were planted by one of Whroo's long vanished residents.

Make your way along a narrow track, past deep fissures that miners gouged into the hillside in search of gold, and wander on beyond the yawning mouths of shafts that spear down into the bowels of the earth, and you'll discover Balaclava Hill where Whroo's greatest wealth was discovered. You might gasp in amazement as you peer down into the vast open cut mine where some 9,000 men once spent their days at back-breaking labour. And as you walk down the countless steps that lead beyond high walls pocked marked with as many holes as an Indian beggar's trousers, to the base of the 25 metre deep pit, perhaps you'll experience fleeting dreams of discovering a nugget of gold unearthed by the latest downpour of rain.

It's the picturesque camping area, in a clearing among the forest, that's the real treasure here. The site can be accessed by large vehicles and rigs, and there's adequate room to set up camp if other visitors have not already claimed the largest campsites. And although there are no facilities here other than pit toilets, the tranquillity you'll find is worth its weight in gold.

Just The Facts

Rushworth And Whroo

Getting there: The Victorian town of Rushworth is 170 kilometres north of Melbourne. The Whroo Historic Reserve is approximately 7kms from the town, with the camping area located 500 metres along Green's Road. The road to the reserve is unsealed.

Town facilities: There are hotels, a museum which is open on Tuesdays from 2-5pm, a laundromat, a supermarket, cafes, and a range of other shops at Rushworth.

Camping area facilities: There is ample room for large vans, motorhomes, and fifth wheelers at the camping area. The only facilities are pit toilets. There are picnic tables and additional toilets near the site's information centre which is no longer operational.

The walking track to the open cut mine is 360 metres one way, with a series of steps leading up to a viewing platform. The track to the tunnel that leads into the base of the open cut mine is 460 metres one way.

Charges: There is no charge for camping here.

Pets: Pets are permitted but should be kept under control so they do not disturb wildlife.

Contact: For additional information, phone 03 5856 1117, send e-mail to info@rushworthtourism.com.au, or log onto www.rushworthtourism.com.au

Free Campsites in Victoria

569. Burough Huts Campground
Map Ref: MAP 4 D8 GPS: 37 13 27 S 142 32 25 E
Camping area 11km S of Halls Gap via Grampians Road. Ph: 03 5361 4000

570. Pyrenees Waterfalls
Map Ref: MAP 4 F8 GPS: 37 05 55 S 143 22 01 E
Camp area 12.5kms W of Avoca. Turn W 200m N of PO onto Duke St then R at T intersection onto Vinoca RD, Waterfall track. Ph: 03 5465 1000

571. Waterfalls Campground - Goldfields
Map Ref: MAP 4 F8 GPS: 37 05 36 S 143 22 06 E
In the Pyrenees State Forest W of Avoca. From Duke St, turn R onto Vinoca Rd. Ph: 03 5465 1000

572. Paddys Ranges State Park
Map Ref: MAP 4 G8 GPS: 37 04 58 S 143 41 27 E
Camping area 8km SW of Maryborough via Karri Track from Old Avoca Rd. Dirt rd. Ph: 13 19 63

573. Karri Track Camping Area - Goldfields
Map Ref: MAP 4 G8 GPS: 37 05 00 S 143 41 45 E
From Maryborough take the Old Avoca Rd off the Pyrenees Hwy. Follow this for 1.7km to the all weather track into the campsite. Ph: 13 19 63

574. Hamiltons Crossing
Map Ref: MAP 4 G8 GPS: 36 56 33 S 143 56 01 E
Camp area 12km S of Eddington via Baringhup-Eastville Rd, Baringhup. S side of bridge to sites.

575. Butt's Reserve Camping Area - Goldfields
Map Ref: MAP 4 G8 GPS: 36 59 20 S 144 03 23 E
Within the Maldon historic reserve close to town take the signposted Mt Tarrengower Road. Ph: 13 19 63

576. The Oaks - Mount Alexander Regional Park
Map Ref: MAP 4 H8 GPS: 36 59 54 S 144 17 26 E
Parking area 3km E of Harcourt at 93 Picnic Gully Rd, Harcourt. Follow E end of Market St from servo and follow sign along dirt road then L at Xmas Tree sign then R at Oak Plantation sign. Small vehicles only, overhanging trees. Ph: 13 19 63

577. Picnic Gully
Map Ref: MAP 4 H8 GPS: 36 59 54 S 144 17 26 E
Within the Mt Alexander Regional Park 3km E of Harcourt. E end of Market St follow signs to Picnic Gully. Dirt road. Suitable for small vehicles only. Ph: 13 19 63

578. Leanganook Camping Area - Goldfields
Map Ref: MAP 4 H8 GPS: 37 01 04 S 144 18 24 E
Located in Mount Alexander Regional Park east of Harcourt via the Faraday-Sutton Grange Rd. Take signposted Joseph Young Dve 3km north east of Faraday then 2km to access road. Ph: 13 19 63

579. Red White and Blue Mine Camping Area
Map Ref: MAP 4 G8 GPS: 37 03 33 S 144 06 28 E
Individual camp sites 1.4kms along Bells Lane Track junction with Red White and Blue Track off Muckleford School Rd. Ph: 13 61 86

580. Chokem Flat campground
Map Ref: MAP 4 H8 GPS: 37 08 26 S 144 13 31 E
1.3kms NW of Irishtown along Fryers Rd off Vaughan-Chewton Rd, 1km N of Vaughan Springs Rd. Camping along the banks of Fryers Creek. Ph: 13 19 63

581. Vaughan Springs Reserve - Goldfields
Map Ref: MAP 4 G8 GPS: 37 09 40 S 144 12 52 E
In the Castlemaine Diggings National Heritage Park S of Castlemaine via Yapeen along Vaughan-Springs Rd & Vaughan-Drummond Rd at Loddon River bridge. Ph: 13 11 93

582. Warburton Bridge Reserve - Goldfields
Map Ref: MAP 4 H8 GPS: 37 10 12 S 144 14 15 E
Camp Area 18km S of Castlemaine via Yapeen along Vaughan Springs Rd & Vaughan-Drummond Rd. Camp at Loddon River Bridge. Ph: 13 11 93

583. Dargile camping and picnic area - Goldfields
Map Ref: MAP 4 J8 GPS: 36 51 10 S 144 44 58 E
Within the Heathcote-Graytown NP N of Heathcote via the Heathcote-North Costerfield Rd. Ph: 13 19 63

584. Spring Creek Camping Area
Map Ref: MAP 4 J8 GPS: 36 47 52 S 144 56 35 E
Located in Heathcote-Graytown NP 30kms NE of Heathcote off the Heathcote-Nagambie Rd on Boundary Rd. Ph: 13 19 63

585. Major Creek Streamside Reserve
Map Ref: MAP 4 J8   GPS: 36 51 16 S 145 04 01 E
Beside the creek along the Major Mitchell Trail at the junction of Mitchellstown Rd and Wattlevale Rd 8km west of Goulburn Valley Hwy and 29km N of Seymour. Ph: 13 19 63

586. Falls Creek Reservoir Camping Area - Melbourne
Map Ref: MAP 4 J8   GPS: 37 07 12 S 145 11 35 E
Located in the Tallarook State Forest 80km N of Melbourne between Broadford and Seymour. Access via East Falls Rd via Freemans Rd. Ph: 03 5784 0600

587. Trawool Reservoir Camping Area - Close to Melbourne
Map Ref: MAP 4 K8   GPS: 37 07 13 S 145 11 31 E
Within Tallarook State Forest, from Main Mountain Rd 300m east of Mt Hickey Rd take road north signposted West Falls Rd. Continue north for 5.4km to gate which is 4WD dry weather only track then 730m to signposted Reservoir Track then 100m to camping area beside dam. Ph: 13 61 86

588. Freemans Camping Area
Map Ref: MAP 4 J8   GPS: 37 09 49 S 145 09 47 E
Within the Tallarook SF between Broadford & Seymour 11km E of the Hume Fwy on Freemans Road, off Ennis Road. Ph: 03 5784 0600

589. Long Lead Camp Area
Map Ref: MAP 4 B9   GPS: 37 35 07 S 141 12 33 E
Camp area 18km w of Casterton. Take the Casterton-Penola Rd and turn N onto Long Lead track then L onto Blue Line, veer R.

590. Ess Lagoon
Map Ref: MAP 4 B9   GPS: 37 34 51 S 141 23 56 E
Camp area at Ess Lagoon Rd, Casterton on N side of town via McPherson St. Limit 1 month stay. Ph: 03 5554 2440

591. Mill Swamp - Wilkin Flora & Fauna Reserve
Map Ref: MAP 4 B10   GPS: 37 42 08 S 141 13 29 E
Camp area 12km E of Strathdownie on Grubbed Rd with access via the Glenelg Hwy. Signposted. Small vehicles only. Ph: 03 555 2440

592. Wannon River Camping Area
Map Ref: MAP 4 C10   GPS: 37 40 16 S 141 50 32 E
Located on the Wannon River 18km NW of Hamilton with signposted access off the Glenelg Hwy at Wannon. Ph: 1800 807 056

593. Freshwater Lake Reserve
Map Ref: MAP 4 D9   GPS: 37 35 07 S 142 19 07 E
Camp area located at 753 Victoria Rd 8km N of Dunkeld.

594. Jimmy Creek Campground
Map Ref: MAP 4 D9   GPS: 37 22 19 S 142 30 11 E
Camping area 35km S of Halls Gap via Grampians Rd. Ph: 03 5361 4000

595. Willaura Recreation Ground
Map Ref: MAP 4 E9   GPS: 37 32 41 S 142 44 36 E
Camping area at Delacombe Way Willaura. Ph: 0429 953 150

596. Chinamans Camping Area - Grampians
Map Ref: MAP 4 F9   GPS: 37 14 58 S 143 11 56 E
Within Mount Cole State Forest 25km NW of Beaufort. Access via Mt Cole Road from Warrak. Ph: 13 61 86

597. Greenhill Lake Reserve - Goldfields & Grampians
Map Ref: MAP 4 E9   GPS: 37 17 46 S 142 58 48 E
4km E of Ararat off the Western Hwy. Ph: 1800 657 158

598. Langi Ghiran Campground - Goldfields
Map Ref: MAP 4 E9   GPS: 37 17 40 S 143 05 52 E
Located in Langi Ghiran State Park 12km E of Ararat via Kartuk Rd off Western Hwy. Ph: 13 19 63

599. Mugwamp Camping Area - Mount Cole SF - Goldfields
Map Ref: MAP 4 F9   GPS: 37 17 24 S 143 13 58 E
Small site located near Mugwamp Creek via Dawson Rock Rd from Mt Cole Road in the Mt Cole State Forest, 25km NW of Beaufort. Ph: 13 61 86

600. Smiths Bridge Camping Area - Goldfields
Map Ref: MAP 4 F9   GPS: 37 17 52 S 143 17 30 E
Located 19km NW of Beaufort within the Mt Cole State Forest. Ph: 13 61 86

Major's Creek Reserve No 585

Mitchellstown, Vic

5kms south of Nagambie

By John Mainwaring

A stopover along the Goulburn River, just like Major Mitchell did in 1836.

Here is a great spot for travellers heading along the Hume or along the Goulburn Highways in the central area of Victoria, and with a bit of history thrown in as well. This was the site where Thomas Mitchell crossed the Goulburn on his way back to Sydney after his 1836 winter tour of Australia Felix, more commonly called Victoria nowadays. It is just 20-25 kilometres north of the Hume along the Goulburn Highway then duck left a few kilometres towards the Goulburn River at Mitchellstown. The site is only 6 or 7 kilometres from Nagambie and all your required supplies can be sourced from there. The town has a large IGA and a few servos. Or if you enjoy wineries and feel like spoiling yourself, eating at the Mitchelton Winery just a few kilometres away is always an option.

Location is important with any camp area but access in is even more so for those with larger rigs and 2WD vehicles. This one ticks all the boxes with good quality bitumen practically all the way, then there's just a couple of kilometres of good quality gravel road to finish off. A couple of areas can get a little rutted in the wet but you can avoid these if your vehicle is not high clearance and you will find an expansive area with few obstructions so no worries manoeuvring your van. There would be room for 50 to 100 campsites at several points along this side branch of the Goulburn and many of the sites are right at the water's edge so you can sit back with a drink and watch the yabbies and listen to the froggies. There are plenty of areas that provide shade but if you are wary of the effect gravity can have on eucalypt branches, then there are open areas available as well.

The site is adjacent to a large and sprawling billabong off the Goulburn River which tells the fisher-folks that this is a worthy spot to wet a line and a kayak might give you some enjoyment too. On the other side of the access road is an apparent wilderness area that happens to be the Puckapunyal Military Training Area with a few signs suggesting that you should not stray into the fenced off area. It is rare to hear much ruckus from that zone but tanks and infantry do a little training in there so you never know. Look out for a rocky creation on the road side celebrating Mitchell's passing by this area back in 1836. There have been a few changes in the last 180 years but I'd bet he would still recognise it.

Camping by the Goulburn River at Major's Creek Reserve.

The Major Mitchell Monument.

So this would be a good stopover for a day or so when transiting central Victoria, and since both the Hume and the Goulburn Highways are popular migration routes and very nearby, this is a handy hideaway to know about.

Just The Facts

Major's Creek

Getting there: Around 5 kilometres south of Nagambie off the Goulburn Highway, and about 5 kilometres along Mitchellstown Road then just over the bridge crossing the Goulburn River. 2WD access.

Facilities:A couple of long-drop bush toilets.

Pets: Pets allowed under control.

Rates: Free

Free Campsites in Victoria

601. Fortes Picnic & Camping Area - Goldfields
Map Ref: MAP 4 F9 GPS: 37 17 57 S 143 21 16 E
Located in Mount Cole SF 25kms north west of Beaufort. From Smiths Bridge take Flume Gully Rd and proceed east for 2.6km. Keep right along Ridge Rd for 2.6kms to SP Fortes Rd and continue for 1.5km to signposted F3 Rd then 110m to camping area. Ph: 13 61 86

602. Middle Creek Campground - Goldfields
Map Ref: MAP 4 F9 GPS: 37 19 56 S 143 14 45 E
Located in Mt Buangor State Park 20km W of Beaufort. Access by Jimmy Smith Rd from Ferntree Gully Rd. Ph: 13 19 63

603. Ditchfields Camping Area - Grampians
Map Ref: MAP 4 F9 GPS: 37 19 01 S 143 16 22 E
Located in Mount Cole State Forest 25km NW of Beaufort. Signposted access via Camp Road from Mt Cole Road. Ph: 13 61 86

604. Red Kangaroo Roadhouse
Map Ref: MAP 4 F9 GPS: 37 25 28 S 143 21 14 E
Camping area 3km W of Beaufort. Fee for showers. Limited stay. Ph: 03 5349 3180

605. Lake Burrmbeet
Map Ref: MAP 4 F9 GPS: 37 29 53 S 143 36 59 E
Camp area 23km W of Ballarat in Dobsons Lane, Burrumbeet. W side of lake, 16km W of Cardigan Village. Ph: 03 5320 5500

606. The Cork Oaks Picnic Area - Mount Beckworth Scenic Reserve
Map Ref: MAP 4 G9 GPS: 37 18 36 S 143 42 29 E
Camp area 8km W of Clunes on Cork Oaks Track, Mount Beckworth via Kierces Rd and Mountain Creek Rd. Rough, dirt road and limited caravan sites. Ph: 13 19 63

607. Cork Oaks Camping Area - Goldfields
Map Ref: MAP 4 G9 GPS: 37 18 35 S 143 42 29 E
Within Mount Beckworth Scenic Reserve 8km west of Clunes and accessed along Mountain Creek Rd. Once in reserve proceed north following signs for 3.5km to camp area. Ph: 13 19 63

608. Slaty Creek Campground - Goldfields
Map Ref: MAP 4 G9 GPS: 37 27 45 S 143 54 16 E
3 campgrounds located in the Creswick Regional Park some 5km S of Creswick. Access via Slaty Creek Rd off Creswick-Bungaree Rd. Ph: 13 19 63

609. Mount Franklin Reserve Campground - Close to Melbourne
Map Ref: MAP 4 G9 GPS: 37 15 48 S 144 08 58 E
Located 11km N of Daylesford. Access off the Midland Highway. Steep Access. Ph: 13 19 63

610. Upper Loddon Bush Camps - Goldfields
Map Ref: MAP 4 H9 GPS: 37 15 23 S 144 14 41 E
Located in Upper Loddon SF north of Glenlyon which is 11kms north east of Daylesford. From Glenlyon take Ford St to the west for 1.2kms turn right at signposted Green Gully Rd. Continue north for 3.6km to Walls Lane then east to track on left before causeway over river. Follow on this track north for 900m for campsites along the western banks of Loddon River. Ph: 13 61 86

611. Kyneton Mineral Springs Reserve
Map Ref: MAP 4 H9 GPS: 37 14 09 S 144 25 10 E
Camping 3.5km W of Kyneton on Burton Ave. Limited stay.

612. Upper Chadwick Campground
Map Ref: MAP 4 H9 GPS: 37 29 06 S 144 23 13 E
Campground located along Upper Chadwick track off O'Briens Road, E of O'Briens Crossing. Ph: 13 19 63

613. Firth Park Campground - Close to Melbourne
Map Ref: MAP 4 H9 GPS: 37 28 10 S 144 24 44 E
Camp Area 24km W of Gisborne. Turn W off C704 11km W of Gisborne or 20km N of Darley onto Carrolls Lane & Firth Rd. 12km dirt road. Ph: 13 11 86

614. O'Briens Crossing - Goldfields
Map Ref: MAP 4 H9 GPS: 37 29 48 S 144 21 36 E
Within the Lerderderg State Park. 8km E of Blackwood on the Lerderderg River. Take Golden Point Rd then in to O'Brien's Rd. Ph: 13 19 63

615. Lerderderg Campground - Close to Melbourne
Map Ref: MAP 4 H9 GPS: 37 29 06 S 144 23 11 E
Located in Lerderderg State Park via Firth Rd off Bacchus Marsh-Gisborne Rd. Located 1.5km north of O'Briens Rd via Upper Chadwick Track which is signposted 4.8km east of O'Briens Crossing. 4WD recommended. Dry weather only. Ph: 13 19 63

616. No 1 Camping Area - Close to Melbourne
Map Ref: MAP 4 J9 GPS: 37 19 16 S 145 10 19 E
Mt Disappointment State Forest 60km N Melbourne & SE of Broadford. Located at the junction of Main Mountain and Flowerdale roads. Ph: 03 5784 0600

617. Andersons Garden Camping Area - Mount Disappointment State Forest - Yarra & Dandenongs
Map Ref: MAP 4 J9 GPS: 37 21 08 S 145 09 28 E
Located 3.5km along Raynors Road off Main Mountain Road from Heathcote junction. Ph: 03 5784 0600

618. Princess Margaret Rose Caves
Map Ref: MAP 4 A10 GPS: 37 59 12 S 140 59 31 E
Located in Lower Glenelg NP. Camping area 16km N of Nelson. Turn N 4km W of Nelson off Hwy. Permit required. Ph: 08 8737 4171

619. Red Gum Camping Area -Otways & South-West
Map Ref: MAP 4 B10 GPS: 38 02 03 S 141 09 19 E
Within the Lower Glenelg NP from Dartmoor via Wanwin Rd. Then via River Fireline Track. Ph: 13 19 63

620. Fort O'Hare Campground - Otways & Sth West
Map Ref: MAP 4 B10 GPS: 37 55 55 S 141 17 11 E
On the bank of the Glenelg River and less than 1km from the centre of Dartmoor in SW Victoria. Ph: 08 8738 4051

621. Digby Hotel
Map Ref: MAP 4 B10 GPS: 37 48 17 S 141 31 51 E
Camp at hotel on Portland-Casterton Rd in Digby. Limited stay. Ph: 03 5579 3281

622. Hiscocks Crossing - Otways Sth West
Map Ref: MAP 4 B10 GPS: 37 56 21 S 141 26 46 E
Camp Area 16km W of Hotspur. Turn W off C195, 600m N of Hotspur Bridge onto Mill Rd & The Boulevard. Dirt road. Bush camping beside river. Dry weather only Ph: 13 19 63

623. Hotspur Bridge
Map Ref: MAP 4 C10 GPS: 37 55 33 S 141 34 58 E
Located on Crawford River 20km NW of A1/C195 junction or 13km S of Digby.

624. The Neck Camping Area - Otways
Map Ref: MAP 4 B10 GPS: 37 56 40 S 141 27 35 E
Located in Crawford River Regional Park 2.5kms east of Cowlands Rd junction. Cross the bridge and turn east to follow the river for 2.1kms to signposted access. Drive 60m to camp area. Ph: 13 19 63

625. Crawford River Camping Aea - Otways
Map Ref: MAP 4 C10 GPS: 37 55 32 S 141 33 39 E
Located in the village of Hotspur on C195 road on the southern end of the bridge over the Crawford River. Suits overnight stop.

626. Wrights Campground
Map Ref: MAP 4 B10 GPS: 38 02 07 S 141 23 24 E
Located in Cobboboonee NP 34km NW of Heywood. Take Pacific Hwy NW for 29km turn S into rights Swamp Rd then 5km to camp spot. Ph: 13 19 63

627. Annya Camp Camping Area - Annya SF - Otways & Sth West
Map Ref: MAP 4 C10 GPS: 38 01 07 S 141 34 58 E
This site is via the Portland - Casterton Road off the Princes Hwy within the Annya SF. Ph: 03 5527 0444

628. Jackass Fern Gully Campground - Otways & Sth West
Map Ref: MAP 4 B11 GPS: 38 04 45 S 141 25 42 E
Cobboboonee State Forest is NW of Portland from the Portland-Nelson Rd take the T&W Rd to the signposted turn-off to the camp area. Dry weather only Ph: 13 61 86

629. Lake Surprise Camping Area -Otways & South-West
Map Ref: MAP 4 C10 GPS: 38 03 25 S 141 55 20 E
Mt Eccles NP 10km W of Macarthur via Mt Eccles Rd. Ph: 13 19 63

630. Lake Surprise Campground
Map Ref: MAP 4 C10 GPS: 38 03 30 S 141 55 22 E
Located within Mount Eccles NP. Camping area 10km SW of Macarthur. Ph: 13 19 63

631. Lake Bolac Foreshore Camping Area - Goldfields & Grampians
Map Ref: MAP 4 E10 GPS: 37 43 16 S 142 51 22 E
2km S of the town of Lake Bolac. Access via signposted Montgomery St off the Glenelg Hwy. Ph: 03 5350 2204

632. East Beach Reserve
Map Ref: MAP 4 E10 GPS: 37 42 17 S 142 52 43 E
Camping area 4km SE of Lake Bolac. Turn off highway 3km E of Lake Bolac.

633. Derrinallum Recreation Reserve
Map Ref: MAP 4 F10 GPS: 37 56 56 S 143 13 59 E
Camping at E end of town. Limited stay.

634. Happy Valley Crossing - Happy Valley Streamside Reserve
Map Ref: MAP 4 F10 GPS: 37 45 02 S 143 34 49 E
Camp area 8km SE of Linton at 264 Happy Valley Crossing Rd, Happy Valley. Exit Glenelg Hwy S to Linton-Naringhil Rd for 5km then E 3km to creek. Small vehicles only. Ph: 13 19 63

635. Surface Point Camping Area
Map Ref: MAP 4 G10 GPS: 37 46 11 S 143 44 17 E
Located 30km S of Ballarat via Misery Creek Road off the Ballarat - Colac Road, 25km S of Ballarat Ph: 13 19 63

636. Hunts Bridge
Map Ref: MAP 4 G10 GPS: 37 42 37 S 144 05 41 E
Camp area 13km NE of Elaine. From N side of town take Settlement Rd for 5.5km then R at T intersection onto Dorn-Egerton Rd for 5km, L at T intersection for 400m, l at jcn for 2km. Beside river. Dirt rd for 6km. Ph: 13 19 63

637. Boar Gully Camping Area - Close to Melbourne
Map Ref: MAP 4 H10 GPS: 37 46 01 S 144 15 47 E
Numerous sites within Brisbane Ranges NP. Access via Reids Rd off Brisbane Ranges Road, Ph: 13 19 63

638. Cape Bridgewater Coastal Camp
Map Ref: MAP 4 B11 GPS: 38 22 15 S 141 24 05 E
Camping area 300m from beach on S side of town of Cape Bridgewater. Ph: 03 5526 7247

639. Surry Ridge Campground - Otways & Sth West
Map Ref: MAP 4 B11 GPS: 38 11 06 S 141 30 25 E
Turn west off A1 21kms north of Portland on to Coffeys Road, left on to Jacky Swamp Rd, right on to Cutout Dam Rd and continue to camp. Dry weather only. Ph: 13 61 86

640. Sawpit Campground - Otways & Sth West
Map Ref: MAP 4 C11 GPS: 38 14 14 S 141 41 22 E
1km W of Narrawong, then 3km N on the Boyers Rd. Ph: 13 61 86

641. Fitzroy River - Otways & Sth West
Map Ref: MAP 4 C11 GPS: 38 13 26 S 141 45 47 E
25kms N of Portland across the Fitzroy River Bridge.

642. Fitzroy River Coastal Reserve - Otways & South-West
Map Ref: MAP 4 C11 GPS: 38 15 29 S 141 50 52 E
25km NE of Portland on the Fitzroy River along Thompsons Rd from the Princess Hwy. Ph: 03 5523 2671

643. Tyrendarra Princes Hwy-Fitzroy River - Otways & Sth West
Map Ref: MAP 4 C11 GPS: 38 15 28 S 141 50 49 E
On the Princes Hwy 1km west of Tyrendarra on the eastern side of Fitzroy River.

644. Yambuk Lakes Camping Ground - Otways & South-West
Map Ref: MAP 4 C11 GPS: 38 20 22 S 142 03 12 E
Yambuk Coastal Reserve 15km W of Port Fairy via Princess Hwy then Carrolls Rd. Ph: 0419 006 201

645. Lake Elingamite
Map Ref: MAP 4 E11 GPS: 38 20 56 S 143 00 56 E
7km SW of Cobden. Turn W off Cobden-Warrnambool Rd 5km SW of Cobden on to Oates Rd and travel 2km on dirt rd.

646. Lake Bullen Merri Reserve
Map Ref: MAP 4 E11 GPS: 38 15 45 S 143 05 41 E
Camping area 4km SW of Camperdown. Turn W on to Naroghid Rd then N on to Bullen Merri Rd.

647. Meredith Park - Otways & Sth West
Map Ref: MAP 4 F11 GPS: 38 16 09 S 143 36 41 E
Located 7kms E of Colac on the road to Ballarat. Ph: 03 5232 3730

648. Tanners Road Bend
Map Ref: MAP 4 G11 GPS: 38 19 49 S 144 04 38 E
Camp area S from Princes Hwy at Winchelsea to Barwon Tce/Atkins Rd, then S to Gherang Rd then Tanner Rd.

649. Hammonds Road Campground - Otways & Sth West
Map Ref: MAP 4 G11 GPS: 38 23 52 S 144 01 21 E
10km N of Aireys Inlet via Bambra Rd. Situated in the Great Otway NP. Dry weather only Ph: 13 19 63

650. Big Hill Campground - Otways & Sth West
Map Ref: MAP 4 G11 GPS: 38 28 30 S 143 55 58 E
Access via Deans Marsh Rd 11kms from intersection with Princes Hwy E of Lorne. Ph: 13 19 63

651. Dando's Campground - Otways & Sth West
Map Ref: MAP 4 F12 GPS: 38 33 18 S 143 37 12 E
Located between Apollo Bay and Colac 13km SE of Gellibrand. Take the Gellibrand East Rd. Ph: 13 19 63

652. Lake Elizabeth Camping Area - Otways Sth West
Map Ref: MAP 4 G12 GPS: 38 33 04 S 143 44 59 E
Signposted access along Kaanglang Road from Forrest. Ph: 13 19 63

653. Stevensons Falls Scenic Reserve - Otways & Sth West
Map Ref: MAP 4 F12 GPS: 38 33 52 S 143 39 25 E
From Barramunga take a left-hand turn on to Upper Gellibrand Rd and follow the signs for 4kms to camp. Dry weather only. Ph: 13 19 63

654. Fork Paddock Camping Area - Otways & Sth West
Map Ref: MAP 4 G12 GPS: 38 34 42 S 143 43 22 E
Within the Great Otway NP located on West Barwon Track, 6km N of Benwerrin Road. Dry weather only Ph: 13 19 63

655. Sharps Track Camping Area - Otways & Sth West
Map Ref: MAP 4 G12 GPS: 38 33 06 S 143 55 56 E
In the Hinterland behind Lorne take Allenvale Rd then on to Garvey Track then signposted turn in to Sharps Track. Dry weather only Ph: 13 19 63

656. Jamieson Track Camping Area - Otways & Sth West
Map Ref: MAP 4 G12 GPS: 38 35 59 S 143 55 04 E
Located 10km S of Lorne on the Great Ocean Road. Dry weather only Ph: 13 19 63

657. Wye River Road campsite - Otways & Sth West
Map Ref: MAP 4 G12 GPS: 38 37 45 S 143 54 16 E
Located 2km inland on Wye River Road off the Great Ocean Rd. Ph: 13 19 63

658. Beauchamp Falls Reserve Otways & Sth West
Map Ref: MAP 4 F12 GPS: 38 39 10 S 143 36 22 E
The camp is located 4km SE of Beech Forest via Aire Valley and Beauchamp Falls Rd. Dry weather only. Ph: 13 19 63

659. Princetown Recreation Reserve
Map Ref: MAP 4 F12 GPS: 38 41 56 S 143 09 31 E
Camping area 1km S of Princetown on Old Coach Rd beside Gellibrand River. Dirt rd & bridge load limits APPLY. Ph: 0429 985 176

660. Johanna Beach Campground - Otways & Sth West
Map Ref: MAP 4 F12 GPS: 38 45 41 S 143 22 32 E
On the Great Ocean Rd 38kms W of Apollo Bay. Turn left on to Red Johanna Rd. Ph: 13 19 63

661. Aire River East Camping Area - Otways & Sth West
Map Ref: MAP 4 F12 GPS: 38 48 02 S 143 28 39 E
Located on the Eastern bank of Aire River near its mouth, the site is along Horden Vale Road off Great Ocean Road, 3.3km W of Cape Otway Lighthouse Road Ph: 13 19 63

662. Aire River West Campground - Otways & Sth West
Map Ref: MAP 4 F12 GPS: 38 48 06 S 143 28 38 E
Within the Great Otway NP located on Sand Rd off the Great Ocean Rd signposted at Glenaire. Ph: 13 19 63

663. Barham Paradise Reserve - Otways Sth West
Map Ref: MAP 4 F12 GPS: 38 44 27 S 143 37 23 E
7kms from Apollo Bay on Barham River Drive (C119). From the Great Ocean Road turn inland at the intersection with the War Memorial centre-piece. Ph: 1300 689 297

664. Parker Hill Camping Area - Otways & Sth West
Map Ref: MAP 4 F12 GPS: 38 50 54 S 143 33 31 E
Take the Otway Lighthouse Rd off the Great Ocean Rd for 5kms, then left in to Blanket Bay Rd. Ph: 13 19 63

Featured Campsite

Dandos Campground

No 651

Gellibrand, Vic
39km south of Colac

Catherine Lawson and David Bristow

From Victoria's rugged southern coastline, the Otway Range rises inland, flanked by colourful coastal heathlands that merge into ancient myrtle beech and mountain ash forests.

A vast network of fern-fringed streams flow over Beauchamp, Little Aire and Triplet Falls and a handful of excellent forest camps ensure travellers don't need to rush on.

One of my favourites is Dandos Campground, located southeast of the tiny town of Gellibrand in Otway Forest Park on the northern fringe of the Otway Range.

Shaded by tall eucalypts, this spacious campground is one of the largest in the region, with dozens of grassy campsites each with firepits, and plenty of picnic tables and a wheelchair-accessible toilet nearby.

Here kookaburras cackle from the pine trees and superb fairy-wrens flit through the undergrowth.

A chilly mountain stream runs past the camp, with stairs leading to a couple of deep pools where you might spot platypus at dusk and dawn.

After dark, keep an eye out for nocturnal creatures like owls, gliders and possums, all found along the Otway Range.

You'll find Dandos Campground about halfway between Apollo Bay and Colac, 13km southeast of Gellibrand via Gellibrand East Road and Lardners and Sayers Tracks.

From the south, head east of Beech Forest's high altitude village on Turtons Track and turn north onto Lardners and then Sayers Tracks.

Dandos campground makes a great base for explorations in the region, with plenty of scenic towns, walking trails and picnic spots within easy reach.

Just east of Beech Forest, Binns Road cuts a winding path through cool temperate rainforest to a picnic area beside a magnificent stand of Californian Redwoods (sequoia sempervirens) planted in 1938, with tables, toilets and water nearby.

Binns Road also leads past walking trailheads for Hopetoun Falls (moderate, 1km return) and Beauchamp Falls (moderate, 1 hour/3.5km return), a lovely trail that descends to Deppeler Creek beneath giant mountain ash trees – the tallest flowering plants in the world.

Enjoy walking amongst streams flowing over rocks through ferns and mountain ash.

BYO firewood is needed for firepits at the picnic area.

Just The Facts

Dandos Campground

Location: Dandos Campground is located about halfway between Apollo Bay and Colac, 13km southeast of Gellibrand. Take Gellibrand East Road, a kilometre south of town, turn onto Lardners Track and then Sayers Track and continue to camp. Travelling east of Beech Forest, turn north off Turtons Track onto the signposted Lardners Track.

Facilities: Toilets, picnic tables and firepits. BYO drinking water and firewood and take away all rubbish.

Rates: Free.

Wheelchair Access: To Toilets.

Pets: Yes.

Contact: Phone Apollo Bay Visitor Centre on 1300 OTWAYS or visit www.visitotways.com where you can download a copy of the "Walks and Waterfalls" guide.

Reverse Camera
Internal Fans
External Shower
Various Sinks
Hatches (all sizes)
Windows (all sizes)
Steps (Single & Double)
Autory
12.8V300Ah
LITHIUM ION BATTERY
LiFePO4
Lithium Batteries
Autory
INTELLIGENT
INVERTER/CHARGER
HICP-3000
3000W/100A
Inverters
Various Toilets
Wall Mounted Washing Machine

Free Campsites in Victoria Index

Free Campsites in Victoria Index

MOBILE POWER MADE EASY

Victoria Map 1

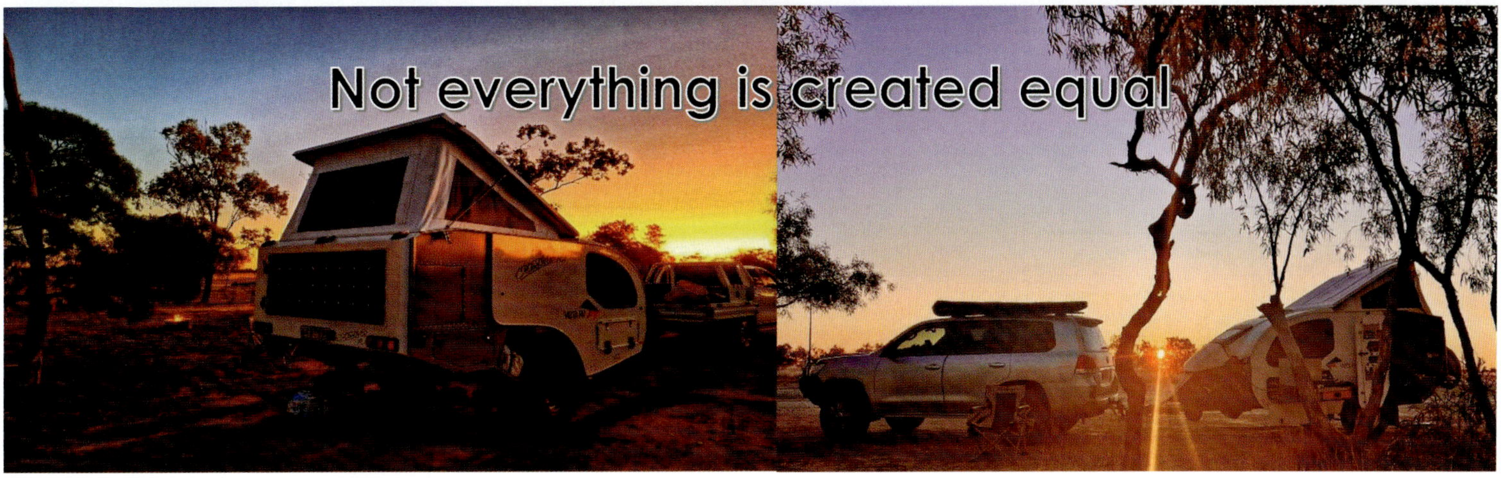
Not everything is created equal

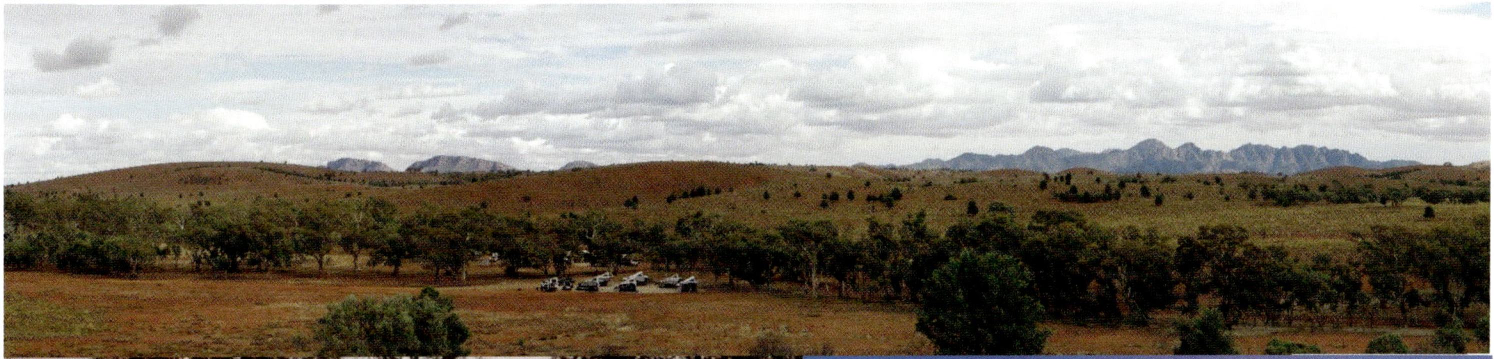

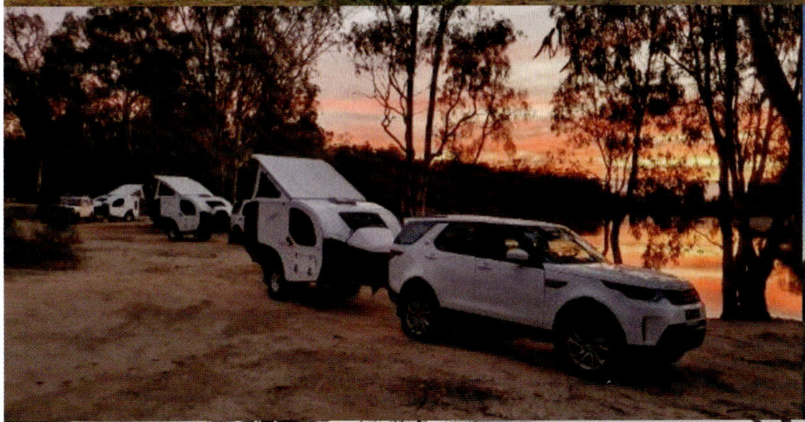

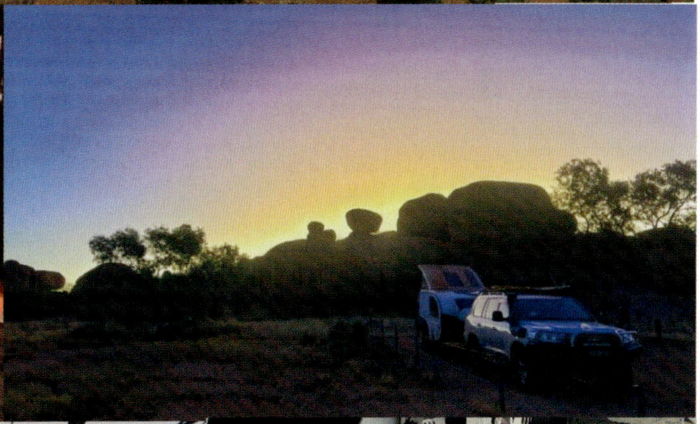

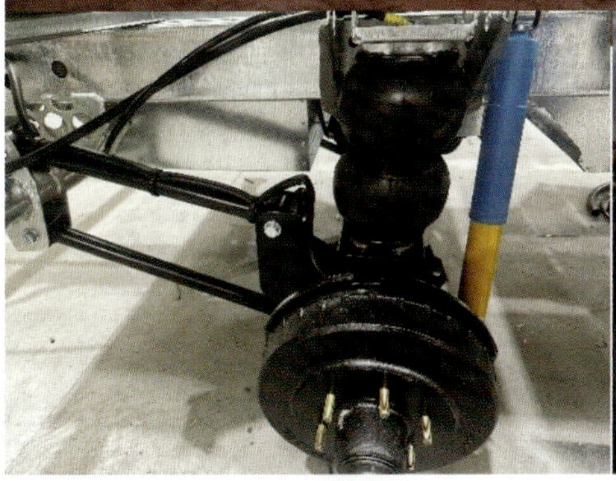

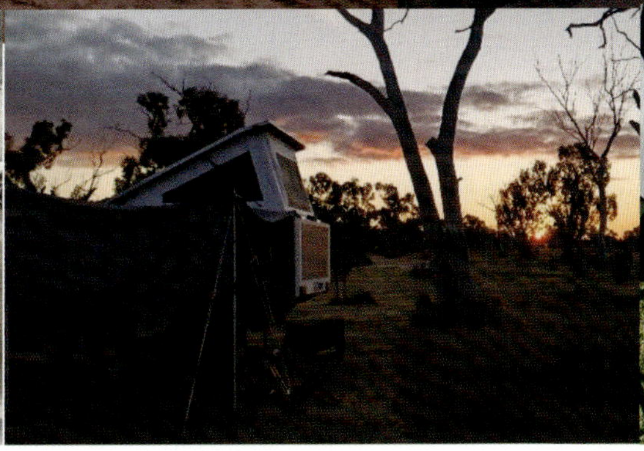

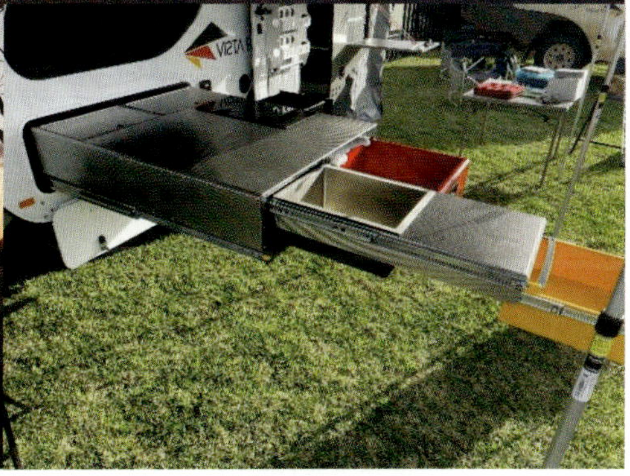

Victoria Map 2

Victoria Map 3

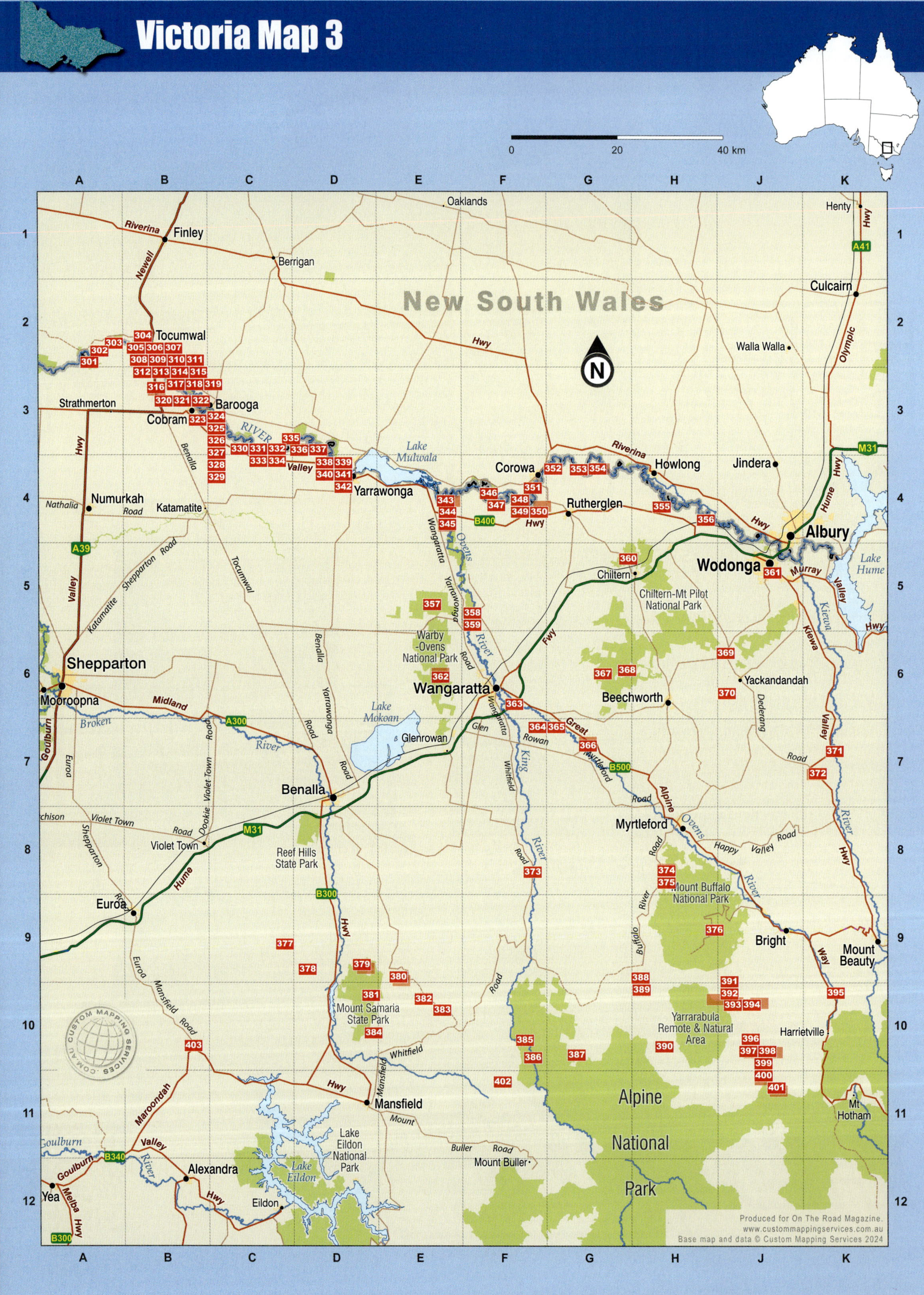

Victoria Map 4

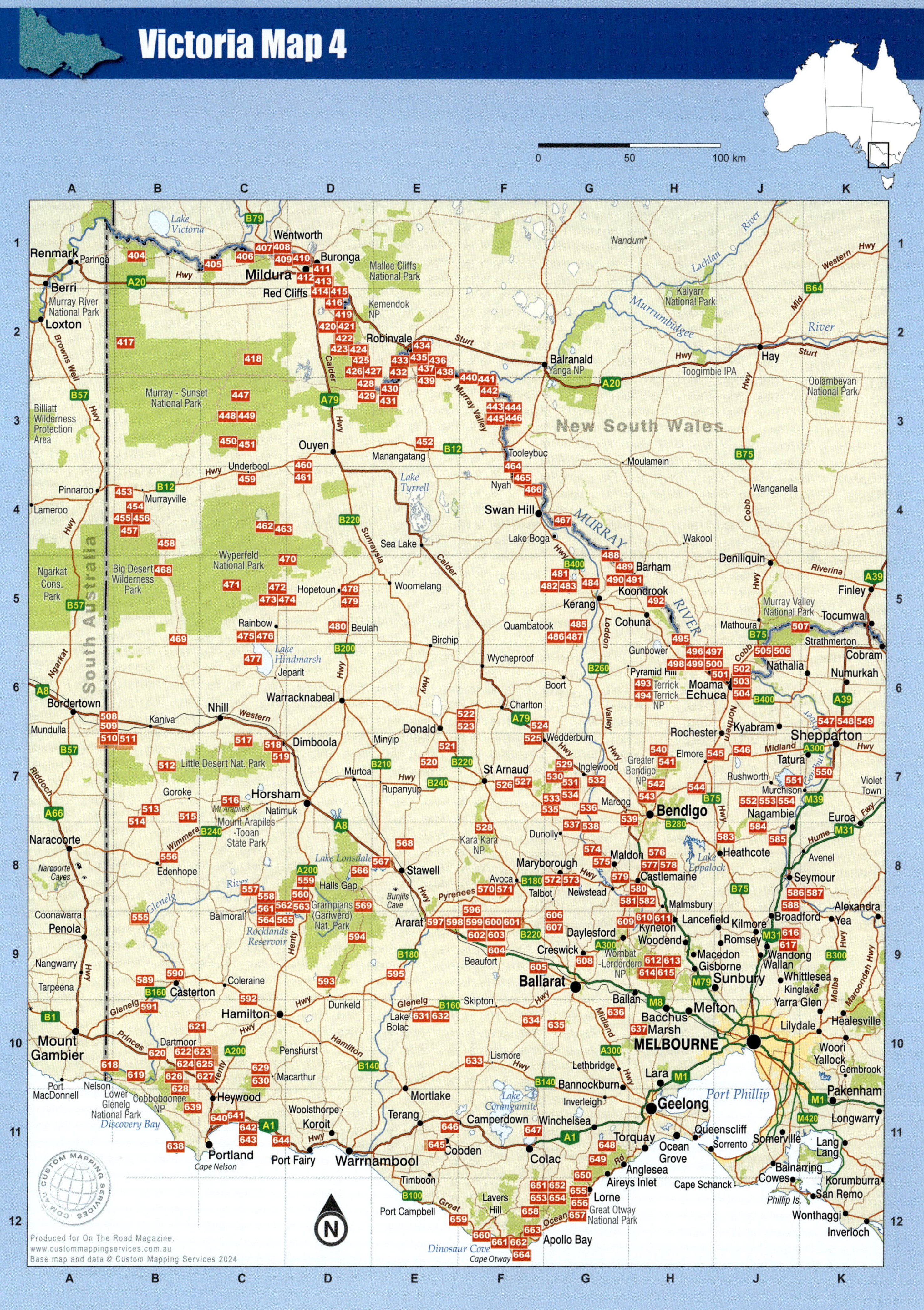

Queensland

Free Camps Guide – Useful Resources & Contacts – QLD

Queensland Parks & Wildlife Service
Smart Service Queensland
General Enquiries and Campsite Bookings
Ph: 13 13 04
Web: www.qld.gov.au/camping

Environmental Protection Agency
Queensland Parks & Wildlife Service
Ph: 1300 130 372
Web: www.epa.qld.gov.au

DPI – Fisheries
Ph: 13 25 23 (QLD only) or (07) 3404 6999
Web: www.dpi.qld.gov.au/fishweb

Department of Primary Industries
Ph: 13 25 23 (QLD only) or (07) 3404 6999
Web: www.dpi.qld.gov.au

Department of Natural Resources and Mines
Licencing Enquiries
Ph: (07) 3238 3775
Web: www.nrm.qld.gov.au

Queensland Fire & Rescue Service
Ph: (07) 3247 8100
Web: www.fire.qld.gov.au

Queensland Main Roads
Ph: (07) 3834 2011
Web: www.mainroads.qld.gov.au

Queensland Travel Centre
Ph: 13 88 33
Web: www.Queenslandholidays.com.au

RACQ – road reports
Ph: 1300 130 595
Web: www.racq.com.au

Bureau of Meteorology
Ph: 1900 926 102
Web: www.bom.gov.au

Royal Flying Doctors Service
QLD Medical & Emergency Calls (Charleville)
(07) 4654 1443

QLD Medical & Emergency Calls (Mt Isa) (07) 4743 2802

Queensland DPI & F Coen Quarantine & Inspection Point
Ph: 13 25 23
Web: www.dpi.qld.gov.au

Free Campsites in Queensland

1. Pajinka (The Tip) - Cape York
Map Ref: MAP 1 D1 GPS: 10 41 32 S 142 31 54 E
Take the signposted turn-off beside Bamaga's BP fuel station, continue N and where road forks veer to the left to reach the Tip. Dry weather only. Ph: 07 4069 1369

2. Somerset - Cape York
Map Ref: MAP 1 D1 GPS: 10 44 30 S 142 35 50 E
Take signed turn-off from Bamaga BP's fuel station, head N to where road forks and veer right for 11km to reach Somerset ruins. Campground lies at end of a side road to the left.

3. Mutee Head - Cape York
Map Ref: MAP 1 D1 GPS: 10 54 41 S 142 15 16 E
Travel N of the Jardine River ferry on the Bamaga Rd for 27km, take the signposted turn-off to Mutee Head for 20km. Campgrounds on either side of headland. Dry weather only. www.tourismcapeyork.com

4. Old Telegraph Track North
Map Ref: MAP 1 D1 GPS: 11 27 15 S 142 25 04 E
Numerous camp spots along 48km of Old Telegraph Track between junction Northern Bypass Rd to S and Jardine Ferry Crossing to N. 4WD only. Ph: 07 4082 0500

5. Captain Billy Landing Camp Area - Cape York & Gulf
Map Ref: MAP 1 D1 GPS: 11 37 55 S 142 51 21
Signposted access along the Southern Bypass Road 67km north of Bramwell Junction. Travel 27.2km east to the camping area. Self-sufficient campers. Bring drinking water and clean firewood. Ph: 137 468

6. Pennefather River
Map Ref: MAP 1 D2 GPS: 12 14 07 S 141 43 06 E
Camp area 84km N of Weipa. Turn W off Andoom Rd 50km N Weipa then to Pennefather Rd for 27km.Access tracks N either via beach or inland track with sand driving closer to camp at river mouth. Check availability, alcohol restrictions. 4WD only. Ph: 07 4090 5600

7. Old Telegraph Track South
Map Ref: MAP 1 D2 GPS: 12 05 33 S 142 33 29 E
Numerous camp spots along 75km of Old Telegraph Track between Bramwell Jctn to S and Northern Bypass Rd Jctn to N. 4WD only. Ph: 07 4082 0500

8. Schramm Creek
Map Ref: MAP 1 D2 GPS: 12 22 23 S 142 36 55 E
Camp spot between Bramwell Roadhouse and Moreton Telegraph Station. Turn E off Peninsula Dev Rd 32 S of the roadhouse. Track to W 100m off Hwy. Ph: 07 4082 0500

9. Moreton Telegraph Station Camping Area - Cape York & Gulf
Map Ref: MAP 1 D2 GPS: 12 27 12 S 142 38 17 E
Located 125km north of Archer River Roadhouse and 73 km north of Peninsula Developmental Road junction. Bring clean firewood. Ph: 07 4060 3360

10. Brown Creek Crossing
Map Ref: MAP 1 D2 GPS: 12 45 19 S 143 06 19 E
Camp on Portlands Rd S side of road 72km NE of junction with Peninsula Dev Rd, or 12km W of entry to Kutini-Payamu NP.

11. Batavia Goldfield Ruins
Map Ref: MAP 1 D2 GPS: 13 05 15 S 142 56 48 E
Camp at ruins. Take LH track just E of Wenlock River crossing, then veer R at fork and follow narrow track 1km to ruins. Bush camping around ruins.

12. Lilly Lagoon
Map Ref: MAP 1 D2 GPS: 13 26 57 S 142 58 43 E
Camp spot between Coen & Archer River Roadhouse. Turn SE off Peninsula Dev Rd 62km N of Coen onto track for 1km, then R on track for 2.5km. 4WD recommended.

13. The Bend - The Gulf
Map Ref: MAP 1 E3 GPS: 13 55 25 S 143 11 35 E
The campground is 3km N of Coen about 310km N of Lakeland on the Peninsula Development Rd. Dry weather only. Ph: 07 4069 6004

14. Lukin River camp area - Cape York
Map Ref: MAP 1 E3 GPS: 14 23 43 S 143 21 42 E
On the Peninsula Development Rd 192km N of Laura, 53km N of Musgrave Roadhouse and 55km S of Coen.

15. Old Faithful Waterhole camping area - Cape York and Gulf
Map Ref: MAP 1 E3 GPS: 15 03 57 S 144 20 01 E
Located within Lakefield NP. Off Battle Camp Rd. Ph: 13 74 68

16. Horseshoe Lagoon camping area - Cape York and Gulf
Map Ref: MAP 1 E4 GPS: 15 17 02 S 144 36 41 E
Located within the Lakefield NP. 92km NW of Cooktown. Access off Battle Camp Road. Ph: 13 74 68

17. Home Rule Rainforest Lodge & Campground - Cape York & Gulf
Map Ref: MAP 1 F3 GPS: 14 55 40 S 145 17 14 E
34kms SE of Cooktown. From Rossville turn E onto River Rd. Travel 2km along gravel rd to entrance. Bookings advised Ph: 07 4060 3925

18. Connies Beach - Cape York
Map Ref: MAP 1 F3 GPS: 14 57 23 S 145 19 40 E
Located 120km N of Cooktown via Battle Camp Rd, Starcke Homestead and Cape Flattery, Silica Mine to Connies Beach on the Cape's northern side.

19. Endeavour River Escape - Cooktown
Map Ref: MAP 1 F4 GPS: 15 24 21 S 145 11 29 E
Camp area 17km N of Post Office. Turn right after airport for 5km, located on Barretts Creek Rd, Cooktown. Closed from Dec-April. Ph: 07 4069 5084

20. Cooktown Racecourse RV Stop - Cooktown
Map Ref: MAP 1 F4 GPS: 15 28 27 S 145 14 09 E
Located on Racecourse Rd, Cooktown off Endeavour Valley Rd. Donation box. Ph: 07 4082 0500

21. Archer Point Conservation Park - Cooktown
Map Ref: MAP 1 F4 GPS: 15 36 11 S 145 19 35 E
Dispersed camping 24km SE of Cooktown. Travel S on Mulligan Hwy for 15km then E 11km, signposted. Dirt rd with tight bends, creek crossings, narrow & steep access to lighthouse. 14 day limit. Permit applies. Ph: 07 4069 6957

22. Wuhal Wujul Sportsground Cape York & Gulf
Map Ref: MAP 1 F4 GPS: 15 56 43 S 145 19 27 E
Camp area on Cape Tribulation Rd at Wuhal Wujul. Permit & kay from Bana Yirriji Centre. Ph: 07 4060 8333

23. Yindilli Camping Ground - Cape York & Gulf
Map Ref: MAP 1 F4 GPS: 16 03 19 S 145 18 23 E
Camp area at Chinacamp 26kms S of Bloomfield on the CRED Track, 38kms N Daintree Village. 4WD & dry season only. Ph: 07 4098 6248

24. Noah Beach Campground - Cape York & Gulf
Map Ref: MAP 1 F4 GPS: 16 08 01 S 145 27 09 E
Signposted access along Cape Tribulation Rd 55km north of Mossman or 8km south of Cape Tribulation. Bring drinking water Ph: 137 468

25. Pebbles Drop
Map Ref: MAP 1 D4 GPS: 16 41 34 S 141 57 01 E
Camping spot 175km NE of Karumba on Burke Development Rd at Wyaaba Creek. Off road tracks.

26. Staaten River - Savannah Way
Map Ref: MAP 1 D4 GPS: 16 31 55 S 142 03 21 E
Staaten River crosses the Burke Developmental Rd about 155km E of the Karumba-Normanton junction. Ph: 07 4745 1065

27. Walsh River West
Map Ref: MAP 1 E4 GPS: 16 32 43 S 143 46 58 E
Camping spot 120km W of Chillagoe on Burke Development Rd.

28. Cooktown Crossing - Mareeba
Map Ref: MAP 1 E4 GPS: 16 33 49 S 144 53 24 E
Camp area 35km NW of Mount Carbine on Kondaparinga Rd, Mareeba. Exit Mulligan Hwy S to Hurricane Rd for 8km then E for 900 m to river camp. 4WD only.

29. Beames Brook
Map Ref: MAP 1 B5 GPS: 17 52 37 S 139 20 35 E
Camping area 27km S of Burketown 3km S of Great Top Rd junction. Off road tracks.

30. Albert River - Savannah Way
Map Ref: MAP 1 B5 GPS: 17 45 56 S 139 33 43 E
228kms W of Normanton on the Savannah Way. Dry weather only. Ph: 07 4745 5111

31. Adels Grove Camping Park
Map Ref: MAP 1 B5 GPS: 18 41 24 S 138 31 54 E
Located 88km W of Gregory Downs.
Fuel for both petrol and diesel available
Email: reservations@wugudaji-adelsgrove.com.au

32. Gregory Downs - The Gulf
Map Ref: MAP 1 B5 GPS: 18 38 59 S 139 15 10 E
Camp area located at Gregory Downs near bridge off Wills Developmental Rd. Ph: 07 4748 5566

Connies Beach No 18

Cape Flattery, Qld

120km north of Cooktown

Catherine Lawson and David Bristow

Driving a 4x4 along the 20km-long beach drive, ideally at low tide.

For 4WD enthusiasts, this remote beach on the northern side of Cape Flattery ticks all the boxes of a grand adventure. It promises great fishing, provides a shady camp just above the high tide mark, spring water flows from the dunes, and very, very few people discover it.

Seagrass beds grow in shallow waters around the cape, feeding green turtles and dugongs, there's rich coral reef just offshore, and the fishing is particularly good. Troll a line from a tinnie for catches of mackerel or try for mangrove jacks, barramundi and crabs from the beach.

This very remote spot on the traditional land of the Guugu Yimithirr people provides no facilities and with no assistance available for miles, 4WD vehicles should be well equipped and carry ample supplies, including recovery gear.

There are no restrictions on a stay at Connies Beach, except that you'll want to stay clear of the water where estuarine crocodiles are commonly spotted. Freshwater that springs from the dunes in the middle of the beach helps to stretch your water supplies, and can be boiled over your campfire before drinking.

The main reason for coming to this secluded beach is for the solitude it offers as you beachcomb and fish. Head to the oyster-covered rocks at the eastern end of the beach (watch your lures!) or launch a boat off the sand to fling a lure around the mangroves.

You can climb a trail that leads to vantage points high above the beach and from the saddle offers views south over the silica mine.

Named by James Cook, Cape Flattery is a source of rich mineral sands that rate as the world's purest. This is a fact that wasn't discovered until the late 1960s, but today, the mine supplies up to 2.2 million tonnes of silica sand a year, making it the biggest such operation in the world.

One of the best parts of any journey to Connies Beach will be navigating the rugged access track that begins in Cooktown. Head northwest past the airport and the turnoff to Hope Vale Aboriginal Community and take the next right-hand turn towards Mt Webb and Starcke Homesteads. Push on and where the track veers left towards Starcke Homestead, head right through a patch of rainforest, across a creek and along a sandy track that ends 15km on at the beach. From here, turn north and begin the 20km-long beach drive, ideally at low tide.

At the end of the beach, turn into the dunes and stick to the track that leads through the mining area before crossing the headland and from the top of a sandy rise you'll have incredible water views across the bay before cruising downhill to Connies Beach.

Ron & Viv Moon's Cape York, An Adventurer's Guide provides maps, detailed track notes and GPS markers for this route and others in the region. Before setting out, obtain permission to camp by phoning the Hope Vale Community Ranger (07 4060 9130), and remember to check local tide times.

The best time to tackle this adventure is during the north's dry winter months. A popular date not to be missed is Cooktown's Discovery Festival which takes place over the Queen's Birthday long weekend in June.

From up high you get a beautiful view of the beach.

Just The Facts

Connies Beach

Location: 120km north of Cooktown via Battle Camp Road, Starcke Homestead and Cape Flattery Silica Mine to Connies Beach on the Cape's northern side.
Facilities: None.
Rates: Free.
Wheelchair Access: N/A.
Pets: Yes.
Contact: Check out Cooktown's visitor information site at www.cook.qld.gov.au.

33. Leichhardt Falls - Savannah Way
Map Ref: MAP 1 B5 GPS: 18 13 10 S 139 52 32 E
On The Savannah Way, about 150km W of Normanton and 77km E of Burketown. Cross the river causeway and camp on northern side of river. Ph: 07 4745 1065

34. Little Bynoe River
Map Ref: MAP 1 C5 GPS: 17 52 00 S 140 49 28 E
Camping spot 37km W of Normanton SW side of river.

35. Bynoe River bush camping
Map Ref: MAP 1 C5 GPS: 17 52 39 S 140 49 29 E
Campsites overlook river 38km W of Normanton at the Burke and Wills Monument. Ph: 07 4747 8444

36. Burke & Wills Camp 119 - Savannah Way
Map Ref: MAP 1 C5 GPS: 17 52 42 S 140 49 38 E
Follow the Savannah Way west of Normanton for 30km and take the signposted turn-off to the south. Camping on banks of Little Bynoe River.

37. Leichhardt Lagoon Camping - Normanton
Map Ref: MAP 1 C5 GPS: 17 51 02 S 141 07 43 E
Camp area 24km SE of Normanton on Gulf Developmental Rd, Normanton. Enter at white tyres near signs. Seasonal closures. Ph: 07 4745 1330

38. Walker Creek - Savannah Way
Map Ref: MAP 1 C5 GPS: 17 28 09 S 141 10 48 E
On a sealed section of the Burke Developmental Rd, 41km S of Karumba and 29km from Normanton. Ph: 07 4745 1065

39. Gilbert River - Cape York
Map Ref: MAP 1 C5 GPS: 17 10 14 S 141 46 02 E
30km N of Normanton turn east on to the Burke Developmental Rd at Walkers Creek rest area and continue for 70km to the Gilbert River.

40. Cumberland Mine Historic Site - Savannah Way
Map Ref: MAP 1 D5 GPS: 18 17 55 S 143 21 11 E
Signposted off the Savannah Way 20km W of Georgetown. Ph: 07 4062 1485

41. Walsh River
Map Ref: MAP 1 E5 GPS: 16 59 24 S 144 17 58 E
Camping spot 32km W of Chillagoe on Burke Development Rd.

42. Dinden camping area -North Queensland
Map Ref: MAP 1 F5 GPS: 17 01 01 S 145 35 06 E
From Mareeba follow the Kennedy Hwy for 14km to signposted turn off to the Dinden NP. Ph: 13 74 68

43. Lower Davies Creek Camping Area
Map Ref: MAP 1 F5 GPS: 17 00 13 S 145 34 09 E
From Mareeba take Kennedy Hwy east for 15km to signposted turn off to Davies Creek NP. Follow this road south for 6.2km to camping area. Bring drinking water. Ph: 137 468

44. Eureka Creek - Cairns
Map Ref: MAP 1 E5 GPS: 17 11 13 S 145 02 27 E
On the Burke Developmental Rd, 10km west of Dimbulah. During wet season flash flooding can occur and cut the route west at Eureka Creek. Ph: 07 4093 5265

45. Rocky Creek - Cairns
Map Ref: MAP 1 F5 GPS: 17 10 59 S 145 27 25 E
Located 8km north of Tolga on the Kennedy Highway. Ph: 07 4043 4444

46. Little Mulgrave Creek
Map Ref: MAP 1 F5 GPS: 17 08 22 S 145 43 26 E
Camp Area at Little Mulgrave 10km W of Gordonvale, short walk to Hotel. Must be self-sufficient.

47. Downfall Creek Camp - Tinaroo
Map Ref: MAP 1 F5 GPS: 17 08 52 S 145 35 18 E
Camp area 8km NE of Tinaroo off Danbulla Forest Drive, 5km dirt road. Pre-book. Ph: 137 468

48. Jumna Dam Camp
Map Ref: MAP 1 E5 GPS: 17 23 49 S 145 13 29 E
Camp spot beside dam 7km E Irvinebank. Turn S off Herberton-Petford Rd 21km W of Herberton. 1.5km to dam.

Featured Campsite

Brought to you by

kokodacaravans.com.au

Leichhardt Falls No 33

Savannah Way, Qld

77km east of Burketown

Catherine Lawson & David Bristow

A day's drive west of Normanton where the 4300km-long Savannah Way hits the dirt and turns rugged, a long, low-slung causeway crosses the Leichhardt River. Just downstream, a short hop across bedrock, the river plunges suddenly over the edge of a broad, arcing falls before continuing to the Gulf of Carpentaria, 50km away.

In the right season, there's a dramatic flurry of whitewater to enjoy from a camp high on the river's banks. Here 4WD travellers set up their off-road caravans, campers and tents under the shade of pandanus palms and eucalypts, and settle in to enjoy the grand views of a rugged, rocky landscape that extends along the river.

This top spot on the remote journey across Queensland's far northwest provides no facilities. But travellers who tackle the route aren't really looking for them anyway. What they'd rather arrive to find are the enormous flocks of sulphur-crested cockatoos bending the canopies along the river, perhaps the sight of a distant croc through the binoculars and most definitely a good-sized barramundi in the deep pools downstream of the falls.

On a leisurely stroll over the expanse of exposed river bedrock near the causeway you might spot some Aboriginal grinding slits. You can explore the riverbanks upstream and rockhop with care beneath the falls for a different view.

The Leichhardt River is a mixture of rockpools and waterfalls.

Just be sure to keep an eye out for estuarine crocodiles that, with a bit of determination, can reach pools upstream of the falls. If it's a swim you are after, your best bet is the local swimming pool in Burketown, 77km and about a 90-minute drive further to the west.

The river takes it name from pioneering explorer Ludwig Leichhardt who led a successful, year-long, 4800km-long overland expedition from Jimbour in Queensland's Darling Downs to Port Essington, 300km north of Darwin.

Considered to be in near-pristine condition, the Leichhardt River winds for 621km from a spot far to the south near Rifle Creek, flowing under the Barkly Highway and into Mt Isa's Lake Moondarra where a dam wall tempers its flow. On its journey across Gulf Country to the sea, 41 creeks and rivers fuel its flow, yet in the dry season, upper reaches retract to still waterholes and even the falls can stop running.

Passing through an area east of Riversleigh's famous fossil fields, Leichhardt River contains prehistoric fossil remains, including the unidentified ancient marsupial unearthed in 2011.

Crossing the river causeway.

Just The Facts

Leichhardt Falls

Location: On the Savannah Way, about 150km west of Normanton and 77km east of Burketown. Cross the river causeway and camp on the northern side the river.
Facilities: None
Rates: Free.
Wheelchair Access: N/A
Pets: Yes.
Contact: Phone the Normanton Visitor Information Centre on (07) 4745 1065 or visit www.carpentaria.qld.gov.au or find information on the entire route at www.savannahway.com.au.

Free Campsites in Queensland

49. Baldy Mountain Forest Reserve Bush Camping
Map Ref: MAP 1 F5 GPS: 17 16 15 S 145 27 20 E
Dispersed bush camping within the Herberton Range State Forest. From the Atherton-Herberton Rd 1.6km south of Atherton take signposted Rifle Range Rd and follow west for 2.1km to forest entrance gate and information board. Self-sufficient campers. Bring drinking water. Ph: 137 468

50. The Boulders Campsite - Cairns
Map Ref: MAP 1 F5 GPS: 17 20 35 S 145 52 15 E
64kms south of Cairns. From the Bruce Highway turn on to Babinda's main street and follow 7kms to the end. Ph: 07 4067 1008

51. Babinda Creek Rotary Park camping area - Innisfail
Map Ref: MAP 1 F5 GPS: 17 21 05 S 145 55 55 E
On the Bruce Hwy 24km N of Innisfail take the road opposite the visitor information centre. Ph: 07 4067 1008

52. Bramston Beach campground -North QLD
Map Ref: MAP 1 F5 GPS: 17 21 09 S 146 01 23 E
Small village on the coast from the Bruce Hwy at the S end of Miriwinni. Take road E to Bramston Beach for 17km. Ph: 07 4067 4121

53. Tully Gorge Campground - Cardstone
Map Ref: MAP 1 F5 GPS: 17 46 22 S 145 38 59 E
Camp area 44km NW of Tully on Tully Rd, Cardstone. Pre-book. Ph: 07 4066 8601

54. Bingil Bay Campground
Map Ref: MAP 1 F5 GPS: 17 49 40 S 146 06 03 E
Beachfront camp area at Bingil Bay 3km N of Mission Beach. Not suitable for large vehicles. Max stay 4 weeks. Ph: 07 4030 2222

55. Hull Heads Camping Ground -North QLD
Map Ref: MAP 1 F5 GPS: 17 59 42 S 146 04 18 E
From the Bruce Hwy 5.3km S of Tully take road signposted to Tully Heads/Hull Heads for 16km then turn left into Luft St and camping area. Ph: 07 4068 2288

56. Murray Falls Camping Area
Map Ref: MAP 1 F5 GPS: 18 09 12 S 145 48 55 E
From Cardwell travel north along the Bruce Hwy for 21km to Bilyana and take road west signposted to Murray Falls then 8km to Murray Upper Rd to the north. Bring drinking water and clean firewood. Ph: 137 468

57. Copperfield Dam Camp Area
Map Ref: MAP 1 E6 GPS: 19 02 09 S 144 07 17 E
72km S of Einasleigh or 98kms SW of Lynd Oasis Roadhouse. Turn SW off Gregory Hwy 26km S of Einsleigh on Gilberton Rd, then L onto Dam Rd. Check website for access updates.

58. Emu Swamp Dam Campsite
Map Ref: MAP 1 E6 GPS: 19 25 02 S 144 09 47 E
Located in Blackbraes NP. From the Kennedy Developmental Rd take track to the west signposted to Blackbraes Homestead which leads 4.1km to homestead and registration area. Follow signage westerly for 700m to a Y-junction then right and proceed north for 15.3km to junction. Turn right for 1.5km to camping area. Bring drinking water. Fires in fire rings only. Ph: 137 468

59. Jourama Falls Camping Area - North QLD
Map Ref: MAP 1 F6 GPS: 18 51 20 S 146 07 36 E
From the Bruce Hwy 24km south of Ingham take signposted Jourama Rd and follow west for 5.2km to camping area. Brink drinking water. Ph: 137 468

60. Lake Paluma camping area - North QLD
Map Ref: MAP 1 F6 GPS: 18 57 21 S 146 08 51 E
From Paluma 21km W of the Bruce Hwy via the Paluma Range NP access roads, take the signposted Paluma Dam Road in NW direction for 12km to the lake. Ph: 07 4727 9000

61. Bushy Parker Park - Rollingstone
Map Ref: MAP 1 F6 GPS: 19 02 46 S 146 23 37 E
Camp area 58km S of Ingham or 54km N of Townsville on Rollingstone St, Rollingstone. Pre-book. Ph: 134 810

62. Balgal Beach
Map Ref: MAP 1 F6 GPS: 19 00 37 S 146 24 18 E
Camp area 65km S of Ingham, 5km E off hwy. Limited sites. Pre-book. Ph: 134 810

63. Bluewater Park - Bluewater
Map Ref: MAP 1 F6 GPS: 19 10 34 S 146 33 06 E
Rest area on Bruce Hwy, Bluewater 80km S of Ingham or 29km N of Townsville. Enter via Forestry Rd. Beside creek. Pre-book. Ph: 134 810

64. Fletcher Creek Campground - Townsville
Map Ref: MAP 1 F6 GPS: 19 48 59 S 146 03 20 E
Follow the Lynd Highway for 46kms north of Charters Towers.

Featured Campsite

Brought to you by

The Boulders Campsite No 50

Babinda, QLD

64km south of Cairns
Catherine Lawson & David Bristow

Enormous granite boulders channel the waters of Babinda Creek.

THE Boulders is a magical place, capable of drawing visitors in and captivating them so that they linger a little longer in the refreshing granite pools shaded beneath a lush, rainforest canopy.

Indeed, Aboriginal legend warns that unsuspecting visitors may fall under the spell of the beautiful young maiden Oolana, who dwells eternally beneath the swift waters and beckons travellers into her raging waters.

The Yidinji tribe believe the spirit of Oolana lives on at The Boulders, her anguished cries for her young, lost lover still heard today.

But whether its Oolana or the irresistible deep, sandy swimming pools on a hot summer's day, it's impossible to stay dry at this refreshing oasis.

You'll find Babinda on the Bruce Highway, 57km south of Cairns.

The friendly town sits nestled in a magnificent rainforested valley in the eastern foothills of Mt Bartle Frere, Queensland's highest mountain at 1622 metres.

Head down Babinda's main street and follow this road for seven kilometres until it ends at The Babinda Boulders Scenic Reserve.

Travellers won't want to rush on from this relaxing spot and you don't have to because the campground permits free, 48-hour stays.

This lovely camp spot, just a short walk from the creek, provides five shady campsites with picnic tables, wood barbecues (BYO wood), toilets, cold water showers, rubbish bins and drinking water that comes straight from the hills.

Each year, more than four-and-a-half metres of rain falls on Babinda, turning the creek into a raging, wet season torrent that carves a broad path through lush, tropical jungle.

Enormous granite boulders divert Babinda Creek's flow into deep, sandy pools that are perfect for swimming.

The large swimming hole near the picnic ground is a popular spot and a stone staircase makes access easy.

Head to this deep, green pool at first light to spot a couple of hungry platypus or the large population of freshwater turtles.

A dip in the shockingly cold water is the perfect way to start the day.

Although much of the park's amazing scenery is inaccessible, you can stroll along one of the most picturesque sections of Babinda Creek via an easy, sealed path to Devils Pool Lookout (470 metres one-way).

Visit here at dusk or dawn to enjoy some quiet solitude beside the roaring waters of the creek.

The track continues for 130 metres beneath a dense canopy of lowland riverine tropical rainforest, to a final lookout over Boulders Gorge.

The Goldfield Track (19km one way) through Wooroonooran National Park to Goldsborough Valley State Forest, remains closed due to cyclone damage but this magnificent creekside walk is highly recommended if you find it open when you visit.

If the campground at The Boulders is full (as it usually is by mid-afternoon during the on-season), take a short drive back through town and cross the Bruce Highway to the much larger overflow campground.

The campsite is just lovely, with shady areas and an excellent outlook.

This is also the place to head to if you have pets on board.

Neither campground charges fees or takes bookings, and both permit a 48-hour stay.

Just The Facts

The Boulders Campsite

Getting there: Babinda Boulders lies about 64km south of Cairns. From the Bruce Highway, turn onto Babinda's main street and follow this road for seven kilometres to its end.

Facilities: The campground at The Boulders provides toilets, cold water showers, picnic tables, drinking water and wood barbecues.

Rates: Free camping is permitted for two nights (48 hours) on a first-come first-served basis (no bookings). Pick up supplies in Babinda en route.

Pets: Not allowed.

Contact: For more information, phone the Babinda Information Centre on (07) 4067 1008 or visit www.cityofcairns.qld.gov.au

Free Campsites in Queensland

65. Big Bend
Map Ref: MAP 1 F6 GPS: 19 51 41 S 146 08 11 E
Camping spot 32km NW of Charters Towers. Turn off Gregory Development Rd on to Big Bend Rd to sites by river. 4WD only

66. Macrossan Park
Map Ref: MAP 1 F7 GPS: 20 00 12 S 146 26 22 E
Rest area 22km E of Charters Towers on Fanning Downs Rd, Dotswood. Turn S off Flinders Hwy E of Burdekin River railway bridge. Take exit off Hwy and veer left and follow signs. 1km dirt road. 7-day limit. Donation box Ph: 07 4761 5533

67. Ravenswood Reserve Camping Ground - Charters Towers
Map Ref: MAP 1 F7 GPS: 20 05 51 S 146 53 35 E
Signposted access in Ravenswood along the road to Ayr. Bring firewood and own fire drum. Ph: 07 4761 5300

68. Wunjunga Camp Area
Map Ref: MAP 1 G7 GPS: 19 45 43 S 147 36 12 E
30km SE of Homehill on Wunjunga Rd. Travel 19km from Homehill turn R via Beachmont Rd

69. Camooweal Billabong - Mt Isa
Map Ref: MAP 1 A6 GPS: 19 55 39 S 138 06 55 E
750 metres from the town across the Georgina River bridge. Ph: 07 4748 2160

70. Mary Kathleen camping area - Outback QLD
Map Ref: MAP 1 B7 GPS: 20 45 10 S 139 55 50 E
Mary Kathleen is a 1km from the Barkly Hwy with the turn-off being 60kms E of Mt Isa and 92km W of Cloncurry. Ph: 1300 659 660

71. Lake Corella - Outback QLD
Map Ref: MAP 1 B7 GPS: 20 50 14 S 140 02 52 E
The turn-off to Lake Corella is on the Barkly Hwy 54kms W of Cloncurry and 65kms E of Mt Isa. A 2km long unsealed track leads from highway to the lake while the riverbank camping area is 5kms further on at Clem Walton Park. Ph: 1300 659 660

72. Clem Walton Park
Map Ref: MAP 1 C7 GPS: 20 49 36 S 140 02 56 E
Camping at Corella Dam 53km W of Cloncurry.

73. Dangi Bush Resort
Map Ref: MAP 1 A7 GPS: 21 36 33 S 138 19 00 E
Camp area at Urandangie free if you spend a gold coin in the pub. Ph: 07 4748 4988

74. Dinner Camp - Outback QLD
Map Ref: MAP 1 A7 GPS: 21 37 28 S 138 18 38 E
Urandangi is 185km SW of Mt Isa. Camping area is 3km SE of Urandangi beside the Georgina River. Ph: 07 4748 4988

75. Dajarra Dam
Map Ref: MAP 1 B7 GPS: 21 40 30 S 139 20 21 E
Camp area off Boulia Mount Isa Hwy, Dajarra 19km W of Dajarra or 137km S of Mt Isa. Ph: 07 4742 4100

76. Dajarra campground - Outback QLD
Map Ref: MAP 1 B7 GPS: 21 41 46 S 139 30 49 E
In Dajarra on the Diamantina Developmental Road 40km S of Mt Isa. Ph: 1300 659 660

77. Prairie Hotel
Map Ref: MAP 1 E7 GPS: 20 52 14 S 144 36 01 E
Camping area behind the hotel. Check with publican.

78. Boulder Creek - Mackay Region
Map Ref: MAP 1 G7 GPS: 21 00 44 S 148 43 12 E
Turn off Bruce Hwy at Calen and drive a further 18km. www.mackayregion.com

79. Ball Bay camping reserve - Mackay Region
Map Ref: MAP 1 G7 GPS: 20 50 11 S 148 59 44 E
From Mackay NW via the Bruce Hwy for 20km to the signposted rd to Seaforth. Then 21km to Ball Bay. Ph: 07 4968 4444

80. Eungella Dam - Mackay Region
Map Ref: MAP 1 G7 GPS: 21 09 07 S 148 22 47 E
Signposted access along Eungella Dam Rd, 30km SW of Eungella at the junction of Eungella Dam Rd and Lizzie Creek Rd. Drive in to the camping area. Ph: 13 15 89

Featured Campsite

Brought to you by

kokodacaravans.com.au

Boulder Creek No 78

Mackay Region, Qld

18km from Calen

John Mainwaring

Boulder Creek downstream from the campground.

A free campsite which can be used as a base to explore the Mackay Region in Queensland

When travelling north or south during the winter months on the "grey nomad stimulus package" my wife and I are always on the lookout for a free campsite. Around Mackay these campsites are few and far between but Boulder Creek in this area is a little gem.

It is a little out of the way and inland from the coast but this makes it attractive and we always spend a couple of nights here. From the south take the Marani – Mt Ossa Road and drive 28km to Mt Charlton. Turn onto a good dirt road to Calen for 5km or turn off the Bruce Highway just north of Mt Ossa and drive 20km to the Mt Charlton turnoff. If travelling from the north turn off the Bruce Highway at Calen and travel for 18km via Cameron Pocket, 7km of this road is good gravel.

The campsite is on private land and is relatively small accommodating twelve to fifteen vehicles so arrive early to get a spot. The campground is surrounded by sugarcane fields and rainforest covered mountains. If the weather is overcast the mist hangs around the mountains and is quite a sight to behold. The campground is on the banks of Boulder Creek and is skirted by rainforest. The Creek is boulder by name and boulder by nature. It is strewn with brown and green mossy rocks. It is quite picturesque and very relaxing. The campsite is flattest near the creek and slopes gently below the cane fields.

Across the narrow sealed road is a day use area which is a very popular spot of a weekend. The "Windyloo" toilet is here as is a number of picnic tables and playing equipment for the kids. There is also a wood barbecue here for your use. There is a couple of decent sized holes in the creek which make for good swimming in the warmer months.

Picnic table beside Boulder Creek.

The community built the day use area in 1995 and is well used by the locals. The Mackay Council erected the "Windyloo" and local cane farmer, Eric Jackson, comes down each morning and replenishes the supply of toilet paper. Council also erected the playing equipment but Eric mows and maintains the area. Council also supplied the trees which make the picnic area quite colourful. Eric's son, Warren, died in 1997 aged 22 and a memorial plaque is on one of the picnic tables near the creek. Have a look for it on the campground side of the road.

Many campers use this delightful little campground as a base to explore the Mackay region. Apart from the northern seaside towns of St Helens and Seaforth, Cape Hillsborough National Park is worth visiting. You can also head up the Pioneer Valley through the towns of Marian and Marani before venturing onto Finch Hatton. From here you can visit Finch Hatton Gorge and do the scenic rainforest walk. The steep drive up the range to Eungella is worthwhile and here you can visit Eungella National Park and view platypus at Broken River.

The campsite is quiet apart from the gurgling creek and it is a great spot to relax and check out all Mackay has to offer. If you are into photography then this is the place for you. Early morning and in the evenings the photo opportunities in the creek are amazing. The Photographic Club from Mackay runs regular field trips here and also to Finch Hatton Gorge.

If you are looking for a free camp spot near Mackay where all you will hear is the bubbling creek, the birds and the rustle of sugarcane, then check out Boulder Creek Campground. You will not be disappointed. It is one of our favourite campsites.

Just The Facts

Boulder Creek

Location: Take the Marani-Mt Ossa Road and drive through Mt Charlton for 33 kms. Turn off the Bruce Highway at Calen and drive 18 kms.

Facilities: Flat campsites beside Boulder Creek accommodating approx.15 vehicles. Picnic Tables,Wood Barbecue and Toilet.

Wheelchair: The area is relatively flat.

Rates: Free

Pets: Yes.

Contact: For more information www.mackayregion.com

Free Campsites in Queensland

81. Platypus Bush camping -Mackay Region
Map Ref: MAP 1 G7 GPS: 21 04 31 S 148 38 16 E
Located in the Finch Hatton Gorge. From the Eungella Mackay Rd, take the road N and follow for 7.4km. Ph: 07 4958 3204

82. Lake Elphinstine - Mackay Region
Map Ref: MAP 1 G8 GPS: 21 32 20 S 148 14 12 E
Head 81km W of Mackay on the Peak Downs Hwy then left onto Nebo-Glenden Rd. Continue for 50km turn left on to Suttor Development Rd and continue 4km to the lake. Ph: 07 4950 5133

83. Mount Britton
Map Ref: MAP 1 G8 GPS: 21 24 13 S 148 32 41 E
Camp area located on Homevale Rd, Mount Britton, 42km N of Nebo or 122km SW of Mackay via Turrawulla Rd. 8km of dirt road. Donation box. Ph: 07 4944 5888

84. Rocky Dam Creek
Map Ref: MAP 1 H8 GPS: 21 32 57 S 149 18 00 E
Camping area 10km NE of Koumala. Turn E onto Landings Rd N of Koumala.6km dirt road.

85. Yarrawonga Park Reserve
Map Ref: MAP 1 H8 GPS: 21 44 28 S 149 28 28 E
14km E of Ilbilbie travel E to Greenhill Rd the right to Notch Point Rd and travel 9km to gate. 3km narrow sandy track. 4WD only.

86. Notch Point Campground
Map Ref: MAP 1 H8 GPS: 21 44 37 S 149 28 38 E
Camp area in Yarrawonga Park Reserve, Notch Point Rd, Ilbilbie. 14km E of Ilbilbie. Turn E to Greenhill Rd SE of Notch Point Rd, 9km to gate then 3km of narrow rough sandy track. 7-day limit. Ph: 1300 472 227

87. Carmila Beach - Mackay Region
Map Ref: MAP 1 H8 GPS: 21 55 06 S 149 28 04 E
101kms S of Mackay and 6kms from Carmila on the coast. Ph: 07 4964 5400

88. Clairview Rest Area - Mackay Region
Map Ref: MAP 1 H8 GPS: 22 06 20 S 149 31 35 E
Take the signposted turn-off on Bruce Hwy at Clairview, 120km S of Mackay, cross the railway line and continue past the Clairview Beach Holiday Park to the northern end of Colonial Drive.

89. St Lawrence Rec area - Rockhampton
Map Ref: MAP 1 H8 GPS: 22 21 10 S 149 31 12 E
155kms S of Mackay and 177km N of Rockhampton.

90. Georgina River - Outback QLD
Map Ref: MAP 1 B8 GPS: 22 54 42 S 138 52 20 E
Close to the NT border 3km from Urandangi. Ask at the pub. Ph: 07 4748 4988

91. Burke River
Map Ref: MAP 1 B8 GPS: 22 53 24 S 139 56 19 E
Camping spot 5km NE of Boulia on Chatsworth-Boulia Rd. Veer left and follow track behind racecourse to river.

92. Old Police Barracks Waterhole
Map Ref: MAP 1 B8 GPS: 22 43 12 S 140 01 52 E
Camping spot 25km N of Boulia via Selwyn Rd. Signposted. Dirt road.

93. Middleton Hotel Camping Area
Map Ref: MAP 1 C8 GPS: 22 21 10 S 141 32 54 E
170kms W of Winton on the Kennedy Developmental Rd. Ph: 07 4657 3980

94. Old Cork Ruins bush camping area - Outback QLD
Map Ref: MAP 1 C8 GPS: 22 55 28 S 141 52 19 E
104km S of Winton via Winton-Jundah Rd. The right to signposted Old Cork Rd for a further 68km. Camping near old homestead. Ph: 07 4657 1466

95. Dinosaur Creek - Twin Hills
Map Ref: MAP 1 D8 GPS: 21 57 47 S 142 39 25 E
Camp area 67km NW of Winton via Landsborough Hwy, Corfield. 1km after rest area head NW past Twin Hill to camp on riverbank. Ph: 1300 665 115

96. Mistake Creek
Map Ref: MAP 1 D8 GPS: 22 25 14 S 143 01 56 E
4kms S of Winton via Winton-Jundah Rd along Western River.

Carmila Beach No 87

Carmila, Qld

101km south of Mackay and 240km north of Rockhampton.

Glenn Gilligan

Carmila Beach is a fabulous free campsite only 70km south of the busy township of Sarina. It would be very expensive to stay anywhere else along the coast and get the views you enjoy from your RV at Carmila Beach. Here it doesn't cost you a cent.

To get there you leave the Bruce highway at the small township of Carmila. This quaint little village comprises a service station, club, sporting fields and caravan park. The town is in the region of Isaac Council and has a population of 340. Fill up at the service station as it is usually cheaper than Mackay and Rockhampton.

The road into Carmila Beach is sealed and passes through picturesque cane fields. It is approximately 6km from the highway into this unspoilt paradise. You are able to stay 72 hours and it is a welcome respite on the road between Mackay and Rockhampton. The campsite is suitable for tents, caravans, camper trailers and motorhomes.

Access to the campgrounds is along a 1km sandy track which has been compressed so 2WD is not a problem. The last 200m however are sandy and narrow and should only be attempted in a 4WD. There is a number of campsites along the beachfront and each can hold five or six vehicles comfortably. These campsites are extremely sandy and it is a good idea to walk the area and pick out where you would like to camp and the best route over the sand. I've witnessed a number of unwary travellers become stuck and have to be pulled out.

Once you have set up it is a charming campsite. Not only do you have uninterrupted views of the water but the sand is white and clean. Swimming is great at high tide but at low tide the water recedes hundreds of metres leaving a sandy base. Sheoaks and rainforest provide shelter from the wind and sun. Small rainforest birds and kangaroos as well as brush turkeys frequent the campsites. We had a yellow sunbird flitting around our camper. Further up the beach in the quiet we spotted a pair of beach stone curlews.

Sunset at Carmila Beach.

Sandy campground at Carmila Beach.

At the first campsite and further along are two strategically placed drop toilets. These are the only amenities as no water or firewood are supplied. Fires are allowed. Large skip bins are on hand for your rubbish.

At the northern end of the beach is a visitor day use area. Here you will find the boat ramp, children's playing equipment, shelters, barbecues and toilets. This is lovely area set under sheoaks and figs. A short stroll from here takes you to the creek and to the beach.

Fishing is a favourite for travellers and locals alike. The boat ramp comes in handy but you need to be careful as the two creeks which border the camping area to the north and south can be very tidal and the water can flow extremely strongly. Many fishermen try their luck from the beach in front of the campground and are able to catch bream, whiting and flathead.

Walking is a favourite with the campers and the energetic nature lovers are able to walk the length of the beach from the northern creek to the southern creek. Look for the many shells scattered after high tide. Cowries are my favourite. A walk can also be taken along the track into the campground and through the rainforest. Queensland Parks are regenerating the rainforest and have fenced off some areas so it's a good idea to stick to the worn tracks.

If you are looking for a free campsite with million dollar views, right on a white sandy beach, with fishing, walking and swimming right at your fingertips then Carmila Beach is for you. Oh! And did I mention it's free.

Just The Facts

Carmila Beach

Location: 101kms south of Mackay and 851 kms north of Brisbane, 6kms from Carmila on the Queensland coast.

Facilities: Sandy camping area where care needs to be taken when driving in. Drop toilets, no water. There is a Day Use Area with a boat ramp, playing equipment, picnic tables, shelters, barbecues and toilets. Dump point is available.

Rates: Free.

Wheelchair Access: Toilets have wheelchair access but moving around the sandy campground could be a problem.

Pets: Pets are allowed.

Contacts:
Carmila Caravan Park
(07) 4950 2227
Isaac Regional Council – 1300 472 227
www.isaac.qld.gov.au
Isaac Visitor Information Centre
(07) 4983 4755
Qld Parks and Wildlife Service – 13 13 04
www.derm.qld.gov.au
Qld Barrier Reef Marine Park Authority
1800 990 177 www.gbrmpa.gov.au

97. Long Waterhole - Winton
Map Ref: MAP 1 D8 GPS: 22 24 44 S 143 03 31 E
Travel S on the Winton-Jundah Rd for 2km then take signposted turn to E on a dirt road for 2km to waterhole. Ph: 1300 665 115

98. Pump Hole
Map Ref: MAP 1 E8 GPS: 22 34 59 S 144 33 57 E
Camping spot 4km W of Muttaburra.

99. The Broadwater
Map Ref: MAP 1 E8 GPS: 22 39 39 S 144 34 06 E
Bush camping spot 6km S or Muttaburra along Thomson River.

100. Muttaburra Broadwater Camp Spot
Map Ref: MAP 1 E8 GPS: 22 41 15 S 144 34 11 E
Locates 11km S of Muttaburra. Take Cornish St S onto Straight Rd for 8kms,veer L onto Steep Gully Rd for 3km. Various spots along channel.

101. 5 Emu Camp
Map Ref: MAP 1 E8 GPS: 22 58 31 S 145 14 13 E
Camp spot 700m SW of Aramac on Raven St, Aramac. Turn W off Barcaldine-Aramac Rd 100m S of bridge. Camp areas along waterway. GPS at turn off. 4WD only. Ph: 07 4651 5600

102. Darr River Camp Area
Map Ref: MAP 1 E8 GPS: 23 12 52 S 144 04 50 E
32km NW of Longreach via Landsborough Hwy, E side of RL Davison bridge. Bush camping along river.

103. Apex Riverside Park - Longreach
Map Ref: MAP 1 E9 GPS: 23 24 33 S 144 13 46 E
Take the signposted turn-off on Matilda Hwy 4km N of Longreach and continue 1km to camp. Ph: 07 4944 5888

104. Bedourie Racecourse Overflow
Map Ref: MAP 1 B9 GPS: 24 21 30 S 139 26 39 E
Camp area on Racecourse Rd, Bedourie off Diamantina Developmental Rd. Overflow only. Ph: 1300 794 257

105. Kings Creek Crossing bush camp - Outback QLD
Map Ref: MAP 1 B9 GPS: 24 31 53 S 139 33 49 E
Bush camp 22km S of Bedourie located on the Eyre Developmental Road near the junction with Diamantina Developmental Road. Ph: 07 4656 3300

106. King Creek Crossing bush camp
Map Ref: MAP 1 B9 GPS: 24 31 53 S 139 33 50 E
Bush camp 22km S of Bedourie on the Eyre Developmental Rd near junction with Diamantina Developmental Rd. Ph: 07 4656 3300

107. No 3 Bore
Map Ref: MAP 1 B9 GPS: 24 28 31 S 139 48 33 E
Rest area 28km E of Eyre Development Rd on Diamantina Development Rd.

108. Eyre Creek - Bedourie
Map Ref: MAP 1 B9 GPS: 24 50 06 S 139 37 26 E
Camp area 61km S of Bedourie on Eyre Developmental Rd, Bedourie, next to creek. Tracks on E side of road S of bridge. 4WD only. Ph: 07 4564 2000

109. Cacoory Homestead Ruins Bush Camp - Outback QLD
Map Ref: MAP 1 B9 GPS: 25 14 34 S 139 33 30 E
Bush camping 81km N of Birdsville and 109km S of Bedourie. Camping on N and S side of creek. Bring drinking water. Ph: 07 4656 3300

110. Monkira Rest Area
Map Ref: MAP 1 C9 GPS: 24 49 11 S 140 32 28 E
Camping spot on Diamantina Development Rd 138km W of Birdsville Development Rd junction.

111. Gum Hole camping area - Outback QLD
Map Ref: MAP 1 C9 GPS: 23 40 20 S 141 59 11 E
Within the Diamantina NP, along side Whistling Duck Creek off Springvale Rd. Ph: 13 74 68

112. Mayne River bush camping area - Outback QLD
Map Ref: MAP 1 D9 GPS: 23 38 10 S 142 19 56 E
Found off the Winton-Jundah Rd from Winton, then Old Cork Rd a further 78km to Mayne River. Ph: 07 4657 1466

Featured Campsite

Brought to you by

Apex Riverside Park

No 103

Longreach, Qld

673km west of Rockhampton

Catherine Lawson and David Bristow

This riverside campground on the Thomson River is an immensely popular freebie that accommodates big rigs, welcomes pets and provides boat access for anglers who disappear all day and return to camp with catches of fat yellowbelly and crayfish.

Located a kilometre off the Matilda (Landsborough) Highway at the northern end of Longreach, the campground is best described as an enormous parking area alongside a grassy hub of toilets, picnic shelters and woodfired barbecues. A pedestrian bridge across the Thomson River leads to waterfront fishing spots that are perfect for those without boats and provides a pleasant stroll.

That said, this is not the most scenic of campgrounds and won't appeal to solitude-seekers looking to get away from the rest of us. There's almost no shade, and come mid-June, don't be surprised to find up to 100 motorhomes and caravans racked and stacked by day's end.

What draws the big crowd then? Without a doubt, Longreach is home to some of the most popular outback tourist attractions in the state, and parking your rig at this free riverfront campground means there's more left in the travelling kitty to pay for those tempting ticket prices.

Topping the list of things to do is a visit to the Australian Stockman's Hall of Fame which pays tribute to outback pioneers and heroes, and the QANTAS Founders Museum where you can walk the wings of a 747 or 707. Explore the Powerhouse Museum, take a Cobb & Co coach ride, cruise the Thomson River aboard a paddle wheeler and indulge in some bush poetry and a 2-course campfire dinner.

Back at camp you can dangle a handline from the bridge or stroll around camp to catch up with all the travellers you've already met elsewhere along the Matilda Highway.

Destinations worth detouring to include Ilfracombe's Great Machinery Mile, a stretch of the Matilda Highway 27km east of Longreach lined with colourfully restored tractors, engines and long superseded farm relics. While in Ilfracombe discover 100-year-old heritage-listed Langenbaker House, which provides a rare insight into pioneer living, and the Jackson Brother's collection of around 30,000 bottles that is said to be Australia's largest.

Travel 56km north of Longreach to catch a sunset from Starlight's Lookout, the watching post of Australia's most notorious cattle duffer Harry Redford, immortalised as Captain Starlight in the Rolfe Boldrewood's novel "Robbery Under Arms".

Run by the Longreach Council, Apex Riverside Park has a maximum stay of four nights, which is ample time to get a good feel for the town, enjoy the sights and barbecue a couple of yellowbelly dinners.

Dates not to be missed include the Australian Stockman's Hall of Fame Horse Expo & Campdraft (July) and the Longreach Yellowbelly Classic in August (www.longreach.net.au/fishing).

This campsite is very popular however there is plenty of room.

There is good boat access to the river.

Just The Facts

Apex Riverside Park

Location: Take the signposted turn off the Matilda (Landsborough) Highway 4km north of Longreach and continue 1km to camp.

Facilities: Toilets, picnic shelters, woodfired barbecues, bins, non-potable water and a boat ramp. Water and a dump point is available at the town's showground.

Rates: Free.

Wheelchair Access: Yes.

Pets: Yes.

Contact: Phone the Longreach Visitor Information Centre on (07) 4658 4150 or visit www.longreachtourism.com.au.

Free Campsites in Queensland

113. Thomson River - Longreach Area
Map Ref: MAP 1 D9 GPS: 24 49 45 S 143 03 10 E
Located 1km E of Jundah on the Thomson Development Rd beside the Thomson River. Ph: 07 4658 6133

114. Royal Mail Hotel Site - Longreach
Map Ref: MAP 1 E9 GPS: 23 39 23 S 144 30 29 E
At Ilfracombe turn S off the Matilda (Landsborough) Hwy towards Isisford for 20km to signposted site. Ph: 07 4658 4150

115. Jericho Community Park - Outback QLD
Map Ref: MAP 1 E9 GPS: 23 39 03 S 145 12 42 E
Within the town of Jericho on Jordan Creek with signposted access along Lyon St at E end of town. Ph: 07 4651 4129

116. Lloyd Jones Weir camping area - Longreach
Map Ref: MAP 1 E9 GPS: 23 39 06 S 145 12 59 E
19kms from Barcaldine. 5kms S turn west on Barcaldine-Downs rd for 9kms to camp area. Ph: 07 4651 1724

117. Oma Waterhole camping area - Outback QLD
Map Ref: MAP 1 E9 GPS: 24 16 56 S 144 19 22 E
From Isisford take the signposted Oma Road towards Yaraka. Follow this road for 14km to the signposted access to the camping area. Ph: 07 4658 8900

118. Yuranigh Ponds
Map Ref: MAP 1 E9 GPS: 24 17 59 S 144 28 44 E
7km S of Isisford on the Isisford Emmet Rd.

119. Barcoo river camping area - Outback QLD
Map Ref: MAP 1 E9 GPS: 24 25 29 S 145 27 41 E
Camping on the N Banks of the Barcoo River, along Garden St within the town of Blackall. Access is along Coronation Dve. Ph: 07 4657 4637

120. Stubby Bend
Map Ref: MAP 1 F10 GPS: 24 52 34 S 146 15 46 E
Camping spot 2km NE of Tambo. Turn right after bridge on Alpha-Springsure Rd. Signposted. Limited stay.

121. Birdsville Windmill
Map Ref: MAP 1 B10 GPS: 25 54 22 S 139 22 24 E
Parking area 2km E of Birdsville on riverbank by windmill.

122. Birdsville Camping Area
Map Ref: MAP 1 B10 GPS: 25 53 58 S 139 21 41 E
1km E of Birdsville. Both sides of the road, large area with various tracks.

123. Old Diamantina Crossing - Birdsville
Map Ref: MAP 1 B10 GPS: 25 54 36 S 139 21 58 E
Camp area 2km SE of Birdsville on Birdsville Developmental Rd, Birdsville. Camp both sides of road by riverside. Ph: 07 5464 2000

124. Cuppa Creek Rest Area
Map Ref: MAP 1 B10 GPS: 25 40 00 S 140 04 01 E
Located 85km E of Birdsville on Birdsville Development Rd.

125. Brown Springs Creek Camp
Map Ref: MAP 1 B10 GPS: 25 41 53 S 140 44 56 E
Camp spot at Betoota. Turn S onto track just E of hotel, follow to waterhole (behind hotel)

126. Betoota Environmental Park
Map Ref: MAP 1 C10 GPS: 25 42 03 S 140 45 39 E
Camp spot 1.5km E of Betoota, turn N just W of cattle grid, follow track through gate.

127. Deons Lookout Rest Area
Map Ref: MAP 1 C10 GPS: 25 43 04 S 140 53 40 E
200km W of Windorah or 20km E of Betoota on the Birdsville Developmental Rd.

128. Haddon Corner
Map Ref: MAP 1 C10 GPS: 25 59 46 S 140 59 58 E
Camping spot 55km SW of Birdsville Development Rd. Sandy rd.

Featured Campsite

Brought to you by

Royal Mail Hotel Site

No 114

Near Ilfracombe, Qld

47km southeast of Longreach

Catherine Lawson and David Bristow

A quiet, skinny stretch of bitumen between the tiny outback towns of Ilfracombe and Isisford, passes the little-known ruins of 12-Mile Dam. More than 100 years ago when Cobb & Co coaches plied the route and drovers moved stock from Wellshot Station to Ilfracombe's railhead, the Royal Mail Hotel was a much-relied upon watering hole that refreshed drovers and teamsters, local shearers and Cobb & Co coach passengers and the horses that pulled them.

Little remains of the old hotel that disappeared sometime in 1916 after the coaches stopped running, but just behind the pub site lies a magnificent example of 19th Century bush craftsmanship that is sure to pique your interest.

Incredibly, despite more than 100 years passing since it was handcrafted, the stone pitched wall that once held back floodwaters at 12 Mile Dam remains marvellously intact. The dying art of carefully selecting flagstones and wedging them together without the use of mortar to create a sturdy tapestry of stone was used extensively around this region, but the overshot at 12 Mile Dam is one of the most accessible, surviving works.

With its leak-proof reservoir, 12 Mile Dam would have provided a reliable water source for those tackling the journey between Isisford and Ilfracombe – a two-day ride for drovers, one day for teamsters and a journey of just a few hours for coaches, riders and buggies.

A wallaby stands by the windmill at sunset.

You can camp amongst the trees.

Signage helps to interpret the site, and because the tradition of resting travellers continues, you can set up camp under the trees beside the dam or alongside the road where there's a nice bit of shade, a picnic shelter and a rubbish bin. Either camp is suitable for big rigs, pets are permitted and you'll get mobile coverage. Because it's a quiet spot, you might well encounter as we did, great flocks of budgies and galahs, and common wallaroos at dusk.

Most travellers discover this spot by detouring off the Matilda (Landsborough) Highway at Ilfracombe, famous for its Great Machinery Mile. The road continues to Isisford, a great little town with a couple of friendly pubs, a small supermarket, post office, fuel station, a free museum, free hot showers and another great camp on the bank of the Barcoo River where a week-long stay costs just $10.

The best time of year to explore this inland region is during the mild winter months when temperatures average 12-23°C. If you go, don't miss the Isisford Fishing Competition and Ilfracombe Picnic Races, both held in July.

All that remains of the Royal Mail Hotel.

Just The Facts

Royal Mail Hotel Site

Location: At Ilfracombe, turn south off the Matilda (Landsborough) Highway towards Isisford and continue for 20km to the signposted site on your left.

Facilities: Picnic tables and bins.
Rates: Free.
Wheelchair Access: N/A.
Pets: Yes.
Contact: Phone the Longreach Visitor Information Centre on (07) 4658 4150 or visit www.ilfracombe.com.au or www.longreachtourism.com.au

129. Cooper Creek - Corner Country
Map Ref: MAP 1 D10 GPS: 25 22 12 S 142 44 45 E
10kms E of Windorah along the riverbank. Ph: 07 4658 6133

130. Adavale Camping Area - Adavale - Charleville
Map Ref: MAP 1 E10 GPS: 25 54 38 S 144 36 03 E
100kms north of Quilpie. Located on the Charleville Rd 1km east of the town. Ph: 07 4656 0500

131. Ambathala Creek - Adavale
Map Ref: MAP 1 E10 GPS: 26 00 54 S 145 20 18 E
Camp area on Adavale Rd, Adavale 107km NW of Charleville on N side of Lake Dartmouth.

132. Quilpie River
Map Ref: MAP 1 D10 GPS: 26 36 55 S 144 17 03 E
Camp at Quilpie. Turn S 1km E of Quilpie just W of John Waugh Bridge (Bulloo River). Follow track to camp spots along river near old crossing.

133. Lake Houdraman - Quilpie - Charleville
Map Ref: MAP 1 E10 GPS: 26 35 22 S 144 18 38 E
7km NE of Quilpie via the Old Adavale Rd. Road is unsealed and impassable in wet weather. Ph: 07 4656 0540

134. Ward River Camping Area - Charleville
Map Ref: MAP 1 E10 GPS: 26 28 30 S 146 06 10 E
20km west of Charleville via the road that leads to Quilpie and located on eastern bank of the river Ph: 07 4654 7771

135. Burke & Wills Dig Tree camping area - Outback QLD
Map Ref: MAP 1 C11 GPS: 27 37 19 S 141 04 24 E
Located NE of Innamincka. Follow signs to the Dig Tree and Nappa Merrie, then a further 72km to the camping area above Cooper Creek. Ph: 07 4655 3399

136. Wilson River Camp - Outback QLD
Map Ref: MAP 1 C11 GPS: 27 49 12 S 142 35 24 E
Located at Noccundra. S of hotel, beside river. Facilities at hall opposite. Ph: 07 4655 3055

137. Hilton Hotel bush camp - Outback QLD
Map Ref: MAP 1 D11 GPS: 27 49 14 S 142 35 31 E
Opposite the Middleton Hotel along the Kennedy Development Rd 168km SW of Winton. Ph: 07 4657 3980

138. Coochin Creek
Map Ref: MAP 1 D11 GPS: 26 52 52 S 143 02 46 E
Camp area 30km NE of Caboolture on Roys Rd, Coochin Creek. Exit Bruce Hwy at Bells Creek Rd interchange, then S to Roys Rd for 5km. Pre-book. Ph: 137 468

139. Tarynya Hole Camp Area
Map Ref: MAP 1 E11 GPS: 26 52 48 S 144 19 41 E
35kms S of Quilpie or 160kms NE of Thargomindah on Quilpie Thargomindah Rd. Unsealed N side of Hwy.

140. Railway Access Rd
Map Ref: MAP 1 E11 GPS: 26 38 11 S 145 06 58 E
125kms from Charleville or 87kms E of Quilpie on Diamantine Developmental Rd.

141. Old Quilpie Rd Camp Spot
Map Ref: MAP 1 E11 GPS: 26 48 20 S 145 20 53 E
25kms SW Cooladdi Foxtrap Roadhouse or 114km NW from Wyandra. Turn 2 off Diamantina Dev Rd 2km NW of Roadhouse onto Yarronvale Rd for 23km then W on Old Quilpie Rd 500m. 4WD recommended.

142. Bulloo River bush camping area - Outback QLD
Map Ref: MAP 1 D11 GPS: 27 11 21 S 144 14 30 E
Bush camping beside the Bulloo River N of Toompine. Take the Ingleberry Rd just N of Toompine for 15km to camping area beside river. Ph: 07 4656 0540

143. Toompine Campsite - Quilpie
Map Ref: MAP 1 D11 GPS: 27 13 31 S 144 22 13 E
Camping in the vicinity of the Hotel on the Quilpie Thargomindah Rd 76km s of Quilpie. Ph: 07 4656 4863

144. Wyandra Campground
Map Ref: MAP 1 E11 GPS: 27 14 37 S 145 58 36 E
Camp area N end of town behind school at 55 Moody St, Wyandra. 7 day limit. Ph: 07 4655 8470

Burke & Wills' Camp

No.135

Savannah Way, Qld

32km west of Normanton

Catherine Lawson and David Bristow

Plenty of space tp camp on your own.

Pulling into camp on the banks of Little Bynoe River, fully loaded with fresh supplies picked up in nearby Normanton, it's difficult to imagine the conditions that Burke and Wills endured here at the site of their most northerly known camp, more than 150 years ago.

On 10th February, 1861, Robert O'Hara Burke and William John Wills set out from Camp number 119 with a horse and three-days worth of provisions, leaving companions John King and Charley Grey behind with the expedition party's camels and equipment.

Having successfully navigated their way inland and north from Melbourne, the pair anticipated a swift journey to the mouth of the Flinders River on the Gulf of Carpentaria, around 60km away. Instead, they were thwarted by a wet season now in full force that turned swampy the mangroves, wetlands and vast saltpans.

The difficulty of the journey was compounded by chart errors, and Burke and Wills never reached the sea. Instead they retraced their steps two days later to Camp 119 and the next day, after jettisoning unnecessary equipment and blazing 15 trees around camp, all four men set off towards home on foot. Their camels carried meagre food supplies, only around half of what was required for the journey to Coopers Creek.

Only King survived the journey, Grey dying en route and Burke and Wills succumbing to starvation at Depot 75 at Coopers Creek. Tragically the men missed a rescue party waiting for the men at camp by just nine hours.

Today, the old blazed trees and a memorial cairn mark the site of Camp 119, listed as a place of historical significance. It's a poignant spot to visit if, like us, you are about to surge forth on your own adventure across the north's remote Savannah Way.

Apart from some information boards and a sheltered picnic table, the camp itself offers no facilities, but the Little Bynoe River on the edge of the Savannah's golden grasslands, is a scenic, very quiet place to overnight.

The camp might well be the first on a journey west to Burketown, through Hells Gate's rocky sandstone escarpments and across the NT border to Borroloola and beyond to Broome. You'll find Camp 119 signposted off the Savannah Way, about 30km west of Normanton. The road is accessible to conventional vehicles, making it a worthwhile detour out of Normanton, even if you're not heading further west.

In Normanton, you can fish the Norman River, watch the great flocks of brolgas and sarus cranes that gather at Mutton Hole Wetlands, ride the Gulflander train to the historical gold rush town of Croydon, and drink a coldie at the impossible to miss 'Purple Pub'.

The river and wetlands offer great views.

Just The Facts

Burke and Wills Campsite

Location: Follow the Savannah Way west of Normanton for 30km and take the signposted turnoff to the south. There is plenty of room to camp on the banks of Little Bynoe River.

Facilities: None

Rates: Free.

Wheelchair Access: N/A

Pets: Yes.

Contact: Phone the Normanton Visitor Information Centre on (07) 4745 1065 or visit www.carpentaria.qld.gov.au or www.savannahway.com.au.

145. Wild Camp Spot
Map Ref: MAP 1 D11 GPS: 27 48 28 S 144 11 41 E
148km S of Quilpie or 47kms NE of Thargomindah on Quilpie Thargomindah Rd. Unsealed road.

146. Alroy Camping Grounds
Map Ref: MAP 1 E11 GPS: 27 48 08 S 144 42 32 E
Camp area 61km NW of Eulo at 4252 Eulo Toompine Rd, Eulo. Turn N 18km W of Eulo and travel 40km along Yowah Creek. Ph: 0427 992 889

147. Lake Bindegolly Camping Area - Charleville
Map Ref: MAP 1 D11 GPS: 28 05 35 S 144 12 15 E
35kms east of Thargomindah and is on the southern side of the Bulloo Developmental Rd. Dry weather only. Ph: 07 4655 3173

148. Yowah Camping Area - Charleville
Map Ref: MAP 1 E11 GPS: 27 58 08 S 144 37 59 E
Located 85km NW of Eulo and is on the northern side of town Ph: 07 4655 4793

149. Paroo River Camping Area - Charleville
Map Ref: MAP 1 E11 GPS: 28 09 40 S 145 02 15 E
70kms west of Cunnamulla on the western bank of the Paroo River. Ph: 07 4655 8470

150. Paddabilla Bore
Map Ref: MAP 1 E11 GPS: 28 07 23 S 145 11 40 E
Camping spot 16km E of Eulo behind bore.

151. Cameron Corner camping area - Outback QLD
Map Ref: MAP 1 C12 GPS: 28 59 52 S 140 59 57 E
140km NW of Tibooburra. Bush camping at Cameron Corner near the store. Ph: 08 8091 3872

152. Ourimperee Waterhole
Map Ref: MAP 1 E12 GPS: 28 52 59 S 144 30 36 E
Located in Currawinya NP. Camp area behind Currawinya Woolshed, 25km N of Hungerford entry or 105km S of Eulo. Small vehicles only. Pre-book. 4WD only Ph: 137 468

153. Warrego River
Map Ref: MAP 1 E12 GPS: 28 44 04 S 145 36 38 E
Bush camping spot 96km S of Cunnamulla. Turn W into Tinnenburra Rd and travel for 7km to river.

154. Theresa Creek Dam camping area - Central QLD
Map Ref: MAP 2 C3 GPS: 22 58 16 S 147 33 13 E
From Clermont take Rubyvale Road for 7.5km then Peakvale Rd for a further 8km then left in to Percy Albert Dve for 6km to dam. Ph: 07 4983 4755

155. Bundoora Dam - Emerald Region
Map Ref: MAP 2 D3 GPS: 22 57 22 S 148 32 20 E
Access via the Capella-Middlemount Rd which is 35km NE of Capella on the Gregory Hwy. Ph: 07 4944 5888

156. Yaamba Rest Area - Rockhampton
Map Ref: MAP 2 F3 GPS: 23 08 06 S 150 22 07 E
On the left-hand side of the Bruce Hwy at Yaamba.To reach Alligator River continue S past camp on the road that parallels the hwy and just before the bridge take the track to the left that leads down to the riverbank. Ph: 07 4921 2311

157. Upper Stony Camping Area
Map Ref: MAP 2 G3 GPS: 22 53 32 S 150 37 06 E
Located north of Yeppoon in Byfield SF. Accessed off Stony Creek Rd signposted on the Byfield Rd 12.5km north of Farnborough Rd. Proceed on Stony-Creek Rd in west north west direction for 10km to camping area. Bring water & clean firewood. Ph: 137 468

158. Five Rocks Camping Area
Map Ref: MAP 2 G3 GPS: 22 48 33 S 150 48 16 E
Within Byfield Conservation Park access is well signposted along Water Park Rd. From Byfield Rd follow Water Park Rd in a north east direction for 22.6km to camping area located just north of the Stockyard Point area. Bring drinking water Ph: 137 468

159. Pandanus camping area - Central QLD Coast
Map Ref: MAP 2 G3 GPS: 22 51 51 S 150 47 21 E
Within the Byfield NP north of Yeppoon access via Water Park Rd S of Byfield. Ph: 13 74 68

160. Casuarina camping area - Central QLD Coast
Map Ref: MAP 2 G3 GPS: 22 52 03 S 150 47 21 E
Within the Byfield NP north of Yeppoon access via Water Park Rd S of Byfield. Ph: 13 74 68

Featured Campsite

Brought to you by

kokodacaravans.com.au

Paroo River Camping Area No.149

Eulo, Qld

Stephanie Jackson

Head out into the south-western Queensland outback and there's a good chance you'll pass through Eulo, but don't expect to find a bustling metropolis here. With a population of merely 60 people, Eulo is as quiet as an ice factory in Alaska, but that doesn't mean there's nothing to do.

A good time begins at the free camping area on the bank of the Paroo River that flows past the western side of the town, and if fishing is your passion, you might be in luck, for locals insist there are plenty of yellow belly to be caught here. You'll have no chance of spotting any fish in the river's perpetually muddy waters, but waterbirds know a good spot when they find one. You'll see white necked herons, cormorants, and egrets snatching a meal from the river, and if you've got the right bait and a little bit of patience, fresh fish might be on your evening menu too.

The river is the star attraction here, and with the Paroo's waters retained by a low weir that's only a short distance from the camping area, you can get out and about and explore this normally calm waterway with a kayak or canoe, or simply cool off with a swim.

The camping area, which can easily accommodate large vans, buses, and fifth wheelers, has no facilities other than an old concrete picnic table, but it's only about 500 metres from all the attractions of Eulo, and believe me, some are certainly worth seeing.

The historic Eulo Queen Hotel serves good meals, and here and at the adjacent general store where you can have a snack or a cup of coffee at footpath tables, you'll meet locals and other travellers. You can drool over works of art and jewellery featuring glittering opals at the Bilby Burrow Art Gallery, and if you don't mind getting a little dirt on your hands, you can scoop up some rubble, brought in from the Yowah opal fields, and for a measly $5, hunt for opal in the most leisurely of ways.

Eulo general store.

The Paroo River.

There are public toilets in the town and showers too, but you'll need to be covered in mud before you can get into the hot water here. The showers at the Palm Grove Winery's famous mud baths are simply to wash off the grime after having soaking in a tub of artesian mud. But it might take a drop of date wine from the winery and date farm, which is Eulo's major tourist attraction, to help you pluck up the courage to get into a mud filled bath tub.

Back at the camping area, with delicious date based products to nibble and wine to share with old mates and new friends, you can relax in the shade of the yapunyah trees that line the Paroo's banks, drop a line in the water, or sit around a campfire and chat about where you've been and where you're heading next. And as a quiet night descends over Eulo, you'll have to agree that the Paroo River camping area is a pleasant corner of the outback in which to spend an idle day or two.

Lots of bird watching, White Necked Heron.

Just The Facts

Paroo River Camping Area

Getting there: The camping area is on the western bank of the Paroo River that borders the south-western Queensland town of Eulo and is approximately 500 metres from the town. Eulo is 70kms west of Cunnamulla on the Bulloo Developmental Road (The Adventure Way).

Facilities: There are no facilities at the camping area other than an old picnic table. Public toilets are available at the hall in Eulo.

Pets: Pets are permitted.

Charges: There is no charge for camping here.

Contact: For further information, contact the Cunnamulla Visitor Information Centre by phoning (07) 4655 8470 or log onto www.paroo.info

Free Campsites in Queensland

161. Redbank Park - Outback QLD
Map Ref: MAP 2 A4 GPS: 23 36 19 S 146 07 57 E
Jericho is on the Capricorn Hwy 500km W of Rockhampton. Turn off eastern end of main street then turn in to Bessemer St and follow signs. Ph: 07 4651 4129

162. Alpha Clermont Rd Camp
Map Ref: MAP 2 B4 GPS: 23 29 04 S 146 39 20 E
Camp area 23km N of Alpha via Alpha Clermont Rd, Alpha. High Clearance vans only, subject to flooding. 4WD only.

163. Bedford Weir Camping Area - Gladstone
Map Ref: MAP 2 E4 GPS: 23 22 25 S 148 50 29 E
Located 25kms north of Blackwater via Cooroorah Road which turns off the Capricorn Hwy. Ph: 07 4986 1247

164. Munall Campground - Central QLD
Map Ref: MAP 2 E4 GPS: 23 47 41 S 149 04 06 E
From the Capricorn Hwy 16km east of Bluff and 11km west of Dingo take signposted road to Blackdown Tableland NP (Wafer Way). Proceed south for 22.9km to information bord then south for 7.9km to camping area. Bring drinking water & clean firewood. Ph: 137 468

165. Neville Hweitt Weir camping area - Baralabra
Map Ref: MAP 2 F5 GPS: 24 11 10 S 149 48 27 E
Within the town of Baralaba on the Dawson River which is 160km SW of Rockhampton or 96 NW of Biloela. Ph: 07 4998 1142

166. Dan River
Map Ref: MAP 2 F5 GPS: 24 05 54 S 150 07 04 E
Camp spot at Rannes via Rannes Station Access.

167. Lake Victoria
Map Ref: MAP 2 F5 GPS: 24 02 03 S 150 17 53 E
Camp area at 412 Dooneys Rd, Smoky Creek 25km S of Dululu via Burnett Hwy. Private property, close gates & control pets.

168. Lake Pleasant Camp Area
Map Ref: MAP 2 F5 GPS: 24 06 57 S 150 18 14 E
6km NW of Goovigen via Goovigen & Lake Pleasant Rds.

169. Goovigen Sportsground
Map Ref: MAP 2 F5 GPS: 24 08 44 S 150 17 08 E
Camp area at 5 Stone Cr, Goovigen. Fee to hotel. Limit 7 nights. Ph: 07 4992 9500

170. Dawson River Rest Area - Moura
Map Ref: MAP 2 F5 GPS: 24 35 58 S 149 54 36 E
Camping area is on the eastern side of the Dawson River and adjacent to the Dawson Hwy approx. 6kms W of Moura. Ph: 07 4997 2084

171. South End Settlement - Curtis Island - Gladstone
Map Ref: MAP 2 G4 GPS: 23 45 14 S 151 18 27 E
1km from ferry drop-off on Curtis Island. Camping area is just a short walk to front beach. Curtis Island is accessed by ferry or private vessel. Ph: 07 4972 9000

172. The Oaks - Facing Island - Gladstone
Map Ref: MAP 2 H4 GPS: 23 49 43 S 151 20 21 E
Campground located 2km from Ferry drop-off point on Oaks Island. Access to island via ferry or private vessel. Dry weather only. Ph: 07 4972 9000

173. Calliope River Camping Ground
Map Ref: MAP 2 G5 GPS: 23 57 51 S 151 09 15 E
Via the old Bruce Hwy which is signposted off Bruce Hwy 4kms N of the Dawson Hwy. Follow Old Bruce Hwy for 3km to track on left for 100m to large grassed area located on bank of river. Ph: 07 4972 9000

174. Boynedale Bush Camp - Gladstone Region
Map Ref: MAP 2 G5 GPS: 24 12 58 S 151 14 35 E
31kms S of Calliope and 2kms E of the Gladstone-Monto Rd, beside Lake Awonga. Ph: 07 4972 9548

175. Workman's Beach Campground - Central QLD Coast
Map Ref: MAP 2 H5 GPS: 24 12 45 S 151 54 51 E
From Agnes Waters follow the signposted Springs Rd in a SE direction to the signposted access road to campsite. Ph: 07 4970 0700

176. Middle Rick Camping Area
Map Ref: MAP 2 H5 GPS: 24 17 26 S 151 57 08 E
Within Deepwater NP signposted access along park's main access track which is 7km south of Springs Rd from Agnes Water. Drive 20m to camping area. Bring drinking water. Ph: 137 468

Free Campsites in Queensland

177. Dragonelly Rock Hole camping area -Central QLD
Map Ref: MAP 2 C6 GPS: 25 01 33 S 147 53 57 E
Within the Carnarvon NP N of information board for 7.5km then left at junction for 3km to signposted camping area. Ph: 13 74 68

178. Junction Park
Map Ref: MAP 2 F6 GPS: 24 57 14 S 150 04 29 E
Camp area S end of The Boulevard, Theodore. 7 night limit. Donation box. Ph: 07 4992 9500

179. Cracow Camping Area - Theodore
Map Ref: MAP 2 F6 GPS: 25 17 43 S 150 18 09 E
In the town of Cracow which is 50km SE of Theodore. Ph: 07 4993 7118

180. George Hamilton Park - Bundaberg
Map Ref: MAP 2 F6 GPS: 25 17 43 S 150 18 11 E
Campground at Cracow on Eidsvold-Theodore Rd. Ph: 07 4993 7118

181. Wuruma Dam - Bundaberg
Map Ref: MAP 2 G6 GPS: 25 10 42 S 150 59 12 E
Abercorn is signposted just off the Burnett Hwy halfway between Monto and Eidsvold. Continue through town to reach dam. Dirt road Ph: 07 4165 7200

182. Old Forestry Camp Camping Area - Central QLD
Map Ref: MAP 2 H5 GPS: 24 31 37 S 151 28 16 E
From Builyan which is 18km south of Ubobo take Gladstone-Monto Rd then signposted Dalga Rd and follow easterly for 3.5km where road becomes Bulburin Forest Drive then 12km to information board and camping area. Bring water & firewood. Ph: 137 468

183. Mount Maria Rest Place
Map Ref: MAP 2 H6 GPS: 24 34 33 S 151 49 04 E
Camp area 19km SE of Lowmead via Lowmead, Tableland & Tesch Rds. Donation please. Ph: 0423 571 269

184. Sharon Nature Park - Bundaberg
Map Ref: MAP 2 J6 GPS: 24 53 05 S 152 14 38 E
12kms NW of Bundaberg on the Bundaberg to Gin Gin Rd. Ph: 1300 722 099

185. Beilba Bush Camp
Map Ref: MAP 2 D7 GPS: 25 33 40 S 148 54 18 E
Within Expedition NP via Beilba Rd, Beilba. Camp area 55km E of Injune, travel N on Carnarvon Hwy for 26km then E to Fairview Rd for 14km then N to Beilba Rd, 15km to camp. Pre-book. Ph: 137 468

186. Chain Lagoons camping area -Roma
Map Ref: MAP 2 E7 GPS: 25 31 14 S 149 46 59 E
Approx 15km from Taroom along the Leichhardt Hwy, camping beside the lagoon. Ph: 07 4628 6113

187. Wandoan Showgrounds
Map Ref: MAP 2 F7 GPS: 26 06 55 S 149 58 58 E
Camp are 3km NE of Wandoan Post Office on Roche Creek Rd.

188. Auburn River Camping Area - Mundubbera
Map Ref: MAP 2 G7 GPS: 25 43 12 S 151 03 11 E
Camping area is 46km SW of Mundubbera.Begin on Mundubbera to Durong Rd, continue along the Hawkwood Rd for approx 31kms then road turns abruptly south. Camp area is on SW side of the bridge that crosses the river. Ph: 1300 696 272

189. Booyal Crossing - SE QLD
Map Ref: MAP 2 H6 GPS: 25 13 45 S 152 00 34 E
Turn S off the Bruce Hwy onto the Booyal-Dallarnil Rd then take Causeway Rd for 4km. Ph: 07 4153 8888

190. Paradise Dam camping area - SE QLD
Map Ref: MAP 2 H7 GPS: 25 21 17 S 151 55 10 E
Located W of Childers on the Burnett River along Grills Rd off the Biggenden-Booyal Rd. Ph: 13 74 68

191. Lawless Park - Goomerie - Maryborough
Map Ref: MAP 2 H7 GPS: 25 56 38 S 151 57 05 E
Lawless Park is on the Burnett Hwy 42kms N of Goomeri. Ph: 07 4168 4488

192. Lake Lenthall Recreation Park camping area - SE QLD
Map Ref: MAP 2 J7 GPS: 25 24 11 S 152 32 03 E
From Bruce Hwy take Warrah Rd (10km N of Maryborough and follow signs to Lenthalls Dam. Tent based camping only Ph: 07 4129 4833

193. Petrie Park - Tiaro
Map Ref: MAP 2 J7 GPS: 25 42 55 S 152 34 40 E
Follow the Bruce Hwy N through Maryborough for 1km and take signposted turn-off W on to Jacobsend St. Cross railway line and immediate right on to Blackmount Rd, drive 200m turn left on to Vandoorn Rd and continue to camp.

194. MV Natone camping area - Sunshine Coast
Map Ref: MAP 2 J7 GPS: 25 48 43 S 153 04 07 E
Located on Inskip Peninsula, access via Inskip Point Rd. Ph: 13 74 68

195. Morven Recreational Reserve- Charleville
Map Ref: MAP 2 B8 GPS: 26 25 10 S 147 06 58 E
Morven is halfway between Mitchell and Charleville on the Warrego Hwy. Ph: 07 4654 3057

196. Fisherman Rest camping area - Roma
Map Ref: MAP 2 C8 GPS: 26 28 51 S 147 55 59 E
5km from Mitchell along the Warrego Hwy. Camping beside the Maranoa River. Ph: 07 4624 6923

197. Neil Turner Weir camping area - Roma
Map Ref: MAP 2 C8 GPS: 26 28 45 S 147 57 36 E
Approx 4km from Mitchell west along the Warrego Hwy. Access via River St beside the Maranoa River Ph: 07 4624 6923

198. Bungeworgorai Creek
Map Ref: MAP 2 D8 GPS: 26 35 32 S 148 41 39 E
Camping spot 10km W of Roma on S side of road E of bridge.

199. Judds Lagoon - Roma
Map Ref: MAP 2 E8 GPS: 26 38 12 S 149 23 46 E
4kms off the Warrego Hwy 60km W of Roma, then Forestry Rd on to Moongool Rd. Unsealed Rd. Ph: 07 4623 5155

200. The Maryanne Camp Area
Map Ref: MAP 2 E8 GPS: 26 43 48 S 149 19 33 E
16km S of Yuleba on the Yuleba Surat Rd (Cobb & Co Way) travel past the windmill and follow track to lagoon and open area.

201. Old Yuleba Camp Spot
Map Ref: MAP 2 E8 GPS: 26 41 50 S 149 25 59 E
13km SE of Yuleba via Forestry Rd & then Moongool Rd for 8km. Signposted Historic Site, 2km dirt road. Ph: 1300 007 662

202. Gil Weir - Miles
Map Ref: MAP 2 F8 GPS: 26 42 44 S 150 10 56 E
5.5km S of Miles. Signposted access off the Leichhardt Hwy. Ph: 07 4627 1492

203. Chinchilla Weir camping area - Chinchilla
Map Ref: MAP 2 F8 GPS: 26 48 05 S 150 35 02 E
9km S from Chinchilla heading towards Tara and Condamine. Ph: 07 4627 1492

204. Grays Reserve - Chinchilla
Map Ref: MAP 2 F8 GPS: 26 49 38 S 150 30 24 E
Located opposite property called "Chinta" 16km S of Chinchilla along the Chinchilla-Tara Rd. Ph: 07 4668 9564

205. Archers Crossing North camping area - Chinchilla
Map Ref: MAP 2 F8 GPS: 26 47 59 S 150 40 58 E
6km SE of Chinchilla via the Warrego Hwy. Take the signposted Archers Crossing Rd to the northern bank of the river. Ph: 07 4668 9564

206. Archers Crossing South camping area
Map Ref: MAP 2 F9 GPS: 26 47 57 S 150 40 46 E
Located 9kms SE of Chinchilla from the Warrego Hwy take signposted Chinchilla-Kogan Rd. Continue S for 8km turn right into Hopeland-School Rd and go for 2km to Archers Crossing Rd. Riverside camping. Ph: 07 4668 9564

207. Proston Golf Club
Map Ref: MAP 2 G8 GPS: 26 09 42 S 151 35 31 E
Camp area W side of town at 81 Brigooda Rd, Proston. Patrons & golfers welcome. Donation welcome. Ph: 0474 741 822

208. Kinbombi Falls
Map Ref: MAP 2 H8 GPS: 26 13 19 S 152 04 08 E
Camping spot 11km E of Goomeri. Turn S off Wide Bay Hwy and follow signs to Kinbombi Falls.

Neil Turner Weir No 197

Mitchell, Qld
3km west of Mitchell
Glenn Gilligan

Well known for its soothing mineral springs, Mitchell is a great spot to break your travels through the Central West of Queensland. Located 87 kms west of Roma, this vibrant rural community is noted for its warm, friendly locals who are always willing to share the town's varied history and culture including the pioneering, bushranging (the notorious Kenniff Brothers), the Aboriginal heritage of the area and of course, plenty of information on the renowned outback explorer Major Thomas Mitchell, after whom the town was named.

Located in the town's aquatic centre, the splendid artesian spa pools are a real delight … and so relaxing! One of the features here is the warm (38°C) and cool (19°C) pool where visitors can move from one pool to another – a really great experience. This whole therapeutic process is designed to soothe body muscles and joints and generally relax tired, aching bodies. Even if your body is still in top shape, the relaxing power of these warm artesian waters is sure to do you good!

After you have had your fill of local attractions, soaked away your troubles in the spas and perhaps checked out the yummies (and good coffee) in the beaut town bakery, a great (free) spot to camp can be found at Neil Turner Weir, just a couple of kilometres out of town.

Located on the banks of the Maranoa River, this well spread out campsite, run by the local Booringa Council, is extremely popular with travellers, particularly during the annual winter tourist season. At the time of our recent visit, there were over 40 units (caravans, campervans, big rigs, camper trailers, etc) camped here for the night.

In the centre of this lovely riverbank campground, the local Rotary Club has set up a splendid grassy picnic area where there is a children's playground, toilets, barbeques, water, bins as well as tables, chairs and shelters – all available for use by the riverside campers.

The campground here includes quite a few shady sites, has mobile/internet service, small campfires are allowed, there are walk trails along the river and at the time of our visit we saw wallabies, ducks, egrets, white cockatoos and other wildlife, all close to our campsite. Dogs are also allowed as long as they are kept on a leash. For the keen fishos, locals report that yellow belly are often caught here as well as yabbies. The Neil Turner Weir is located along the river near the eastern section of the riverbank campground.

Without doubt, this is one of Queensland's great outback camping experiences and at the end of the day, sit in your camp chair around the fire with a cool drink in hand watching the local birdlife and one of the area's usual colourful sunsets.

Just The Facts

Neil Turner Weir Campsite

Location: Three kilometres west of Mitchell in the Central West of Queensland (87 kms west of Roma). Turn off the Warrego Highway 2 kms west of Mitchell along Alexandra Street and follow approximately 1 km to River Street on the banks of the Maranoa River.
Facilities: Picnic area, toilets, water, gas barbeques, tables and chairs, bins, children's playground. No powered sites. Generators allowed but please respect other campers. There is a nearby boat ramp. Some shady sites.
Wheelchair Access: Flat campground and access to picnic area and toilets.
Rates: Free - maximum of 48-hour stay.
Pets: Dogs allowed on leash.
Contact: Mitchell Visitor Information Centre – phone (07)4624.6923

Featured Campsite

Brought to you by

Judds Lagoon No 199

Yuleba, Qld

60km east of Roma

Catherine Lawson and David Bristow

The campsite is a peaceful setting by the water.

The campground 'welcoming party' greeted us on arrival, circling our camp chairs and poking hungry, loudly quacking beaks through the door of the caravan. Only when they were convinced that there was no meal forthcoming did the big pairs of ducks and geese wander back down to the water's edge, pushing off through the lillies floating on Judds Lagoon.

This picturesque waterfront camping spot at Yuleba (pronounced Yool-bah), west of Roma, is a particularly scenic place to spend a few days. It's flat, spacious and shady and the excellent facilities include wheelchair-accessible eco-friendly toilets, a bush shower room (BYO hot water), rubbish bins and firepits.

A few kilometres away in Yuleba you can top up drinking water and make use of the sheltered picnic area with free barbecues and a kids' playground. There's mobile coverage, campfires are permitted and there is no time limit on how long you can stay. Pets are welcome, just be sure to keep them tethered and away from the wandering waterbirds.

Judds Lagoon is a pretty spot to swim or paddle a kayak, cast a line or just rest on its banks and watch the waterbirds cruise on by. Take a walk along the bush tracks at dawn to catch the wildlife starting to stir and if you've set a yabby pot overnight, you might spend a morning stoking up the campfire to cook your catch.

The campground lies a suitable distance off the Warrego Highway to buffet any traffic noise, so you can expect a genuinely restful stay. You'll find Judds Lagoon on the eastern edge of Yuleba, about 60km from Roma and 417km west of Brisbane.

Taking its name from the Aboriginal word meaning 'the place of water lillies', Yuleba is tiny town of just 200 people that was once a bustling railway line and Cobb & Co coach hub, servicing pastoral stations for miles around. Things slowed down and on August 16th 1924, driver Fred Thompson brought the very last Cobb & Co coach ever to run in Australia home to Yuleba.

Today the Yuleba to Surat stagecoach route is lined with historical markers that signpost old corduroys - stretches of cypress pine saplings laid across difficult-to-cross gullies - and horse changing posts. Along this scenic 75km-long drive to Surat you'll also pass the Native Wells, an important Aboriginal reservoir and picnic spot, and The Maryanne where you can fossick for agates and opalised and petrified wood.

Painted with murals, Yuleba's Cobb & Co information shed can tell you more, and once you reach Surat, check out the Cobb & Co Changing Station that now houses a 14-seater Cobb & Co coach in its museum.

Services in Yuleba include a small general store and newsagency, post office, butcher, fuel station, library, skate park and walking circuit with an outdoor gym. You can join the locals in town for a game of bowls, golf or a game of cards on Fridays at the Arts Cottage.

In nearly Wallumbilla, 40km west, don't miss a stop at the Heritage Complex's free museum where a great little collection of photographs and memorabilia related to Yuleba includes an old horse and cart and a restored 1925 vintage Model T Ford. The museum opens from 9am-4pm Monday to Saturday and from 10am on Sundays. Next door are picnic tables, wheelchair-accessible toilets and Calico Cottage has crafts, homemade goodies and Devonshire teas for sale.

Just The Facts

Judds Lagoon

Location: 3.5km off the Warrego Highway, 417km east of Brisbane and 60km west of Roma. To get there, turn south onto Forestry Road just before the town cemetery, then onto Moongool Road and follow the unsealed road for 2km to camp.

Facilities: Wheelchair-accessible toilets, bush shower room (BYO hot water), firepits and rubbish bins.

Rates: Free.

Wheelchair Access: Yes.

Pets: Yes.

Contact: Find out more about local events and attractions at www.visitmaranoa.com.au.

Throw in a line and try your luck.

taking it easy, has never been so easy.
KOKODA
STRENGTH • PASSION • PRIDE
2025
CARAVAN OF THE YEAR
SPONSORED BY
CARAVAN
Winner
MOST INNOVATIVE & HIGHEST X-FACTOR
KOKODA
KOKODA

Free Campsites in Queensland

209. Broadwater Recreational Reserve - Nanago
Map Ref: MAP 2 H8 GPS: 26 30 10 S 152 02 14 E
Off the Burnett Hwy 22km N Nanango via Broadwater Access Rd. Ph: 07 4171 0100

210. Cedar Grove Campground
Map Ref: MAP 2 J8 GPS: 26 21 58 S 152 35 13 E
Within Amamoor SF 12km W of Amamoor on Amamoor Creek Rd. 5km dirt road. Pre-book. Ph: 137 468

211. Kadanga RV Park
Map Ref: MAP 2 J8 GPS: 26 23 12 S 152 40 37 E
Located in the town of Kadanga 8km N of Imbil and 9km S if Amamoor opposite the Jack Spicer Park and pool. Ph: 07 5488 4605

212. Belli Creek Park
Map Ref: MAP 2 J8 GPS: 26 29 57 S 152 51 47 E
17km NE of Kenilworth on Eumundi-Kenilworth Rd

213. Persimmon Tree Park bush camp
Map Ref: MAP 2 H8 GPS: 26 39 36 S 152 28 00 E
40km N of Kilcoy and 70km SE of Murgon on the banks of the Yabba Creek in the village of Jimna, 300m N of visitor info centre on Borgan Rd. Ph: 07 5497 3174

214. Charlie Moreland camping area - Sunshine Coast
Map Ref: MAP 2 J8 GPS: 26 36 59 S 152 39 02 E
Located 12km SW of Kenilworth off the Maleny-Kenilworth Rd and then Sunny Creek Rd. Ph: 13 74 68

215. Kenilworth Recreation Grounds - Sunshine Coast Hinterland
Map Ref: MAP 2 J8 GPS: 26 35 56 S 152 43 34 E
Located within the town of Kenilworth. Signposted access along Elizabeth St at the S end of town. Ph: 07 5446 0131

216. Obi Obi Creek Crossing No.2 Camp Area
Map Ref: MAP 2 J8 GPS: 26 38 08 S 152 47 02 E
Situated at 1127 Obi Obi Rd Kidaman Creek. 10km SE of Kenilworh via Eumundi Rd. Both sides of crossing.

217. Warroo Bridge camping area - St George
Map Ref: MAP 2 D9 GPS: 27 38 57 S 148 44 45 E
60km from St George via the Carnarvon Hwy for 51km and then the Warroo Bridge Rd for 9km to the camping area. Camping on north side of bridge only. Ph: 07 4625 9147

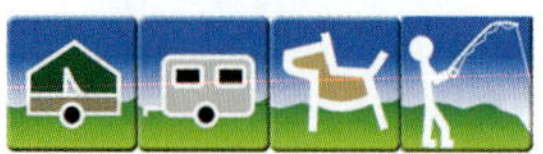

218. Green Timbers Fishing Reserve - Surat - St George
Map Ref: MAP 2 D9 GPS: 27 15 55 S 148 55 57 E
Off the Carnarvon Hwy 18km S of Surat. Ph: 07 4626 5136

219. Surat Fishing & Restocking Club Park
Map Ref: MAP 2 D9 GPS: 27 08 57 S 149 04 23 E
Camp area 1km N of Surat on Carnarvon Hwy Surat, just over bridge on Balconne River. Dirt surface and grass. Limit 4 days. Donation box. Ph: 07 4626 5136

220. Fishermans Park camping area - Surat
Map Ref: MAP 2 E9 GPS: 27 08 57 S 149 04 22 E
Camping area on the Carnarvon Hwy on the Northern Side of Surat, beside the Balonne River. Ph: 07 4626 5136

221. Balonne Bridge - Surat - St George
Map Ref: MAP 2 E9 GPS: 27 08 58 S 149 04 24 E
On the Carnarvon Highway on the north side of Surat. 78km S of Roma. Ph: 07 4626 5136

222. Cow Paddocks - Surat - St George
Map Ref: MAP 2 E9 GPS: 27 08 48 S 149 05 26 E
On Sawmill Rd 2km E of Surat. Surat is on the Carnarvon Hwy 116km N of St George. Ph: 07 4626 5136

223. Caliguel Lagoon - Condamine - Chinchilla
Map Ref: MAP 2 F9 GPS: 26 59 01 S 150 06 40 E
Located 7km S of Condamine. 33km S of Miles. Access via the Condamine-Meandarra Rd. Ph: 07 4627 1492

224. Rocky Waterhole - Toowoomba
Map Ref: MAP 2 F9 GPS: 27 37 49 S 150 17 37 E
Along the Leichhardt Hwy cross the Moonie River at Wild Horse Paradise Crossing then on to Old Moonie Rd. Ph: 07 4665 0189

Featured Campsite

Brought to you by

kokodacaravans.com.au

Rocky Waterhole

No 224

Moonie, Qld

14kms north of Moonie

Stephanie Jackson

Native woodlands hide the river from view.

"There's a great spot to camp beside the Moonie River," an old bloke I met at the Queensland town of Dalby told me many years ago. "It's near the Moonie crossroads, but I'm not tellin' ya exactly where it is," he added with a mischievous chuckle. Now his secret's out however, for I've finally discovered the place that locals know as 'the Rocky Waterhole', and unlike that old fella, I can't keep a secret to myself for too long.

If you're travelling along the Leichhardt Highway, you'll cross the Moonie River at the curiously named Wild Horse Paradise Crossing that's 14kms north of the crossroads at the settlement of Moonie. A few metres further on, you'll find a dirt road that spears east through native woodlands and that, after around 500 metres, crosses a diminutive waterway. The concrete causeway here acts as a low weir and holds back the dawdling waters of the Moonie River to create a relatively wide expanse of water. And it's at this secluded spot, on the shaded banks of this scenic stream, that you can set up camp and enjoy the serenity of the bush without coughing up a single razoo for the privilege.

If you're driving a gargantuan motorhome or towing a van of huge dimensions you can easily access the area, but with only a small area of level ground, and limited space to manoeuvre, you might find some problems if you pull in here.

The ground can become boggy even after light rain, and that means that the camping area, on the eastern side of the river, is not the best place to be if there's any hint that wet weather is on the way.

With the highway not far away, you might assume that there'd be little peace and quiet, but with the surrounding woodlands muffling the incessant grumble of traffic, it's a spot that's almost as quiet as an ice factory in Alaska. Water that might be tumbling repetitiously over the edge of the causeway and a breeze muttering through the canopy of the eucalypts that grasp the river's sandy banks with gnarled and contorted roots are all that shatter the silence here - until the locals inevitably arrive.

If you're quiet, superb blue wrens, blue faced honeyeaters, king parrots, and other woodland birds will all drop by to entertain you and to add their voices to the subtle sounds of the great outdoors. You might also hear the sound of fish leaping from the coffee coloured water, for this is a popular fishing spot where, if Lady Luck is on your side, golden perch might be on the evening menu.

There are no facilities here, but if you want to enjoy a picnic by the river, have a swim to cool off on a steamy summer's day, indulge a passion for fishing, or spend a few days doing nothing other than soaking up the serenity of the bush, you'll be pleased I let you in on what was once a well kept secret.

The muddy waters of the Moonie River are home to golden perch.

Just The Facts

Rocky Waterhole

Getting there: To reach the riverbank camping area, follow the Leichhardt Highway north from the Queensland settlement of Moonie. After 14kms the road crosses the Moonie River at the curiously named Wild Horse Paradise Crossing, and a few metres beyond the low bridge, there's a turnoff, to the east, onto the Old Moonie Road. This is a dirt road that becomes impassable after rain. The Moonie River camping area is approximately 500 metres along this road on the eastern side of the causeway. The camping area is not suitable for large vehicles and rigs.

Facilities: There are no facilities here.

Pets: Pets are permitted.

Charges: There is no charge for camping here.

Contact: For further details, contact the Moonie Rural Transaction Centre by phoning 07 4665 0189

225. Tara Lagoon Parklands
SITE CLOSED
Map Ref: MAP 2 F9 GPS: 27 16 2[illegible] S 150 27 36 E
Camp area on Showground Rd, Tara. 14 day limit. Fees applicable. Ph: 07 4679 4000

226. Rangers Bridge Camping area - Dalby
SITE CLOSED
Map Ref: MAP 2 G9 GPS: 27 07 17 S 151 05 21 E
From Dalby via the Warrego Hwy for 5km then on to Kogan/Condamine Rd. After 11km left on to Dalby/Kogan Rd to camp beside river. Ph: 07 4662 1066

227. Loudoun Bridge camping area -Dalby
Map Ref: MAP 2 G9 GPS: 27 13 12 S 151 11 01 E
From Dalby along the Moonie Hwy to 10.5km to Loudan Bridge. Bush camping on the E and W side of the bridge. Dry weather access only. Ph: 07 4662 1066

228. Wilga Bush campinga area - Dalby
Map Ref: MAP 2 G9 GPS: 27 19 55 S 151 05 46 E
28km SW from Dalby, after 20km turn off Moonie Hwy to Lake Broadwater Conservation Park. Ph: 07 4663 3562

229. Lakeside Camping Area - Dalby
Map Ref: MAP 2 G9 GPS: 27 21 09 S 151 05 33 E
Follow the Moonie Hwy for 19km SW from Dalby in a SW direction from Dalby to the signposted turn-off. Then drive for a further 11km to camping area on bank of Lake Broadwater. Ph: 07 4663 3562

230. Bowenville Reserve - Toowoomba
Map Ref: MAP 2 G9 GPS: 27 19 41 S 151 27 21 E
Located on Warrego Hwy 56km NW of Toowoomba on the banks of Oakey Creek Ph: 07 4691 1388

231. Oakey Creek Reserve - Toowoomba
Map Ref: MAP 2 G9 GPS: 27 19 40 S 151 27 17 E
Turn S off the Warrego Hwy at Bowenville on to the Bowenville-Norwin Rd and continue for 5km to campsite. Ph: 07 4679 4461

232. Swinging Bridge Park camping area - Toowoomba
Map Ref: MAP 2 H9 GPS: 26 59 04 S 151 50 02 E
Located within the village of Cooyar which is on the New England 90km N of Toowoomba. Accessed along Fergus Street. Ph: 07 4692 6185

233. Clancy's Camping Area
Map Ref: MAP 2 H9 GPS: 26 58 17 S 152 09 51 E
Located in the Blackbutt Range 11.5km south of the D'Anguilar Hwy along Benarkin Forest Drive. Dry weather access 4WD recommended. Bring firewood. Ph: 137 468

234. Captain Logan Camp
Map Ref: MAP 2 J9 GPS: 27 21 01 S 152 32 58 E
25km south of Esk take signposted Hay Road off the Brisbane Valley Hwy. Follow 1.1km to signposted Logan Inlet Rd which leads 2.4km to a road on the right signposted to Captain Logan Camp/Lumley Hill. Follow this road for 440m to a junction and take the left road for 220m to camp area. Bring firewood. Ph: 07 5426 4729

235. Maleny Showgrounds
Map Ref: MAP 2 J9 GPS: 26 45 47 S 152 50 44 E
Camp area located at 13 Maleny Stanley River Rd, Maleny. Pay at Secretary's office near pavilion. Ph: 07 5494 2008

236. Poverty Point Camping - Bribie Island
Map Ref: MAP 2 J9 GPS: 26 59 27 S 153 05 44 E
Located on western shore of Bribie Island north of Gallaghers Point 7.2km from White Patch Ranger Base. From here follow signage to Poverty Creek. Soft, sandy access track. Bring water & firewood Ph: 137 468

237. Gallagher Point Camping Area - Bribie Island
Map Ref: MAP 2 J9 GPS: 27 01 01 S 153 06 07 E
Located on western shore of Bribie Island 3.4km from White Patch Ranger Base. Follow signage to Gallagher Point on soft sandy track. Bring water & firewood. Ph: 137 468

238. Neebine Creek- St George
Map Ref: MAP 2 B10 GPS: 27 59 49 S 146 48 46 E
60kms W of Bollon beside the Neebine Creek. Ph: 07 4625 6108

239. Wallam Creek Camping Area - St George
Map Ref: MAP 2 C10 GPS: 28 01 45 S 147 28 48 E
Bollon is on the Balonne Hwy 114km W of Saint George. Camping area is on Fire Station Rd on the western side of town. Ph: 07 4620 8888

240. Whyenbah Bridge -St George
Map Ref: MAP 2 C10 GPS: 28 23 24 E 148 19 04 S
53kms SW of St. George off Whyenbah Rd.

Wallam Creek Camping Area No 239

Bollon, Qld

114kms west of Saint George

Stephanie Jackson

The creek's calm waters are perfect for kayaking.

The south-western Queensland town of Bollon is home to around 500 people, but you're more likely to see emus wandering along the footpaths than any of the town's human residents. It's a sleepy little spot that boasts little more in the way of commercial facilities than a pub, a café/general store, a post office, and a small museum that's only open on request, but there's one very good reason to stop here. Wallam Creek meanders along the edge of the town, and with a free camping area on the shaded bank of this quiet waterway, setting up home for a day, a week, or even longer in this pleasant corner of the outback won't cost you a single cent.

The camping area, locals will tell you with a laugh, is at the dead centre of Bollon, for it's next to the cemetery, and being on Fire Station Road which, predictably, is next to the fire station, it's not hard to find.

There have been several changes to the camping area in recent times, the most welcome of which is the construction of a cubicle with a flushing toilet and a wash basin. A concrete pathway that winds along the creek's bank links the camping area to the highway and to the town itself, and with park benches positioned along it, you can take it easy and watch the birds that make themselves at home among the river red gums that drape their great branches over this idle stream.

More than 100 species of birds thrive in the Bollon region, and many visit the creek on a regular basis. It's easy to spot white necked herons, greater egrets, and nankeen night herons that, despite their common name, are often out and about in daylight hours. And if you turn your gaze away from the creek, there's a good chance that, at dusk or dawn, you'll see brolgas performing their elegant dance in the grasslands beside the camping area.

You won't be so lucky if you try to spot the koalas that once spent their days dozing in the arms of ancient eucalypts that shaded the camping area, for now they're nowhere to be seen. "It's the recent floods that have chased them away," one camper insisted, but there's a more conspicuous reason for their absence. The camping area has become too civilised. Large trees have been removed, and smaller ones and tall grasses on the creek's bank have been cleared to provide visitors with an improved view of the creek and better access to the water. The area is now more reminiscent of a neat and tidy town park than the wild corner of the bush it had once been, and koalas were perhaps not impressed with the new face of the landscape.

Progress has had both positive and negative affects on the area, but you can swim, fish for the yellow belly that hide in the creek's calm waters, explore the waterway in a kayak or canoe, or wander into the sleepy heart of Bollon to meet the invariably friendly locals. And with ample room for vehicles and rigs of every size imaginable, it's still a pleasant place to relax for a while.

Brolgas are frequently seen near the camping area.

Nankeen night herons rest at the water's edge.

Just The Facts

Wallam Creek Camping Area

Location: The Queensland town of Bollon is on the Balonne Highway 114kms west of Saint George. The camping area is on Fire Station Road which is on the western side of the town.

Facilities: There is a flushing toilet, which is wheelchair accessible, at the northern end of the camping area, there are several taps to provide water, and there is a dump point nearby.

Town facilities: A concrete pathway links the camping area to the town which is about 500 metres away. There is a café/general store, a post office, and a pub in the town, and there are public toilets and hot showers in the park in the main street.

Charges: There is no charge for camping.

Pets: Pets are permitted.

Contact: For further information, phone the Bollon Heritage and Craft Centre on (07) 4625 6108. Additional regional information is available by visiting the Balonne Shire Visitor Information Centre, at 114 The Terrace, Saint George, by logging onto www.balonne.qld.gov.au/web/guest/visitors/index.shtml, or by phoning (07) 4620 8877.

Free Campsites in Queensland

241. Jack Taylor Weir camping area -St George
Map Ref: MAP 2 D10 GPS: 28 03 04 S 148 34 06 E
Just outside the town of St George on the western side of the weir access via the Andrew Nixon Bridge. Ph: 07 4625 4996

242. Beardmore -St George
Map Ref: MAP 2 D10 GPS: 27 57 22 S 148 40 54 E
14km N of St George. At the turn off to Beardmore Dam. Ph: 07 4620 8877

243. Moonie River -St George
Map Ref: MAP 2 D10 GPS: 28 21 26 S 148 49 26 E
Located at Flinton via the Moonie Hwy. Ph: 07 4677 6116

244. Nindigully Pub
Map Ref: MAP 2 D10 GPS: 28 21 17 S 148 49 15 E
Camp beside Moonie River across and along from the pub. Donation box. Ph: 07 4625 9637

245. Millmerran Golf Club
Map Ref: MAP 2 G10 GPS: 27 53 05 S 151 16 18 E
Parking area S side of town at 8 Golf Club Rd, Millmerran. Honesty box. Ph: 07 4695 1476

246. Lemontree Weir -Toowoomba
Map Ref: MAP 2 G10 GPS: 27 45 10 S 151 18 40 E
20km N of Millmerran. Access via Lemontree Rd off the Gore Highway. Ph: 07 4695 1399

247. Yarramalong Weir - Toowoomba
Map Ref: MAP 2 G10 GPS: 27 50 10 S 151 27 10 E
Located 11km N of Millmerran which is on the Gore Hwy. Travel on Leyburn Rd for 11km, then along Yarramalong Rd for 3km to weir. Ph: 07 4695 1399

248. Passmore Reserve
Map Ref: MAP 2 G10 GPS: 27 56 11 S 151 43 01 E
From Clifton take the road west towards Leyburn for 19kms to Passmore Rd. Camping beside the Condamine River Ph: 07 4688 6611

249. Leyburn Recreation Ground
Map Ref: MAP 2 G10 GPS: 28 00 27 S 151 34 58 E
Camp area at Leyburn across bridge near General Store. Showers behind tennis courts.

250. Rockland Camping Reserve
Map Ref: MAP 2 H10 GPS: 28 16 03 S 151 51 19 E
Camp area 27km SW Warwick. Travel 14km S on New England Hwy turn R onto Pikedale Rd then R again onto Rockland Rd to site. Self Contained vehicles only.

251. Kalbar Showgrounds camping area - Kalbar
Map Ref: MAP 2 J10 GPS: 27 56 15 S 152 37 32 E
2oo metres N of the town shopping centre. Open, grassed areas around the showgrounds arena. Kalbar is located just off the Cunningham Hwy S of Ipswich. Ph: 07 5463 7360

252. Boonah Showgrounds
Map Ref: MAP 2 J10 GPS: 27 59 52 S 152 41 06 E
Located in Boonah and access along Melbourne Street. Melbourne Street is signposted off Church St then follow signage to Showground CP. Bring firewood Ph: 07 5463 4080

253. Flinders Beach Camping Area - Stradbroke Island
Map Ref: MAP 2 K10 GPS: 27 24 24 S 153 28 15 E
Located on North Stradbroke Island. Beach camping behind sand dune along the northern shore. From Dunwich proceed north along East Coast Rd for 11km to Amity Point turnoff. Then 3.3km to T-intersection turn right to Flinders Beach Rd for 1.7km to beach. Bring drinking water & firewood.

254. Canungra Showgrounds
Map Ref: MAP 2 J10 GPS: 28 01 15 S 153 09 32 E
Reserve is located at the Canungra Sports & Recreation Ground with access signposted along the Lamington NP Rd. From Canungra proceed south to Lamington NP and after 700m take signposted Coburg Rd/Showgrounds which leads 250m to Showgrounds. Bring firewood. Ph: 07 5543 5904

255. Bokhara River - Hebel- St George
Map Ref: MAP 2 C11 GPS: 28 58 02 S 147 47 45 E
Located on the Bokhara River in Hebel. Hebel is located 162km S of St George. Ph: 07 4625 4996

256. Narran River - Dirranbandi - St George
Map Ref: MAP 2 C11 GPS: 28 50 20 S 148 03 18 E
Located on the Narran River. Access via the Dirranbandi-Hebel Road 37km S of Dirranbandi. Ph: 07 4625 4996

Free Campsites in Queensland

257. Barney's Beach - Thallon - St George
Map Ref: MAP 2 D11 GPS: 28 38 17 S 148 49 27 E
On the Thallon-Dirranbandi Road, 3km west of Thallon beside the Moonie River. Ph: 07 4625 4996

258. Major Mitchell Campground - Central QLD
Map Ref: MAP 2 D11 GPS: 28 58 34 S 148 59 00 E
From Thallon travel south along the Carnarvon Hwy for 40km to bridge over Barwon River, 650m N of Mungindi. On the northern side of the bridge is a track on the west, which leads in 100m to camping area beside the river. Ph: 07 4624 6923

259. Barwon River - Mungindi -St George
Map Ref: MAP 2 D11 GPS: 28 58 41 S 148 59 51 E
On the banks of the Barwon River in Mungindi. Mungindi is 118km SE of St George. Ph: 07 4625 4996

260. Lee's Reserve Camping Area - Goondiwindi
Map Ref: MAP 2 F11 GPS: 28 32 47 S 150 18 26 E
Located on the tourist drive between Goondiwindi and Yelarbon and approx. 13km from Goondiwindi on a dirt rd. Ph: 07 4671 2653

261. Rainbow Reserve - Goondiwindi
Map Ref: MAP 2 F11 GPS: 28 37 46 S 150 25 07 E
17km from Goondiwindi via the Kildonan Rd. Camping beside the MacIntyre River. Ph: 07 4671 2653

262. Yellowbank Reserve - Goondiwindi
Map Ref: MAP 2 F11 GPS: 28 39 10 S 150 31 48 E
Camp spot 28km SE of Goondiwindi via Border Rivers Tourist Drive, 25km to reserve. Bush track to river. 14 day limit. Ph: 07 4671 7400

263. Bengall Reserve
Map Ref: MAP 2 F11 GPS: 28 39 29 S 150 35 56 E
Camp spot 36km SE of Goondiwindi. Follow Borders Rivers Tourist Drive for 33km to gateway & reserve sign. Bush track to river.

264. Yelarbon Recreation Grounds - Central QLD
Map Ref: MAP 2 F11 GPS: 28 34 33 S 150 45 24 E
Yelarbon on the Cunningham Hwy 50km E of Goondiwindi. Camping area along Wyemo St E end of town. Ph: 07 4671 2653

265. Carisbrooke Camping & Fishing Reserve
Map Ref: MAP 2 F11 GPS: 28 27 58 S 150 57 32 E
Camping area 15km SW of Inglewood on Cunningham Hwy, 300m N of McDougalls Rd on N side of river.

266. The Pocket Reserve
Map Ref: MAP 2 F11 GPS: 28 27 52 S 150 57 34 E
Camp area at Whetstone Weir, 15km SW of Inglewood on Cunningham Hwy. Travel 300m N of McDougalls Rd, N side of road on riverside. 14 night limit. Ph: 132 523

267. Dumaresq River Texas Camping
Map Ref: MAP 2 G11 GPS: 28 52 03 S 151 09 51 E
Camping spot opposite stock inspection station 1km S of Texas.

268. Stanthorpe Showground
Map Ref: MAP 2 H11 GPS: 28 38 27 S 151 56 50 E
Camp area NE side of town at 8 High St Stanthorpe. Entry via Showground Lane & Club Rd. Caretake. Pre-book. Ph: 0493 088 769

269. Castle Rock Camping Area
Map Ref: MAP 2 H11 GPS: 28 50 03 S 151 56 17 E
Access via Pyramids Rd signposted off the New England Hwy 10km north of Wallangarra and 7.5km south of Ballandean. Follow Pyramids Rd 8.7km to signposted access to camping area. Bring water & clean firewood. Ph: 137 468

270. Bald Rock Creek camping area - Brisbane and surrounds
Map Ref: MAP 2 H11 GPS: 28 49 58 S 151 56 16 E
Within the Girraween NP, access via Pyramids Rd off the New England Hwy. Ph: 13 74 68

271. Burgess Park camping area - Beaudesert
Map Ref: MAP 2 H11 GPS: 28 14 20 E 152 29 45 E
Located 20km S of the Mt Lindesay Hwy. From Beaudesert follow hwy to Christmas Creek Road then to campsite. Ph: 07 5544 8120

272. Flanagan's Reserve bush camping - Beaudesert
Map Ref: MAP 2 J11 GPS: 28 12 50 S 152 45 54 E
Situated 13km W of Rathdowney via Upper Logan Rd. Ph: 07 5544 3128

Free Campsites in Queensland

273. Andrew Drynan Park camping area - Beaudesert
Map Ref: MAP 2 J11 GPS: 28 19 08 S 152 56 59 E
Located on Running Creek Road S of Beaudesert. 18km from Rathdowney.
Ph: 07 5544 1281

274. The Settlement Camping Area
Map Ref: MAP 2 J11 GPS: 28 11 36 S 153 16 20 E
Within Springbrook NP located along Carricks Rd signposted off Springbrook Rd. From Mudgeeraba follow Gold Coast-Springbrook Rd for 19km to junction with Pine Creek Rd. Continue south for 5.7km to signposted Carricks Rd then 400m to camping area. Boil water first. Ph: 137 468

Featured Campsite

Brought to you by

Lee's Reserve Camping Area No 260

Goondiwindi, Qld

Stephine Jackson.

I headed out of the Queensland border town of Goondiwindi hoping that the words 'gold' and 'rainbow' had more than a fabled connection, and when I arrived at the Rainbow Reserve..

As I wandered towards the water, an aging drover told me that was a better camping area a few kilometres further east, he mumbled in a gruff and inhospitable welcome. , I took the hint and left. And I was glad I did, for merely 13kms away, and at the end of a one kilometre long rough dirt track, I discovered Lee's Reserve and the picturesque Dumaresque River.

Tranquil river camping

Travellers with a four wheel drive can camp on a small sandy 'beach' that's right at the water's edge, and fishermen who had already set up their temporary home here bragged of their success.

With a four wheel drive and a little bit of skill, a small boat can be launched into the river - if no campers are blocking access to the water .. Only a short section of the river can be accessed by power boats however, but as all I had was a kayak, getting my craft into the water was easy, and the limit to which I could explore the river had no boundaries.

I'd planned to stay at this idyllic free camping area for several days, but with a prolonged period of wet weather predicted, I made the decision to leave while I was still able to do so. but as I made my retreat, there was no question in my mind that, in the future, I would enjoy the pleasures of Lee's Reserve once again.

Free Campsites in Queensland Index

Free Campsites in Queensland Index

Queensland Map 1

0 200 400 km

Base map and data © Custom Mapping Services 2024
www.custommappingservices.com.au
Produced for On The Road Magazine.

Queensland Map 2

0 100 200 km

Mackay
Walkerston
Hay Point
Sarina
Moranbah
Clermont
Dysart
Middlemount
Emerald
Blackwater
Capella
Alpha
Rockhampton
Yeppoon
Emu Park
Gracemere
Mt Morgan
Gladstone
Tannum Sands
Calliope
Biloela
Moura
Banana
Theodore
Monto
Bundaberg
Childers
Hervey Bay
Maryborough
Gympie
Noosa Heads
Sunshine Coast
Nambour
Maroochydore
Caloundra
Caboolture
BRISBANE
Gold Coast
Toowoomba
Dalby
Chinchilla
Miles
Roma
Mitchell
Morven
Charleville
Augathella
Tambo
Taroom
Wandoan
Kingaroy
Nanango
Gayndah
Mundubbera
Warwick
Stanthorpe
Goondiwindi
St George
Dirranbandi
Cunnamulla
Bourke
Lightning Ridge
Walgett
Moree
Inverell
Glen Innes
Tenterfield
Lismore
Casino
Ballina
Byron Bay
Tweed Heads
Murwillumbah
Yamba
Grafton

New South Wales

Free Camps Guide – Useful Resources & Contacts – NSW

Parks & Wildlife Service NSW National Parks and Wildlife Service
Ph: 1300 361 967 or 02 9995 5550
Web: www.environment.nsw.gov.au/nationalparks or www.nationalparks.nsw.gov.au

Forests New South Wales
Ph: 1300 655 687
Web: www.dpi.nsw.gov.au/forests

Fisheries: Department of Primary Industries – Fisheries & Aquaculture
Ph: 1300 550 474
Web: www.dpi.nsw.gov/fisheries

NSW Rural Fire Service
Bushfire Information Hotline
Ph: 1800 679 737
Web: www.bushfire.nsw.gov.au

Department of Lands
Ph: (02) 9228 6666
Web: www.lands.nsw.gov.au

Fossicking Department of Primary Industries
Ph: 1300 736 122
Web: www.dpi.nsw.gov.au

Roads and Traffic Authority Road Conditions
Ph: 131 700
Web: www.rta.nsw.gov.au

Road Conditions NSW Outback
Ph: 08 8082 6660
Web: www.exploroz.com

Royal Flying Doctors Service – NSW Medical & Emergency Calls (Broken Hill)
Ph: 08 8088 1188

Vehicle Assistance
NRMA
Ph: 132 132
Web: www.nrma.com.au

Weather Information
Bureau of Meteorology
Ph: 1900 926 102
Web: www.bom.gov.au

Tourism New South Wales
Ph: 132 077
Web: www.visitnsw.com.au

Free Campsites in New South Wales

1. Koreelah Creek camping area - New England
Map Ref: MAP H2 GPS: 28 18 30 S 152 27 58 E
23km W of Woodenbong. Access via White Swamp Rd off Mt Lindesay Highway. Dry weather only. Ph: 02 6632 0000

2. Woodenbong Camping Area - North Coast
Map Ref: MAP 1 J2 GPS: 28 23 19 S 152 36 22 E
Located on Mount Lindesay Hwy at western end of Woodenbong Village. Bring firewood. Ph: 02 6635 1471

3. Urbenville Forest Park - New England
Map Ref: MAP 1 H2 GPS: 28 28 06 S 152 32 55 E
Located at N End of Urbenville - 400m from village. Signposted access along the Urbenville-Woodenbong Rd. Ph: 02 6634 1254

4. Tooloom Falls Campground - New England
Map Ref: MAP 1 H3 GPS: 28 30 46 S 152 31 37 E
6km S of Urbenville off Urbenville-Warwick Rd. 3km SW of Urbenville onto Tooloom Falls Rd. Ph: 02 6632 0000

5. Iron Pot Creek Camping Area - North Coast
Map Ref: MAP 1 J3 GPS: 28 31 19 S 152 44 52 E
Within Toonumbar NP which is located 35kms northwest of Kyogle and accessed from Afterlee via Toonumbar Forest Drive. Signposted access along Murray Scrub Rd off Afterlee Rd. Ph: 02 6632 0000

6. Peacock Creek Rest Area - North Coast
Map Ref: MAP 1 J3 GPS: 28 39 36 S 152 42 57 E
Within the Richmond Range NP located on Peacosk Creek Rd 36kms north of Mallanganee. Access via Cambridge Plateau Forest Drive from Mallanganee. Bring drinking water & firewater. Ph: 02 6632 0000

7. Bells Bay
Map Ref: MAP 1 J3 GPS: 28 37 03 S 152 47 37 E
Camping spot at Toonumbar Dam 29km W of Kyogle via Afterlee and Dam Access rds. Ph: 02 6633 9140

8. Lynchs Creek Reserve camping area - North Coast
Map Ref: MAP 1 J3 GPS: 28 26 42 S 152 59 58 E
Located next to the old school building 10kms NE of Wiangaree on the Summerland Hwy within the Border Ranges NP. Ph: 02 6632 1611

9. Sheepstation Creek camping area - North Coast
Map Ref: MAP 1 J2 GPS: 28 24 47 S 153 01 22 E
17km NE of Wiangaree via Lynchs Creek Rd and Tweed Range Scenic Dve. Ph: 02 6632 0000

10. Forest Tops Camping area - North Coast
Map Ref: MAP 1 J2 GPS: 28 23 15 S 153 03 50 E
6.5km NW of Sheepstation Creek Camping area along Tweed Range Scenic Dve. Ph: 02 6632 0000

11. Cutters Camp camping area - North Coast
Map Ref: MAP 1 J3 GPS: 28 26 42 S 153 11 39 E
Within the Mebbin NP 12km S of Tyalgum and 11km W of the Murwillumbah-Kyogle Rd. Ph: 02 6670 8600

12. Rummery Park
Map Ref: MAP 1 K3 GPS: 28 35 54 S 153 22 42 E
Within Whian Whian State CA 32km NE of Lismore travel N off Dunoon Rd to Minyon Falls Rd. A further 7km narrow winding dirt rd. Ph: 02 6627 0200

13. The Old Teven School
Map Ref: MAP 1 K3 GPS: 28 48 48 S 153 29 45 E
Camp area at Teven 15km W of Ballina on Teven Rd. Must be self sufficient. Ph: 02 6687 8927

14. Alstonville Showground
Map Ref: MAP 1 K3 GPS: 28 50 23 S 153 26 26 E
Camp area at Alstonville via South St cnr Commercial Rd. Contact caretaker. Ph: 02 6628 0358

15. Barwon River Crossing Park
Map Ref: MAP 1 B3 GPS: 28 58 33 S 148 59 01 E
Parking area on N side of Mungindi Bridge on Carnarvon Hwy, Mungindi. Ph: 07 4620 8877

16. Boomi River Picnic Area
Map Ref: MAP 1 C3 GPS: 29 01 18 S 149 03 57 E
Camp area 20km S of Mungindi. Turn E on track S side of bridge. Large flat area 300m from Carnarvon Hwy. Ph: 02 6757 3350

Free Campsites in New South Wales

17. Lemon Tree Flat Camping Area - New England
Map Ref: MAP 1 F3 GPS: 29 08 51 S 150 59 27 E
Located in Kwiambal NP 90km north of Inverell. Access is singposted from Ashford via Limeston Rd or Coalmine Rd which is 2.8km north of town. Camp area is 3.3km along Lemon Tree Flat Rd which is signposted off access road to MacIntyre Falls. Bring water & firewood. Ph: 02 6736 4298

18. Bonshaw Weir - North East
Map Ref: MAP 1 F3 GPS: 28 59 12 S 151 16 42 E
On the banks of the Dumaresq River. Signposted access along the Bruxner Hwy 8km N of Bonshaw. Ph: 02 6728 8161

19. Bald Rock Camping Area - New England
Map Ref: MAP 1 H3 GPS: 28 50 42 S 152 02 43 E
Bald Rock NP is signposted 29km north of Tenterfield along Mount Lindesay Hwy. Then 6km to camping area in bush setting. Bring water & firewood. Ph: 02 6736 4298

20. Basket Swamp Campground - North East
Map Ref: MAP 1 H3 GPS: 28 54 33 S 152 09 11 E
Located in the Boonoo State Forest. 24km NW of Tenterfield. Off Mt Lindesay Hwy via Lindbrook Rd & Basket Swamp Rd. Dry weather only. Ph: 02 6736 4298

21. Woolloo Woollooin
Map Ref: MAP 1 H3 GPS: 28 56 39 S 152 11 01 E
Camp area located in Basket Swamp NP 22km NE of Tenterfield. Take Mt Lindsay Rd to Black Swamp Rd & continue to Wellington Rock Trail. Only 3 sites. 4WD only.

22. Crooked Creek Rest Area - New England
Map Ref: MAP 1 H3 GPS: 28 55 48 S 152 18 59 E
Situated 38km NE of Tenterfield near Drake. Signposted access via Richmond Rd from Bruxner Hwy. Dry weather only. Ph: 02 6662 0900

23. Mount Pikapene Campground
Map Ref: MAP 1 J4 GPS: 29 02 02 S 152 43 06 E
22kms S of Mallanganee via Old Lawrence Rd then Busby's Flat Rd. Ph: 1300 655 687

24. Braemar Park Camp
Map Ref: MAP 1 J4 GPS: 29 05 16 S 153 00 07 E
Within Ellangowan State Forest on Summerland Way, Ellangowan, 28kms S of Casino or 22kms N of Whiporie. Ph: 1300 655 687

25. Rocky River
Map Ref: MAP 1 D4 GPS: 29 24 36 S 149 55 09 E
Camp spot 11km NE of Moree. Tracks either side of Gwyder River bridge W of Hwy.

26. Tareelaroi Weir - Outback
Map Ref: MAP 1 D4 GPS: 29 26 50 S 150 01 53 E
20kms E of Moree. Northern side of Gwydir Hwy. 4km unsealed track and impassable in wet weather. Dry weather only. Ph: 02 6757 3350

27. Pallamallawa - Moree - Outback
Map Ref: MAP 1 D4 GPS: 29 27 33 S 150 05 00 E
32km E of the town of Moree on the Gwydir Hwy.

28. Gum Flat Public Reserve - North West
Map Ref: MAP 1 D4 GPS: 29 27 55 S 150 04 55 E
Camp Spot 28km E of Moree. Signposted access along the Gwydir Hwy. Ph: 02 6757 3350

29. Gravesend Hotel
Map Ref: MAP 1 E4 GPS: 29 34 59 S 150 20 15 E
Camp spot in Railway Pde Gravesend at rear of hotel. Check in with publican. Ph: 02 6729 7005

30. Ezzy's Crossing Camp Area
Map Ref: MAP 1 E4 GPS: 29 34 37 S 150 21 31 E
Camp area 4kms E of Gravesend via Gwydir Hwy. Entry north side of bridge. Ph: 02 6729 0046

31. Cranky Rock Recreation Reserve - North West
Map Ref: MAP 1 E4 GPS: 29 33 40 S 150 38 45 E
Access signposted off Gwydir Hwy 6km E of Warialda and then 3km into camping area. Access road can be rough in sections. Ph: 02 6729 1402

32. Delungra Hotel
Map Ref: MAP 1 E4 GPS: 29 39 11 S 150 49 40 E
Located at 28 Inverell St Delungra - behind the hotel. Ph: 02 6724 8405

Brought to you by

kokodacaravans.com.au

Tareelaroi Weir No 26

Near Moree, NSW

20kms east of Moree

Stephanie Jackson

If you rush blindly along the Gwydir Highway that links the NSW town of Moree to urban centres further east and west, you might never notice the tiny sign that points to the Tareelaroi weir. It's on the northern side of the Gwydir Highway, 20kms east of Moree, and if you're not averse to rattling along a 4km long dirt track, you'll be able to camp, free of charge, on the shaded banks of the Gwydir River.

The camping area can, with care, be accessed by all vehicles and rigs, but the final black soil section of the track can become impassable during or after wet weather.

The camping area is upstream of the junction where the diminutive Mehi River joins the waters of the larger Gwydir River that, further along its meandering route, is confined by the Tareelaroi weir.

It's a popular fishing and camping spot for locals, and there are several fairly large flat areas where you can camp close to the water's edge, further back from the river, or close to the water regulating facility at the Gwydir's junction with the Mehi. There's ample room to set up your temporary home well away from the tall gum trees that are in and around the area and that might drop limbs during a storm or strong winds, but you won't find any manicured lawns here. It's volunteers who maintain the area, and if the seasons have been good and it's been some time since anyone rolled onto the scene with a mower, the camping area will be overgrown with tall and luxuriant weeds.

A composting toilet and a muddy boat ramp are the only facilities on offer here, but if fishing and taking it easy in a quiet location that seems a million miles from civilisation head your list of pleasurable ways to spend a day or two, you're sure to have a good time.

If you want to explore the adjacent bushland or check out other nearby camping areas, you can walk or drive along the narrow track that links the main camping area to one further east, near the junction with the Mehi. Take care when walking along this meandering trail however, for it's lined with an avenue of prickly acacias and invasive and aggressive weeds such as cobbler's pegs and ngurra burr, the prickly seeds of which will eagerly attach themselves to your clothing.

In late winter, native clematis bloom in profusion and fill the air with their subtle perfume, and this and the other unkempt vegetation that surround the camping area provide a habitat for a diverse community of small birds. If bird watching is your passion, you'll be mesmerised by superb blue wrens and diminutive honeyeaters that dance before you. And you'll see larger species, including corellas, galahs, and king parrots that are more at home among the taller vegetation that lines the river's reed hemmed banks.

This secluded camping area hides in a tranquil corner of the great outdoors, and if you genuinely want to take it easy, it's an ideal place to do just that.

Boats can be launched into the calm waters of the Gwydir River.

There's plenty of level ground where you can set up camp close to the river.

A winding narrow track links the main camping area to the weir itself.

Just The Facts

Tareelaroi Weir

Getting there: The turnoff to the camping area is on the northern side of the Gwydir Highway 20kms east of the NSW town of Moree. Access is then via a 4km long unsealed track, with the track on the right hand side before the third grid leading to the main camping area. The area can be accessed by all vehicles and rigs with care, but the final section of the route can be impassable in wet weather.

Facilities: A composting toilet and a boat ramp are the only facilities here.

Pets: Pets are permitted.

Charges: There is no charge for camping here.

Contact: For more information, contact the Moree Visitor Information Centre by phoning 02 6757 3350, or log onto www.moreetourism.com.au

33. Graman Hotel
Map Ref: MAP 1 F4 GPS: 29 28 09 S 150 55 41 E
Located in Yetman Rd Graman. Large grassed area behind hotel. Check in with publican. Ph: 02 6725 6482

34. Graman Hotel
Map Ref: MAP 1 F4 GPS: 29 28 09 S 150 55 41 E
Camp area 41kms NW of Inverell. Large grassed area behind hotel 4150 Yetman Rd, Graman. Check in with publican. Free for patrons. Ph: 02 6725 6491

35. Wells Crossing - New England
Map Ref: MAP 1 F4 GPS: 29 21 45 S 151 08 38 E
Camp Area located 7km E of Ashford on the Pindari Dam Rd - beside Severn River Ph: 02 6725 4455

36. Pindari Dam - North East
Map Ref: MAP 1 F4 GPS: 29 23 51 S 151 15 54 E
Located 24km SE of Ashford on the Severn River via Pindari Dam Rd. Ph: 02 6728 8288

37. Kings Plain Creek camping area - Kings Plains National Park - North East
Map Ref: MAP 1 F4 GPS: 29 35 02 S 151 23 22 E
Access via Jindalee Rd from Kings Plains Rd West of Wellingrove then W about 2km from Jindalee. Dry weather only Ph: 02 6739 0700

38. Ironbark camping area - New England
Map Ref: MAP 1 F4 GPS: 29 35 42 S 151 23 44 E
Within the Kings Plain NP. 50km NW of Glen Innes via Kings Plain Rd and the park's access track. Ph: 02 6739 0700

39. Blatherarm Creek
Map Ref: MAP 1 G4 GPS: 29 14 25 S 151 41 58 E
Camp area 11km N of Torrington via Blatherarm Rd which is off Silent Grove Rd. Ph: 02 6736 4298

40. Gunyah-Deepwater River Camping Ground
Map Ref: MAP 1 G4 GPS: 29 26 40 S 151 51 03 E
Camping area at gunya 1km E of Deepwater. Travel along Simpson St off New England Hwy and follow sign to area. Ph: 0429 462 642

41. North Washpool camping area - New England
Map Ref: MAP 1 H4 GPS: 29 16 12 S 152 26 02 E
Located in the NE corner of the Washpool NP. Access via Washpool Rd off Lionsville Rd from Baryulgil. Ph: 02 6739 0700

42. The Gorge
Map Ref: MAP 1 H4 GPS: 29 23 28 S 152 34 18 E
Camp area on Heifer Station. 2568 Gorge Rd - 27kms from Lilydale Bridge via Copmanhurst. Dirt rd. Recommend call before arrival. Ph: 02 6647 2173

43. Bellbird Camping Area - New England
Map Ref: MAP 1 H4 GPS: 29 28 24 S 152 18 58 E
Within Walshpool NP 75km east of Glen Inness and 90km west of Grafton. Unsealed access is signposted along the Gwydir Hwy. Signposted access 3.3km north of Gwydir Hwy on Coachwood Rd then 200m to camp area. Ph: 02 6739 0700

44. Mulligans Camping Area - New England
Map Ref: MAP 1 H4 GPS: 29 30 56 S 152 21 32 E
Located 9.5km along Mulligans Dve, which is signposted off Gwydir Hwy 92km west of Grafton. Unsealed access road is beside the NPWS visitor centre. Bring drinking water & firewood. Ph: 02 6739 0700

45. Cangai Bridge
Map Ref: MAP 1 H4 GPS: 29 29 24 S 152 27 53 E
Camp area 20km W of Jackadery via Gwydir Hwy & Cangai Bridge Rd. Small vehicles only - narrow bridges.

46. Broadwater Bridge Camp Area
Map Ref: MAP 1 H4 GPS: 29 27 07 S 152 29 36 E
Camp spot located on Hanging Rock Rd, Cangai, 26km W of Jackadery via Gwydir Hwy to Cangai Bridge Rd. Beware narrow bridges, small vehicles only. Ph: 02 6643 0800

47. Lilydale Primitive Camp Ground
Map Ref: MAP 1 H5 GPS: 29 32 46 S 152 40 16 E
Camp area 12km from Copmanhurst via Clarence Way in Winegrove Rd. SW side of Lilydale Bridge. Ph: 1300 886 235

48. Copmanhurst Primitive Camping Ground
Map Ref: MAP 1 J5 GPS: 29 35 24 S 152 46 50 E
Camp area at Copmanhurst in Lawrence St 31kms NW of Grafton via Clarence Way. Ph: 1300 886 235

Free Campsites in New South Wales

49. Grafton Showground
Map Ref: MAP 1 J5 GPS: 29 41 03 S 152 56 24 E
Camp area at Grafton cnr Prince St & Dobie St. Ph: 0468 482 919

50. Woody Head Camping Area - North Coast
Map Ref: MAP 1 K4 GPS: 29 21 58 S 153 22 17 E
Bundalong NP is situated between Iluka and Evans Head. Signposted access along Iluka Rd 13km east of Pacific Hwy 15km north of Maclean. Then 900m to camping area with beach frontage. Ph: 02 6627 0200

51. Lake Arragan Camping Area - North Coast
Map Ref: MAP 1 J5 GPS: 29 34 01 S 153 20 11 E
Access road is signposted off Brooms Head Rd 4km north of Brooms Head and 20km southeast of the Pacific Hwy at Maclean. Continue 2km to camping area. Bring drinking water & firewood. Ph: 02 6640 2500

52. Diggers Headland Reserve camping area - North Coast
Map Ref: MAP 1 J5 GPS: 29 48 55 S 153 17 19 E
12km N of Wooli along Nugget St in Diggers Camp Village. Check information board for camping locations. Ph: 02 6643 0200

53. Pebbly Beach Camping Area - North Coast
Map Ref: MAP 1 J5 GPS: 29 56 45 S 153 15 24 E
Located in Yuraygir NP from Angourie 6km south of Yamba. Access track is located 13km along Barcoongere Way to information board. Track leads through car park for 2.5km to beach. Follow beach north for 2.1km to exit track which leads 200m to creek crossing then 200m to camp area. Bring drinking water & firewood. Ph: 02 6640 2500

54. Pilliga Baths - Central West
Map Ref: MAP 1 B6 GPS: 30 21 20 S 148 54 25 E
Located 96kms from Narrabri and 55kms W of Wee Waa on the Wee Waa/ Pilliga Rd. Ph: 02 6799 6866

55. Burren Junction Bore - Far West
Map Ref: MAP 1 B5 GPS: 30 06 51 S 148 59 44 E
The bore is on the Kamilaroi Hwy 4kms E of Burren Junction which is 115kms NW of Narrabri. Ph: 1800 659 931

56. Artesian Bore Baths Reserve - North West
Map Ref: MAP 1 B5 GPS: 30 06 52 S 148 59 44 E
3 km E of Burren Junction township on the Burren Junction-Wee Waa Road. Ph: 02 6828 6139

57. Yarrie Lake camping area - North West
Map Ref: MAP 1 C6 GPS: 30 22 07 S 149 31 05 E
Located around 30km W of Narrabri off the Newell Hwy along Yarrie Lake Rd. (Tourist Drive #2) Ph: 02 6799 6760

58. Bellata Golf Club
Map Ref: MAP 1 D5 GPS: 29 55 08 S 149 47 57 E
Parking area 800m E off Newell Hwy at 80 Berrigal Rd, Bellata. Check in at bar. Ph: 0467 937 559

59. Namoi River
Map Ref: MAP 1 D6 GPS: 30 24 18 S 149 53 39 E
Camp spot 15km SE of Narrabri via Old Gunnedah Rd. Tracks W to river. Use 2nd entry after bridge if towing a van.

60. Dawsons Springs camping area - North West
Map Ref: MAP 1 D5 GPS: 30 16 51 S 150 09 48 E
Within the Mt Kaputar NP 33km E of Narrabri off the Newell Hwy off the Kaputar road. No caravans. Ph: 02 6792 7300

61. Little Creek Recreation Reserve - North West
Map Ref: MAP 1 E6 GPS: 30 18 37 S 150 26 04 E
Small camping area 20km NW of Barraba via Trevallyn Rd. Ph: 02 6782 1255

62. Bingarra Riverside Camping
Map Ref: MAP 1 E5 GPS: 29 51 45 S 150 34 45 E
Camp spot at Bingarra. 3 area of riverside camping on Copeton Dam Rd. Info & map on board at entrance to S side of camp area. Self contained vehicles only. Max 7 night stay.

63. Gwydir River Camps - New England
Map Ref: MAP 1 E5 GPS: 29 53 27 S 150 37 18 E
Camp spots 8km E of Bingara via Keera Rd. Various campsites along riverbank. Ph: 02 6724 0066

64. Glen Riddle Reserve camping area - North West
Map Ref: MAP 1 E6 GPS: 30 27 02 S 150 41 35 E
Located 17km S of Barraba on the Split Rock Dam. Access is signposted via Crow Mountain Road at Black Springs turn-off on Fossickers Way. Ph: 02 6782 1255

Free Campsites in New South Wales

65. Split Rock Dam camping area - North West
Map Ref: MAP 1 E6 GPS: 30 33 50 S 150 40 34 E
Situated 20km N of Manilla. Access signposted via Oakhampton turn-off at Upper Manilla on Fossickers Way. Good fishing. Ph: 02 6785 1207

66. Bundarra Lions Park - New England
Map Ref: MAP 1 F5 GPS: 30 11 37 S 151 04 41 E
Located 2.5km south of Bundarra along Thunderbolts Way beside the Gwydir River. Bring water & firewood.

67. Mann River Nature Reserve - North East
Map Ref: MAP 1 G5 GPS: 29 41 32 S 152 06 19 E
Located 48km SE of Glen Innes. 10km unsealed road from Gwydir Hwy to the reserve is windy and steep. Not suitable for large rigs or towing vans. Ph: 02 6732 5133

68. Nymboida River camping area - North Coast
Map Ref: MAP 1 H5 GPS: 29 43 02 S 152 33 52 E
Located 52km W of Grafton on T-Ridge Rd - 7km NW of T-Ridge Rd and Ramornie Forest Rd. Lovely site above the Nymboida River. Ph: 02 6641 1500

69. Dalmorton camping area - New England
Map Ref: MAP 1 H5 GPS: 29 51 56 S 152 26 51 E
Guy Fawkes River Conservation Area on the banks of the Boyd River along Chaelundi Rd 1km S of Old Grafton-Glen Innes Rd. Ph: 02 6657 2309

70. Buccarumbi Primitive Camp Ground
Map Ref: MAP 1 H5 GPS: 29 50 07 S 152 35 16 E
Camp area 50km SW of Grafton via Old Grafton Rd adjacent to Buccarumbi Bridge. Ph: 1300 886 235

71. Blaxland Creek Riverside Reserve
Map Ref: MAP 1 H5 GPS: 29 54 26 S 152 47 10 E
Located 33km SW of Grafton with camping spot just N of bridge

72. Clouds Creek Camp Ground
Map Ref: MAP 1 H5 GPS: 30 00 01 S 152 40 51 E
Camp spot at Armidale Rd 23kms S of Nymboida to Hortons Creek Nature Reserve.

73. Cod Hole camping area - North Coast
Map Ref: MAP 1 H6 GPS: 30 07 57 S 152 42 12 E
At the end of Moses Rock Rd which is signposted off Moonpar Forest Dve. Dry weather only Ph: 02 6657 2309

74. Platypus Flat camping area - North Coast
Map Ref: MAP 1 H6 GPS: 30 11 07 S 152 41 30 E
29km N of Dorrigo. Access via Mills Road from Moonpar Forest Dve. Ph: 02 6657 2309

75. Timms Park
Map Ref: MAP 1 J6 GPS: 30 13 59 S 152 53 01 E
Located at 9 Timmsvale Rd. From Dorrigo-Coffs Harbour Rd turn into Timmsvale Rd.

76. Ulong bush camping area
Map Ref: MAP 1 J6 GPS: 30 14 43 S 152 53 15 E
Located in Toonumbar NP 32kms W of Coffs Harbour. Access on Pine Avenue N of Eastern Dorrigo Way in Ulong Village behind the Eastern Dorrigo Community Hall. Ph: 02 6648 4000

77. Coffs Harbour Camping & 4WD
Map Ref: MAP 1 J6 GPS: 30 08 28 S 153 03 24 E
Located at 1119 Bucca Rd on a 230 acre estate 15 minutes north of Coffs Harbour and only 8 mins from glorious Moonee Beach. 4WDs and motorbikes are NOT to be ridden on the property. Best to pre-book. Ph: 0421 748 895

78. Orara East bush camping - North Coast
Map Ref: MAP 1 J6 GPS: 30 11 30 S 153 07 40 E
9km W of Coffs Harbour in the Orara East State Forest via Bruxner Park Rd off the Pacific Hwy. Numerous bush camping areas located throughout the forest. Ph: 02 6652 0111

79. Yarrowyck Gwydir River Camp Area
Map Ref: MAP 1 F6 GPS: 30 28 03 S 151 21 34 E
Camp area 25km NW of Uralla via Thunderbolts Way & Yarrowyck Crossing Rd - 5km dirt road. Causeway can be cut due to floods.

80. Dumaresq Dam Recreation Area - North East
Map Ref: MAP 1 F6 GPS: 30 25 33 S 151 35 34 E
14kms NW of Armidale. Turn N off Boorolong Rd onto Dumaresq Dam Rd. Ph: 02 6770 3880

Mann River Nature Reserve No 67

Glen Innes area, NSW

48kms south-east of Glen Innes
Stephanie Jackson

It was the lure of water that persuaded me, several years ago, to drive along the old coach road that links the NSW town of Grafton to its westerly neighbour of Glen Innes. I'd followed the meandering trail that shadows the Mann River and that slithers through a low-roofed tunnel carved through the rocky hillside by convicts more than 100 years ago, and I'd eagerly anticipated the adventure that awaited me at my destination. But when I finally reached the Mann River Nature Reserve, my vision of kayaking along a wild river was shattered, for only a narrow stream mutters through this picturesque camping area.

A few months ago I retraced that journey and was as excited as in the past about the prospect of camping beside the Mann River, but this time there would be no hint of disappointment, for I knew exactly what to expect. Kayaking wouldn't be on the agenda, but I'd be able to explore the region on foot, to wander through the bushland and along the riverbank that's congested with massive granite boulders, and if a bout of laziness came my way, I'd sit in the shade of the forest and do nothing other than watch the antics of the kangaroos and wallabies that have also discovered that life was meant to be easy in this secluded and scenic spot.

I set up camp on a wide expanse of grass, close to rock pools where, in a warmer season and with no other campers in sight, I'd have exuberantly cast off my clothes and leapt into the cool, inviting, and bubbling water. On a winter's day there were other ways to have a good time however, and with no defined walking tracks, I explored the landscape by scrambling across boulders shaded by she-oak trees where black cockatoos fed on ripening seeds, and slowly followed the river's meandering course upstream.

The forest was alive with crimson rosellas, superb fairy-wrens, and yellow robins, and as I eventually wandered back to my campsite, I grabbed some fruit from a wild lemon tree to add a little flavour to the fish I'd be cooking for my evening meal.

The tunnel on the old coach road prevents some campers from accessing the nature reserve via this scenic route from Grafton.

A joey peered from its furry pouch as its mother cautiously approached my campsite in anticipation of a free handout of food, and a magpie waited optimistically too. Being a firm believer that campers should not feed the wildlife, I ignored their silent, pleading stares, for Mother Nature had provided all they needed for their survival in this forest environment.

Only minimal facilities have been provided for human visitors however. There are composting toilets that can be accessed by disabled travellers, picnic tables, and fireplaces, but visitors must bring their own firewood as collecting it within a nature reserve is prohibited.

Night time temperatures in the region frequently drop to below zero, and as grey clouds unfurled across the sky I lit a small fire to chase away the increasingly cold grasp of the approaching night. A feeble shower of rain attempted to snuff out the flames, leaving me enveloped in a haze of smoke before I conceded defeat and took shelter in my tent.

My campervan, with the kayak lashed to its roof, had squeezed through the 3.27 metre high tunnel, through which the road that links Grafton to the camping area passes, with only inches to spare. The steep and winding section of the road to the west of the reserve is unsuitable for large vehicles and for those towing caravans, and although there's ample room for the largest of vehicles at this quiet riverbank camping area, the road conditions ensure that it's rarely crowded. Kangaroos and wallabies routinely outnumber humans, and for travellers who revel in sharing their campsite with some of Australia's most beautiful wild creatures, the Mann River Nature Reserve is the perfect place to be.

A stream crosses the road on its way to unite with the Mann River at the nature reserve.

Just The Facts

Mann River Nature Reserve

Getting there: The Mann River Nature Reserve is 48kms south-east of the NSW town of Glen Innes that sits at the intersection of the Gwydir and New England highways. The10km long unsealed road leading from the Gwydir Highway to the reserve has a steep and winding descent that makes it unsuitable for large vehicles or those towing caravans. Access via the unsealed old coach road from Grafton is limited by the height of the tunnel (3.27 metres) through which the road passes.
Facilities: There are picnic tables and composting toilets.
Pets: Pets are permitted but should not be allowed to harass the wildlife.
Charges: There is no charge for camping here.
Contact: Additional information is available from the Glen Innes Visitor Information Centre by phoning (02) 6730 2400 or by logging onto www.gleninnestourism.com. For travellers intending to access the nature reserve via the old coach road from Grafton, the Clarence River Visitor Information Centre can also provide information.
The centre can be contacted by phoning (02) 6645 4121 or via their website at www.clarencetourism.com.

Free Campsites in New South Wales

81. Woodridge Fossicking Reserve & Rocky River Fossicking Area camp ground
Map Ref: MAP 1 F6 GPS: 30 37 42 S 151 28 13 E
Located 6km W of Uralla beside Rocky River. From New England Hwy take the road to Kingstown 45/Fossicking Area 6 for 3km then Devoncourt Rd/ Fossicking Area and follow signs. Ph: 02 6778 6420

82. Wooldridge Recreation & Fossicking Reserve
Map Ref: MAP 1 F6 GPS: 30 37 45 S 151 28 18 E
Camp area 6km W of Uralla. Go 4.5 km on Kingstown Rd then turn N onto Devoncourt Rd and follow to end. Cattle grid at entrance.

83. Uralla Fossicking Area - North East
Map Ref: MAP 1 F6 GPS: 30 37 46 S 151 28 21 E
Turn west off New England Hwy at Uralla's BP Roadhouse onto Kingston Rd then right on to Devoncourt Rd to the river. Ph: 02 6778 4496

84. Dangars Falls camping area - New England
Map Ref: MAP 1 G6 GPS: 30 40 20 S 151 43 34 E
22km S of Armidale within the Oxley Wild Rivers NP via the Dangars Falls Rd. Ph: 02 6777 4700

85. Green Gully (Wollomobi Falls) camping area - New England
Map Ref: MAP 1 G6 GPS: 30 31 54 S 152 01 39 E
Signposted access off the Waterfall Way - 37km E of Armidale then drive 1.5km S to camping site. Best suited for Tent and campervan sites. Ph: 02 6776 0000

86. Barokee campground - New England
Map Ref: MAP 1 H6 GPS: 30 26 36 S 152 15 08 E
Within the Cathedral Rock NP off the Waterfall Way - 6km S of Ebor. Follow track West 8km. Limited turning area. Ph: 02 6657 2309

87. Ebor Sports & Recreation Reserve
Map Ref: MAP 1 H6 GPS: 30 24 28 S 152 20 46 E
Located 11822 Waterfall Way, Ebor 600m W of town next to sportsground. Opposite Ebor Falls turnoff. Donation. Ph: 02 6770 3888

88. Little Styx River Campground
Map Ref: MAP 1 H6 GPS: 30 30 17 S 152 21 36 E
21km S of Ebor turn E off Waterfall Way to Point Lookout Rd and travel 10km on dirt rd to camp spot.

89. Hyatts Flat camping area - New England
Map Ref: MAP 1 H6 GPS: 30 31 14 S 152 20 02 E
65km E of Armidale via Point Lookout Rd then Forest Way and Hardwood Rd. Ph: 1300 655 687

90. Wattle Flat Camping Area - New England
Map Ref: MAP 1 G6 GPS: 30 34 24 S 152 14 13 E
Within the Styx River SF 65km E of Armidale. Located along Wattle Flat Rd which is signposted off Loop Rd. Ph: 1300 655 687

91. Schwagers Bore picnic & camping area - North West
Map Ref: MAP 1 C6 GPS: 30 36 14 S 149 18 58 E
Located in the Pilliga SF. 61km SW of Narrabri via the Pilliga Forest Way. Ph: 02 9871 3377

92. The Aloes Camping area - North West
Map Ref: MAP 1 B6 GPS: 30 44 58 S 149 06 40 E
88km from Narrabri within the Pilliga SF. Signposted access 23km north of Baradine at junction of Cumbil Rd and Forest Way opposite the historic Aloes site and close to Etoo Creek. Ph: 02 9871 3377

93. Rocky Creek Mill - North East
Map Ref: MAP 1 B6 GPS: 30 42 54 S 149 08 44 E
5km NE of The Aloes CA. Signposted access on Forest Way. Ph: 1300 655 687

94. Salt Caves Picnic & Camping area - North West
Map Ref: MAP 1 C6 GPS: 30 44 46 S 149 17 29 E
Located in Timallallie NP. 68km SW of Narrabri or 37km NE of Baradine. Turn SW on to Pilliga Forest Way 27km SW of Narrabri then S on to County Line Rd. Dirt Road. Dry weather only. Ph: 02 6943 4003

95. Sculptures in the Scrub camping area - Timallallie NP - North West
Map Ref: MAP 1 C7 GPS: 30 59 50 S 149 14 03 E
Located 33km NE of Baradine at Dandra Gorge via No 1 Fire Break Road then Top Crossing Road (SW of Narrabri) Dry weather only. Ph: 02 6843 4011

96. Yarrigan camping area - Central West
Map Ref: MAP 1 B7 GPS: 31 04 48 S 149 04 31 E
Within the Yarrigan NP. Located along Ridge Road via Forest Way. Ph: 02 6943 4003

Featured Campsite

Brought to you by

Dangars Gorge Campground No 84

Oxley Wild Rivers National Park, New England Region NSW
22kms south of Armidale

Miriam Blaker

Wild terrain is never too far away here. Rushing water has carved its way to the ocean through ancient rainforest and around resilient granite over millennia, leading to some of Australia's most thrilling gorges, waterfalls and walking trails. Dangars Gorge along the Waterfall Way in NSW gives you a taste of that and it's literally on the doorstep of Armidale. The Dangars Gorge campground, at the start of the Waterfall Way is a perfect base.

There are only seven sites at this campground so make sure to book before you arrive to ensure your spot. New South Wales National Parks Campgrounds charges a small booking fee but apart from that it's free to stay.

We were on our way north and had just passed through Armadale in the scenic New England area. Our plan was to experience some of the spectacular scenery that the area is famous for, although we didn't want to take our van too far along the Waterfall Way. The road to Dangars Gorge Campground at Oxley Wild Rivers National Park is easily accessible to all size rigs and sites are big and spacious.

Each campsite has a fire pit and some have picnic tables. There's one well maintained drop toilet and a very peaceful vibe in this small National Park campground set in native bush land. It was dry and dusty when we visited (in February 2023) so the water taps located conveniently near the campsites were very welcome.

If you're here after heavy rain the falls will be thundering but even in the dry the gorge is spectacular. It's only a short walk to the Gorge lookout from the campsite with lots of steps along the way. There you'll find a jaw dropping view as you look out over the waterfall and down into the deep gorge.

At various times of the day the colours change as it hits the gorge walls. It's a photographers dream. The Dangars Falls Walking Track packs in six lookouts in 600 metres so it's a popular spot for day trippers. Really keen hikers can check out the 6kms McDirty's walking track which takes 2-3 hours or the 16kms epic Salisbury Waters Walking Track which includes a steep descent to a pristine and secluded pool. Back at camp the wildlife is abundant at night so don't be surprised if you're sharing your site with a possum or two. We had a regular brush tailed fella who liked to visit each night.

While you're based at Dangars Gorge Campground take the chance, while being unhitched and minus the caravan, to continue down the Waterfall Way and explore some of the many other beautiful waterfalls of the area.

Sunset over the Oxley Wild River.

Looking over the gorge is breathtaking.

There are some great walking paths.

Just The Facts

Dangars Gorge Campground
Where: Dangarsleigh, NSW
Facilities: Picnic tables, barbeque facilities, carpark, drinking water, toilets
Rates: $6 booking fee applies
Contact www.nationalparks.nsw.gov.au/camping or 1300 072 757

Free Campsites in New South Wales

97. Camp Blackman Camping Area - North West
Map Ref: MAP 1 B7 GPS: 31 16 37 S 148 59 49 E
Within Warrumbungle NP west of Coonabarabran and signposted from centre of town. Take signposted turn-ff for park visitor information centre along John Renshaw Parkway. Camp area located 2.5km north of information centre. Bring drinking water & firewood. Ph: 02 6825 4364

98. Coonabarabran Golf Club RV
Map Ref: MAP 1 C7 GPS: 31 16 14 S 149 17 45 E
Located in River Rd, Coonabarabran, 2km W of PO. 7 day limit. Ph: 02 6842 1292

99. Currabubula Recreation Ground
Map Ref: MAP 1 E7 GPS: 31 15 40 S 150 44 22 E
Located 35km SW of Tamworth at 25 Alford St Currabubula. Donation appreciated. Ph: 02 6747 1226

100. Attunga Creek Camp
Map Ref: MAP 1 E7 GPS: 30 55 45 S 150 50 48 E
Area opposite pub on Manilla Rd, Attunga 24kms S of Manilla or 21km N of Tamworth. Check signs. Ph: 13 22 13

101. Bendemeer Rest Area - New England
Map Ref: MAP 1 F7 GPS: 30 53 14 S 151 09 26 E
Camp Spot at Bendemeer. Access via 800m dirt road parallel to Hwy - between Hwy & service station. Behind showgrounds.

102. Cockburn River campsite - North East
Map Ref: MAP 1 F7 GPS: 31 03 07 S 151 08 38 E
Access via the Kootingal-Limbri Rd 30 km NE of Tamworth beside Cockburn River. Ph: 02 6764 5100

103. Peel River Campground
Map Ref: MAP 1 F7 GPS: 31 12 08 S 151 05 13 E
Camp area 1229-1523 Tamworth-Nundle Rd near river 20kms SE of Tamworth on W side of road.

104. Youngville camping area - The Hunter
Map Ref: MAP 1 F7 GPS: 31 11 57 S 151 18 34 E
From Singleton take Richmond Rd and then Mount Royal Rd for nearly 7 kms to the part entrance. Ph: 02 6574 5555

105. Cobrabold Fishing & Fossicking Camp Area
Map Ref: MAP 1 F7 GPS: 31 06 04 S 151 28 24 E
Camp area 17km SW of Walcha on Aberbaldie Rd. Signposted, 1km of dirt road. 4WD recommended. Ph: 02 6774 2460

106. Apsley Falls Camping Area - New England
Map Ref: MAP 1 G7 GPS: 31 03 51 S 151 45 44 E
Signposted access on Oxley Hwy 18km east of Walcha. Drive 600m to large camping area. Bring water & firewood. Ph: 02 6777 4700

107. Tia Falls Campground - North East
Map Ref: MAP 1 G7 GPS: 31 09 40 S 151 51 20 E
Located in Oxley Wild Rivers NP. Signposted access on the Oxley Hwy 42km SE of Walcha. Then 5km to camp area. Ph: 02 6777 4700

108. Budds Mare Campground
Map Ref: MAP 1 G7 GPS: 30 59 01 S 151 58 14 E
Located in Oxley Wild Rivers NP. Camp area 45km E of Walcha via Fitzroy/ Oxley Hwy. Take Emu Creek Rd then Moona Plains Rs, then Kanangra Vale Rd to trail. Very remote, pre-book suggested. Ph: 1300 072 757

109. George's Junction Reserve camping area - Mid North Coast
Map Ref: MAP 1 G7 GPS: 30 45 05 S 152 11 27 E
Within the Macleay River Rec Reserve - grassy riverside flat 26km W of Blackbird Flat camping area along the Kempsey-Armidale Rd. Ph: 02 6563 1555

110. Blackbird Flat Camping Area - Mid North Coast
Map Ref: MAP 1 H7 GPS: 30 45 49 S 152 21 47 E
Located 72km west of Kempsey on the old Armidale Rd. Unsealed road and after heavy rain only for 4WD vehicles. Ph: 02 6563 1555

111. Daisy Plains Huts Carrai NP - North East
Map Ref: MAP 1 G7 GPS: 30 54 18 S 152 17 40 E
4 maintained forestry huts. Located at junction of Carrai Cochrane and Mines roads - 61km W of the Kempsey-Armidale Rd. Ph: 02 6777 4700

112. Mooraback campground - North East
Map Ref: MAP 1 G7 GPS: 31 08 51 S 152 12 54 E
Situated in Werrikimbe NP 83km SE of Walcha. Access via Mooraback Rd from Oxley Hwy. Ph: 02 6777 4700

Featured Campsite

Brought to you by

kokodacaravans.com.au

Blackbird Flat Camping Area No 110
Kempsey, NSW

72km west of Kempsey, NSW
Stephanie Jackson

You're certainly not crowded here.

YOU can do the sensible thing and travel from the NSW city of Armidale to Kempsey along a modern highway, but if you're like me, and regularly avoid the easy options, there's a more challenging and scenic route. A journey along this winding mountain trail is a hair-raising experience that's not for the faint hearted, and at mid-afternoon, still some 70km from Kempsey, we were in desperate need of a break. And who could go past a riverbank recreation area with the appealing name of Blackbird Flat, particularly when camping is permitted free of charge?

We were to share the large grassy paddock with two bulls that I nicknamed, with dazzling imagination, Mr Black and Mr Brown. I'm no city slicker so was unfazed by their presence, and once they had dawdled past on a lap of inspection, they settled down beneath a shading she-oak tree to chew their cud.

I'd hoped to launch my kayak here and spend some time drifting idly along the shallow waters of the Macleay River that borders the recreation area, but recent floods had eroded the riverbank and washed away the area that had once acted as a boat ramp. My disappointment was brief, however, for there were plenty of other ways to pass the time including swimming and fishing, and with forested ranges all around, bird watching was on the agenda, too.

As the only human residents of the recreation area, we commandeered the large covered picnic area as our private domain, and while my other half likes the simple comforts of the campervan, I rolled out my self inflating mat and sleeping bag on the floor, rather than bother to erect my tent for a night or two.

The beautiful Macleay River borders the recreation area.

When Mr Black and Mr Brown awoke from their siesta, I was pleased that our temporary home was surrounded by gated railings to keep these curious and overly friendly beasts at bay.

They did what cattle inevitably do, and left sloppy cow pats just beyond the gate of the picnic area, and I hoped that when I wandered across to the toilet in the darkness of the night, I wouldn't return with my boots smelling of the countryside. But when the worst inevitably happened, there was plenty of water in the recreation area's large water tank for a thorough clean up. It was stagnant, infested with mosquito larvae, and definitely unsuitable for drinking, but it did the job. With barely a hint of a breeze, it was safe to light a campfire, and in a silence broken only by the calls of an owl, we watched occasional golden sparks drift skywards like rising stars. Silence would continue to rule the night, for although the recreation area is next to the road, there was unlikely, in this quiet neck of the woods, to be any passing traffic, and no late arrivals would be calling in to share "our" camping area. There's ample room for large vans and motorhomes, but only small vehicles, and those without trailers, are permitted to travel along the track that heads west beyond the recreation area towards Armidale.

Morning peered hesitantly from a cloak of mist that hung tenuously over the surrounding hills; dewdrops, on cobwebs strewn among the tangled riverbank vegetation, glinted in the first rays of sunshine; crimson rosellas darted among the foliage. And Mr Black and Mr Brown grazed contentedly. As we finally packed up camp and prepared to hit the road once again, I was confident that we'd be back again some day to enjoy more of the quiet life that Blackbird Flat has to offer.

Just The Facts

Blackbird Flat Camp Area

Getting there: The recreation area is 72km west of Kempsey on the old Armidale Road. The majority of the road is unsealed, but the recreation area is accessible to two-wheeldrive vehicles, except after heavy rains.
Facilities: There is a large covered picnic area, and there are pit toilets.
Wheelchair access: Nothing specific.
Rates: There is no charge for camping.
Pets: Dogs are permitted, but must not be allowed to chase the cattle that routinely graze in the recreation area.
Contact: Additional information is available from the Kempsey Visitor Information Centre on the Pacific Highway at South Kempsey, phone (02) 6563 1555, www.macleayvalleycoast.com.au

Free Campsites in New South Wales

113. Plateau Beech campground - North Coast
Map Ref: MAP 1 G8   GPS: 31 10 48 S 152 19 34 E
Within the Werrikimbe NP 90km SW of Walcha. Signposted access on Cockerawombeeba Rd - 10km S of Hastings Forest Way. Ph: 02 6588 5555

114. Brushy Mountain Campground - North East
Map Ref: MAP 1 H7   GPS: 31 08 49 S 152 21 41 E
Located in Werrikimbe NP. Signposted access along Hastings Forest Way 47km NW of Wauchope. Dry weather only Ph: 02 6586 8300

115. Wild Bull Camping Area
Map Ref: MAP 1 H8   GPS: 31 14 43 S 152 30 46 E
42km NW of Wauchope signposted off the Cobrabald Rd in the Mt Boss State Forest. Dry weather only Ph: 02 9871 3377

116. Bluff picnic and camping area
Map Ref: MAP 1 H8   GPS: 31 14 33 S 152 31 35 E
Located inn the Mt Boss State Forest. Signposted access along Cobrabald Rd 1.4km N of Wild Bull Park camping area. Ph: 02 6585 3744

117. Gumma Crossing Reserve
Map Ref: MAP 1 J7   GPS: 30 42 24 S 152 59 00 E
Camp are 7km E of Macksville. Turn E off Pacific Hwy S of bridge at Macksville onto Partridge St then onto Gumma Rd for 5km. 2km dirt road. Narrow access. Ph: 02 6568 2555

118. Smoky Cape camping area - Mid North Coast
Map Ref: MAP 1 J7   GPS: 30 55 44 S 153 04 38 E
9km SE of South West Rocks via Arakoon and Lighthouse Rds. First class fishing. Ph: 02 6566 6168

119. Hungry Gate camping area - Mid North Coast
Map Ref: MAP 1 J7   GPS: 31 04 44 S 153 02 30 E
5km S of Hat Head village access via Hungry Road off The Gap Rd. Ph: 02 6566 6168

120. Racecourse Campground - North Coast
Map Ref: MAP 1 H8   GPS: 31 14 57 S 152 57 36 E
Located in Goolwah Reserve 8km south of Crescent Head. Signposted access along Point Plomer Rd. Bring water & firewood. Ph: 02 6563 1983

121. Delicate Beach Camping Area - North Coast
Map Ref: MAP 1 J8   GPS: 31 15 37 S 152 58 05 E
Located in Goolwah Reserve 12km south of Crescent Head. Signposted access along Point Plomer Rd. Bring water & firewood. Ph: 02 6563 1983

122. Point Plomer Camping Area - North Coast
Map Ref: MAP 1 H8   GPS: 31 18 46 S 152 58 16 E
Located in Limeburners Creek Nature Reserve 12kms south of Crescent Head along Point Plomer Rd. Bring drinking water & firewood. Ph: 02 6566 6168

123. Mendooran Rest Area - Central West
Map Ref: MAP 1 B8   GPS: 31 49 28 S 149 06 52 E
Mendoran is 75kms from Dubbo - 71kms from Coonabarabran and 56kms from Gilgandra in the central West. Ph: 1800 242 881

124. Binnaway Pumphouse Camping Ground - North East
Map Ref: MAP 1 C8   GPS: 31 33 08 S 149 22 43 E
35km south of Coonabarabran. Located in Bullinda Street on the bank of the Castlereagh River. Ph: 1800 242 881

125. Coxs Creek - Central West
Map Ref: MAP 1 D8   GPS: 31 43 57 S 150 00 39 E
Situated in the Coolah Tops NP 32km E of Coolah. Coolah Creek Rd leads you to the parks main entrance then turn off Forest Rd on to Pinnacle Rd. Ph: 02 6372 7199

126. The Barracks Campground - Central West
Map Ref: MAP 1 D8   GPS: 31 43 50 S 150 00 55 E
275kms NW from Newcastle. Follow the Golden Hwy to Coolah then E along Coolah Creek Rd. Sections are unsealed. Ph: 02 6372 7199

127. Bald Hill - Central West
Map Ref: MAP 1 D8   GPS: 31 45 25 S 150 00 45 E
Via Bald Hills Rd off Hildegard Rd from Forest Rd. Ph: 02 6372 7199

128. The Pines Campground - Central West
Map Ref: MAP 1 D8   GPS: 31 44 51 S 150 01 50 E
Located in Coolah Tops NP. Camp Area 37km NW of Coolah via Hildegarde Rd. Ph: 02 6372 7199

Featured Campsite

Brought to you by

Mendooran Rest Area No 123

Mendooran, NSW

56 kilometres east of Gilgandra

Barbara and Kevin Weimer

Mendooran free campsite - not too squeezy.

Mendooran, on the banks of the Castlereagh River in Central North-West NSW provides travellers with a quiet place to stay a night or two. This free campsite is a large, flat, grassy rest area at the end of the main street. Shade gum trees line the river edge and the largest rigs would have no difficulty finding a suitable spot.

Facilities include covered picnic tables and barbecues. There are flushing toilets and a cold water shower, both of which at the time of our visit were in need of a clean. A notice board advertises meals at the local pub and lists places in the near vicinity worth visiting. The village is a short walk from the riverfront rest area. In addition to the pub and shops, a bowling club, a 9-hole golf course, an RSL club and tennis courts all service the town and surrounding rural area.

Mendooran offers a peaceful centrally located diversion via good roads for travellers on the Mitchell, Oxley, Newell, Castlereagh and Golden Highways. The iconic poet, Banjo Paterson, in his poem "The Travelling Post Office," makes reference to "Mundooran," an early spelling of Mendooran, which was the first town on the Castlereagh River. Settled in the 1840s, this quaint village still retains its old-time charm and traditional wide streets. However, as has happened in many small rural communities, some businesses have closed down. A few years ago, in an effort to bring more tourists into town, over ten colourful murals, depicting scenes from local history and rural life, were painted on the walls of buildings in the main street, making Mendooran one of the iconic mural towns of NSW. Today, the murals would benefit from a face lift.

One of the Mendooran town murals.

Fishing for yellow belly, catfish and carp is a popular pastime on the Castlereagh River. Bait is available at the newsagency. The area is also popular with fossickers. Agate, petrified wood and jasper have been found and recommendations for possible fossicking sites can be gained from the gem and herb shop in Bundulla Street.

Close by is the small village of Merrygoen, where a number of scenes from the ABC mini-series "The Leaving of Liverpool" were shot. Gilgandra is also a short drive away where a day trip could include a visit to the Coo-ee Heritage Centre with its wonderful eclectic range of arts and crafts. Another worthwhile day trip is to Dubbo and the Western Plains Zoo, perhaps hiring a tandem bicycle to ride the 6 km loop road that runs through the zoo.

Coolah Tops National Park and the Warrumbungle National Park are both within easy reach from Mendooran. Coolah Tops features a picturesque landscape of tall eucalypt forests, giant grass trees, scenic views and great bushwalks, while the Warrumbungles are famous for their volcanic outcrops, spectacular rock formations and magnificent bushwalks.

Mendooran rest area is a pleasant peaceful spot to rest and refresh before continuing your travels.

Castlereagh River runs past the campsites.

Just The Facts

Mendooran Rest Area

Getting there: Mendooran is 75 kilometres from Dubbo, 71 kilometres from Coonabarabran and 56 kilometres from Gilgandra in the Central West of NSW.

Facilities: There are covered picnic tables, flushing toilets and cold showers.

Wheelchair Access: Nothing specific, although the area is flat.

Rates: Free.

Pets: Pets are permitted.

Contact: Warrumbungle Shire Council www.warrumbunglewired.com.au Phone: 1800 242 881

129. Walshpools Camping Area - Hunter Region
Map Ref: MAP 1 E9 GPS: 31 54 07 S 150 47 07 E
Towarri NP is located 20 morth west of Scone. From Scone take Tourist Drive 27 for 1.5km then turn into signposted Middlebrrok Rd. Signposted access 3.8km north of its junction with Cressfield Rd then 130m to camping area. Bring water. Ph: 02 6540 2300

130. Burning Mountain Reserve
Map Ref: MAP 1 E9 GPS: 31 51 21 S 150 53 58 E
On New England Hwy, Wingen 10kms S of Blandford. 200m in from highway on sloping parking area. Check all signs. Ph: 13 22 13

131. Woolomin Reserve - New England
Map Ref: MAP 1 F7 GPS: 31 18 13 S 151 08 51 E
Camp Area at Woolomin. Beside Peel River 21km N of Nundle. Access via Fossicker's Way. Ph: 02 6764 2243

132. Bowling Alley Point Recreation Reserve - New England
Map Ref: MAP 1 F8 GPS: 31 21 34 S 151 08 00 E
Located 14km north west of Nundle and 45km south east of Tamworth on foreshor of Chaffey Dam. Signposted access on the Fissickers Way. Ph: 02 6769 3374

133. Swamp Creek - North East
Map Ref: MAP 1 F8 GPS: 31 26 15 S 151 08 40 E
Located 4km N of Nundle. Beside Peel River. Ph: 02 6764 5100

134. Teamsters Rest Campground - New England
Map Ref: MAP 1 E8 GPS: 31 33 24 S 151 03 22 E
14km S of Nundle via Crawney Rd. Camping on the banks of the Wombramurra Creek. Dry weather only. Ph: 02 6764 5100

135. Sheba Dams Camping Area - North East
Map Ref: MAP 1 F8 GPS: 31 29 58 S 151 11 47 E
11km from Nundle which is 400km north of Sydney via the New England Hwy and about 70km south of Tamworth. Ph: 02 6764 5100

136. Ponderosa Park - New England
Map Ref: MAP 1 F8 GPS: 31 27 48 S 151 15 25 E
Located within Hanging Rock SF. Camp Area 17km E of Nundle. Turn N off Hanging Rock Rd after 8 km onto Forest Way. Dirt road - dry weather only. Ph: 02 6777 4100

137. Jacky Barkers Camp Ground
Map Ref: MAP 1 F8 GPS: 31 35 30 S 151 43 28 E
Located in Nowendoc NP 13km S of Nowendoc via Thunderbolts Way and Wrights Rd. 4WD vehicles only. Ph: 02 6777 4700

138. New Country Swamp - North East
Map Ref: MAP 1 G8 GPS: 31 19 45 S 151 52 09 E
In the Mummel Gulf NP Signposted access 13km along Enfield Forest Rd. Signposted off the Oxley Hwy. Ph: 02 6777 4700

139. The Cells Camping Area - Mid North Coast
Map Ref: MAP 1 G8 GPS: 31 27 13 S 152 05 58 E
Beside the Cells River 8km W of Knodingbul Rd via Blue Mountain Creek Rd in the Cells State Conservation Area. Ph: 02 6588 5555

140. Maxwells Flat - North East
Map Ref: MAP 1 G8 GPS: 31 29 20 S 152 11 20 E
Situated in the Cootan-Bimbang NP. Reached via Causeway Rd off Knodingbul Rd. 9km S of Oxley Hwy. Ph: 1300 655 687

141. Ellenborough West campsite
Map Ref: MAP 1 H8 GPS: 31 26 25 S 152 27 40 E
Located at Ellenborough west of Wauchope. 500m N of highway on east side of bridge next to the Hastings River.

142. Dingo Tops Camping Area - North Coast
Map Ref: MAP 1 G8 GPS: 31 40 01 S 152 08 38 E
Within Tapin Tops NP 30kms northwest of Wingham. Access is via Knodingbul Rd off the Oxley Hwy. Camp area located at junction of Knodingbul Rd & Dingo Tops Rd via the Wherrol Flat Rd. Bring drinking water & firewood. Ph: 02 6552 4097

143. The Rapids Camping Area - North Coast
Map Ref: MAP 1 G8 GPS: 31 35 35 S 152 15 38 E
Elands Village is located 35kms north of Wingham and access is 2.1kms along Rapids Rd signposted 7.4kms north of Elands General Store. Overnight only. Bring water & firewood. Ph: 02 6550 4440

144. Swans Crossing camping area - North Coast
Map Ref: MAP 1 H8 GPS: 31 36 30 S 152 34 55 E
Camp area located 16km NW of Kendall. From the Kendall-Lorne Rd onto the signposted Upsalls Creek Rd. Ph: 1300 655 687

Featured Campsite

Brought to you by

Sheba Dams Camping Area No 135

Hanging Rock, New South Wales

11km from Nundle, NSW
Stephanie Jackson

THE tiny NSW town of Nundle has a reputation for being a bitterly cold spot in winter.

It's even colder, locals said, at the settlement of Hanging Rock that sits on the summit of the ranges that rise sharply beyond Nundle.

When we arrived there at four in the afternoon, it was obvious that they were right.

The sun had cast its warming rays across the streets of Nundle but at Hanging Rock and the nearby Sheba Dams snow that had fallen during the previous night lay thick on the ground in patches of shade.

Our decision to camp beside the Sheba Dams meant we were in for a cold, cold night.

But, determined to tough it out and camp in what is unquestionably a quiet and attractive location, we set about collecting wood for a fire that would keep us from shivering too intensely in the hours before we hit the sack.

Other firewood scavengers had been there before us but we gathered a considerable heap of twigs that, with the wood we had brought with us, would keep the cold at bay.

The travelling clock/thermometer that had been in our campervan's glove box registered a pleasant 14 degrees but in the outside air that figure rapidly fell to eight, to four, to two, and eventually to an icy minus-two degrees by six in the evening.

Sulphur crested cockatoos screamed as the sun took its final bow for the day.

And, as the cold bit into fingers that were briefly ungloved as we ate our evening meal, it was obvious that, even with the insulation provided by our sleeping bags with their stuffing of goose down, this would be an uncomfortably cold night.

We survived the night and woke to see patches of snow still scattered across the landscape.

A small fire soon sent glimmers of warmth into the air and I was eager to launch my kayak and paddle about on the waters of the small dam.

Sunrise changed the olive foliage of the forest to a warm golden hue.

But as winds whipped up the surface and flecks of snow drifted through the air, that plan was promptly cancelled.

We scoffed our hot porridge as we warmed ourselves by our small fire, then took a stroll along the 12km track that leads through the forests that hem the larger of the two dams that is next to the camping area.

Gold had been discovered near Hanging Rock in 1851 and, in 1888, with picks and shovels and horse-drawn earthmoving equipment, gangs of men began to excavate the two dams to meet the increasing demand for water for mining operations.

In merely three weeks, the earthen walled dams, with a total surface area of 36 hectares, were completed.

Today, their sole purpose is to provide pleasure for visitors who come to fish for the trout and salmon with which the largest of the dams is regularly stocked, and to camp and picnic on its shaded banks.

The dam, beside the camping area, is set among eucalypt forest.

The majority of the birds that normally inhabit the forest that envelopes the dams were nowhere to be seen.

Only a solitary kookaburra, seemingly frozen to its perch on a branch overhanging the water, put in an appearance.

We were frozen, too, but despite the icy wind and biting cold, our brief stay at Sheba Dams, a place we had visited in more pleasant weather, was once again a memorable experience.

Just The Facts

Sheba Dams Camping Area

Where: Nundle is about 400km north of Sydney via the New England Highway, and about 70km south of Tamworth

Facilities: There are picnic tables and pit toilets at Sheba Dams. There is a general store at Nundle and fuel is available in the town.

Wheelchair access: Nothing specific.

Rates: There is no charge for camping at Sheba Dams.

Pets: Pets are permitted at the camping area.

Contact: For additional regional information contact the Nundle General Store on (02) 6769 3374.

145. Diamond Head Camping Area - North Coast
Map Ref: MAP 1 H9 GPS: 31 43 08 S 152 47 41 E
Signposted access on Diamond Head Rd 9km south of Laurieton in Crowdy Bay NP. Drive 200m to camping area with beach frontage. Bring water & firewood. Ph: 02 6586 8300

146. Coopernook Forest Park - Mid North Coast
Map Ref: MAP 1 H9 GPS: 31 47 25 S 152 36 40 E
Located in Coopernook SF 5km W of Moorland. Turn onto Forest Rd for 4km to camp area. Ph: 1300 655 687

147. Crowdy Gap Cultural Camp - North Coast
Map Ref: MAP 1 H9 GPS: 31 49 57 S 152 43 48 E
Located in Crowdy Bay NP 5km south of Laurieton with signposted access on Crowdy Bay Rd 6km south of Coralville Rd. Bring water & firewood. Ph: 02 6586 8300

148. Farquhar Park Reserve Camping Area - North Coast
Map Ref: MAP 1 H9 GPS: 31 56 39 S 152 36 32 E
Located 8km south of Manning Point near mouth of Manning River in Manning Entrance State Park. Bring drinking water & firewood. Ph: 02 6552 1900

149. Cooyal Hotel
Map Ref: MAP 1 C9 GPS: 32 26 27 S 149 47 18 E
Camp area at 1765 Wollar Rd, Cooyal on N side of road. Register at bar and pre-book. Donation Ph: 02 6373 5353

150. The Drip - Central West
Map Ref: MAP 1 C9 GPS: 32 13 14 S 149 47 37 E
50kms N of Mudgee along the Ulan-Cassilis Rd. Turn right 50m past the cement bridge over the Goulburn at 'The Drip" sign. Ph: 1800 816 304

151. Spring Gully Camp Ground - Central West
Map Ref: MAP 1 D9 GPS: 32 14 32 S 150 02 44 E
Located in Goulburn River NP 15km NW of Wollar via Mogo Rd. Dry weather only. Ph: 02 6372 7199

152. Big River Campground- Central West
Map Ref: MAP 1 D9 GPS: 32 14 26 S 150 03 34 E
From Wollar take the Mogo Rd NE for approx 15kms to park entrance. From Mudgee take the Wollar Rd for 38kms. Ph: 02 6548 2340

153. Lake Liddell Recreation Airea - Hunter Region
Map Ref: MAP 1 D9 GPS: 32 21 03 S 150 29 47 E
16kms S of Muswellbrook along the Hebden Rd from its junction with the New England Highway. Ph: 02 6541 2010

154. Jerry Plains Recreation Ground
Map Ref: MAP 1 E10 GPS: 32 29 52 S 150 54 36 E
Located south end of town of Jerry Plains.

155. Bridge Reserve - Williams River Holiday Park camping area - Hunter Region
Map Ref: MAP 1 E10 GPS: 32 34 55 S 151 00 50 E
On The banks of the Williams River at east end of Clarence Town. Access is off Durham St. Locked gate access. Check times. Bookings recommended Ph: 02 4996 4231

156. Bulga Recreation Ground
Map Ref: MAP 1 E10 GPS: 32 39 12 S 151 01 06 E
Parking area on The Inlet Rd, Bulga 22km SW of Singleton. Ph: 02 6578 7290

157. Glennies Creek Camp
Map Ref: MAP 1 E10 GPS: 32 27 36 S 151 07 04 E
Camp area 18kms NW of Singleton. Travel NW oh Singleton Hwy for 16km then N to Glennies Creek Rd for 4km, then E for 650m to creek side. Small vehicles only. Ph: 02 6578 7290

158. Belmadar camping area - Hunter Region
Map Ref: MAP 1 F9 GPS: 31 55 25 S 151 14 12 E
On the Hunter River in the historic village of Moonan Flat. Hotel nearby. Ph: 02 6546 3130

159. Cologolies (Moonan Outlook) camping area
Map Ref: MAP 1 F9 GPS: 31 55 47 S 151 20 46 E
Located in Stewart Brook SF at western boundary of Barrington Tops NP along Boundary Rd signposted off Barrington Tops Forest Rd. Dry weather only. Ph: 1300 655 687

160. Horse Swamp camping area
Map Ref: MAP 1 F9 GPS: 31 55 36 S 151 23 14 E
Signposted on Tubrabucca Rd 2.3kms NE of Barrington Tops Forest Rd. Ph: 02 6540 2300

The Drip Goulburn River Reserve No 150

Central West NSW
50kms north of Mudgee
Glenn Gilligan

The first time we visited "The Drip" we had travelled from Newcastle through Denman and we were heading to Mudgee on the Ulan – Cassilis Road when we saw the sign "The Drip Picnic Area" and as it was lunchtime we decided to investigate.

This small reserve has space for about six campers on flat sites and is approximately 100m off the road. There are picnic tables, garbage bins and a drop toilet. The camping area is situated just above the Goulburn River, which is really a shallow stream but can flood in heavy rain.

While the camping area is a great overnighter the highlight is the 2.7km walk along the river to "The Dripping Wall" and is about an hour return walk. It is an easy grade walking trail that leads you through sandstone cliffs riddled with caves which shelter weeping ferns. The gorge walls tower above and are made of sedimentary rock, many of which are honeycombed. The area harbours a great range of flora and fauna. The bottle brush were a striking red and activity was evident around the wombat holes along the track.

When you reach "The Dripping Wall" it is an amazing site. It rises sheer to the sky and the orange rock is covered with grasses, mosses and ferns which are fed constantly by the dripping water seeping from the plateau above. It is a great place to sit and enjoy the ambience, swim, rock hop, explore or take a photo or two. The river continues on gurgling over the huge rocks and you can explore down river as far as your energy levels allow.

Brett Whitely, the famous Australian artist camped here with his family in the 1970s and apparently stripped off and painted aboriginal designs under an overhang. It was to pay homage to aboriginal art in the area. The paintings have survived a number of floods but you have to know where to look. We have never found them.

We were so impressed with this scenic area we decided to stay the night. It is a great spot as the road isn't very busy. Many people believe that "The Drip" is situated in the Goulburn River National Park but this is not the case. The National Park is situated downstream from the "The Dripping Wall". "The Drip" was originally on Crown Land but is now controlled by Moolarben Coal, whose plans for the area are still unclear. I hope their mining plans don't interfere with this wonderful icon.

About 3km up the road you will find "Hands on Rock" which is an historic aboriginal site. You will see a sign Bobadeen Road and you won't see the "Hands on Rock" sign until you turn onto this gravel road. It can be a bit confusing. This area was used by aboriginals as a major trading route between the coast and the western plains. From the carpark you follow the walking track for about 600m through natural bushland past grass trees and banksias to the boardwalk and heritage cave. The cave bears evidence of ancient hand stencils created by spraying red, white and yellow clay pigments with the mouth over a hand held against the rock. It is easy to envisage the activity of the aboriginal people who hundreds of years ago sat around fires, painted the walls, sheltered from the sun and cooked their meals.

Since our first visit to "The Drip", we have returned a couple of times in our travels west and we would recommend you do too. Even if you don't stay overnight, just drop into The Drip' for a cuppa and do the magnificent walk, you will be amazed.

The track beside the Goulburn River leading to "the Drip".

Just The Facts

The Drip Goulburn River Reserve

Getting there: 50km north of Mudgee along the Ulan-Cassilis Road. 37km from Gulgong and 10km north of Ulan Mine. Turn right 50m past the small cement bridge over the Goulburn River at "The Drip" Picnic Area sign.

Facilities: Drop toilet, picnic tables, approximately 6 campsites and garbage bins.

Wheelchair Access: No special facilities but the camping area is flat.

Rates: Free.

Pets: Pets not allowed.

Contact: Mudgee Visitor Information Centre.
Ph 1800 816 304 or
www.visitmudgeeregion.com.au
Gulgong Visitor Information Centre.
Ph (02) 6374 2691
National Parks and Wildlife Service.
Mudgee Ph (02) 6370 9000
www.environment.nsw.gov.au or
www.nationalparks.nsw.gov.au
Mudgee Region Tourist Booklet.
Ph 1800 816 304 for a free copy.

Free Campsites in New South Wales

161. Manning River - Hunter Region
Map Ref: MAP 1 F9   GPS: 31 52 36 S 151 29 38 E
Access off Pheasant Creek Rd 15km W of the junction of Dilgry Circle and Barrington Tops Forest Rd. Located in the Barrington Tops State Forest. Ph: 1300 655 687

162. Gummi Falls Camping Area - Hunter Region
Map Ref: MAP 1 F9   GPS: 31 54 10 S 151 28 07 E
Within the Barrington Tops NP 45km west of Gloucester. Located 2.8km along Bullock Brush Rd which is signposted off Tubrabucca Rd. Dry weather only. Bring water & firewood. Ph: 02 6540 2300

163. Dilgry River Camping Area - Hunter Region
Map Ref: MAP 1 F9   GPS: 31 53 38 S 151 31 33 E
Camp beside the Dilgry River via the Dilgry Circle Rd within the Barrington Tops SF. Ph: 1300 655 687

164. Banksia Camping Area - Hunter Region
Map Ref: MAP 1 F9   GPS: 31 53 20 S 151 32 17 E
Camp beside the Dilgry River. Access along the Dilgry Circle Rd. Ph: 1300 655 687

165. Devils Hole campground - Hunter Region
Map Ref: MAP 1 F9   GPS: 31 54 58 S 151 28 59 E
Signposted access along Barrington Tops Forest Road. West of Dilgry Circle Rd Turn-off. Ph: 02 6538 5300

167. Lake St Clair Park - Hunter Region
Map Ref: MAP 1 F9   GPS: 32 20 04 S 151 17 30 E
35kms N of Singleton on the eastern shore of the Lake via Bridgemann Rd. Ph: 02 6577 3370

167. Polblue camping area
Map Ref: MAP 1 F9   GPS: 31 57 41 S 151 25 56 E
68kms W of Gloucester and signposted along the Barrington Tops Forest Rd. Ph: 02 6540 2300

168. Little Murray Camping Area - Hunter Region
Map Ref: MAP 1 F9   GPS: 31 58 53 S 151 27 30 E
Signposted access along Barrington Trail which is signposted off Barrington Tops Forest Rd. Access track is signposted 4.5km south of the Forest Rd. Ph: 02 6538 5300

169. Junction Pools campground -Hunter Region
Map Ref: MAP 1 F9   GPS: 32 01 48 S 151 26 36 E
Located beside the Barrington River from the Barrington Trail which is signposted off Barrington Tops Forest Road. Dry weather only. Ph: 02 6538 5300

170. White Rock camping Area. - Hunter Region
Map Ref: MAP 1 F9   GPS: 32 07 49 S 151 29 08 E
Located in the Barrington Tops NP. Accessed off Allyn River Rd which is signposted along Allyn River Forest Rd. Ph: 1300 655 687

171. Pademelon Park camping area - Hunter Region
Map Ref: MAP 1 F9   GPS: 32 09 23 S 151 29 05 E
Situated in Chichester SF. Located on Mt Allyn Forest Rd which is signposted off Allyn River Forest Rd. Ph: 1300 655 687

172. Old Camp - Hunter Region
Map Ref: MAP 1 F9   GPS: 32 09 40 S 151 29 30 E
Past Dobbie Rim camp ground along the Allyn River Rd which is reached via Salisbury Gap Rd W of Salisbury. Ph: 1300 655 687

173. Dobbie Rim - Hunter Region
Map Ref: MAP 1 F9   GPS: 32 09 40 S 151 29 32 E
Signposted access along Allyn River Forest Rd in the Chichester State Forest Ph: 1300 655 687

174. Gloucester River campground - Hunter Region
Map Ref: MAP 1 F9   GPS: 32 03 30 S 151 41 01 E
Signposted access on Gloucester Tops Rd 24km W of Bucketts Way. Ph: 02 6538 5300

175. Woko Camping Area - Hunter Region
Map Ref: MAP 1 G9   GPS: 31 48 01 S 151 47 32 E
Woko NP is situated 30km north west of Gloucester. Aaccess is via Curricabark Rd off Thunderbolts Way (Gloucester-Nowendoc Rd). Access is signposted off Thunderbolts Way 10.9km north of Gloucester-Sconee Rd. Bring water & firewood. Ph: 02 6538 5300

176. Bretti Reserve - Mid North Coast
Map Ref: MAP 1 G9   GPS: 31 47 24 S 151 54 01 E
North of Gloucester on Thunderbolts Way beside Manning River. Ph: 02 6558 1408

177. Rocks Crossing Reserve - North Coast
Map Ref: MAP 1 G9 GPS: 31 46 08 S 152 04 31 E
Signposted access on Nowendoc Rd - 21km NW of Mount George village which is 21km W of Wingham. Ph: 02 6552 1900

178. Gloryvale Reserve - Mid North Coast
Map Ref: MAP 1 G9 GPS: 31 51 31 S 151 52 56 E
23km N of Gloucester along the Thunderbolts Way beside Manning River. Dry weather only. Ph: 02 6558 1408

179. Copeland Reserve - Mid North Coast
Map Ref: MAP 1 G9 GPS: 31 58 22 S 151 51 42 E
13 km W of Gloucester along the Gloucester-Scone Rd. Ph: 02 6558 1408

180. Frying Pan Creek Camping Area - Hunter Region
Map Ref: MAP 1 F9 GPS: 32 13 07 S 151 45 42 E
Located 33kms north of Dungog. Accessed via the unsealed Chichester Dam Road. Dry weather only. Ph: 02 4927 0977

181. Telegherry Forest Park - Hunter Region
Map Ref: MAP 1 F9 GPS: 32 13 30 S 151 44 52 E
On the banks of the Telegherry River. Signposted off Middle Ridge Rd - 4.5km past Frying Pan camping area in Chichester State Forest. Dry weather only. Ph: 1300 655 687

182. The Knob picnic & camping area
Map Ref: MAP 1 F9 GPS: 32 15 31 S 151 45 22 E
From Dungog go N to Stroud and take signposted Monkerai Rd until you reach Main Creek Rd. Follow to Skimming Gap Rd 2.6km N of junction with Frying Pan Rd. Ph: 1300 655 687

183. Gumleaf Hut - Hunter Region
Map Ref: MAP 1 G9 GPS: 32 15 44 E 151 45 27 E
Within Chichester SF. Signposted access on Skimming Gap Rd 1.7km west of its junction with Frying Pan Rd. Ph: 1300 655 687

184. Coachwood Camping Area
Map Ref: MAP 1 F9 GPS: 32 12 58 S 151 45 39 E
Located off Frying Pan Rd 2.5km E of Middle Ridge Rd. Beautiful camp area on the bank of the Telegherry River. Dry weather only Ph: 02 4927 0977

185. Currawong camping area - Chester State Forest - Hunter Region
Map Ref: MAP 1 G9 GPS: 32 13 12 S 151 44 42 E
4WD only as you need to cross Telegherry River. Closed during winter with the wetter months. Dry weather only Ph: 02 9871 3377

186. Wards Glen camping area - Mid North Coast
Map Ref: MAP 1 G9 GPS: 32 10 42 S 152 00 40 E
Situated in the Glen Nature Reserve 25km SE of Gloucester reached of Glen Rd via Bucketts Way. Ph: 02 4984 8200

187. Blueberry Mill camping area
Map Ref: MAP 1 G10 GPS: 32 18 28 S 152 05 11 E
Located 10km NW of Bulahdelah and 6km E of Stroud in the Myall River SF. Area is along Johnsons Creek Rd close to Mammy Johnsons River. Ph: 02 4997 4981

188. Strike a Light Campground - Hunter Region
Map Ref: MAP 1 G10 GPS: 32 17 41 S 152 05 30 E
Within the Myall River SF. Camp Area 24km SNW of Bulahdelah. Via Cabbage Tree Creek & Strike a Light Rds. Ph: 02 4997 4981

189. Wallingat River camping area - Hunter Region
Map Ref: MAP 1 G10 GPS: 32 19 39 S 152 24 10 E
Access off the Lakes Way via Sugar Creek Rd then in to River Rd. Ph: 02 6591 0300

190. The Ruins Camping Area - Hunter Region
Map Ref: MAP 1 H10 GPS: 32 18 37 E 152 31 07 E
Located within Booti Booti NP 16km south of Forster. Camp area situated at the southern end of Seven Mile Beach and signposted access along The Lakes Way. Ph: 02 6591 0300

191. Branxton Oval
Map Ref: MAP 1 F10 GPS: 32 39 18 S 151 21 05 E
Parking are 400m north of PO on John Rose Ave, Branxton. Limited stay Ph: 02 4993 6700

192. Wharf Reserve
Map Ref: MAP 1 F10 GPS: 32 35 25 S 151 46 38 E
Located on Rifle Street - Clarence Town. Ph: 02 4996 4231

Frying Pan Creek Camping Area No 180

Chichester State Forest, Vic

33km north of Dunog

Stephanie Jackson

Telegherry River at the Frying Pan Creek camping area.

After several days spent exploring towns and villages I'd had enough of urban life and was eager to escape to the bush, and when an elderly woman at the museum in the NSW town of Dungog suggested I should visit the nearby Chichester State Forest, I leapt at the idea as quickly as a ravenous fox snatches a dozing hen from its perch.

The forest covers around 15,000 hectares, and my new friend reckoned that if I set up camp at the Frying Pan Creek camping area, 33kms from Dungog, a quiet and relaxing escape from urban life would be guaranteed. And it didn't take me long to realise that she was right.

The journey to the camping area took a considerable time however, for the unsealed road, with its rough and stony surface and hairpin bends, demanded cautious driving, and I'd been warned that the greatest danger was from wallabies leaping out from the shadows of the forest.

At mid afternoon, beyond a landscape congested with tall flooded gums, tangled vines, tree ferns, and moss coated logs, I arrived at the camping area - a large grassy clearing beside the Telegherry River that is merely a shallow stream. It would offer a welcome chance to cool off on a summer's day, but with the weather too cold to even dip my toes into the fast flowing water, I opted to simply sit back and take it easy for the rest of the day.

There are no facilities here other than pit toilets – but with no charge for camping, it's certainly good value. Firewood can be collected in the forest, but should always be done in a way that has a negligible impact on the environment, and I was disgusted to see that previous campers had cut down saplings on the bank of the creek, only to find that green timber doesn't burn. I scrounged the more useful firewood that other campers had generously left behind, lit a small fire, and sat back with a cuppa to watch the antics of the neighbours. Currawongs, scrub turkeys, eastern yellow robins, and crimson rosellas all dropped by, bellbirds twittered among the dense vegetation, and satin bower birds scrounged for anything blue with which to decorate their well concealed bowers.

Another camper, a resident of Dungog, arrived to warn me that packs of wild dogs frequently roam throughout the forest. He'd heard them howling and barking outside his caravan the previous night, and he warned me, in a neighbourly way, to ensure that I didn't leave any food scraps outside at night that would attract either the dogs or the large goannas that inhabit the forest..

The camping area is close to the road that slices through the forest, but with few vehicles passing this way, the night was draped in silence that was torn apart only by the snarling sounds of a possum and the repetitious hooting of a boobook owl.

Night temperatures in the region can be extremely cold from June through to November, and dawn arrived with an anticipated icy bite, and as I emerged into the crisp morning air, corellas screeched a warning of my presence, and a camper, wandering past with an armful of firewood, called out a cheerful 'G'day'.

This was a place where it was easy to pass the hours doing little more than watching the birds, chatting with new friends, and exploring through the forest to see what wonders it concealed. And with the Chichester dam only 13kms away, and the picturesque Jerusalem Creek falls, in the adjacent Barrington Tops National Park, being on my must-see list, I was in no hurry to leave the Frying Pan and jump back to the hustle and bustle of urban life.

Just The Facts

Frying Pan Creek Camping Area

Getting there: The camping area is 33kms north of Dungog, which is 215kms north-east of Sydney, and is accessed via the Chichester Dam Road. The road is unsealed, and while it is suitable for all vehicles in dry weather, it may become impassable in wet weather.

Facilities: There are no facilities other than pit toilets. There is ample room for large vehicles and rigs.

Pets: Pets are permitted.

Charges: There is no charge for camping here.

Contact: For additional information, phone the NSW Forests Information Line on 1300 655 687 or contact the Dungog Visitor Information Centre by phoning (02) 4992 2212 or by logging onto www.visitdungog.com.au.

Free Campsites in New South Wales

193. Tattersalls camping area - Karuah Nature Park - Hunter Region
Map Ref: MAP 1 G10 GPS: 32 35 08 S 151 58 06 E
Located on the Karuah River. Access is via Hobart Rd from Limeburners Creek. Access via 4WD only. Self-sufficient campers only. Ph: 02 4984 8200

194. Double Wharf campground - Mid North Coast
Map Ref: MAP 1 G10 GPS: 32 34 44 S 151 57 50 E
On the banks of the Caruah River in the Caruah Nature Reserve. By Googes Rd off Hobarts Forest Rd. Dry weather only Ph: 02 4984 8200

195. Little Mountain camping area - Karuah Nature Park - Hunter Region
Map Ref: MAP 1 G10 GPS: 32 36 21 S 151 56 45 E
Off Buckets Way. Just N of Limburners Creek. Ph: 02 4984 8200

196. Violet Hill Camping Area - Hunter Region
Map Ref: MAP 1 G10 GPS: 32 28 14 S 152 19 36 E
Signposted access 1.7km south of Bungarie Bay at the end of Violet Hill Rd off The Lakes Way. Bring water & firewood. Ph: 02 6591 0300

197. White Tree Bay Camping Area - Hunter Region
Map Ref: MAP 1 G10 GPS: 32 31 39 S 152 19 26 E
Within Myall Lakes NP signposted access along Mungo Brush Rd 22km north of Hawks Nest. Bring water. Ph: 02 6591 0300

198. Abermain Bowl & Recreation Club
Map Ref: MAP 1 F10 GPS: 32 48 26 S 151 25 36 E
10kms W of Kurri Kurri on corner of Goulburn & Armidale Sts, Abermain. Parking area beside club. Ph: 02 4930 4285

199. Stockton Beach bush camping - Hunter Region
Map Ref: MAP 1 F10 GPS: 32 50 03 S 151 52 18 E
Do not camp on vegetated dunes. Access via Lavis Lane off the Nelson Bay Rd. Ph: 02 4984 8200

200. Ponto Falls
Map Ref: MAP 2 C4 GPS: 32 27 57 S 148 49 12 E
Located 19kn NW of Wellington. Turn W off Mitchell Hwy travel 10km. Take dirt road to campsites along river. Maximum stay applies.

201. Cudgegong Waters Park - Central West
Map Ref: MAP 2 E5 GPS: 32 48 43 S 149 49 24 E
Located at Windamere Dam 24km south east of Mudgee. Camp area is 1km east of Castlereagh Hwy and 20km west of Rylstone. Access is signposted off the hwy 35km south of Mudgee and 19km north of Ilford. Bring firewood. Ph: 02 6358 8462

202. Dunns Swamp camping area - Hunter Region
Map Ref: MAP 2 F5 GPS: 32 50 08 S 150 12 26 E
25km E of Rylstone with access signposted along Narrango Rd. Ph: 02 6372 7199

203. Kelgoola picnic and camping area - Central West
Map Ref: MAP 2 F5 GPS: 32 51 34 S 150 18 51 E
Located in the Coricudgy State Forest 34km E of Rylstone camping ground is less than 2km NE of forest gate via Narango Rd from Rylstone. Ph: 1300 655 687

204. Federal Falls camping area - Mount Canobolas State Conservation Area - Central West
Map Ref: MAP 2 C6 GPS: 33 20 56 S 148 58 41 E
Follow Pinnacle Rd from Orange and turn onto Towac Rd. Ph: 02 6332 7640

205. Four Mile Creek - Central West
Map Ref: MAP 2 C6 GPS: 33 24 56 S 148 59 09 E
Camp Area 23km SW of Orange via Peosley and Forest Rds. Cadia Rd. Giles Rd & Four Mile Creek Rd. Located in Canobolas State Forest. Ph: 02 9871 3377

206. The Junction Campground - Central West
Map Ref: MAP 2 C6 GPS: 33 10 11 S 149 14 22 E
Camp Area 26km NE of Orange via Ophir Rd or Punds Rd. Steep sections. Ph: 1800 069 466

207. Heritage Grove - Central West
Map Ref: MAP 2 D6 GPS: 33 24 34 S 149 18 44 E
Located 29km W of Bathurst via Cashens Lane off the Mitchell Hwy. Ph: 1300 655 687

208. Macquaire Woods - Central West
Map Ref: MAP 2 D6 GPS: 33 24 35 S 149 18 44 E
Camp Area 28km W of Bathurst within the Vittoria SF access via the Mitchell Hwy. Ph: 02 6331 2044

209. Glendora Camping Area - Central West
Map Ref: MAP 2 D5 GPS: 33 01 24 S 149 24 19 E
Located 1km north of Hill End which is 85km north of Bathurst and 72km south of Mudgee. Access via Lees Lane off Beyers Ave. Bring firewood. Ph: 02 6337 8206

210. Village Campground - Central West
Map Ref: MAP 2 D6 GPS: 33 02 02 S 149 24 50 E
Located in the centre of Hill End Village on Warry Road off Clarke St. Closed during winter. Ph: 02 6337 8206

211. Bruinbun Reserve camping area - Central West
Map Ref: MAP 2 D6 GPS: 33 08 50 S 149 27 19 E
Located on Bridle Track between Bathurst and Hill End. Signposted access along the Bridle Track 4.1km north of Bathurst and 1.3km south of Amy Anderson Reserve. Bring water & firewood. Ph: 02 6391 4300

212. Amy Anderson Reserve
Map Ref: MAP 2 D6 GPS: 33 09 04 S 149 26 51 E
Camp area on The Bridle Track, Killongbutta, 43km N of Bathurst. Contact Info Centre for road update. Ph: 1800 681 000

213. Coles Bridge - Central West
Map Ref: MAP 2 D6 GPS: 33 03 50 S 149 37 26 E
Located 14km W of Sofala. Take Hill End Rd W from Sofala and turn into Turondale Rd and follow to the bridge and camping area on the Turon River. Ph: 1800 681 000

214. Wallaby Rocks Crossing - Central West
Map Ref: MAP 2 D6 GPS: 33 04 29 S 149 38 58 E
Located 5km W of Sofala on Hill End Rd. Situated on the Turon River. Dry weather only. Ph: 02 6332 1444

215. Crossley Bridge - Central West
Map Ref: MAP 2 D6 GPS: 33 04 45 S 149 41 12 E
Less than 1km from Sofala on the northern banks of the Turon River. Access track is off the Mudgee-Bathurst Rd. Ph: 1800 681 000

216. Ration Point - Central West
Map Ref: MAP 2 D6 GPS: 33 05 30 S 149 42 55 E
Camp Spot 3km E of Sofala via Upper Turon Rd. Beside river. Ph: 02 6332 1444

217. First Crossing camping area - Central West
Map Ref: MAP 2 D6 GPS: 33 06 01 S 149 44 10 E
Located 6km E of Sofala on the banks of the Turon River. Only 45km N of Bathurst. Ph: 1800 681 000

218. Green Point
Map Ref: MAP 2 D6 GPS: 33 05 44 S 149 43 55 E
Located 6km E of Sofala via Upper Turon Rd beside river.

219. The Diggings - Central West
Map Ref: MAP 2 E6 GPS: 33 11 02 S 149 57 23 E
Located in Turon NP on the Turon River. Campground is 2km S of the park entrance. Dry weather only Ph: 02 4787 8877

220. Glen Davis - Central West
Map Ref: MAP 2 F6 GPS: 33 07 32 S 150 16 54 E
Situated in Glen Davis Village some 35km E of Capertee via the Glen Davis Rd off the Castlereagh Hwy. Ph: 02 6353 1859

221. Coorongooba Campground
Map Ref: MAP 2 F6 GPS: 33 07 21 S 150 19 20 E
Camp area in western area of Wollemi NP. Turn E off Hwy at Capertee then turn onto Goora St. Turn right onto Nioka St and follow signs. 4WD only- river crossing. Ph: 02 4787 8877

222. Newnes Campground - Central West
Map Ref: MAP 2 F6 GPS: 33 10 21 S 150 14 20 E
35km NE of Lithgow in the Wollemi NP via Wolgan Rd. Ph: 02 4787 8877

223. Little Capertee Newnes - The Blue Mountains
Map Ref: MAP 2 F6 GPS: 33 10 20 S 150 14 17 E
35kms NE of Lidsdale on the Castlereagh Hwy. Access to the campground via Wolgan Rd. Ph: 1300 760 276

224. Newnes Ruins camping area
Map Ref: MAP 2 F6 GPS: 33 10 38 S 150 14 13 E
Numerous sites on eastern side of Wolgan River 300m north of river crossing to Newnes Industrial Ruins. Dry weather only. Ph: 02 4588 5247

Little Capertee Camping Area No 223

Newnes, NSW
35kms north-east of Lidsdale, NSW
Stephanie Jackson

An early morning mist hovers over Mystery Mountain that lies at the edge of the camping ground.

Newnes. Every time I hear that simple word I'm keen to hit the road and head for this secluded corner of the NSW bush once again. It's a delightful place to camp at any time of the year, but when late winter transforms the landscape with golden wattle blooms, it's nothing short of spectacular.

The town of Newnes, in the picturesque Wolgan Valley, was established in 1906 for the sole purpose of mining and processing shale oil. At its peak, it had more than 2,000 residents, but when the industry came to a halt in the 1930s, Newnes was doomed. The only surviving building is the old pub, but it's no longer a popular watering hole. It now houses a small museum and a kiosk that's open at very erratic hours, but if you drop in at the right time of day, you can enjoy a cuppa and a yarn with the building's friendly owner.

Shaded campsites are here, for a fee, but some 400 metres further along the road, in the Wollemi National Park, there's a scenically stunning location where campers can set up home free of charge.

The Little Capertee camping area is an immense grassy clearing among the forest, and although it can accommodate motorhomes and rigs of gargantuan proportions, there's barely room for an anorexic centipede to slither through the crowd of campers during holiday periods and on weekends. When the area is almost devoid of humans however, silence descends across the landscape, and hordes of other residents move in.

The cavernous holes excavated in the camping area and the surrounding bushland provide evidence of the creatures that live here, but the region's wombats, inflicted with a severe mange-like disease, are a sorry sight to see. If you're hoping to see other wildlife – including satin bowerbirds, king parrots, superb fairy-wrens, eastern yellow robins, and wallabies - you won't be disappointed, for they're all here in abundance.

The camping area's only facilities are two pit toilets, but, for a fee of $5 per visit, you can use the hot showers and flushing toilets at the old pub's camping area.

This is an ideal place to relax and take it easy, but if you want to add some energetic activities to your holiday agenda, there are several options at Newnes. There are forests and rugged mountains to explore, but if you're searching for a real challenge, you won't need to look any further than Mystery Mountain, the conical peak that rises above the shallow Wolgan River that mutters past the southern end of the camping area. The record for climbing to its summit is an almost unbelievable 22 minutes, and while you might not expect to equal that Herculean effort, the view is sure to be worthwhile however long the ascent takes.

On the far side of the river, a 7km long walking trail winds through woodlands that conceal the extensive ruins associated with the shale oil industry. While you might not think that the remains of an industrial complex would be of any interest, there's a good chance that you'll be pleasantly surprised by the picturesque landscapes and fragments of the region's history that you'll discover as you walk along the track.

A tinge of sadness may surface as your stay at Newnes comes to its inevitable conclusion, but you'll be itching to return to this spectacular neck of the woods when the opportunity for another adventure in the great outdoors arises.

The old coke ovens are among the many ruins of the shale oil industry.

Just The Facts

Little Capertee Camping Area

Getting there: Newnes is 35kms north-east of Lidsdale which is on the Castlereagh Highway approximately 150kms north-west of Sydney. Access to the camping area is via the Wolgan Road, with the route including around 25kms of unsealed roads that are suitable for two wheel drive vehicles.

Facilities: There are only pit toilets at the camping area, and generators are not permitted. Flushing toilets and hot showers are available, for a fee of $5, beside the old pub where firewood can be purchased for $30 a barrowful.

The 7km long ruins walking track begins 1.5kms from the sandy river crossing, which can usually only be negotiated by four wheel drive vehicles.

There is no mobile phone reception at Newnes.

Pets: Pets are not permitted in the national park camping area.

Charges: There is no charge for camping here.

Contact: For additional information contact the Lithgow Visitor Information Centre by phoning 1300 76 02 76 or by logging onto www.tourism.lithgow.com

225. Grey Gum Café
Map Ref: MAP 2 F6 GPS: 33 01 49 S 150 40 25 E
Camp area 86kms S of Singleton on the Putty Rd. Pay for showers. Ph: 02 6579 7015

226. Blue Gums Campground
Map Ref: MAP 2 G6 GPS: 32 57 22 S 150 53 14 E
Camp area 42.5kms W of Wollombi. From Yango Creek rd take Finchley Track then Yango Track and Wollombi Arm Trail to Big Yengo Loop Trail in Big Yengo. Ph: 02 6574 5555

227. Mountain Arm Campground
Map Ref: MAP 2 G6 GPS: 32 59 03 S 150 53 26 E
Located in Yengo NP 44km W of Wollombi. From Yango Creek rd take Finchley Track then Yango Track and Wollombi Arm Trail to Big Yengo Loop Trail in Big Yengo. Ph: 02 6574 5555

228. Finchley Campground -Blue Mountains
Map Ref: MAP 2 G6 GPS: 32 58 47 S 151 00 50 E
Signposted access on Yango Track some 800m S of its junction with Finchley Track. Ph: 02 4320 4200

229. Mogo Creek Campground - Blue Mountains
Map Ref: MAP 2 G6 GPS: 33 08 42 S 151 05 27 E
At the top end of the Old Great North Rd. Signposted access on Mogo Creek Rd. Ph: 02 4320 4200

230. St Albans Reserve
Map Ref: MAP 2 G6 GPS: 33 17 33 S 150 58 14 E
Camp spot in Wollombi Street - St Albans near the Settles Arm Inn.

231. Watagan Headquarters camping area - Hunter Region
Map Ref: MAP 2 H6 GPS: 32 58 57 S 151 25 01 E
Within the Heaton SF. Signposted access on Watagan Rd 3km N of Watagan Forest Rd. Ph: 1300 655 687

232. Gap Creek camping area - Hunter Region
Map Ref: MAP 2 H6 GPS: 33 00 51 S 151 25 48 E
Located in Watagans NP on Bangalow Rd. 3km W of Mt Faulk Rd. Bangalow Rd is signposted off Mt Faulk Rd. Ph: 02 4358 0400

233. Bangalow Road camping area - Hunter Region
Map Ref: MAP 2 H6 GPS: 33 00 59 S 151 25 32 E
Located in Watagans NP on Bangalow Rd. 4km W of Mt Faulk Rd. Bangalow Rd is signposted off Mt Faulk Rd. Ph: 02 4358 0400

234. Olney HQ Camping Area
Map Ref: MAP 2 H6 GPS: 33 03 47 S 151 19 53 E
Located in Olney SF16kms W of Cooranbong via Martinsville Rd & Watagan Forest Rd. 8km dirt road. Ph: 1300 655 687

235. Casuarina camping area - Hunter Region
Map Ref: MAP 2 H6 GPS: 33 03 50 S 151 20 08 E
Located 100m E of Watagan Forest Rd. Signposted access along Watagan Forest Rd - N of the junction of Watagan Forest & Walkers Ridge Forest roads. Ph: 1300 655 687

236. The Pines Campground - Hunter Region
Map Ref: MAP 2 H6 GPS: 33 03 50 S 151 20 14 E
Within the Onley State Forest on the Watagan Forest Rd just past the junction of Watagan Forest & Walkers Ridge Rds. Ph: 1300 655 687

237. The Basin - Hunter Region
Map Ref: MAP 2 H6 GPS: 33 06 14 S 151 13 50 E
Camping ground is on Walkers Ridge Forest Rd. 8km E of The Letter A on George Downes Dve. Ph: 1300 655 687

238. Turpentine camping area - Hunter Region
Map Ref: MAP 2 H6 GPS: 33 03 59 S 151 20 23 E
Within the Onley SF located 400m E of Watagan Forest Rd with signposted access along Watagan Forest Rd. 300m N of the junction of Watagan Forest and Walkers Ridge Forest Rds. Ph: 1300 655 687

239. Wattle Tree camping area
Map Ref: MAP 2 H6 GPS: 33 04 01 S 151 20 34 E
Within the Onley SF. Signposted access along Watagan Forest Rd. 1km S of the junction of Watagan Forest and Walkers Ridge Forest Rds. Ph: 1300 655 687

240. FreemanS Camping Ground - Close to Sydney
Map Ref: MAP 2 H6 GPS: 33 12 04 S 151 36 12 E
Within Munmorah State Conservation Area 40km north of Gosford between Budgewoi and Catherine Hill Bay. Signposted off Pacific Hwy at Lake Monmorah. Take Birdie Beach Dve 1.1km from the park's entrance station then 300m to camp area. Ph: 02 4358 0400

Free Campsites in New South Wales

241. Bakers Shaft Reserve - Central West

Map Ref: MAP 2 C7 GPS: 33 36 34 S 149 00 43 E
15km N of Mandurama. Turn W off Mandurama-Burnt Yards Rd after 10km onto Makers Rd then into Junction Park Rd. Dry weather only. Ph: 02 6391 4300

242. Carcoar Dam - Central West

Map Ref: MAP 2 C7 GPS: 33 36 39 S 149 10 46 E
8km E of Carcoar. Signposted off Mid Western Hwy. Ph: 02 6367 3103

243. Mary's Park At Sunny Corner - Central West

Map Ref: MAP 2 E6 GPS: 33 22 40 S 149 51 37 E
Located 40kms east of Bathurst. After 7kms nor on Great Western Highway turn on to Sunny Corner Road at Meadow Flat. Ph: 02 6331 2044

244. Sunny Corner Recreation Reserve - Central West

Map Ref: MAP 2 E7 GPS: 33 23 16 S 149 53 35 E
36km E of Bathurst signpost access from Great Western Hwy via Sunny Corner Rd. Ph: 02 6393 4384

245. Bungleboori Campground - The Blue Mountains

Map Ref: MAP 2 E7 GPS: 33 24 16 S 150 11 57 E
Located in the Newnes State Forest 12km NE of Lithgow via State Mine Hill Rd. Dry weather only. Ph: 02 6331 2044

246. Flat Rock

Map Ref: MAP 2 E7 GPS: 33 32 54 S 149 47 31 E
Located 7km E of O'Connell on Mutton Falls Rd.

247. Lake Lyell Camping Ground - Blue Mountains

Map Ref: MAP 2 E7 GPS: 33 31 30 S 150 04 37 E
Camp area located 13kms SW of Lithgow along the Rydell-Lithgow Rd. Good facilities. Ph: 02 6355 6347

248. Lockyers Track Head Campground

Map Ref: MAP 2 E7 GPS: 33 32 09 S 150 13 58 E
Camp area 12km SE of Lithgow via Hartley Vale Rd. Small vehicles only limited caravan sites. Ph: 02 6350 3230

249. Millionth Acre Picnic Area

Map Ref: MAP 2 E7 GPS: 33 40 37 S 150 03 01 E
Located intersection of Jenolan Caves Rd and Oberon Rd 4km S of Hampton. Ph: 1300 655 687

250. Jenolan Campground - Blue Mountains

Map Ref: MAP 2 E7 GPS: 33 44 59 S 150 02 26 E
Camp area 13km S of Hampton on Jenolan Caves Rd. Small site good for overnight. Ph: 02 9871 3377

251. Dunphy's Camping Area

Map Ref: MAP 2 E8 GPS: 33 47 24 S 150 13 48 E
Located in Blue Mountains NP on Bellbird Ridge Firetrail, 23kms S of Blackheath via Megalong Rd. Donation box. Ph: 02 4787 8877

252. Blackheath Glen Reserve

Map Ref: MAP 2 E7 GPS: 33 40 30 S 150 16 08 E
Camp area 6.5kms S of Blackheath via Megalong Valley Rd.

253. Cathedral Reserve

Map Ref: MAP 2 F7 GPS: 33 30 07 S 150 23 26 E
Camp area in Mount Irvine Rd at Mt Wilson.

254. Upper Colo Reserve camping area

Map Ref: MAP 2 F7 GPS: 33 25 13 S 150 43 50 E
West of Colo on banks of Colo River. Accessed by signpost along Colo Heights Rd. Ph: 02 4560 4444

255. Mill Creek Camping Ground - Close to Sydney

Map Ref: MAP 2 G7 GPS: 33 24 04 S 151 02 36 E
Located in Dharug NP 55km north of Sydney. Access to the park is via Old Northern Rd to Wisemans Ferry. Signposted access along Wisemans Ferry Rd. 5.6km east of Wisemans Ferry ferry. Drive a further 1.9km to camping area. Bring water & firewood. Ph: 02 4320 4200

256. Wheeny Creek camping area - Central Coast

Map Ref: MAP 2 F7 GPS: 33 27 24 S 150 43 20 E
In Wollemi National Park. 30 camping sites available in southern section of park. It's on Comleroy Road off Bells Line of Road. 14km N of Kurrajong. Ph: 02 4588 5247

Free Campsites in New South Wales

257. Burralow Creek camping area - The Blue Mountains
Map Ref: MAP 2 F7 GPS: 33 33 22 S 150 36 13 E
Family friendly camping ground. Access via a fire trail off Burralow Road from Kurrajong Heights or via the Patterson Range fire trail from Bilpin. 4WD only. Ph: 02 4588 5247

258. Burralow Creek Camping Ground
Map Ref: MAP 2 F7 GPS: 33 33 31 S 150 36 20 E
4.5km E of Bilpin take signposted Patterson Range Fire Trail for 10.6kms Ph: 02 4588 2400

259. Murphy's Glen Camp Ground
Map Ref: MAP 2 F8 GPS: 33 46 09 S 150 27 13 E
Situated 6kms S of Woodford. Dry weather only. Ph: 02 4588 2400

260. Murphys Glen Campground - The Blue Mountains
Map Ref: MAP 2 F8 GPS: 33 46 10 S 150 29 16 E
Located in the Blue Mountains NP 6km S of Woodford via Bedford Rd off Railway Parade. Ph: 02 4588 5247

261. Euroka Campground - Close to Sydney
Map Ref: MAP 2 F8 GPS: 33 47 55 S 150 37 01 E
Located within Blue Mountains NP. From Glenbrook follow Ross St and turn into signposted Burfitt Parade which leads to Bruce Rd. Follow further 1.6km to park entrance. Continue for 3.9km to camping area. Bring water & firewood. Ph: 02 4588 5247

262. Darby's Falls River Reserve
Map Ref: MAP 2 C8 GPS: 33 56 55 S 148 51 45 E
26km SE of Cowra on Darbys Falls Rd, Darby Falls. Beside Lachlan Rivers 2kms S of township. Ph: 02 6342 4333

263. Bigga Recreation Ground
Map Ref: MAP 2 C8 GPS: 34 04 59 S 149 09 06 E
Camp area at Mulgowrie Street - Bigga. Ph: 02 4835 2234

264. Trunkey Creek Showground - Central West
Map Ref: MAP 2 D7 GPS: 33 49 03 S 149 19 24 E
Located within Trunkey Creek Village on Arthur St. Ph: 02 6368 8604

265. Abercrombie Caves Reserve - Central West
Map Ref: MAP 2 D8 GPS: 33 54 52 S 149 21 30 E
Signposted access 12km S of Trunkey Creek along the Bathurst-Crookwell Road. Ph: 02 6368 8603

266. Abercrombie River Camp - Central West
Map Ref: MAP 2 C8 GPS: 33 57 30 S 149 19 11 E
Along the banks of the Abercrombie River 19km S of Trunkey Creek. Signpost access along the Bathurst-Crookwell Rd. Dry weather only. Ph: 02 4830 1000

267. Tuena Camping & Picnic ground - Central West
Map Ref: MAP 2 D8 GPS: 34 00 59 S 149 19 48 E
On Bathurst Rd within the village of Tuena. Ph: 02 4834 5235

268. Campbells River - Central West
Map Ref: MAP 2 D7 GPS: 33 47 12 S 149 36 36 E
Located in Dog Rocks State Forest 20km W of Oberon. Great campground on the Campbells River. Take Rockley Rd from Rockley then Dog Rocks Rd then Swallows Nest Rd. Ph: 1300 655 687

269. Black Springs camping area - Blue Mountains
Map Ref: MAP 2 D8 GPS: 33 50 51 S 149 44 38 E
Located in village of Black Springs 26km SW of Oberon at the junction of the Oberon-Black Springs Road and the Goulburn Rd. Ph: 1300 655 687

270. Burraga Dam - Central West
Map Ref: MAP 2 D8 GPS: 33 56 20 S 149 33 10 E
Burraga is 70km S of Bathurst. Camp area is 2km NE of Burraga access via Arkstone Rd. Dry weather only. Ph: 02 6367 3103

271. The Sink - Canberra
Map Ref: MAP 2 D8 GPS: 34 05 51 S 149 39 31 E
Next to Retreat River on the Retreat Fire Trail via Arkston Rd. Dry weather only. Ph: 02 6336 1972

272. The Beach - Canberra
Map Ref: MAP 2 D8 GPS: 34 07 44 S 149 38 05 E
Located next to Abercrombie River via Abercrombie Fire Trail from Arkstone or Emden Vale. Ph: 02 6336 1972

Featured Campsite

Brought to you by

Bummaroo Ford

No 273

Oberon, NSW

75kms south of Oberon

Stephanie Jackson

It was early afternoon when we rolled into the Bummaroo Ford camping area, and with the dark sky threatening a deluge of rain, we hurriedly set up camp, expecting the worst, yet hoping for a positive change in the weather.

We scrounged the firewood that previous campers had generously left behind, stashed it under our campervan where it would remain dry if rain eventually fell, and set out to explore every nook and cranny of our new surroundings.

The camping area, which is beside the Abercrombie Road that links the NSW city of Goulburn to its northern neighbour of Oberon, is a small parcel of land that's an unconnected fragment of the vast Abercrombie River National Park. It's bordered by the Abercrombie River, and as we meandered through the forest of casuarinas that line the banks of this narrow stream, black cockatoos screeched a warning of our approach, and gang gang cockatoos, feeding in the treetops, fled in a moment of panic.

There were plenty of other wild creatures here too, and while eastern grey kangaroos were easy to spot as they grazed on frosted grass, wombats were dozing in their cavernous subterranean burrows that undermine the camping area and exit at the riverbank.

Much of the river's wide rock-strewn bed is touched by the waters of the Abercrombie only in times of flood, but there's always a narrow stream of water here. With its route across the landscape routinely disrupted by piles of flood debris and fallen trees however, the Abercrombie River is a far from ideal venue for canoeing, but it's a pleasant spot to cool off on a summer's day.

The camping area, a narrow clearing that follows the sinuous curve of the river, and that's sandwiched between a hillside and the forest that hides the river from view, has only the most basic of facilities. In fact, there's nothing more than a few picnic tables and a single pit toilet that's perched on the hillside well beyond the reach of floodwaters.

All vehicles, including immense fifth wheelers, can easily access the area, but travellers with large motorhomes and rigs should only set up camp near the entrance, as other sections of the camping area offer limited room to manoeuvre. An extensive level clearing beside both the Abercrombie Road and the river, and approximately 100 metres south of Bummaroo Ford, is more suitable for large vehicles and rigs, and although it's outside the boundaries of the national park, it's an area where locals frequently camp during holiday periods and on long weekends.

With the approach of nightfall the park's nocturnal residents were out and about, and as a possum arrived to scrounge for food, we tip-toed slowly and quietly into the darkness on a wombat spotting excursion. With the gaping entrances to their maze of burrows scattered across the landscape, caution was a high priority, but as rain began and with our patience exhausted, we abandoned any hopes of glimpsing one of these elusive creatures, and headed off to bed.

With limited vehicular traffic passing the camping area either day or night, the silence of the bush was disrupted only by the melodic patter of raindrops on the roof of the campervan, and we dozed contentedly, knowing there'd be another day to enjoy the simple pleasures of Bummaroo Ford, and another night to search for its elusive wild inhabitants.

Travellers can set up camp on the level grassy area that's close to the river.

The camping area is on the northern side of the bridge across the Abercrombie River.

Kangaroos usually outnumber the human visitors at the camping area.

Just The Facts

Bummaroo Ford

Getting there: The Bummaroo Ford camping area is on the eastern side of the Abercrombie Road where it crosses the Abercrombie River. It is approximately 110kms north of the NSW city of Goulburn and 75kms south of Oberon.

Facilities: There are no facilities other than a pit toilet and picnic tables.

Pets: Pets are not permitted.

Charges: There is no charge for camping here.

Contact: For additional information, contact the National Parks and Wildlife office at Oberon by phoning 02 6336 1972.

Free Campsites in New South Wales

273. Bummaroo Ford - Blue Mountains
Map Ref: MAP 2 D8 GPS: 34 11 41 S 149 33 10 E
Situated on eastern side of Abercrombie Road where it crosses the river approx 75kms S of Oberon. Ph: 02 6336 1972

274. Silent Creek - Canberra
Map Ref: MAP 2 D8 GPS: 34 09 29 S 149 40 41 E
Situated within the Abercrombie River NP. Signposted access along Abercrombie Fire Trail 6km S of The Beach access track. Ph: 02 6336 1972

275. Dingo Dell - The Blue Mountains
Map Ref: MAP 2 E8 GPS: 33 58 30 S 149 58 04 E
Located 13.3km SW of the Kanangra Walls Rd signposted 5km W of Jenolan Caves. 4WD access via Kowmung River Fire Trail and is signposted off the Kanangra Walls Road. 15km S of the Jenolan Caves-Oberon Road. Ph: 02 4787 8877

276. Boyd River Campground - The Blue Mountains
Map Ref: MAP 2 E8 GPS: 33 58 20 S 150 03 40 E
Access via Kanangra Walls Rd 22km S of Jenolan Caves Rd. Dry weather only Ph: 02 4787 8877

277. Mt Werong Campground - The Blue Mountains
Map Ref: MAP 2 E8 GPS: 34 04 48 S 149 55 38 E
Located in the Blue Mountains NP. From Oberon head S along Shootershill Rd left into Gurnang Forest Rd and left again at the correctional centre sign. Dry weather only. Ph: 02 4320 4203

278. Batsh Camp Camping area - The Blue Mountains
Map Ref: MAP 2 E8 GPS: 34 08 36 S 150 05 32 E
One of the few camping areas in the southern end of the national park. Via the Oberon-Colong Stock Route. Dry weather only. Ph: 02 6336 1972

279. Private Town Camping Area - Close to Sydney
Map Ref: MAP 2 E8 GPS: 34 07 01 S 150 12 40 E
Signposted access at Yerranderie via the Old Oberon-Colong Stock Route 62km east of Goulburn/Wombeyan Caves access road junction with the Old Oberon-Colong Stock Route. Ph: 02 4659 6165

280. Government Town - The Blue Mountains
Map Ref: MAP 2 E8 GPS: 34 07 06 S 150 13 26 E
On the edge of the Blue Mountains NP access is via Old Oberon-Colong Stock Route. Ph: 02 4720 0300

281. Wombeyan Caves Campground - Southern Highlands
Map Ref: MAP 2 E9 GPS: 34 18 18 S 149 58 17 E
Located 60km west of Mittagong. Access via Wombeyan Caves Rd. Bring firewood. Ph: 02 4843 5976

282. Dalys Clearing Campground - Southern Highlands
Map Ref: MAP 3 H1 GPS: 34 32 10 S 150 14 30 E
Camp Area 10km W of Moss Vale. Turn W off Hume Hwy 6km N of Illawarra Hwy junction then Bunnigalore Rd & Dalys Rd. Ph: 02 6458 3177

283. Carrington Falls - South Coast
Map Ref: MAP 3 K1 GPS: 34 37 17 S 150 39 40 E
Within the Budderoo NP small camping area. Find it on Carrington Falls access Rd off Jamberoo Mountain Rd which is 4km E of Robertson. Ph: 02 4236 0469

284. Killalea camping area - South Coast
Map Ref: MAP 3 K1 GPS: 34 36 38 S 150 51 13 E
6km S of Shellharbour off Shellharbour Rd. Closed gate access. Check times. Bookings essential Ph: 02 4237 8589

285. Jugiong Showground
Map Ref: MAP 3 B2 GPS: 34 49 34 S 148 19 34 E
Jugiong Showground camping area at Jugiong signposted off the Hume Hwy. Donation box.

286. Browning Recreation Ground
Map Ref: MAP 3 D1 GPS: 34 46 13 S 148 49 17 E
Located on Minehan Lane, Browning 11kms NW of Yass. Donation box. Ph: 1300 886 014

287. Gundaroo Sport & Recreation Ground
Map Ref: MAP 3 E3 GPS: 35 01 25 S 149 15 57 E
Camp area in Cork St, Gundaroo W side of town, N of David St. Short term only, tents in designated area and donation for general store upkeep. Ph: 0411 400 897

288. Bungonia State Conservation Camping Area - Southern Highlands
Map Ref: MAP 3 G2 GPS: 34 48 26 S 150 00 10 E
Located 35km east of Goulburn near Bungonia. From the Hume Hwy take the signposted access road 2.3km south of the Marulan service centre and follow this road for 14.9km to Bungonia. Then take signposted Lookdown Rd for 8.7km to signposted camping area. Bring drinking water. Ph: 02 4844 4341

290. Forest Headquarters camping area
Map Ref: MAP 3 H2 GPS: 34 42 31 S 150 10 37 E
Set in pine plantation in Wingello SF 4kms SE of Wingello via Caoura Rd. Ph: 1300 655 687

291. HQ Camp
Map Ref: MAP 3 H2 GPS: 34 42 57 S 150 11 20 E
Located in Wingella SF 4km SE of Wingella via Forest Rd. Ph: 1300 655 687

292. Wingello State Forest - Goulburn
Map Ref: MAP 3 H2 GPS: 34 42 56 S 150 11 21 E
Camp Area 4km SE of Wingello via Forest Rd. Ph: 02 6458 3177

293. Gambells Reast Camping Area - Southern Highlands
Map Ref: MAP 3 J1 GPS: 34 40 07 S 150 17 47 E
Located in Morton NP near Moss Vale. From the village of Bundanoon take the road signposted to NP and signposted Church St which becomes The Gullies Rd. Camping area is 1.4km along this road. Ph: 02 4887 7270

294. Bendeela Recreation Area - South Coast
Map Ref: MAP 3 J2 GPS: 34 44 30 S 150 28 25 E
Near the village of Kangaroo Valley between Moss Vale and Nowra. Approx 200km south of Sydney. Ph: 1300 722 468

295. Grassy Gully camping area -Bundundah Reserve - South Coast
Map Ref: MAP 3 J2 GPS: 34 51 25 S 150 24 30 E
Bush camping with no facilities beside Grassy Gully Creek. 25km W of Nowra via Grassy Gully Road. Ph: 02 4428 6300

296. Danjera Dam - South Coast
Map Ref: MAP 3 J2 GPS: 34 55 15 S 150 23 32 E
Located 25km W of Nowra. Access signposted along Yalwai Rd from Nowra and Burrier. Dry weather only. Ph: 02 4421 0778

Featured Campsite

Bendeela Recreation Area

No 294

Near Kangaroo Valley , NSW
180 kms south of Sydney

Errol Kurth

Kangaroos share the campground.

Bendeela has few facilities, no staff, and no shops within walking distance. It is simply a patch of grass to erect your tent or park your van. But it is this simplicity and easy comfortable access to nature which makes the Bendeela Recreation Area a must see for everyone. Bendeela is located near Kangaroo Valley village. The bitumen extends all the way to the front gate, so this place is accessible to all. The recreation area is managed by Sydney Catchment Authority as a wildlife reserve, and offers free camping for up to 14 consecutive nights.

The recreation reserve is split into two areas, with the second area only open to camping/caravanning in times of peak demand (school holidays, long weekends). I think for any nature enthusiast, a visit in the off-season would be the most appropriate time to plan your stay. The only facilities on site are the two flush toilet blocks with disabled access and two portable toilet dump points. Tapped drinking water is available at five sites within the recreation area. Campfires are not permitted anywhere in the reserve area.

To fill in the day, campers can fish, bushwalk, swim or use their own non-powered boating devices on the Kangaroo River. A canoe portage is available in the upper camping area. As a nature reserve, kangaroos and birdlife are abundant. However, it is the nightly visit from wombats that provides that up close and personal nature experience.

Free Campsites in New South Wales

297. Yalwal Campground
Map Ref: MAP 3 H2 GPS: 34 55 23 S 150 23 03 E
Camp area at Yalwal 24km W of Nowra via Burrier & Yalwal Rds overlooking Danjera Dam. 17km dirt road not suitable for caravans. Bookings required. Ph: 1300 662 808

298. Danjera Dan camping area
Map Ref: MAP 3 J3 GPS: 34 55 38 S 150 23 06 E
27km W of Nowra along Yalwal Rd from Nowra and Burrier. Steep and unsealed road. Dry weather only. Ph: 02 4421 0778

299. Tumblong Rest Area
Map Ref: MAP 3 A3 GPS: 35 08 07 S 148 00 39 E
Travel 1km N of Tumblong. Only overnight.

300. Careys Reserve - Snowy High Country
Map Ref: MAP 3 C3 GPS: 35 05 30 S 148 40 20 E
Located 3km N of Wee Jasper Village via Caves Rd. Ph: 02 6227 9626

301. Fitzpatrick Trackhead Camp Area - The Snowys
Map Ref: MAP 3 C3 GPS: 35 08 20 S 148 40 24 E
Located 4km south of Wee Jasper with access signposted along the Tumut-Nottingham Rd. Ph: 02 6937 2700

302. Billy Grace Reserve - Snowy High Country
Map Ref: MAP 3 C3 GPS: 35 08 15 S 148 41 14 E
4.1km S of Wee Jasper Village along the Wee Jasper- Nottingham Road just W of the Wee Jasper Creek crossing. Ph: 02 6227 9626

303. Swinging Bridge Reserve - Snowy High Country
Map Ref: MAP 3 C3 GPS: 35 09 44 S 148 41 13 E
8km S of Wee Jasper Village via the Wee Jasper-Nottingham Road beside Goodradigbee River. Ph: 02 6227 9626

304. Micalong Creek Reserve - The Snowys
Map Ref: MAP 3 C3 GPS: 35 11 17 S 148 41 15 E
Signposted access 10kms south of Wee Jasper Village along Wee Jasper-Nottingham Rd. Bring water & firewood. Ph: 02 6227 9626

305. McIntyres Hut bush camp
Map Ref: MAP 3 C3 GPS: 35 15 56 S 148 44 17 E
Located in Brindabella NP beside Goodradigbee River - 3.5km along McIntyres Trail from Webbs Ridge Trail and Waterfall Fire Trail. Dry weather only Ph: 02 6229 7166

306. Lowells Flat Bush Camp - The Snowys
Map Ref: MAP 3 C3 GPS: 35 16 47 S 148 44 23 E
Located in Brindabella Np 53km west of Canberra. Camp area is situated beside Goodradigbee River 1.9km along Lowell's Flat Trail which is signposted off McIntyres Trail - 2.8km from its junction with Waterfall Fire Trail. Ph: 02 6299 2929

307. Cotter Campground - ACT
Map Ref: MAP 3 D4 GPS: 35 19 32 S 148 56 52 E
22km W of Canberra along Cotter Road beside Murrumbidgee River. Ph: 02 6207 2425

308. Oallen Ford-Braidwood - South Coast
Map Ref: MAP 3 G3 GPS: 35 09 04 S 149 57 49 E
53kms NE of Braidwood and 4kms S of Nerriga. Ph: 02 4842 1144

309. Corang River - South Coast
Map Ref: MAP 3 G3 GPS: 35 12 22 S 150 03 07 E
Located on the Braidwood-Nowra Rd 12km S of Nerriga. Camping beside river. Ph: 02 4842 1144

310. Endrick River Crossing - South Coast
Map Ref: MAP 3 H3 GPS: 35 05 24 S 150 07 20 E
Nerriga is 55km NE of Braidwood with the camp ground 5km NE of Nerriga on the Braidwood-Nowra Rd. Ph: 02 4842 1144

311. Batlow Showground
Map Ref: MAP 3 A4 GPS: 35 31 09 S 148 09 11 E
Camp area E side of town cnr Memorial Ave & Park ST, Batlow. Ph: 1300 275 782

312. Windy Point - The Snowys
Map Ref: MAP 3 B4 GPS: 35 29 59 S 148 14 56 E
On the western side of Blowering Reservoir within the Bago SF at the end of Yellowfin & Foreshore Rds. Ph: 1300 655 687

Featured Campsite

Brought to you by

Oallen Ford No 308

Near Nerrigan, NSW
75kms south of Oberon

Stephanie Jackson

If you pass through the tiny NSW town of Nerriga, 53kms south-west of Braidwood, you might find nothing to tempt you to spend even a second of your time here, for there's nothing to see other than a pub, a church, a community hall, and a few derelict cottages. There's a pleasant surprise in store beyond the town's boundaries however, and if you've got the time to take a detour a little further west, you won't be disappointed.

The Oallen Ford Road, which heads west towards Goulburn, is 4kms south of Nerriga, and some 13kms along this road, where it crosses the Shoalhaven River at the Oallen Ford, you can camp free of charge for as long as you like.

The wooden bridge over the river has a load limit of 5 tonnes, so if you have a large vehicle or rig you might not be able to travel on beyond the river's western bank that rises steeply above the valley. Fortunately, all the areas where you can camp are on the eastern side of the ford. It's here that the river, when in flood, spreads out across the low lying land, but when it's in a calm mood it leaves much of the stony riverbed high and dry. And that means that whatever form your camping accommodation takes, you'll have no trouble finding somewhere close to the water's edge to set up home.

Well used tracks make it easy for vehicles to access the extensive riverbed where, although there are low shrubs and long grasses that offer some shelter from winds, the majority of the vegetation is not tall enough to offer any shade.

Although many areas beside the water can be easily accessed by two wheel drive vehicles, some sandy tracks can only be negotiated with a four wheel drive, and if you have a large motorhome or a gargantuan rig you won't have to look too hard to find a suitable camping spot. You can make yourself at home on an extensive cleared area near the river and close to the road, or settle in for a relaxing stay a little further from the water's edge. Approximately 100 metres east of the river there's a high ridge with a large and level clearing hidden among tall eucalypts that provide welcome shade in summer months.

With several extensive areas where you can set up home, you won't find other campers crowding onto your doorstep at the Oallen Ford, and although there are no facilities of any kind, there are plenty of relaxing, enjoyable, and even profitable ways to spend your time here. You can swim, explore the river in a kayak or canoe, or try your luck at fishing in this picturesque spot where, with only light traffic using the road, the loudest noises you'll hear are those of the wind, the river, and the birds that frequent the area. You might also hear a shout of excitement, or yell 'Eureka!' yourself, for this is a popular spot for gold panning, and if Lady Luck comes your way, you'll be pleased you stopped at the Oallen Ford.

There is an extensive cleared area to camp near the river.

The wooden bridge over the river.

Just The Facts

Oallen Ford

Getting there: The Oallen Ford Road is 4kms south of Nerriga which is 53kms south-west of the NSW town of Braidwood. The ford is 13kms along this road. All vehicles and rigs can access the camping area. The bridge over the river has a load limit of 5 tonnes, so some travellers might not be able to travel beyond the ford.

Facilities: There are no facilities at the camping area. Nerriga has a pub that serves counter meals, but there are no other commercial facilities in the town.

Pets: Pets are permitted.

Charges: There are no charges for camping here.

Contact: Phone the Braidwood Tourist Information Centre on (02) 4842 1144 for additional information.

Free Campsites in New South Wales

313. Island Picnic Ground
Map Ref: MAP 3 B4 GPS: 35 30 36 S 148 14 22 E
Within Bago SF signposted access along Foreshore Rd 3.8km N of Barrets Bay. Ph: 1300 655 687

314. Willow Bay - Riverina & Murray
Map Ref: MAP 3 B4 GPS: 35 30 36 S 148 14 40 E
Along the western shore of Blowering Reservoir. Signposted access along Foreshore Rd from Island Picnic Ground. Ph: 1300 655 687

315. Barrets Bay camping area
Map Ref: MAP 3 B4 GPS: 35 31 12 S 148 14 33 E
Within Bago SF signposted access along Foreshore Rd 1.6km N of Powerline Park. Ph: 1300 655 687

316. Powerline Park camping area
Map Ref: MAP 3 B4 GPS: 35 31 22 S 148 14 12 E
Within Bago SF signposted access along Foreshore Rd 350m N of Long Point. Ph: 1300 655 687

317. Long Point - The Snowys
Map Ref: MAP 3 B4 GPS: 35 31 40 S 148 14 13 E
On the western side of Blowering Reservoir signposted access along Foreshore Road - 200m N of Junction Park. Ph: 1300 655 687

318. Wilkinsons Point camping area
Map Ref: MAP 3 B4 GPS: 35 32 36 S 148 14 06 E
In Bago SF - 1.2km E of Yellowfin Rd. Take signposted Foreshore Rd to reach campsite. Ph: 1300 655 687

319. Junction Park - The Snowys
Map Ref: MAP 3 B4 GPS: 35 31 49 S 148 14 17 E
Within the Bago SF on the western side of Blowering Reservoir. Access along Foreshore Rd. Ph: 1300 655 687

320. Yellowfin Forest Park camping area
Map Ref: MAP 3 B4 GPS: 35 32 19 S 148 13 55 E
Within the Bago SF camp is signposted access along Yellowfin Rd 5.6km N of Yellowfin Rd and Blowering Camp junction. Ph: 1300 655 687

321. Dormans Point - The Snowys
Map Ref: MAP 3 B4 GPS: 35 32 02 S 148 14 13 E
Within the Bago SF on the shores of Blowering Reservoir. Access along Foreshore Rd which is off Yellowin Rd Ph: 1300 655 687

322. Log Bridge Creek Campground - The Snowys
Map Ref: MAP 3 B4 GPS: 35 25 08 S 148 16 22 E
Located 18km S of Tumut. Turn SE off Hwy and follow road back across Hwy for 1.5km to main camp area. Ph: 02 6947 7025

323. The Pines camping area
Map Ref: MAP 3 B4 GPS: 35 26 52 S 148 17 02 E
Situated near Blowering Reservoir 4km S of Log Bridge Creek on the Snowy Mountains Hwy - 22kms S of Tumut. Ph: 02 6947 7025

324. Blowering Reserve - The Snowys
Map Ref: MAP 3 B4 GPS: 35 26 51 S 148 17 04 E
The waterfront camp begins 17kms south of Tumut on the Snowy Mountains Highway. Ph: 02 6947 7025

325. Humes Crossing - The Snowys
Map Ref: MAP 3 B4 GPS: 35 28 30 S 148 16 20 E
Off the Snowy Mountains Hwy 25km S of Tumut in Kosciuszko NP. Ph: 02 6947 7025

326. Yachting Point - The Snowys
Map Ref: MAP 3 B4 GPS: 35 30 40 S 148 16 04 E
Signposted access along the Snowy Mountains Hwy 10km N of Talbingo turnoff. Dry weather only. Ph: 02 6947 7025

327. Yolde Campground - The Snowys
Map Ref: MAP 3 B4 GPS: 35 32 22 S 148 17 45 E
Signposted access along the Snowy Mountains Hwy 5km N of Talbingo turnoff. Ph: 02 6947 7025

328. Jounama Creek Campground - The Snowys
Map Ref: MAP 3 B4 GPS: 35 33 59 S 148 19 48 E
Off the Snowy Mountains Hwy 40km S of Tumut opposite Talbingo turnoff Ph: 02 6947 7025

Blowering Reservoir

No 324

Northern Kosciuszko National Park, NSW

17km south of Tumut

Catherine Lawson & David Bristow

Blowering Resrvoir is perfect for many water sports.

In this famous national park's north, the Snowy Mountains Highway leads along the eastern shore of Blowering Reservoir to five waterfront camps that permit breezy, unrestricted stays.

Perfect for fishing, paddling, sailing, water skiing and swimming, Blowering Reservoir measures 18 kilometres long and up to four kilometres wide when full, and is stocked with Murray cod and golden perch, plus protected species - silver perch, eel-tailed catfish, river blackfish and Macquarie perch - which must be returned to the water unharmed.

Fisherfolk can also expect catches of redfin and rainbow and brown trout.

Eastern grey kangaroos flourish on the reservoir's grassy foreshores and the woodlands harbour noisy flocks of gang-gang cockatoos and crimson rosellas.

Facilities are limited to toilets, picnic tables and fireplaces, but that doesn't deter the fishing-mad families who set up here over the summer school holidays with ski boats, pool toys and stock piles of fire wood.

Convenient for resupply trips, Tumut is located just 17 kilometres north of the first camp at Log Bridge Creek, a shady choice for bushwalkers and travellers with small rigs.

There are two walking trails close to this camp: the Blowering Cliffs Walk (5km return) which climbs through a cool, steep valley of peppermints and mountain gums to Blowering Falls, and the Warogong Sugarloaf Trail (11km return), rewarding walkers with good views of Tumut Valley and the reservoir.

Water skiers favour The Pines campground, where a boat ramp and grassy foreshore provide easy access to the water. The shady, free-range campsites here allow for big rigs.

Camps at Hume's Crossing and Yachting Point also cater to big rigs, and provide toilets, tables and fireplaces, while the cosy bush sites at Yolde campground well suit compact campers seeking solitude.

Open year-round, all campgrounds on Blowering Reservoir are accessible to conventional vehicles and caravans, and have mobile reception.

Before you take to the water, buy a NSW recreational fishing licence online at www.licence.nsw.gov.au, priced at $6 (valid 3 days), $12 (one month) or $30 for a year. Kids under 18 years fish for free.

The camping ground has a relaxed environment.

Just The Facts

Blowering Reservoir

Location: The waterfront camps begin 17km south of Tumut on the Snowy Mountains Highway.

Facilities: Toilets, picnic tables and fire places are provided. BYO firewood and drinking water.

Rates: Free.

Wheelchair Access: To the toilet at The Pines campground.

Pets: No.

Contact: National Parks in Tumut on (02) 6947 7025 or head to www.environment.nsw.gov.au/nationalparks.

Free Campsites in New South Wales

329. Thomas Boyd Trackhead Camp Area - The Snowys
Map Ref: MAP 3 B4 GPS: 35 22 25 S 148 25 01 E
Located east of Tumut along Goobarragandra Rd. From Tumut take signposted Lacmalac Rd which is accessed off Wynyard St. Take Lacmalac Rd which turns into Goobarragandra Rd for 24kms to camp area. Ph: 02 6937 2700

330. Rock Flat Campground - The Snowys
Map Ref: MAP 3 B4 GPS: 35 24 05 S 148 25 36 E
Located in Kosciuszko NP. Access via Laclamac Rd 26km SE of Tumut on the Goobarragandra River. Ph: 02 6947 7025

331. Broken Cart - The Snowys
Map Ref: MAP 3 C4 GPS: 35 28 32 S 148 35 45 E
8km NW of Long Plain Rd via Broken Cart Trail. Camping area located at junction with Feints Trail. Dry weather only. Ph: 02 6947 7025

332. Wood's Reserve Camping Area - ACT
Map Ref: MAP 3 D4 GPS: 35 28 51 S 148 56 21 E
Wood's Reserve Recreation Area is located on the banks of Gibraltar Creek 30km west of Canberra. Access is signposted 5.3km along Corin Rd from its junction with Tdbinbilla Rd 7km west of Point Hut Rd. Bring drinking water. Ph: 02 6207 2498

333. Honeysuckle Creek Campground - ACT
Map Ref: MAP 3 D5 GPS: 35 34 59 S 148 58 30 E
Located in Namagji NP 35km south of Canberra. Signposted access 9.5km along Apollo Rd which is signposted off Naas Rd 8km south of parks visitor centre. Located at the site of Honeysuckle Tracking Station. Bring firewood. Ph: 02 6207 2900

334. Wilkins Park - South Coast
Map Ref: MAP 3 F5 GPS: 35 35 29 S 149 26 46 E
In the town of Captains Flat 45km S of Queanbeyan. Ph: 02 4842 1144

335. Lowden Forest Park - South Coast
Map Ref: MAP 3 F4 GPS: 35 30 34 S 149 36 17 E
40kms SE of Queanbeyan via Captains Flat Rd and Coxes Creek Rd. Some sections are unsealed. Dry weather only. Ph: 1300 655 687

336. Bombay Reserve
Map Ref: MAP 3 F4 GPS: 35 25 35 S 149 42 50 E
Camping spot located 9km W of Braidwood via Cooma and Bombay Rds beside Shoalhaven River.

337. Warri Reserve - South Coast
Map Ref: MAP 3 F4 GPS: 35 20 37 S 149 44 16 E
Situated on SW bank of the Shoalhaven River 13kms NW of Braidwood. Ph: 02 4842 1144

338. Charleyong Crossing
Map Ref: MAP 3 G4 GPS: 35 14 41 S 149 53 31 E
Located 31km SW of Nerriga. Turn off Braidwood-Nerriga Rd 29km SW of Nerriga on to Mayfield-Tarago Rd. travel 3km on dirt rd.

339. Stuart's Crossing camping area - South Coast
Map Ref: MAP 3 G4 GPS: 35 14 48 S 149 53 31 E
24km N of Braidwood off the Turpentine Rd. Located on Stuart's Crossing Rd. On the banks of the Shoalhaven River. Ph: 02 4842 1144

340. Wog Wog Campging Area - Canberra
Map Ref: MAP 3 G4 GPS: 35 16 10 S 150 02 12 E
Located 25km NE of Braidwood. Access is via the Mongarlowe Rd most of which is unsealed. Ph: 02 4423 2170

341. Long Gully - South Coast
Map Ref: MAP 3 H4 GPS: 35 19 26 S 150 11 50 E
In the Budawang NP signposted access off Long Gully Rd. Once having crossed the Clyde River the bridge is 2.5km N of Blue Gum Flat Rd. Ph: 02 4454 9500

342. Yadboro Flat - South Coast
Map Ref: MAP 3 H4 GPS: 35 20 41 S 150 13 10 E
In the Yadboro Sate Forest 30km SW of Milton. On the banks of the Clyde River. Access along the Yadboro State Forest Rd. Ph: 02 4472 6211

343. Blue Gum Flat camping area - South Coast
Map Ref: MAP 3 H4 GPS: 35 22 02 S 150 12 04 E
Located beside Clyde River at end of Blue Gum Flat Rd via Yadboro Rd 35km SW of Milton. A short 32m walk to the campsite from parking area. Ph: 02 4428 6300

344. Termeil Point Campground
Map Ref: MAP 3 H4 GPS: 35 27 35 S 150 23 38 E
Located in Meroo NP. Camp area at Termeil Point 14kms S of Ulladulla. Turn E onto Blackbutt Rd and travel 2km to fork and veer R then 600m to camp area. 4WD only / high clearance offroad vans. Ph: 02 4454 9500

Lowden Forest Park

No 335

Tallaganda State Forest, NSW

40 km south east of Queanbeyan

Stephanie Jackson

The campsite has an old steam engine which is a relic from a past era.

In the past, the harsh sounds of destruction echoed through the Tallaganda State Forest that lies to the south-east of the NSW town of Queanbeyan, but today, in the heart of the forest, there's little evidence that loggers have ever visited the region.

At the site where they had camped in the 1930s, only an old steam engine and a wooden waterwheel, built in 1952 and used to generate electricity to make the simple lives of timber cutters a tad easier, show that men once lived and laboured here. The clearing among the forest is now known as Lowden Forest Park, and here, in this secluded and picturesque neck of the woods, modern day campers can set up home and look forward to days that don't involve even a few moments of hard yakka.

The park is accessed via a narrow and unsealed road that meanders past orderly pine plantations, and weaves its way through native forests where eucalypts tower over a tangled understorey of bracken and tree ferns. It's a road that requires attentive driving, for it's still used by logging trucks that may unexpectedly hurtle around the bend, but fortunately none passes within cooee of the camping area itself.

Wildlife are the only long term residents here now, and in the surrounding forest there's a good chance, if you're quiet and patient, that you'll see swamp wallabies bounding from the shadows and vanishing as quickly as they had appeared. You might be treated to an entertaining avian display of black cockatoos screeching in the forest's lofty canopy; thornbills and superb blue wrens twittering exuberantly as they dart among the tangled undergrowth; and crimson rosellas fluttering past to add a dash of red to a landscape dominated by green.

A tiny stream mutters among the emerald ferns of the forest.

There are no facilities in the camping area, but there's a pit toilet on a nearby hillside, and there are covered picnic tables in the day use picnic area which is about 100 metres away. It's here that you'll find the historic waterwheel, and the picnic area is also where two of the park's most popular walking trails begin.

The Fern Gully walking track, covering a return distance of merely 1.6kms, leads through the tangled and diverse vegetation of a forest that's dominated by lofty eucalypt species - including brown barrel, messmate, narrow leafed peppermint, ribbon gum, and scribbly gum – and down to Lowden Creek that's choked with tree ferns. It's a faint and narrow trail, with some steep sections, and appears to be little more than a wildlife highway linking the wombat burrows that are scattered across the landscape.

The Hopkins Pond walking track, covering a similar distance, is a more clearly defined trail. Leading beyond moss cloaked logs and to a tiny waterfall beside an equally tiny pond that's secluded among the emerald fronds of tree ferns, it's the easiest and most scenically spectacular of the two trails.

Lowden Forest Park is not a safe place to be in excessively wet and windy weather when branches of the trees that are in and around the camping area may come tumbling down with disastrous consequences. At other times, and when fire bans are not in place, it's an idyllic destination in which to take life easy without paying a cent for the luxury of seclusion and serenity. The only negative aspect is that the camping area is inaccessible to travellers with very large vehicles and rigs.

Just The Facts

Lowden Forest Park Camping Area

Getting there: Lowden Forest Park is approximately 40kms south-east of the NSW town of Queanbeyan, and 45kms west of Braidwood, with access being via Captains Flat Road and Coxes Creek Road. Some sections of the route are unsealed and are not suitable for large vehicles and rigs.

Facilities: There are no facilities other than a pit toilet and covered picnic tables in the day use area.

Pets: Pets are permitted.

Charges: There is no charge for camping here.

Contact: For additional information contact Forests NSW by phoning 1300 655 687 or log onto www.forests.nsw.gov.au/visiting/forests/tallaganda

Free Campsites in New South Wales

345. Meroo Head camping area - South Coast
Map Ref: MAP 3 H5 GPS: 35 28 59 S 150 23 35 E
Access via Meroo Point Rd off the Princess Highway - 4km S of Lake Tabourie within the Meroo NP. Ph: 02 4454 9500

346. Mannus Campsite - Riverina & Murray
Map Ref: MAP 3 A5 GPS: 35 46 46 S 147 56 44 E
Located 7km W of Tumbarumba via Linden Roth Drive. Beside Mannus Creek. Ph: 02 6937 2700

347. Lake Mannus Boat Ramp
Map Ref: MAP 3 A5 GPS: 35 48 40 S 147 58 38 E
Camp spot 12km W of Tumbarumba. Turn S at Mannus Campsite on Lake Rd and follow dirt rd for 5km to boat ramp.

348. Mannus Lake camping area
Map Ref: MAP 3 A5 GPS: 35 48 39 S 147 58 39 E
Located 12km W of Tumbarumba beside Mannus Lake via Jingellic Rd and then Mannus Lake Rd. Site is 5km along this road. Ph: 02 6948 3333

349. Henry Angel Flat - The Snowys
Map Ref: MAP 3 A5 GPS: 35 49 42 S 148 03 38 E
Located 8km SE of Tumbarumba beside the Burra Creek. Signposted access along the Khancoban-Corryong Rd. Ph: 02 6948 3444

350. Paddys River Flats - The Snowys
Map Ref: MAP 3 A5 GPS: 35 51 06 S 148 08 24 E
Signposted access along the Tumbarumba-Tomma Rd 17km SE of Tumbarumba. Camping beside river. Ph: 02 6948 9100

351. Paddys River Dam campsite - The Snowys
Map Ref: MAP 3 A5 GPS: 35 43 02 S 148 10 04 E
From Tumbarumba proceed north towards Batlow then at 8km take signposted Bago Forest Road and follow to Hardys Road. Ph: 02 6937 2700

352. Buddong Falls camping area - Kosciuszko NP - The Snowys
Map Ref: MAP 3 B5 GPS: 35 38 34 S 148 13 10 E
4WD vehicles only. Access from Talbingo or via Bago State Forest from Batlow. Dry weather only. Ph: 02 6450 5600

353. Yarrangobilly Village - The Snowys
Map Ref: MAP 3 B5 GPS: 35 39 13 S 148 28 02 E
On the Snowy Mtns Hwy 63kms S of Tumut. Ph: 02 6947 7025

354. Cooleman Mountain - The Snowys
Map Ref: MAP 3 C5 GPS: 35 35 51 S 148 38 23 E
Located on Blue Waterholes Access Road 2.5km E of Long Plain Road. Ph: 02 6947 7025

355. Blue Waterhole Campground - Kosciuszko NP - The Snowys
Map Ref: MAP 3 C5 GPS: 35 37 16 S 148 40 48 E
7.7km along Blue Waterholes road. 5.1km E of Colleman Mountain CA. Access road is closed in Winter (June-Oct). Dry weather only. Ph: 02 6450 5600

356. Magpie Flat Camping Area - The Snowys
Map Ref: MAP 3 C5 GPS: 35 37 17 S 148 40 48 E
Located 7.7km along Blue Waterholes Rd which is singposted off Long Plain Rd 5.1km east of Cooleman Mountain camping area 4km off Cooinbil Rd and 17km north of Snowy Mountains Hwy. No access June to Oct. Steep sections. Bring water & firewood. Ph: 02 6947 7025

357. Cooinbil Hut - The Snowys
Map Ref: MAP 3 C5 GPS: 35 37 53 S 148 35 49 E
Camping near the historic Cooinbil Hut and horse yards. Take the Cooinbil Hut access track from the Long Plain Rd 10km N of Long Plain Hut. Dry weather only. Ph: 02 6450 5600

358. Long Plain Hut camping area - Kosciuszko NP - The Snowys
Map Ref: MAP 3 C5 GPS: 35 41 49 S 148 32 14 E
3.3km NE of Snowy Mountains Hwy along Long Plain Road from Rules Point. 34km S of Talbingo turn-off Ph: 02 6450 5600

359. Ghost Gully Horse Camp - The Snowys
Map Ref: MAP 3 C5 GPS: 35 41 33 S 148 35 32 E
Access camp via Snowy Mountains Hwy along Long Plain Rd after 3km signposted access on to Port Phillip Rd after 3km on to Port Phillip Fire Trail. Ph: 02 6947 7025

360. Ravine camping area (Lobbs Hole) - The Snowys
Map Ref: MAP 3 B5 GPS: 35 47 10 S 148 23 57 E
Dispersed camping beside Yarrangobilly River - 16.4km N off the Kiandra-Cabramurra Rd via Lobbs-Hole Ravine Rd. Lobbs Hole Ravine Rd is signposted off Kiandra - Cabramurra Rd. Ph: 02 6947 7025

Featured Campsite

Brought to you by

Yarrangobilly Village

No 353

Northern Kosciuszko National Park, NSW

63km south of Tumut

Catherine Lawson & David Bristow

Historic Cotterill's Cottage sits nestled on a bend in the Yarrangobilly River, a blink-and-you'll-miss-it spot along the Snowy Mountains Highway.

Built in 1898 by the then local postmaster Walter Hoad, the cottage is one of the oldest in Kosciuszko National Park and the last one standing in a town that once boasted 10 houses, a store, school and a police station constructed to protect the Gold Escort delivering precious cargo from the fields at nearby Kiandra on its journey north to Tumut.

Travellers of a very different kind now stake out the grassy riverside nooks beside Cotterill's Cottage, which was included in Northern Kosciuszko National Park in 1970.

Easily accessible to large rigs, the camping area has picnic tables shaded by riverside trees, fireplaces, bins and a toilet, but no water except what you take from the crystal-clear river.

The camp is ideally located for those visiting Yarrangobilly Caves, part of a system of 200 caves along a 12-kilometre-long limestone belt that has been developed into a popular tourist attraction.

Self-guided tours of South Glory at Yarrangobilly Caves cost $13/adult, $8/concession and $30/family (two adults and up to three children), plus a $3 vehicle entry fee which permits access to a natural thermal bathing pool, short walking trails and a barbecue and picnic area.

To book guided tours, phone Yarrangobilly Caves on (02) 6454 9597.

The Yarrangobilly River.

Cotterill's Cottage is one of the oldest houses in Kosciuszko National Park.

A relic old steam engine sits in the park.

Unlike the southern section of Kosciuszko National Park where toll booths charge vehicles $16 per day, entry to the north is free. The best time to visit is after the snow melts in springtime and Australian brumbies return to the high country.

Just beyond Yarrangobilly Village, 1330 metres above sea level on the vast Treeless Plains, 4WD tracks suitable for mountain bikers and horseriders lead to historic cattlemen's huts, waterholes and more remote camping spots, some that cater to horses with permanent yards and loading ramps.

Here we watched a herd of brumbies grazing on plains peppered with everlasting daisies.

The easiest hut for conventional vehicles to reach is Long Plain Hut, signposted off the Snowy Mountains Highway via Long Plain Road (open during summer only).

Built in early 1900s and restored in 2002, Long Plain Hut provides a campground with picnic tables, fireplaces, a toilet and facilities for horses.

Travelling further across the plains, 4WD vehicles can reach the Blue Waterholes and walkers can tackle Clarke Gorge Track (2.5km return) or Nicole Gorge Track (6.3km return).

The best nearby spot for boat fishing is Blowering Dam, 17 kilometres south of Tumut, popular for its eight free campgrounds, boat ramps, good facilities and unrestricted stays.

It's not just the fish that make this dam popular. Eastern grey kangaroos flourish on the grassy flats, while gang-gang cockatoos, crimson rosellas, wallabies, echidnas and wombats stake out the woodlands.

You can fish Yarrangobilly River for trout between the long weekends in October and June. A NSW recreational fishing licence is easily purchased online, priced at $6 (valid 3 days), $12 (valid one month) or $30 for a year. Kids under 18 years fish for free.

Just The Facts

Yarrangobilly Village

Getting there: Head south of Tumut on the Snowy Mountains Highway for 63km.

Facilities: Picnic tables, fireplaces, bins and a toilet. BYO firewood and water or take it from the river and boil before drinking.

Rates: Free.

Wheelchair Access: No.

Pets: No.

Contact: National Parks in Tumut on (02) 6947 7025 or head to www.environment.nsw.gov.au/nationalparks. To purchase a fishing licence go to www.licence.nsw.gov.au

Free Campsites in New South Wales

361. Bullocks Hill horse camp
Map Ref: MAP 3 C5 GPS: 35 46 37 S 148 31 06 E
Situated 430m along Bullocks Hill Fire Trail which is signposted off the Snowy Mountains Hwy - 11km N of Mt Selwyn turn-off. Dry weather only. Ph: 02 6947 7025

362. O'Hares camping area - Kosciuszko NP - The Snowys
Map Ref: MAP 3 B5 GPS: 35 49 20 S 148 21 55 E
Near site of Sue City. 20km N of Cabramurra beside Talbingo Reservoir. Accessed off Elliott Way. Ph: 02 6450 5600

363. Three Mile Dam - The Snowys
Map Ref: MAP 3 B6 GPS: 35 53 21 S 148 26 54 E
Take the Mt Selwyn turnoff off the Snowy Mountains Hwy for approx 5.5km. Camping areas on both east & west side of dam (fees apply in winter). Ph: 02 6947 7025

364. Eucumbene River - The Snowys
Map Ref: MAP 3 C6 GPS: 35 53 05 S 148 30 48 E
Access to the Eucumbene River with Great fishing off the Snowy Mountains Hwy just N of The Resthouse. Or 5.5km off the Mt Selwyn turnoff. Ph: 02 6947 7025

365. Wares Yard Horse Camp - The Snowys
Map Ref: MAP 3 C6 GPS: 35 52 43 S 148 37 51 E
Signposted access along Tantangara Rd - 7km N of the Snowy Mountains Hwy which is signposted 19km NW of Adaminaby. Ph: 02 6947 7025

366. Rocky Plain horse camp - The Snowys
Map Ref: MAP 3 C6 GPS: 35 53 50 S 148 32 58 E
Signposted access on Snowy Mountains Hwy - 500m E of Sawyers Hut. Horse yards and loading ramp. Ph: 02 6947 7025

367. Tumut Pond Bush camping area - The Snowys
Map Ref: MAP 3 B6 GPS: 35 57 59 S 148 25 19 E
6km E of Cabramurra. Road closed during winter. Signposted off the King's Cross Rd. Dry weather only. Ph: 02 6947 7025

368. Denison camping area - The Snowys
Map Ref: MAP 3 C6 GPS: 35 56 46 S 148 36 20 E
With access to Lake Eucumbene this camping ground is located off the Snowy Mountains Hwy 2km W of Tantangara Rd. Ph: 02 6947 7025

369. Berlang camping area - South Coast
Map Ref: MAP 3 F5 GPS: 35 43 28 S 149 38 46 E
Within the Deua NP 41Km S of Braidwood near Shoalhaven River. Signposted access along Krawarree Road Ph: 02 6496 1500

370. Wyanbene Caves - South Coast
Map Ref: MAP 3 F6 GPS: 35 47 41 S 149 40 59 E
48km S of Braidwood on the Wyanbene Rd signposted off the Krawarree Rd. Ph: 02 4476 2888

371. Araluen Creek - South Coast
Map Ref: MAP 3 G5 GPS: 35 37 35 S 149 47 50 E
Located 3km west of the Araluen Valley Hotel 50kms west of Moruya. Ph: 02 4842 1144

372. Currowan Creek - South Coast
Map Ref: MAP 3 G5 GPS: 35 34 31 S 150 04 39 E
Within the Currowan State Forest 15km NW Batemans Bay. From the Kings Hwy take the signposted Lyons Rd to the bridge over the creek and to the camp area. Ph: 02 9871 3377

373. Pretty Beach Camping Area - South Coast
Map Ref: MAP 3 H5 GPS: 35 34 03 S 150 21 56 E
Take signposted road to Bawley Point from Termeil on the Princes Hwy 20km south of Ulladulla. Follow for 5.5km to Bawley Point then take signposted Murramarang Rd for 7km south to signposted Merry Beach Rd. Follow this road for 500m and take signposted Pretty Beach Rd then 800m to camp area. Ph: 02 4454 9500

374. Depot Beach Camping Ground - South Coast
Map Ref: MAP 3 H5 GPS: 35 37 43 S 150 19 17 E
Within the Murramarang NP and accessed via the signposted Mt Agony Rd/ Depot Beach Rd 13km north of Batemans Bay off the Princes Hwy at East Lynne. Follow MtAgony Rd for 5km to signposted Depot Beach and follow for 3km to signposted Depot Beach access rd. Ph: 02 4454 9500

375. Deua River camping area - South Coast
Map Ref: MAP 3 G5 GPS: 35 44 54 S 149 54 58 E
36km NW of Moruya located in the Deua NP on the near the Deua River via Araluen Rd. Ph: 02 4476 2888

376. Bakers Flat camping area - South Coast
Map Ref: MAP 3 G5 GPS: 35 44 50 S 149 55 36 E
35km NW of Moruya located in the Deua NP on the near the Deua River. Access via Araluen Rd. Ph: 02 4476 2888

Featured Campsite

Brought to you by

Three Mile Dam

No 363

Northern Kosciuszko National Park, NSW
6kms from Kiandra

By Gregg Haythorpe

Finding that 'special'camping location is a little like winning at the races or the footy, you try many times but only get lucky on a few occasions. Well for us the Three Mile Dam campsite in the Kosciuszko National Park is one such camping location.

The camping grounds are located in the Kosciuszko NP on the northern side of Mt Selwyn just off the Cabramurra-Kiandra Road, (about 6 kms from Kiandra and 14 kms before Cabramurra). The camp grounds are on both sides of the picturesque Three Mile Dam, the dam which is fringed with hundreds of snow gums is about 1400 metres above sea level. Built in the 1880s by Chinese gold miners to provide water for their gold sluicing operations, then many years later in the 1950s it became a base camp during the building of the Snowy Mountains Hydro-electric scheme.

Today its location and beauty have made it a top class camping and picnic location that is popular with many in particular during the summer months. The other great attraction of this campsite is the presence of wild brumbies. Now I can't promise that they are there all year round but your chances of a close encounter with these wild beautiful creatures is high and is a memorable experience.

There is plenty of space to set up and relax.

Brumbies aside, the Three Mile Dam has plenty of other options to tempt, the dam waters hold a healthy population of trout and there are great options for bushwalking and mountain bikes. Winter has the campsite closed as it spends many months covered in the white stuff, the normal opening time is the long weekend in October depending on snow conditions and it closes with the Queen's birthday weekend in early June.

So if you are travelling the NSW High Country and looking for a great overnight campsite or a place to enjoy for a few days then check out Three Mile Dam, equipped with pit toilets, picnic tables and fireplaces on both sides of the dam it's a top class campsite that you may get to share with the mountain brumbies.

You'll see wild brumbies in the area.

Just The Facts

Three Mile Dam

Getting there. Located in the Kosciuszko NP along the Cabramurra-Kiandra Road ,some 6kms from Kiandra and 14kms from Cabramurra.
Facilities. Plenty of good sizes campsites with pit toilets, fireplaces and picnic tables. Phones do work.
Pets. No pets in the National Park.
Charges. Camping is free.
Contact .NSW National Parks, 1300 361 967 or www.nationalparks.nsw.gov.au

377. North Head Beach - South Coast
Map Ref: MAP 3 H5 GPS: 35 43 10 S 150 16 50 E
From the Princes Hwy take the signposted road to South Durras and Murramarang Resort which is 24km S of Termeil or 9km N of Batemans Bay. Ph: 02 4454 9500

378. Bendethera Valley - South Coast
Map Ref: MAP 3 F6 GPS: 35 58 16 S 149 44 46 E
In Deua NP 46km W of Moruya via the Bendethera Fire Trail from Little Sugarloaf Rd. Ph: 02 4476 2888

379. Congo Camping Area - South Coast
Map Ref: MAP 3 H6 GPS: 35 57 15 S 150 09 25 E
Take the signposted South Head Rd off the Princes Hwy south of Moruya. After 2.1km take signposted Congo Rd and follow for 9.2km to camping area. Ph: 02 4476 2888

380. Towong Reserve - Upper Murray
Map Ref: MAP 3 A6 GPS: 36 07 24 S 147 59 59 E
Located 23km S of Tooma beside Murray River bridge. Ph: 02 6948 3333

381. Leatherbarrel Creek camping area - Kosciuszko NP - The Snowys
Map Ref: MAP 3 A8 GPS: 36 31 33 S 148 11 36 E
16km W of Thredbo on Alpine Way. Ph: 02 6450 5600

382. Ngarigo camping area - Kosciuszko NP - The Snowys
Map Ref: MAP 3 B8 GPS: 36 27 30 S 148 23 04 E
Close to Thredbo River. Access via Alpine Way - 3.6km W of Thredbo Diggins CA and 8.1km E of Thredbo. Ph: 02 6450 5600

383. Thredbo Diggins camping area -Kosciuszko NP - The Snowys
Map Ref: MAP 3 B8 GPS: 36 26 49 S 148 25 31 E
Limited sites. Access via Alpine Way - 1.4km from the park entrance. Ph: 02 6450 5600

384. Island Bend camping area - Kosciuszko NP - The Snowys
Map Ref: MAP 3 B7 GPS: 36 19 37 S 148 28 22 E
Site of former Snowy Hydro work camp near Snowy River. Grassy sites 23km NW of Jindabyne via Guthega Road. Ph: 02 6450 5600

385. Badja Recreation Reserve - South Coast
Map Ref: MAP 3 E7 GPS: 36 10 26 S 149 21 02 E
22kms E of Cooma. Cross bridge over Numeralla River on E side of town. Turn N into Peak View Rd. Reserve is approx 50m from corner. Ph: 02 6450 1777

386. Numeralla camping area - The Snowys
Map Ref: MAP 3 E7 GPS: 36 10 27 S 149 20 56 E
Camping ground is in the village - 22km NE of Cooma. Ph: 1800 636 525

387. Cascades - South Coast
Map Ref: MAP 3 F7 GPS: 36 13 45 S 149 31 12 E
Located in Wadbilliga NP. Access of Petes Road which is signposted off Badja Forest Road. Further signposted off the Braidwood Rd. Camping beside Tuross River. Ph: 02 4476 2888

388. Lake Creek - South Coast
Map Ref: MAP 3 F7 GPS: 36 15 42 S 149 39 21 E
Located in Wadbilliga NP. Signposted access 37km W of Cobargo from Princes Hwy head west along Wandella Rd then take signposted Towrie Rd to Bourkes Rd. Ph: 02 4476 2888

389. Badgerys Lookout
Map Ref: MAP 3 H2 GPS: 34 46 23 S 150 06 08 E
Camp spot 8kms S of Tallong via Caoura Rd & Badgerys Lookout Rd.

389. Bodalla Forest Park Camp Area - South Coast
Map Ref: MAP 3 G7 GPS: 36 09 02 S 150 05 42 E
Signposted acess on the Princes Hwy 9km north of Narooma and 9km south of Bodalla. Overnight only. Ph: 02 4472 6211

390. Brou Lake - South Coast
Map Ref: MAP 3 G7 GPS: 36 07 44 S 150 07 26 E
Off the Princess Hwy 9km N of Narooma take the signposted Brou Lake Rd. Camping on shore of Lake. Ph: 02 4476 2888

391. Wagonga picnic & camping area - South Coast
Map Ref: MAP 3 G7 GPS: 36 13 10 S 150 04 05 E
Outside Narooma take Wagonga Scenic Drive from Princes Hwy and follow signs. Ph: 02 4472 6211

392. Mystery Bay Campground
Map Ref: MAP 3 G8 GPS: 36 17 54 S 150 08 00 E
10km S of Narooma or 27kms NE of Cobargo onto Mystery Bay Rd. Ph: 0428 622 357

Featured Campsite

Brought to you by

Badja Reserve No 385

Numeralla, NSW
22kms east of Cooma

Stephanie Jackson

The Badja reserve is a quiet spot to set up camp.

The tiny NSW town of Numeralla, merely 22kms east of Cooma, is not on the itinerary of many travellers, for there's little to see or do here. There's one good reason to drop into this forgotten corner of the world however, and it's called the Badja Recreational Reserve. Here, where the meandering waters of the diminutive Badja River unite with those of the slightly larger Numeralla River, you can camp free of charge, but I have to warn you that it's a dangerous place.

Prominent signs warn of the risks from falling trees and branches, uneven ground, steep drop offs beside the river, submerged obstacles in the water, and wild animals. If you're careful when selecting a site to set up camp, if you watch your step, and if you don't dive into the inviting water, you'll be safe enough. And if you're wondering what wild animals pose a threat here, I can assure you that no crocodiles will come prowling around your campsite, and that the possums that snarl as darkness descends over the landscape are completely harmless - at least to humans.

I can only surmise that the creator of the reserve's signs regards wombats as dangerous, for unwary campers could tumble into the cavernous burrows they have excavated on the riverbank. Danger might also come from a fox that could mistake a traveller's poodle for one of the succulent lambs in a nearby paddock, and then of course there's Molly. This cattle dog, the best mate of a nearby resident, trots across to the camping area to welcome every visitor, and there's always the risk that she might batter your leg with her vigorously wagging tail.

Molly's jovial owner reckons that the only danger at the Badja Reserve is from the sharp edges of metal signs, but all that gave me a fright were the acorns of an ancient oak tree that, in the middle of the night, unexpectedly rained down onto the roof of my tent.

Other trees, immense and gnarled eucalypts festooned with tattered ribbons of bark, provide some shade and line the banks of the two rivers that separate the reserve from farmlands and from the township that, with a population of merely 50 people and with no shops or other commercial facilities, is never a hive of activity.

The facilities at the reserve include picnic tables and fire places, and flushing toilets in a small brick building on the opposite side of the Jerangle road that borders the camping/ recreation area.

The Badja Reserve, with little passing traffic, is a quiet spot to relax. Magpies will welcome a fine day with their melodic songs, crimson rosellas will chirp, wrens will twitter, and crows will make their familiar and mournful caws. But if tranquillity tops your list of essential ingredients for a good campsite, then the Badja Recreational Reserve won't disappoint you.

Just The Facts

Badja Reserve

Getting there: Numeralla is 22kms east of the NSW town of Cooma. To reach the Badja Reserve, cross the bridge over the Numeralla River on the eastern side of the town and turn north into Peak View Road. The reserve is on the western side of the road and approximately 50 metres from the corner.

Facilities: The reserve's facilities include picnic tables and flushing toilets. Campfires are permitted. There are no shops or other commercial facilities at Numeralla.

Pets: Pets are permitted.

Charges: There is no charge for camping here.

Contact: For additional regional information contact Numeralla and District Activities Inc. by phoning 02 6453 3009.

The reserve is on the bank of the Numeralla River.

393. Cobargo Hotel
Map Ref: MAP 3 G8 GPS: 36 23 22 S 149 53 09 E
Parking area behind Cobargo Hotel on Princes Hwy Cobargo. Check in with publican, fee for showers. Ph: 02 6493 6423

394. Halfway Flat camping area - The Snowys
Map Ref: MAP 3 B9 GPS: 36 45 46 S 148 26 01 E
Signposted access On The Barry Way S of Jindabyne. 2km S of the Jacobs River camping area. Ph: 02 6450 5600

395. Jacobs River camping area - The Snowys
Map Ref: MAP 3 B9 GPS: 36 45 02 S 148 27 04 E
Signposted access on Barry Way - 54km S of Jindabyne. Ph: 02 6450 5600

396. No Name Picnic and camping area - Kosciuszko NP - The Snowys
Map Ref: MAP 3 B9 GPS: 36 46 08 S 148 25 18 E
Near Snowy River (small campsite). 1.7km S of Halfway camp area and 3.4km N of Pinch River camp area on the Barry Way. Ph: 02 6450 5600

397. Pinch River camping area - Kosciuszko NP - The Snowys
Map Ref: MAP 3 B9 GPS: 36 47 31 S 148 25 18 E
From Jindabyne head W on Kosciuszko Rd taking signposted left turn at second roundabout. Campsite on the Barry Way. Ph: 02 6450 5600

398. Running Waters - The Snowys
Map Ref: MAP 3 B9 GPS: 36 48 47 S 148 24 16 E
Signposted access 63km S of Jindabyne via Barry Way. Ph: 02 6450 5600

399. Scotchies Yard camping area - The Snowys
Map Ref: MAP 3 B9 GPS: 36 52 01 S 148 25 02 E
Signposted access on Barry Way - 7.9km S of Running Waters CA and 3km N of Willis CA. Ph: 02 6450 5600

400. Brown Mountain Camp Area
Map Ref: MAP 3 E9 GPS: 36 36 31 S 149 25 58 E
Located on Wattle Rd, Bemboka 22kms SE of Nimmitabel behind truck parking area. Ph: 13 22 13

401. Nunnock Campground - South Coast
Map Ref: MAP 3 E9 GPS: 36 42 12 S 149 26 50 E
Take Tantawangalo Mountain Rd from Mt Darragh Rd then New Line Rd then Packers Swamp Rd and then Cattlemans Link Trail. Dry weather only. Ph: 02 6458 4080

402. Alexanders Hut camping area - South Coast
Map Ref: MAP 3 E9 GPS: 36 43 27 S 149 28 02 E
Located in South East Forests National Park. From Nunnock camping ground continue S past Cattleman's Link trail. Ph: 02 6458 4080

403. Postman's camping area - South Coast
Map Ref: MAP 3 E9 GPS: 36 45 59 S 149 32 36 E
In the South East Forest NP. Signposted access on Tantawangalo Mountain Road - 23km W of Candelo. Ph: 02 6458 4080

404. Six Mile Creek - South Coast
Map Ref: MAP 3 E9 GPS: 36 47 15 S 149 32 26 E
Camp Area 12km W of Candelo on the Tantawangalo Mountain Rd. Dry weather only. Ph: 02 6458 4080

405. Dr William Loftus Park
Map Ref: MAP 3 F9 GPS: 36 46 00 S 149 41 42 E
Area on Williams St Candelo, opposite general store. Donation. Ph: 02 6499 2222

406. Aragunnu Camping Area - South Coast
Map Ref: MAP 3 G9 GPS: 36 35 05 S 150 02 41 E
Located in Mimosa Rocks NP south of Bermagui and north of Tathra. Signposted access along the Bermagui-Tathra Rd 20km south of Bermagui and 2km north of Wapengo Lake Rd. The 2.7km to start of camping areas. Bring drinking water. Ph: 02 4476 2888

407. Gillards Beach Camping Area - South Coast
Map Ref: MAP 3 G9 GPS: 36 39 40 S 149 59 56 E
Signposted along the Bermagui-Tathra Rd 4km south of Middle Beach access road. Then in 3.5 km to camp area. Bring drinking water & firewood. Ph: 02 4476 2888

408. Hobart Beach Camping Area - South Coast
Map Ref: MAP 3 G9 GPS: 36 47 48 S 149 56 23 E
Signposted access of Sapphire Coast Drive 15km north of Merimbula via Bournda Rd. Then in 3.5km to large camping area. Ph: 02 6495 5000

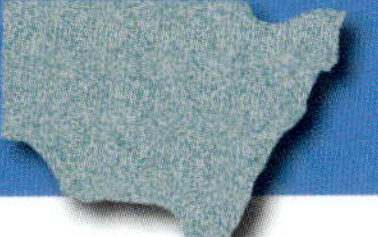

Free Campsites in New South Wales

409. Waratah Gully - South Coast
Map Ref: MAP 3 E10 GPS: 37 00 15 S 149 23 10 E
Located in South East Forest NP the Coollangubra section. Aaccessible from Bombala on Buckley Spring Rd along Coollangubra Way and Wog Wog Way. Ph: 02 6458 4080

410. Newtons Crossing - South Coast
Map Ref: MAP 3 F11 GPS: 37 16 10 S 149 40 40 E
Within Timbillica State Forest 30km SW of Eden via Imlay Rd. On to Allan Brook Rd to the camp area. Dry weather only. Ph: 02 6496 1500

411. Scrubby Creek Picnic & Camping Area - South Coast
Map Ref: MAP 3 F11 GPS: 37 13 20 S 149 49 49 E
Located 23km S of Eden. Signposted access on Princes Hwy. More of an overnight rest area than a long term camp ground. Convenient location. Ph: 02 6496 1500

412. Saltwater Creek Camping Area - South Coast
Map Ref: MAP 3 G11 GPS: 37 10 08 S 150 00 01 E
Located on Saltwater Rd 40km south of Eden. Take Edrom Rd which is signposted off Princes Hwy 18km south of Eden. Follow 5.7km to signposted Green Cape/Saltwater and follow to junction with Duckhole Rd. Take Duckhole Rd north for 4km to signposted Saltwater Creek then 4.1km to camp area. Bring drinking water & firewood. Ph: 02 6495 5000

413. Dead Horse Gully Campground - Outback
Map Ref: MAP 4 B1 GPS: 29 25 03 S 142 00 03 E
Within the Sturt NP signposted access 1km north of Tibooburra on Silver City Hwy then 1.9km to camping area. Bring drinking water. Ph: 08 8091 3308

414. Milparinka Free Camping Area - Outback
Map Ref: MAP 4 B2 GPS: 29 44 01 S 141 53 01 E
Situated 42kms S of Tibooburra and 2kms from the Silver City Hwy. Ph: 08 8091 2524

415. Evelyn Creek - Outback
Map Ref: MAP 4 B2 GPS: 29 44 03 S 141 53 04 E
1km E of Milparinka off the Silver City Hwy via the Milparinka Rd. Ph: 08 8091 3863

416. Cobham Lake North
Map Ref: MAP 4 B2 GPS: 30 08 05 S 142 05 37 E
Camp spot 235km N of Broken Hill - SW off Silver City Hwy. GPS at track entrance. SW side of Hwy.

417. Cobham Lake South
Map Ref: MAP 4 B3 GPS: 30 10 04 S 142 06 08 E
Camp spot 229km N of Broken Hill - NW off Silver City Hwy. GPS at track entrance.

418. Wanaaring - Paroo River camping area
Map Ref: MAP 4 E2 GPS: 29 42 19 S 144 08 55 E
Located in the town of Wanaaring 190km NW of Bourke. Ph: 02 6874 7720

419. Bourke's Fishing Reserve - Outback
Map Ref: MAP 4 G3 GPS: 30 05 04 S 145 53 17 E
Approx 4km west of Bourke via Anson Street. Signposted to multiple camping sites along the Darling River. Ph: 02 6872 1321

420. Mays Bend camping area - Outback
Map Ref: MAP 4 G3 GPS: 30 02 40 S 146 01 50 E
On the banks of the Darling River some 10km N of North Bourke take signposted Mays Bend Road. Ph: 02 6872 1222

421. Four Mile Campground
Map Ref: MAP 4 H3 GPS: 29 59 06 S 146 55 02 E
Camp area 6km E of Brewarrina via Coolabah-Brewarrina Rd & Billybingbone Brae for 5km. Follow blue signs. Ph: 02 6830 5152

422. Brewarrina Boat Ramp camp Area
Map Ref: MAP 4 H3 GPS: 29 56 57 S 146 51 54 E
Camp area 1.5km N side of Brewarrina town at 50953 Kamilaroi Hwy. South side of bridge Ph: 02 6830 5152

423. Four Mile Reserve - Outback
Map Ref: MAP 4 H3 GPS: 29 59 10 S 146 55 03 E
The reserve is approx 4kms S of Brewarrina via Carinda Rd. Ph: 02 6830 5152

424. Culgoa River Campground - North West
Map Ref: MAP 4 J1 GPS: 29 05 53 S 147 05 23 E
Camp Area 100km N of Brewarrina. Signposted access along the Goodooga Rd 9km N of entering the park then Tatala track. Ph: 02 6871 2744

Featured Campsite

Brought to you by

kokodacaravans.com.au

Milparinka Free Camping Area No 414

Milparinka, NSW
42kms south of Tibooburra

Stephanie Jackson

The ruins of the post office are only a short walk away from the camping area.

I rolled into the outback town of Milparinka with a vision of an evening at the pub where I'd tuck into a succulent steak and warm myself beside a roaring log fire. Life at this tiny NSW settlement had virtually ground to a halt since my previous visit however, and today the town has a permanent population of merely two hardy folk, and the pub, with a lack of patrons, closed its doors long ago.

Now the only activity at Milparinka is centred around the historic courthouse where it's tourists, rather a stream of villains and burly coppers, parade through the hallways of this grand old sandstone building. It's here, in rooms that now accommodate the town's information centre, that volunteers welcome visitors with a smile and with reams of information about Milparinka's brief but colourful past. The town had been the hub of a short-lived gold mining boom, but there's little to see here today other than the pub, the courthouse, the adjacent police barracks, and the ruins of the general store and the post office.

What makes Milparinka a worthwhile port of call is not merely its visible links to the past, but the fact that it's a quiet place to spend the night. And there are two camping options - both of which involve no expense at all.

Camping on the shaded banks of Evelyn Creek, which is more often a dry and sandy watercourse than a stream of any significance, was my first preference, but with large mounds of gravel heaped along the road in readiness for road works, the camping area, on the creek's eastern bank, was temporarily inaccessible.

The only other option was to set up camp on the vacant land between the pub and the courthouse. It's a large level area where there's room for vehicles and rigs of every conceivable size, but it has no trees to offer shade or shelter from the cold winds that often sweep across the landscape in winter. The only facilities are flushing toilets, which are modern and immaculately clean, and while there's no charge for camping here, a small donation to assist with the maintenance of the toilets and of the town's historic precinct is appreciated.

With the town being two kilometres west of the Silver City Highway that links the neighbouring town of Tibooburra to the distant city of Broken Hill, the nights here are usually as quiet as the vacuum within a celestial black hole. But when the local dogs decide to bark at nocturnal shadows, the silence of the outback is abruptly shattered, and with no neighbours to complain, the owner of these friendly mutts does nothing to quell the ruckus that's guaranteed to annoy even those who sleep almost as soundly as the dead.

There's no chance to have a friendly yarn with the locals here, for the only people you'll meet, in addition to other travellers, are the volunteers at the information centre who are often travellers themselves who've stopped to lend a hand.

If you dawdle along the town's short historic walking track, you'll see the crumbling visible reminders of a town that has fallen from glory to dust, but spend a night Milparinka and you'll discover that there's still a hint of treasure to be found.

Just The Facts

Milparinka Camping Area

Getting there: Milparinka is 42kms south of the NSW outback town of Tibooburra, and 2kms from the Silver City Highway that links this remote settlement to the city of Broken Hill. The camping area can be accessed by all vehicles and rigs.
Facilities: The only facilities at the camping area are flushing toilets that are clean, and well maintained. There are no facilities in the town, and fuel and food are not available here.
Pets: Pets are permitted.
Charges: There is no charge for camping here, but a small donation towards the maintenance of the toilets and the town's historic buildings is appreciated.
Contact: Phone the Milparinka Visitor Information Centre on 08 8091 2524 for additional details.

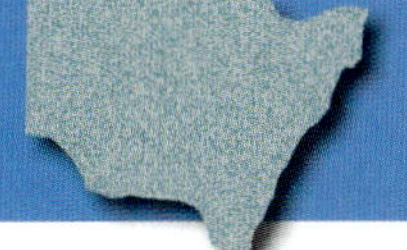

Free Campsites in New South Wales

425. Goodooga Artesian Baths
Map Ref: MAP 4 J1 GPS: 29 06 37 S 147 27 21 E
Camp area on Hammond St, Goodooga N side of town. 74km NW of Lightning Ridge or 40km SW of Hebel. Ph: 02 6830 5100

426. Angledool Weir
Map Ref: MAP 4 K1 GPS: 29 06 48 S 147 54 17 E
Camp spot 19.5km S of Hebel. Areas E side of Hwy and both sides of weir.

427. Glengarry Hilton
Map Ref: MAP 4 J2 GPS: 29 40 11 S 147 36 56 E
Camp area 75km W of Lightning Ridge via Cumborah & Walgett Goodooga Rd. Patronage appreciated. Ph: 02 6829 3983

428. The Sheepyard Inn
Map Ref: MAP 4 J2 GPS: 29 41 20 S 147 37 41 E
Camp area at Grawin opposite the Inn. Approx 73km W of Lightning Ridge via Cumborah & Walgett Goodooga Rd. Ph: 02 6829 3932

429. Cumborah Park Reserve
Map Ref: MAP 4 K2 GPS: 29 44 43 S 147 46 19 E
Camping in Cumborah S end of main road. Ph: 0418 317 002

430. Pagan Creek Bridge
Map Ref: MAP 4 K3 GPS: 29 59 13 S 148 09 18 E
Camping are 6km N of Walgett. 1.5km N of Castlereagh & Kamilaroi Hwys junction.

431. Tilpa Weir - Outback
Map Ref: MAP 4 E4 GPS: 30 55 12 S 144 27 50 E
On the Darling River 6km E of Tilpa on the Tilpa-Louth Rd. Ph: 02 6837 3928

432. Louth Camp St - Outback
Map Ref: MAP 4 F3 GPS: 30 32 08 S 145 06 46 E
Camp Spot at Louth beside Darling River. Camp on both sides of the river. Ph: 02 6872 1222

433. Humes Creek bush camping
Map Ref: MAP 4 G3 GPS: 30 24 51 S 145 28 57 E
56km S of the Kidman Way on the Bourke-Louth Road. Campsites on eastern side of the Darling River. Access is 400m S of the sign on northern banks of Humes Creek. Ph: 02 6872 1321

434. Dry Tank camping ground - Outback
Map Ref: MAP 4 G3 GPS: 30 31 04 S 145 42 52 E
Within the Gundabooka NP. 50km S of Bourke via the Kidman Way. Numerous campsites. Ph: 02 6872 2744

435. Quambone Primitive Campsite
Map Ref: MAP 4 J4 GPS: 30 56 01 S 147 52 16 E
Camp area at Quambone - Mungie St near swimming pool & tennis courts. Keys at General Store. Ph: 03 6827 1923

436. Nakadoo Camp Area
Map Ref: MAP 4 K4 GPS: 30 55 41 S 148 22 28 E
Located 4km N of Coonamble - Castlereagh Hwy. Ph: 0428 221 861

437. Coonamble Showground
Map Ref: MAP 4 K4 GPS: 30 57 58 S 148 23 17 E
Camp area S of town on Castlereagh Hwy, Coonamble. Donation at Visitors Centre. Ph: 02 6827 1981

438. Homestead Creek camping area -Outback
Map Ref: MAP 4 B4 GPS: 31 16 56 S 142 17 38 E
Within the Mutawintji NP. Access signposted off the Broken Hill-White Cliffs Rd - 61km NE of the Silver City Hwy. Then 14km E to the parks information centre. 1.5km from Information centre via signs. Ph: 02 8088 3200

439. Umberumberka Reservoir
Map Ref: MAP 4 A5 GPS: 31 48 52 S 141 12 32 E
Via Silverton 36NW of Broken Hill.

440. Penrose Park - Outback
Map Ref: MAP 4 A5 GPS: 31 52 52 S 141 13 37 E
Signposted access off the Broken Hill Rd 1km east of Silverton then drive 1km to park. Bring drinking water & firewood. Ph: 08 8088 5307

Free Campsites in New South Wales

441. Border Gate Roadhouse
Map Ref: MAP 4 A5   GPS: 32 04 42 S 141 00 06 E
Area on NSW/SA Border 48kms west of Broken Hill on Barrier Hwy. Share with trucks. Ph: 0422 705 571

442. Lake Cawndilla camping area - Outback
Map Ref: MAP 4 B6   GPS: 32 26 05 S 142 15 05 E
4km W of Menindee signposted access along Lake Drive in the Kinchega NP. Ph: 08 8080 3200

443. Darling River Camping Area - Outback
Map Ref: MAP 4 C6   GPS: 32 23 51 S 142 22 30 E
Located in Kinchega NP 5km south of Menindee and 110km south east of Broken Hill. Numerous campsites signposted along 12km of the river and access along River Drive via Old Pooncarie Rd from Menindee. Ph: 08 8080 3200

444. Emu Lake Camping Area - Outback
Map Ref: MAP 4 C6   GPS: 32 28 13 S 142 20 52 E
Signposted access along Emu Lake Drive 400m north of Kinchega NP visitor information centre. Emu Lake Drive is signposted off the Old Pooncarie Rd 14km south of Menindee. Bring drinking water & firewood. Ph: 08 8080 3200

445. Lake Pamamaroo camping area - Outback
Map Ref: MAP 4 C6   GPS: 32 18 41 S 142 29 10 E
In the Menindee Lake system on the lake's foreshore on the Main Weir Rd which is off the Menindee-Broken Hill Rd. Ph: 08 8091 4274

446. Burke and Wills Campground - Outback
Map Ref: MAP 4 C6   GPS: 32 18 17 S 142 29 54 E
Located within the Menindee Lake system. Ssignpost access along Main Weir Rd 8.5km E of the Menindee-Broken Hill Rd. Ph: 08 8091 4274

447. Menindee Lakes - Far West
Map Ref: MAP 4 C6   GPS: 32 18 17 S 142 29 57 E
118km SE of Broken Hill. Turn off is 8km NW of Menindee. Take the dirt road NE to the weir for 9km.

448. Main Weir Campground - Outback
Map Ref: MAP 4 C6   GPS: 32 18 49 S 142 30 25 E
Camp Area 19km NE of Menindee. Turn E off Menindee-Broken Hill Rd onto Main Weir Rd. Camping beside Darling River. Ph: 08 8091 4274

449. Coach and Horses Camping Ground - Outback
Map Ref: MAP 4 D4   GPS: 31 27 22 S 143 49 38 E
Located in Paroo-Darling NP. Ssignposted access 46km north of the Barrier Hwy along the Wilcannia-Bourke Rd. Then 800m to camp area. Bring drinking water. Ph: 08 8088 3200

450. The Newey-Cobar - Outback
SITE CLOSED
Map Ref: MAP 4 G5   GPS: 31 30 33 S 145 49 50 E
Located in the town of Cobar. Ph: 02 6836 2448

451. The Old Res - Outback
Map Ref: MAP 4 G5   GPS: 31 28 53 S 145 51 32 E
Situated approx 3kms N of Cobar with final section unsealed and impassable after rain. Dry weather only. Ph: 02 6836 2448

452. Glenhope Camp Area
Map Ref: MAP 4 G5   GPS: 31 30 17 S 145 54 09 E
Camp area 5.5km E of Cobar on Barrier Hwy Cobar. Ring on arrival for details of camp area. Donation. Ph: 0428 463 413

453. CWA Memorial Park
Map Ref: MAP 4 H4   GPS: 31 14 52 S 146 54 24 E
Camp area 44km NE of Nyngan located in Arcturus St, Girilambone, E of Hwy. See signage for access. Check in at pub opposite. Donation box.

454. Nyngan Weir
Map Ref: MAP 4 J5   GPS: 31 34 50 S 147 10 23 E
Camp spot 5km S of Nyngan. Turn off Barrier Hwy onto Temples Lane for 2km then L onto Ski Lane.

455. Bob Christensen Reserve
Map Ref: MAP 4 J5   GPS: 31 41 08 S 147 50 01 E
Parking area 3km NE of Warren PO on Industrial Access Rd, via Burton & Dubbo Sts. Ph: 02 6847 6600

456. Warren Weir camping area - Central West
Map Ref: MAP 4 J5   GPS: 31 44 08 S 147 51 57 E
Located 5km S of Warren on the Macquarie River. Ph: 02 6847 4186

Menindee Lakes

No 447

South East NSW

118km south east of Broken Hill

Jim & Cheryl Foster

This area is famous for the amazing sunsets over the water.

You can camp beneath the gum trees where the Burke and Wills expedition camped on the shores of Lake Pamamaroo, here Burke and Wills left behind a large part of their expedition between the banks of the Darling River and Lake Pamamaroo. This base camp was occupied from 19th of October 1860 until 26th of January 1861.

Burke and Wills travelled north to Cooper Creek and camped at what is now known as the Dig Tree Reserve on the northern bank of the Cooper before leaving behind another base camp crew and making their ill fated dash for the Gulf of Carpentaria.

Menindee Lakes was a magnet for early explorers. Major Mitchell was the first when he arrived here in 1835. In 1844 Charles Sturt visited the area and camped a little further south at Lake Cawndilla. Then came John McKinlay in 1855 with Burke and Wills following in 1860. Charles Sturt 1841855

This historic spot is in the centre of the famous Menindee Lakes system. The campsite lacks grass and the other amenities of a caravan park but does have toilets. There is also a picnic shelter and fireplaces for campers and day visitors.

This isn't the only spot you can free camp around the lake but it is about the only one that has toilets. There are many spots along the banks of the lake where people come to camp, some return every year for the serenity and simplicity of life on an outback lake.

The fishing can be very good in the river and lakes with Golden Perch (yellowbelly) being the prime target for anglers and yabbies can also be found here in large numbers.

It is unusual to be able to camp, especially for free, in a spot that carries so much Australian history. While camping at Lake Pamamaroo there are many historic and interesting places to visit. Menindee itself has a great fascination to people, especially when they learn that Maiden's Hotel was well established on the banks of the Darling even before Burke and Wills passed through. There are other historic places to visit in the town such as Ah Chung's Bakehouse, Dost Mahomet's grave and Kinchega Homestead site and woolshed to name but a few.

But one historic story that few people have heard is the Menindee Lakes own Tarzan, Norm Edwards. Norm lived with his parents on the small paddle steamer Daisy and settled in the Pamamaroo area in the 1920s. Tiring of life on the river Norm joined a travelling circus and performed on the high trapeze. Returning to the lakes he entertained the locals with feats such as walking a high wire and bending iron bars with his teeth. When a Tarzan movie was to be made in Australia he went into training for the role but unfortunately for Norm the movie was never made and he had to return to making a living from fishing. However, he continued to amaze and entertain the locals at local events and swimming days on the river.

But whether you stay on the banks of the lake for a day or week you will certainly enjoy camping where the most famous of Australian explorers camped so many years before you.

Campsite where Burke and Wills camped with the wall of the weir in the background.

Just The Facts

Menindee Lakes

Getting there: Menindee and the Menindee Lakes can be found 118km south east of Broken Hill on a good sealed road in the west of NSW.

The turnoff to the Burke and Wills Campsite is 110 km south east of Broken Hill or 8km northwest of Menindee. Take the dirt road to the north east and follow it for 9km to the weir then turn right to the campsite at Lat: 32. 18. 17. 09. S. Long: 142. 29. 57. 13. E. The ground in the campsite can get very slippery when wet so be careful during wet weather although the dirt road is an all weather road.

Facilities: The only amenities are the long drop toilets, fire place and picnic shelter.

457. Macks Reserve
Map Ref: MAP 4 K6 GPS: 32 11 45 S 148 14 46 E
Camp 4km N of Narromine. Turn N off Mitchell Hwy onto Warren Rd. Travel 3km to signpost and follow track to campsites beside Macquarie River.

458. Bogan Weir
Map Ref: MAP 4 K7 GPS: 32 43 27 S 148 07 35 E
Camp area 7km W of Peak Hill via Peak Hill-Tullamore Rd.

459. Wanda Wandong Campground - Central West
Map Ref: MAP 4 K6 GPS: 32 38 13 S 148 22 56 E
Located in the Goobang NP 30km from parks off the Newell Hwy then take the Tomingly-Obley Rd 3km N of Tomingley. Dry weather only Ph: 02 6851 4429

460. Greenbah Creek - Central West
Map Ref: MAP 4 K7 GPS: 32 46 10 S 148 21 10 E
Within the Goobang NP. Situated on Sawpit-Gully Trail from the Baldry-Peak Hill Rd. Dry weather only. Ph: 02 6851 4429

461. Willandra Camping Area - Outback
Map Ref: MAP 4 F7 GPS: 33 11 39 S 145 07 08 E
Located in Willandra NP. Access is signposted off the Hillston-Mossgiel Rd 57m east of Mossgiel and 41km west of Hillston. From Hillston take road north towards Ivanhoe for 1kmthen take signposted road towards Roto for 3.8km to signposted road to park. Unsealed roads. Bring water & firewood. Ph: 02 6966 8100

462. Wallanthery Bridge Rest Area - Central West
Map Ref: MAP 4 G7 GPS: 33 20 30 S 145 50 08 E
Wallanthery Bridge crossed the Lachlan River on the Kidman Way N of Hillston. Area is on NE side of bridge. Ph: 02 6967 1549

463. Lake Brewster Weir camping area - Outback
Map Ref: MAP 4 G7 GPS: 33 23 56 S 145 58 46 E
Located 42km W of Lake Cargelligo township. 2WD dry weather only access via Ballyrogan Channel from Hillston Rd. On Lachlan River. Ph: 02 6898 1009

464. Dead Mans Point Camp Area
Map Ref: MAP 4 G7 GPS: 33 16 46 S 146 23 44 E
Camp area 3.5km NE of Lake Cargelligo via Canada & Uabba Sts on McInnes St, Lake Cargelligo. Beside lake. Donation. Ph: 02 6898 1501

465. Lake Cargelligo Weir camping area - Central West
Map Ref: MAP 4 H7 GPS: 33 12 04 S 146 27 12 E
Located 25km NE of Lake Cargelligo township. Access via Lachlan Valley Way on the Lachlan River. Ph: 02 6898 1009

466. Frog Hollow
Map Ref: MAP 4 H7 GPS: 33 18 14 S 146 22 59 E
Camping area at Lake Cargelligo. Travel 1.5km SE of PO via Canada & Narrandera Sts.

467. Booberoi Weir
Map Ref: MAP 4 H7 GPS: 33 02 14 S 146 38 38 E
Located 56km W of Condobolin via Kiacatoo & Euabalong Rds. Turn S opposite radio tower and travel 1km to river. Ph: 02 6836 5888

468. Gum Bend Lake
Map Ref: MAP 4 H7 GPS: 33 04 45 S 147 06 03 E
Camp area 4km W of Condobolin via Bathurst St. Dogs in signed area only. Donation appreciated. Ph: 02 6895 1900

469. Burcher Camping Ground
Map Ref: MAP 4 J8 GPS: 33 31 00 S 147 15 07 E
Camp area S of main street on Kurrajong St, Burcher. Donation to pub, PO or honesty box. Ph: 02 6895 1900

470. Terarra Creek - Central West
Map Ref: MAP 4 K8 GPS: 33 25 11 S 148 29 55 E
Located in Nangar NP 70km W of Orange. This camp ground is 11km E of Eugowra along Dripping Rock Rd which is signposted off The Escort Way. Ph: 02 6851 4429

471. Terrara Creek Camping Area
Map Ref: MAP 4 K8 GPS: 33 25 08 S 148 29 52 E
Within the Nangar NP 76km W of Orange on Escort Way. Turn S 11km E of Eugowra on to Dripping Rock Rd. A further 7km to campsites. Ph: 02 6851 4429

472. Gooloogong Camping Area - Central West
Map Ref: MAP 4 K8 GPS: 33 37 27 S 148 24 32 E
About 45km NW of Cowra on the way to Forbes in central NSW. Ph: 02 6342 4333

Wallanthery Bridge Rest Area No 462

Lachlan River, NSW

36km north of Hillston

Stephanie Jackson

Rain had plagued our journey for day after sodden day, but as we headed through NSW along the Kidman Way the deluge temporarily concluded. After more than 50mm of rain the countryside was awash, and we searched in desperation for somewhere to camp, but didn't dare to put a wheel onto the red soil of any track that might lead to a secluded corner of bushland.

Eventually luck came our way, and as we crossed the Wallanthery bridge over the Lachlan River, 36kms north of Hillston, we discovered the perfect spot to bring our damp day's travels to an end. Here, on the north-eastern side of the bridge, where the river makes a sharp bend along its meandering course, was the perfect camping area for a rainy day. The large flat area on the river's bank has a bitumen surface, and a place where there was no chance of getting bogged was exactly what we had been looking for.

As rain clouds approached and the wind that hurled them in our direction intensified, the idea of having a campfire was scrapped, but we weren't complaining. We were just pleased to be on firm ground for the night in a location that would remain high and dry, unless there were floods of biblical proportions. With only two campers having arrived before us, there was no chance of stepping on anyone's toes in this spacious area that can easily be accessed by vehicles and rigs of the largest size imaginable.

We chatted with our new neighbours, with the conversation, as is so common, beginning with "Where have you come from," and "Where are you going," and just as we said goodnight, another traveller arrived and the evening suddenly became more interesting.

The driver of the ute, with his caravan in tow, rolled across the bitumen, ploughed straight into the thick red mud that had been churned up by earlier visitors, and then attempted to turn around. And it soon became obvious, as wheels spun and mud and colourful words of frustration flew through the air, that he wasn't going anywhere in a hurry. My other half wandered over to lend a hand, but his offer of help was politely declined. "I miscalculated badly, but I'll be right mate," the driver said in a classic understatement of the situation as he wedged sticks and cardboard under the vehicle's wheels in a vain attempt to get some traction.

There's plenty of room for caravans of all sizes.

As darkness enveloped the landscape, we watched the river's muddy waters swirling past. In better weather this great spot, where there are no facilities other than a metal picnic table, would be an ideal place to swim and to do a spot of fishing, but our visions of aquatic fun and games were disrupted by a call for help. The driver of the ute had finally conceded that some assistance was required to get his rig out of the quagmire, and our Land Rover accomplished the job with ease.

The bridge is only a short distance downstream from the camping area.

Travellers are usually happy to assist others who might get themselves into trouble, for who knows, the favour might one day need to be repaid, but this incident was a sharp reminder of the need for caution and common sense, particularly in wet weather. All's well that ends well however, and as we scoffed the chocolates that we'd received as an unnecessary reward for helping fellow travellers, we were grateful that we'd found a safe and pleasant place to spend another wet and wild night.

Just The Facts

Wallanthery Bridge Rest Area

Getting there: The Wallanthery bridge that crosses the Lachlan River is on the Kidman Way 36kms north of the NSW town of Hillston. The rest area is on the north-eastern side of the bridge.
Facilities: There are no facilities other than a picnic table.
Pets: Pets are permitted.
Contact: For more information, contact the Hillston Visitor Information Centre on 02 6967 1594.

Free Campsites in New South Wales

473. Wallaby camping area - Central West
Map Ref: MAP 4 K8 GPS: 33 47 59 S 148 26 31 E
Within the Conimbla NP. Signposted access along Barryrennie Rd - 19km off the Mid Western Hwy. Ph: 02 6851 4429

474. Holy Campground - Central West
Map Ref: MAP 4 J8 GPS: 33 53 53 S 148 00 16 E
In the Weddin NP 15km W of Grenfell via Holy Camp Rd. Dry weather only. Ph: 02 6851 4429

475. Fuzzy Box Camping Area - Central West
Map Ref: MAP 4 J8 GPS: 33 54 24 S 147 57 02 E
Located in Weddin Mountains NP 31km west of Grenfell. From Mid Western Hwy take signposted Back Piney Range Rd 5.4km west of Grenfell. Follow for 18km to singnposted Nowlans Rd then 5.4km to signposted access to park. Drive east for 3km to camp area. Bring water & firewood. Ph: 02 6851 4429

476. Ben Halls Campground - Central West
Map Ref: MAP 4 J8 GPS: 33 54 20 S 147 57 10 E
Located in Weddin Mountains NP 20km SW of Grenfell via Back Piney Range Rd and Weddin View Rd. Dry weather only. Ph: 02 6851 4429

477. Main Camp Camping Area - Outback
Map Ref: MAP 5 C1 GPS: 33 44 08 S 143 00 55 E
Signposted access at Mungo NP boundary on the road to Mildura 100m west of Balranald-Ivanhoe Rd and 2km south west of the visitor information centre. Access from Mildura is signposted via Buronga along Arumpo Rd. Ph: 08 8091 3863

478. Lake Victoria - Riverina & Murray
Map Ref: MAP 5 A1 GPS: 34 04 43 S 141 17 35 E
Situated 55km W of Wentworth on the shores of Lake Victoria. Access via Rufus River Road. Ph: 1300 655 687

479. Frenchman's Creek camping area - Outback
Map Ref: MAP 5 A1 GPS: 34 06 21 S 141 25 23 E
Via Lock 8 access rd from Rufus River Rd. Road is Closed when wet
Ph: 03 5027 5080

480. Lock 10 Wentworth - Riverina & Murray
Map Ref: MAP 5 B1 GPS: 34 06 36 S 141 54 14 E
Located near the town of Wentworth on the Murray just downstream of Lock 10.

481. Manly Beach camping area
Map Ref: MAP 5 B1 GPS: 34 08 11 S 141 58 09 E
From the Sturt Hwy in Curlwaa follow Manly Rd to dirt road and turn left. Follow for 2km to the river. Ph: 03 5027 5080

482. Gol Gol State Forest - Riverina & Murray
Map Ref: MAP 5 B2 GPS: 34 18 21 S 142 18 00 E
Located 24km E of Mildura near Monak. From the Sturt Hwy turn on to signposted track Bottle Bend Picnic Area and follow 2km along the banks of the Murray River. Ph: 1300 655 687

483. Bottle Bend Forest Picnic Area - Riverina & Murray
Map Ref: MAP 5 C2 GPS: 34 18 12 S 142 17 56 E
Camp Area 18km SE of Gol Gol. Beside River.

484. Mallee Cliffs State Forest - Outback
Map Ref: MAP 5 C2 GPS: 34 30 28 S 142 28 27 E
Camp area 40km W of Euston. Take Tapalin Mail Rd which is signposted of the Sturt Hwy. Dry weather only. Ph: 1300 655 687

485. Euston State Forest - Riverina & Murray
Map Ref: MAP 5 A7 GPS: 34 34 58 S 142 44 20 E
Adjacent to Euston town from the Sturt Hwy in to Cowper St on the banks of the Murray River. Ph: 1300 655 687

486. Lake Benanee Rest Area - South West
Map Ref: MAP 5 A7 GPS: 34 31 12 S 142 52 40 E
16kms E of Euston and is located beside the Sturt Hwy. Ph: 03 5020 1599

487. Tooleybuc Bridge
Map Ref: MAP 5 B8 GPS: 35 01 44 S 143 19 58 E
Camp area E off Murray Valley Hwy to Mallee Hwy. N to Tooleybuc Rd.

488. Balranald Low Level Weir Camping Area
Map Ref: MAP 5 B8 GPS: 34 39 52 S 143 29 34 E
Camp area on Balranald Weir Rd, Balranald 6kms W of Balranald on Wentworth Rd/Sturt Hwy. Gravel road. Weir signposted. Ph: 03 5020 1599

Brought to you by

kokodacaravans.com.au

Lock 10 Campsite

No 480

Wentworth, NSW

30km north west of Mildura

John Mainwaring

This camp area is next to the water.

Travellers on the Silver City Highway in NSW will know Wentworth and its claim to fame as "The Junction" of our 2 greatest rivers. In fact for many years that is how the locality was referred to by travellers. At this point, the confluence of these rivers means you are at the point where a large part of the drainage from Queensland, NSW and Victoria is flowing past your feet. This is the drain pipe for a large chunk of our continent.

Just downstream from Lock 10 there is a boat ramp and a track that goes along the river's edge for around a kilometre with flat and nicely shaded spots. Follow the boat ramp signs and you are there. There would be room for 20 or 30 campsites and I have seen it described as "dispersed camping for about 1km along the river below Lock 10". That says it all really. Technically it is within the Thegoa Lagoon and Reserve area.

Lock 10 itself is an interesting spot and not bad for a break with a few picnic tables and nicely tended grass plus a few BBQs provided over the road adjacent to the cemetery. If you are into cemetery history you could spend an hour wandering around in there as well. Lock 10 can be a hive of activity when one of the riverboats is passing through. This lock was constructed in 1929. It has an interesting fishway in place which allows the native fish to pass this river obstacle, but it is a bit of a worry that the entrance and the exit have an almost constant picket line of shags and pelicans that have got wise to this smorgasbord.

Walks around the Thegoa Lagoon and Reserve are very interesting and it is worth a visit to the Wentworth Visitors Centre to pick up the Self-Guided Tour Notes pamphlet. Just 2 kilometres away you have Wentworth with surprisingly good facilities for such a small town. The local IGA is excellent. There are mechanical repair businesses, a servo, several nice pubs and a large club and a caravan park with "The Sturt Tree" within its boundaries. This is the tree that Captain Sturt blazed when he passed here in 1830. Check out the point where the waters of The Darling and The Murray come together and in particular, the lookout overlooking the small island around which the waters come together. Here you can see the milky lime waters from the Darling resisting mixing with the relatively clear waters of the Murray.

The bird life around here is prolific and includes Red Rumps and Rosellas, heaps of aquatic birds and roving kites always on the prowl. Over 100 species have been identified around Thegoa Lagoon and many are unusual enough to have you reaching for the bird identification book.

The camping spot downstream of Lock 10 is your standard primitive, no facilities camping location good for a night or two. It is convenient, quiet and pleasant and if you have a boat you are a minute from the boat ramp for some river exploration as well. Quiet and relaxed and just 2 minutes from town and that will suit plenty of passing travellers.

Take a cruise on a paddle steamer along the Murray River.

Just The Facts

Lock 10 Campsite

Getting there: The camping area is several hundred metres downstream of Lock 10 on the Murray at Wentworth. Just follow the boat ramp signs and then follow the track along the river's edge and find a number of spots within the Thegoa Lagoon Reserve.

Facilities: There are no facilities but 20-30 riverside campsites that make convenient stopover sites. Several hundred metres upstream at Lock 10 there are toilets, BBQs and lunch tables but this is a day use area only.

Charges: Free

Pets: No signage indicates that pets are not welcome, but care should be exercised as there are a lot of water birds

Featured Campsite

Brought to you by

Lake Benanee No 486

Near Euston, NSW

16 km east of Euston

Kathy Littlemore

Lakeside camping is available with plenty of room.

Some places on earth have a mystical attraction. People are drawn to them without ever knowing why. Lake Benanee in south west New South Wales is such a place.

Locals are fascinated by the number of campers their lake lures in for a night, and several nights later those same campers remain in their prized campsites by the lake. Driving by Benanee on the Sturt Highway several times a month at various times of the day and night, over the past eight years, my husband and I routinely count the tents, caravans, RVs, camper trailers, big rigs and small. It is a game we play and only once have we had a zero count. And I might add that for several of those years the lake was drained dry to conserve precious water during the long drought.

House guests with their custom built RV have left our Balranald home, a mere 65kms to the east and camped the very next night at Lake Benanee.

So what is it that attracts people to this part of our wonderful world and keeps them there?

Lake Benanee is the Great Outback escape. The Australian outback romances people from around the world. But for many travellers the prospect of venturing into the outback is both tantalising and daunting. Lake Benanee allows you to wear the "badge" of Outback Adventurer while removing the daunting isolation. Coming from the east coast, you will have officially penetrated a bit over 70kms into the outback and you don't even have to get off-road to do it. Okay, there is an unsealed track of less than 1km from the highway to the lake.

Trucks may be rumbling by just over the rise on the Sturt Highway; a link with civilisation; but lakeside you are a world away.

Early birds get the best spots with shade by the water's edge. Settle in, sit back and relax. Get the billy on to boil, let the little tackers and the dogs run free without annoying fellow travellers and wait for Benanee to work its magic.

If you've got energy to burn, launch the boat at the ramp and get the crew up on skis. You could try catching a Murray cod to cook over the coals or trap some red claw for a tasty treat. The beach is a favourite with kids and adults alike and sometimes you just have to take a dip… clothes and all.

Hardened travellers get excited about the flushing toilets. It really is the small things that count, isn't it? And if you really have to, you can catch up with the folks at home as there is mobile phone coverage.

By dinner time you will have made new friends with travel tales to share as you all sit and gaze, mesmerised into the glowing red coals and flickering orange flames of the campfire. Expect music, games and friendly drinks as the night deepens.

And as the golden sun sinks, making way for the star studded velvety night bathed in white moonlight, it is time to set up the tripod for some evening photos, depicting serenity like no other. World renowned celestial photographer and astronomer Dennis Mammana has captured amazing images of Lake Benanee by moonlight. You can too.

From kites to cormorants, Lake Benanee is home to many bird species, with avid bird watchers excitedly documenting their sightings. You'll hear their chattering dawn chorus.

Early morning when the mirror-like water reflects the banks and the world gently stirs to life, is a special time to let Lake Benanee soothe your soul. Listen to your heart and you'll find yourself spending another day in this enchanting free camping ground.

Hardened travellers get excited about the flushing toilets.

Just The Facts

Lake Benanee Camping Area

Getting there: 16km east of Euston and 65km west of Balranald on the Sturt Highway in south western NSW.

Facilities: Male and female flushing toilets with wheelchair access, picnic tables with shelter, boat ramp. Suitable for large rigs and overnight camping. No Drinking water.

Charges: Free

Pet: Pets

Murray Cod Season: Closed 1 September to 30 November each year. NSW fishing licence required.

Dining Out: Euston Club and the Royal Hotel Euston or border hop to Robinvale.

Contact: Balranald Visitor Information Centre on 03 5020 1599

Free Campsites in New South Wales

489. Mamanga camping area - Riverina & Murray
Map Ref: MAP 5 B8   GPS: 34 39 55 S 143 30 40 E
2.5km E of Balranald. Follow signpost to park then travel for 5.5km to signposted access to camping area Ph: 02 6990 8200

490. The Willows camping area - Riverina & Murray
Map Ref: MAP 5 C8   GPS: 34 44 44 S 143 45 03 E
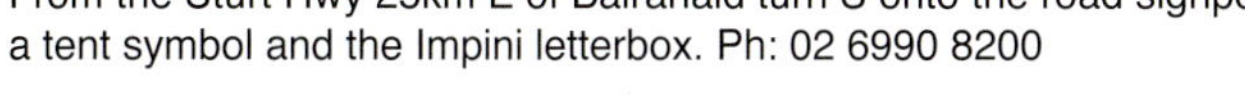
From the Sturt Hwy 25km E of Balranald turn S onto the road signposted with a tent symbol and the Impini letterbox. Ph: 02 6990 8200

491. Redbank Weir
Map Ref: MAP 5 C7   GPS: 34 22 40 S 143 46 52 E
Camp spot 55km N Balranald via Balranald-Ivanhoe and Oxley Rds and Redbank Weir Rd.

492. Yang Yang (Maude) Campground - Riverina & Murray
Map Ref: MAP 5 D7   GPS: 34 28 40 S 144 17 59 E
55km W of Hay. Access via Maude Rd adjacent to the township of Maude on Murrumbidgee River. Dry weather only. Ph: 02 6993 5055

493. Soapworks Bend
Map Ref: MAP 5 D7   GPS: 34 30 26 S 144 49 12 E
Camp spot via Jackson Street - Hay.

494. Sandy Point Reserve
Map Ref: MAP 5 D7   GPS: 34 30 55 S 144 50 08 E
Camp spot at Hay. Turn W off Cobb Hwy N of bridge onto Brunker St then S for 1km to N bank of Murrumbidgee River. Entry from Water St near Hatty St for large vehicles.

495. Nine Mile Reserve - Riverina & Murray
Map Ref: MAP 5 D7   GPS: 34 32 60 S 144 42 50 E
15km W of Hay. Signposted on the Sturt Hwy and located on Murrumbidgee River. Dry weather only Ph: 02 6993 5055

496. Llilalawa Reserve - Riverina & Murray
Map Ref: MAP 5 E7   GPS: 34 29 51 S 144 55 02 E
Camp Spot 8km E of Hay. Turn E off Mid Western Hwy through gate and track to Murrumbidgee River. Dry weather only. Ph: 02 6993 5055

497. Brandons Bend Reserve - Riverina & Murray
Map Ref: MAP 5 E7   GPS: 34 31 11 S 144 51 57 E
Camp Spot 3km E of Sth Hay off the Sturt Hwy take the road signposted "River" Ph: 02 6993 5055

498. Meriola Reserve
Map Ref: MAP 5 E7   GPS: 34 28 01 S 145 00 52 E
19km E of Hay turn S off hwy on to Murrumbidgee River Rd. Travel 3km S at river sign. Through gateway and then 1km to sites beside river.

499. Eli Elwah Reserve - Riverina & Murray
Map Ref: MAP 5 E7   GPS: 34 29 25 S 144 58 03 E
10km E of Hay on the Sturt Hwy signposted off the hwy on the banks of the Murrumbidgee River. Dry weather only. Ph: 02 6993 5055

500. Meriola Reserve - Riverina & Murray
Map Ref: MAP 5 E7   GPS: 34 28 01 S 145 00 57 E
Camp Spot 20km E of Hay via Mid Western Hwy to signposted Carrathool Rd. Dry weather only Ph: 02 6993 5055

501. Burrabogie Reserve - Riverina & Murray
Map Ref: MAP 5 E7   GPS: 34 30 05 S 145 09 32 E
Camp Spot 31km E of Sth Hay. Signposted River &Burrabogie Reserve on the banks of the Murrumbidgee River.

502. Mulberrygong Reserve
Map Ref: MAP 5 E7   GPS: 34 30 41 S 145 13 57 E
Located 135km W of Newell Hwy/Sturt Hwy jcn or 38km E of Hay. Turn N at signs "River" & Mulberrygong Reserve" and travel 1km on dirt rd to riverbank sites.

503. Cooey Point Reserve
Map Ref: MAP 5 F7   GPS: 34 28 33 S 145 19 18 E
Camp area 50 kms E of South Hay via Sturt Hwy Carrathool. Turn N at 'River' sign for 1.3 kms of dirt road to S bank of Murrumbidgee River. Ph: 02 6993 2069

504. Campbells Reserve
Map Ref: MAP 5 F7   GPS: 34 28 00 S 145 23 19 E
Camp spot 58km E of Hay. Turn N at Campbells Reserve sign travel for 1km on dirt road to S bank of Murrumbidgee River.

505. Truss Bridge
Map Ref: MAP 5 F7 GPS: 34 26 54 S 145 25 05 E
Camp spot 5km S of Carrathool or 2km N of Sturt Hwy intersection via Carrathool Rd. N side of bridge on river bank.

506. Tonganmain Reserve
Map Ref: MAP 5 F7 GPS: 34 28 15 S 145 38 17 E
Located 79km S of Hay on Newell Hwy. Turn N at reserve sign and 3km on dirt rd to S bank of Murrumbidgee River.

507. Birdcage Reserve
Map Ref: MAP 5 F7 GPS: 34 31 12 S 145 41 56 E
Camp spot 86km W of Newell Hwy/Sturt Hwy jcn. Turn N at sign "Birdcage Reserve" for 500m to S bank of Murrumbidgee River.

508. Nobles Beach Camp - Riverina & Murray
Map Ref: MAP 5 F7 GPS: 34 33 31 S 145 53 52 E
15km W of Darling Point is Dunoon Lagoon. Turn W 3km N on to Murrumbidgee River Rd. Dry weather only Ph: 1300 655 687

509. Swaggies Beach Camp - Riverina & Murray
Map Ref: MAP 5 G7 GPS: 34 33 33 S 145 57 31 E
Located in Willbriggle SF. 7km W of Darlington Point. Turn W off Kidman Way N of bridge. Opposite Caravan Park following No1 Green sign post 7km to River. Dry weather only. Ph: 02 6851 5288

510. Horries Beach Camp - Riverina & Murray
Map Ref: MAP 5 G7 GPS: 34 33 45 S 145 58 37 E
Camp Spot 5km W of Darlington Point off the Kidman Way. Opposite caravan park into the Willbriggle State Forest on bank of river. Dry weather only. Ph: 02 6851 5288

511. Beaumont Beach - Riverina & Murray
Map Ref: MAP 5 F7 GPS: 34 33 49 S 145 55 42 E
Located In Uri State Forest 9km SW from Darlington Point. Access from Britts Rd from Hay Rd. Ph: 1300 655 687

512. Bunyip Hole Reserve - Central West
Map Ref: MAP 5 G7 GPS: 34 33 39 S 145 59 24 E
Camp Spot at Darlington Point W end of King St on the banks of the Murrumbidgee River. Dry weather only Ph: 02 6962 7522

513. Common Beach - Riverina & Murray
Map Ref: MAP 5 G7 GPS: 34 33 54 S 145 59 42 E
Camp area at Darlington Point W end of Kings St to bank of Murrumbidgee River. Dry weather only Ph: 02 6962 7522

514. Cookoothama Reserve
Map Ref: MAP 5 G8 GPS: 34 32 47 S 145 56 49 E
Camp spot 8km W of Darlington Point. Turn W 3km N of Darlington Point onto Murrumbidgee River Rd. N bank of Murrumbidgee River.

515. Boomerang Beach Camp - Riverina & Murray
Map Ref: MAP 5 G8 GPS: 34 34 56 S 146 01 13 E
Located in Willbriggie State Forest 7km E of Darlington Point off Black Rock Rd. Dry weather only Ph: 02 6851 5288

516. Woolshed Flat - Riverina & Murray
Map Ref: MAP 5 G7 GPS: 34 04 53 S 146 13 17 E
Located in Cocoparra NP 25km NE of Griffith. Signposted access via Mackay Ave and Yenda Rd. N along Myall Park Rd then onto Mt Bingar Rd. Dry weather only. Ph: 02 6966 8100

517. Lake Wyangan camping area
Map Ref: MAP 5 G7 GPS: 34 12 46 S 146 01 01 E
20km N of Griffith via Wyangan Avenue then follow signs to lake. Ph: 1800 681 151

518. Binya Forest Park - Riverina & Murray
Map Ref: MAP 5 G7 GPS: 34 12 58 S 146 16 54 E
Situated in the Binya State Forest 30km W of Griffith. Off the Binya Forest Drive via Whitton Stock Route & Yenda-Ardlethan Rd. Ph: 1300 655 687

519. Beckom RV Stop
Map Ref: MAP 5 J7 GPS: 34 19 30 S 146 57 41 E
Parking area opposite hotel on Ariah St Beckom next to old bowling club. Ph: 02 6930 1831

520. Barmedman Mineral Pool Camp Area
Map Ref: MAP 5 J7 GPS: 34 08 19 S 147 23 10 E
Camp area on grassed area each side of the pool, cnr Nobbys Rd & Goldfield Way, Barmedman. Pool is seasonal. Donation.

Free Campsites in New South Wales

521. Cuba Beach - Riverina & Murray
Map Ref: MAP 5 G8 GPS: 34 37 56 S 146 05 52 E
Located in Cuba State Forest 19km E of Darling Point via Cuba State Forest Drive on the banks of the Murrumbidgee River. Ph: 1300 655 687

522. Tims Beach camping area - Riverina & Murray
Map Ref: MAP 5 G8 GPS: 34 38 02 S 146 06 32 E
Within the Cuba State Forest access track 11km east of Darlington Point along the road to Whitton. Follow this S for 6km to track junction and turn left. Ph: 1300 655 687

523. Brolga Hotel Motel
Map Ref: MAP 5 F8 GPS: 34 48 20 S 145 52 49 E
Located in Brolga Place, Coleambally. Check in with publican. Toilets open during pub hours. Ph: 02 6954 4009

524. Whitton Beach Camp - Riverina & Murray
Map Ref: MAP 5 G8 GPS: 34 36 59 S 146 11 02 E
Located within the MIA No 3 SF. Camp Spot 22km W of Yanco via River Rd & Forest Drive. Dry weather only. Ph: 02 6581 5299

525. Gogeldrie Weir Camping Area - Riverina
Map Ref: MAP 5 G8 GPS: 34 36 54 S 146 15 26 E
Located west of Leeton on banks of Murrumbidgee River. Access is from Irrigation Way 12km west of Leeton. Take signposted road to Golgeldrie Weir and follow for 3.8km to T-junction then right and follow for 1km to junction. Turn left for 6.4km to River Road. Turn right then 100m turn left into Golgeldrie Weir Rd which leads to park entrance. Ph: 02 6955 9267

526. Euroley Beach - Riverina & Murray
Map Ref: MAP 5 G8 GPS: 34 37 49 S 146 21 32 E
8km SW of Yanco on the banks of the Murrumbidgee access from Euroley Rd. Dry weather only. Ph: 02 6951 2508

527. Middle Beach Camp - Riverina & Murray
Map Ref: MAP 5 G8 GPS: 34 37 54 S 146 21 42 E
Located in MIA 2 State Forest 5km SW of Yanco. Access from Euroley Rd to river. Dry weather only. Ph: 1300 655 687

528. Long Beach camping area - Riverina & Murray
Map Ref: MAP 5 G8 GPS: 34 39 02 S 146 23 01 E
Located 10km W of Narrandera in the MIA No.1 State Forest. Access via Forest Drive off the Irrigation Way. Ph: 1300 655 687

529. Broad Beach camping area
Map Ref: MAP 5 H8 GPS: 34 41 46 S 146 24 08 E
From Cunninghams Beach follow Forest Drive for 700m to signposted access. Located 1.8km w of signposted junction. Ph: 02 6966 8100

530. Cunninghams Beach camping area
Map Ref: MAP 5 H8 GPS: 34 42 22 S 146 25 25 E
10km W of Narrandera to MIA 1 NP to signposted Forest Drive. Continue from Anglers Bend to Yanco Weir and a further 500m past the weir is Cunninghams Beach. Ph: 02 6966 8100

531. Anglers Bend camping area
Map Ref: MAP 5 H8 GPS: 34 42 30 S 146 26 13 E
10km W of Narrandera to MIA 1 NP to signposted Forest Drive. Continue on Forest Drive in westerly direction from Markeys Beach access track. After 1.2km left track leads to camp. Ph: 02 6966 8100

532. Markeys Beach Camp - Riverina & Murray
Map Ref: MAP 5 H8 GPS: 34 42 59 S 146 26 45 E
Located in MIA 1 SF 10km W of Narrandera along Forest Drive from Platts Beach access track. Dry weather only. Ph: 1300 655 687

533. Sandy Beach Camp - Riverina & Murray
Map Ref: MAP 5 H8 GPS: 34 43 16 S 146 27 48 E
16km NW of Narrandera S from Irrigation Way at MIA-Rifle Club sign. Follow No 2 State Forest Green Post signs river. Dry weather only. Ph: 02 6851 5288

534. Brewery Flat Reserve
Map Ref: MAP 5 H8 GPS: 34 45 15 S 146 33 00 E
Parking area 1km S of Narrandera via Newell Hwy on Old Brewery Rd, Narrandera, opposite Narrandera Wetlands. Ph: 02 6959 5545

535. Five Mile Reserve - Riverina & Murray
Map Ref: MAP 5 H8 GPS: 34 45 08 S 146 36 12 E
Camp Spot 9km E of Narrandera on Old Wagga Rd via Bolton & Victoria Sts. Ph: 02 6962 7522

536. Buckinbong Reserve - Riverina & Murray
Map Ref: MAP 5 H8 GPS: 34 48 14 S 146 36 59 E
Located next to Murrumbidgee River 16km SE of Narrandera. Via Buckinbong Rd off the Stuart Hwy. Ph: 02 6959 1766

Free Campsites in New South Wales

537. Colombo Creek
Map Ref: MAP 5 G8 GPS: 34 56 11 S 146 17 40 E
Camp spot 1km S of Morundah off The Yamma Rd (Coleambally Rd). Limited spaces - small vehicles only beside creek.

538. Berembed Weir - Riverina & Murray
Map Ref: MAP 5 H8 GPS: 34 52 48 S 146 50 09 E
Camp Spot 19km S of Grong Grong along the Narrandera-Wagga Wagga Rd. Dry weather only. Ph: 02 6959 1766

539. Piper Reserve
Map Ref: MAP 5 H9 GPS: 34 55 13 S 146 51 37 E
Located 57km W of Wagga Wagga on Weir Road then turn right at Riverside Reserve sign. Dirt road.

540. Bethungra Dam
Map Ref: MAP 5 K8 GPS: 34 45 50 S 147 54 27 E
5km E of Bethungra. Turn E 100m N of Bethungra to Bethungra Waterworks Rd then travel along to dam.

541. Kohlhagens Beach
Map Ref: MAP 5 J9 GPS: 35 04 58 S 147 11 34 E
Camp area 20km W of Wagga Wagga on Kohlhagens Rd - Yarragundry via Sturt Hwy.

542. The Shanty Reserve
Map Ref: MAP 5 J9 GPS: 35 06 45 S 147 31 15 E
Camp spot 7km N of Alfred Town. Turn N off Sturt Hwy at Alfred Town onto River Rd. Signposted "Reserve" tracks along the river. 6km dirt road.

543. Oura Beach Reserve - Riverina & Murray
Map Ref: MAP 5 K9 GPS: 35 07 25 S 147 32 32 E
Camp area beside the Murrumbidgee River 19km E of Wagga Wagga. From Oura turn onto Wagga Wagga St. Signposted "The Beach Reserve".

544. Breaden Sportsground
Map Ref: MAP 5 K9 GPS: 35 16 38 S 147 44 12 E
Area 1km NE of Hume Hwy on Sydney Rd, Tarcutta. Sportsground behind servo. Ph: 02 6928 7202

545. Hay Plains
Map Ref: MAP 5 D8 GPS: 34 52 43 S 144 45 34 E
Camp spot on Nyangay Creek 50km S of Hay or 6km N of Booroorban on either side of bridge.

546. Wanganella Weir
Map Ref: MAP 5 D9 GPS: 35 13 03 S 144 48 26 E
At Wanganella turn SW on N side of bridge. Travel 1km along river bank to camping spots.

547. Conargo Rec Grounds
Map Ref: MAP 5 E9 GPS: 35 18 18 S 145 10 53 E
Parking area next to tennis courts on Conargo Rd, Conargo. Time limit. Ph: 1800 650 712

548. Bills Park
Map Ref: MAP 5 E9 GPS: 35 18 24 S 145 10 38 E
Area W end of Conargo town on Conargo Rd near school. Time limit. Ph: 1800 650 712

549. Campbells Island State Forest - Riverina & Murray
Map Ref: MAP 5 C10 GPS: 35 35 26 S 144 06 21 E
Camp Area 5km NW of Barham via Cobwell St & North Barham Rd then Little Murray Rd. Signposted Campbells Island. Ph: 03 5881 9999

550. Koondrook State Forest - Riverina & Murray
Map Ref: MAP 5 C10 GPS: 35 40 28 S 144 11 51 E
Camp Area 12km SE of Barham via East Barham & River Rds. Dry weather only. Ph: 13 19 63

551. Wakool River
Map Ref: MAP 5 D10 GPS: 35 29 57 S 144 27 28 E
Camping spot 11km E of Wakool. Turn E when S of Wakool River bridge then follow along river to sites.

552. Perricoota State Forest - Riverina & Murray
Map Ref: MAP 5 D11 GPS: 35 56 14 S 144 29 31 E
Camp Spot 33km NW of Moama via Perricoota Rd and Nineteen Mile Rd then signposted Perricoota Forest Rd & River Rd. Ph: 02 6851 5288

553. Benarca Campground
Map Ref: MAP 5 D11 GPS: 36 03 15 S 144 37 25 E
Located in Murray Valley Regional Park 18km NW of Moama. Take Perricoota Rd (Moama-Barnham Rd) for 15km turn S onto Benarca Forest Rd and follow signs to campground. Ph: 03 5583 9100

554. Moama Campground
Map Ref: MAP 5 D11 GPS: 36 04 01 S 144 41 29 E
Within Murray Valley NP 8km W of Moama via Perricoota Rd. Ph: 03 5583 9100

555. Bama State Forest - Riverina & Murray
Map Ref: MAP 5 D11 GPS: 36 04 13 S 144 49 58 E
Located in Murray River Forests and Reserves. 13km NE of Moama. Access via Barmah Forest Road from Old Moama-Barmah Road. Ph: 1300 655 687

556. Willoughby's Beach
Map Ref: MAP 5 E10 GPS: 35 31 53 S 144 58 35 E
Within Murray Valley NP. Take Memorial Drive in Deniliquin past showgrounds to park entrance. Ph: 03 5583 9100

557. Gulpa Island State Forest - Riverina & Murray
Map Ref: MAP 5 D10 GPS: 35 48 42 S 144 54 37 E
Camp Spot 3km E of Mathoura via Picnic Point Rd & Gulpa Creek Road. Signposted Gulpa Island Forest Drive. Ph: 02 6851 5288

558. Edward River Campground - Riverina & Murray
Map Ref: MAP 5 D10 GPS: 35 48 39 S 144 57 46 E
Camp Area 8.5km E of Mathoura off Mathoura-Tocumwal Rd beside Edward River. Ph: 02 6851 5288

559. Millewa State Forest - Riverina & Murray
Map Ref: MAP 5 E10 GPS: 35 48 39 S 144 59 13 E
Located 10km E of Mathoura. From the Cobb Hwy take signposted Milewa Rd to Milewa Forest Drive then Milewa River Rd. Dry weather only. Ph: 1300 655 687

560. Moira State Forest - Riverina & Murray
Map Ref: MAP 5 E10 GPS: 35 51 39 S 144 54 34 E
Located 5km SE of Mathoura. From Cobb Highway take the signposted Moira Forest Drive to the forest entrance. Then Poverty Point Rd which then becomes Moira Forest Drive and continues to the river. Ph: 1300 655 687

561. Porters Creek
Map Ref: MAP 5 E11 GPS: 35 53 44 S 144 57 50 E
Within Murray Valley NP 13km SE of Mathoura. 5km S of Mathoura access via Coolamon Rd then Poverty & Porters Creek Rds. Travel 8km to sites beside creek. Dirt road. Ph: 03 5583 9100

562. Swifts Creek Campground
Map Ref: MAP 5 E11 GPS: 35 54 50 S 144 57 20 E
Camp area 15km SW of Mathoura. Turn E off Cobb Hwy 5km S of Mathoura onto Poverty Point Rd. Travel 5km to Porters Creek Rd then R into Hut Rd. Follow river to campground. Ph: 03 5583 9100

563. Fishermand Bend Rd
Map Ref: MAP 5 E10 GPS: 35 49 35 S 145 04 36 E
Located in Murray Valley NP 22kms E of Mathoura on riverside end of Fishermans Bend Rd along Millewa River Rd - Millewa Precinct. Limited spaces and dispersed camping in Millewa Precinct.

564. Scotts Beach
Map Ref: MAP 5 E10 GPS: 35 51 03 S 145 15 53 E
Located in Murray Valley NP 53kms E of Mathoura on riverside end of Scotts & Beach Rds along Millewa River Rd - Millewa Precinct. Limited spaces and dispersed camping in Millewa Precinct.

565. Sonnermans Beach camping area - Riverina & Murray
Map Ref: MAP 5 F10 GPS: 35 48 04 S 145 32 12 E
Located 2km W of Tocumwal. Located along the road to Mathoura (Tuppal Rd). Permit required & available from Tocumwal Information Centre. Ph: 1800 677 271

566. Barooga State Forest - Riverina & Murray
Map Ref: MAP 5 F10 GPS: 35 51 56 S 145 36 37 E
Located E of Tocumwal from the Tocumwal- Barooga Road. Signposted on Smithers Road 6km E of Tocumwal. Ph: 1300 655 687

567. Wattle Tree Beach
Map Ref: MAP 5 F10 GPS: 35 55 27 S 145 40 27 E
Located in Murray Valley Regional Park 2km W of Barooga. Turn S off Cobram-Barooga Rd. Dirt road. Ph: 03 5583 9100

568. Paradise Beach
Map Ref: MAP 5 F10 GPS: 35 55 46 S 145 41 07 E
Located in Murray Valley Regional Park 3km W of Barooga. Turn S off Cobram-Barooga Rd. Dirt road. Ph: 03 5583 9100

Free Campsites in New South Wales

569. Quicks Beach
Map Ref: MAP 5 F10 GPS: 35 55 37 S 145 42 01 E
Located in Murray Valley NP 5km SE of Barooga. Travel S off Mulwala-Barooga Rd - 35km W from Mulwala to Quicks Rd. Ph: 03 5583 9100

570. Quicks Beach (5 Mile) campground
Map Ref: MAP 5 F10 GPS: 35 55 37 S 145 42 01 E
Sandy beach on the river NW of Moama. Access along Perricoota Rd 8km from Cobb Hwy Ph: 03 5583 9100

571. Cottadidda State Forest - Riverina & Murray
Map Ref: MAP 5 F11 GPS: 35 57 00 S 145 45 14 E
Located 8km SE of Barooga. From the Barooga-Mulwala Road take the signposted Seppelts Road and then the signposted Stock Route Road. Ph: 1300 655 687

572. Boomanoomana State Forest
Map Ref: MAP 5 F11 GPS: 35 55 55 S 145 53 26 E
15km W of Mulwala via Mulwala-Barooga Rd. Many camping spots signposted Sandy Beach Ph: 02 6851 5288

573. Mulwala Regional Park
Map Ref: MAP 5 G11 GPS: 35 57 12 S 145 57 40 E
Via Mulwala-Barooga Rd 8km W of Mulwala. Signposted Hinches Beach. Ph: 02 6851 5288

574. Boomanoomana State Forest - Riverina & Murray
Map Ref: MAP 5 F11 GPS: 35 55 56 S 145 53 26 E
Bush camping via Mulwala-Barooga Rd. Numerous sites along the Murray River. Dry weather only. Ph: 02 6851 5288

575. Mulwala State Forest - Riverina & Murray
Map Ref: MAP 5 G11 GPS: 35 57 10 S 145 57 60 E
State Forest is 8km W of Mulwala via Mulwala-Barooga Rd. Signposted. Dry weather only. Ph: 1300 655 687

576. Kyffins Reserve - Riverina & Murray
Map Ref: MAP 5 G11 GPS: 35 58 49 S 146 03 32 E
On the shores of Lake Mulwala 5km E of Mulwala on the Corowa Rd. Ph: 1800 062 260

577. Collendina State Forest - Riverina & Murray
Map Ref: MAP 5 G11 GPS: 36 01 02 S 146 17 58 E
Camp Spots 9km W of Corowa off Mulwala-Barooga Rd onto signposted access track. Numerous campsites beside river. Ph: 1300 655 687

578. Rand Camp Site
Map Ref: MAP 5 H10 GPS: 35 35 36 S 146 34 35 E
Camp area beside Billabong Creek at Four Corners Rd next to bridge in the Rand Township.

579. Billabong Creek
Map Ref: MAP 5 H10 GPS: 35 41 50 S 146 43 34 E
Camp spot at Walbundrie. Turn E over bridge on S side of town.

580. Billabong Creek Camp Area
Map Ref: MAP 5 H10 GPS: 35 41 50 S 146 43 34 E
Camp area S side of town on Urana Rd, Walbundrie. Turn E after bridge.

581. Walla Walla Sportsground
Map Ref: MAP 5 H10 GPS: 35 46 04 S 146 54 09 E
Camp area at Walla Walla in William St. Caretaker on duty. Ph: 0429 039 322

582. Tin Mines Campsite - Riverina & Murray
Map Ref: MAP 5 J11 GPS: 35 51 34 S 147 28 38 E
Located in Woomargama NP along Tin Mine Road. Access is from Woomargama 13km S of Holbrook. Dry weather only. Ph: 02 6937 2700

583. Jingellic Reserve - The Snowys
Map Ref: MAP 5 K11 GPS: 35 55 44 S 147 42 15 E
On the banks of the Murray in Jingellic. Access by the Jingellic-Khancoban Rd. Ph: 02 6037 1290

Free Campsites in New South Wales Index

Free Campsites in New South Wales Index

Free Campsites in New South Wales Index

New South Wales Map 1
0
50
100 km
A B C D E F G H J K
1 2 3 4 5 6 7 8 9 10 11 12
BRISBANE
Gold Coast
Toowoomba
Queensland
Darling
Downs
St George
Dirranbandi
Nindigully
Hebel
Mungindi
Boomi
Goondiwindi
Boggabilla
Toomelah
Yelarbon
Inglewood
Millmerran
Pittsworth
Clifton
Allora
Warwick
Stanthorpe
Texas
Yetman
Tenterfield
Wallangarra
Killarney
Gatton
Laidley
Fernvale
Walloon
Rosewood
Ripley
Cedar Grove
Jimboomba
Beaudesert
Boonah
Aratula
Yangan
Murwillumbah
Tweed Heads
Cudgen
Pottsville
Burringbar
Mullumbimby
Brunswick Heads
Bangalow
Byron Bay
Clunes
Kyogle
Bonalbo
Lismore
Casino
Skennars Head
Ballina
Coraki
Woodburn
Evans Head
Bundjalung National Park
Woombah
Iluka
Yamba
Maclean
Gulmarrad
Ulmarra
Yuraygir National Park
Grafton
Coutts Crossing
Glenreagh
Wooli
Corindi Beach
Arrawarra
Woolgoolga
Sandy Beach
Coffs Harbour
Coramba
Bonville
Dorrigo
Bellingen
Urunga
Valla Beach
Nambucca Heads
Bowraville
Macksville
Scotts Head
Stuarts Point
South West Rocks
Frederickton
Kempsey
Crescent Head
Limeburners Creek National Park
Telegraph Point
Beechwood
Port Macquarie
Wauchope
Lake Cathie
Bonny Hills
Laurieton
Kendall
Crowdy Bay National Park
Harrington
Taree
Wingham
Old Bar
Gloucester
Nabiac
Forster
Green Point
Wallingat National Park
Smiths Lake
Bulahdelah
Stroud
Dungog
Myall Lakes National Park
Hawks Nest
Nelson Bay
Karuah
Raymond Terrace
Maitland
Cessnock
Newcastle
Lake Macquarie
Summerland Point
Morisset
Wyee
Jilliby
Wyong
Gosford
Brooklyn
Wilberforce
Hornsby
Penrith
Wallacia
Warragamba
SYDNEY
Blackheath
Katoomba
Kurrajong
Mt Victoria
Lithgow
Wallerawang
Portland
Oberon
Bathurst
Blayney
Orange
Molong
Cowra
Woodstock
Lyndhurst
Canowindra
Eugowra
Cargo
Cudal
Manildra
Parkes
Peak Hill
Yeoval
Cumnock
Wellington
Dubbo
Narromine
Firgrove
Mudgee
Gulgong
Kandos
Denman
Muswellbrook
Aberdeen
Scone
Singleton
Branxton
Greta
Broke
Merriwa
Murrurundi
Willow Tree
Wallabadah
Quirindi
Nundle
Werris Creek
Tamworth
Kootingal
Walcha
Uralla
Armidale
Manilla
Attunga
Gunnedah
Curlewis
Boggabri
Narrabri
Wee Waa
Pilliga
Baradine
Coonabarabran
Binnaway
Mendooran
Coolah
Dunedoo
Gilgandra
Gulargambone
Coonamble
Walgett
Lightning Ridge
Collarenebri
Moree
Ashley
Pallamallawa
Warialda
Delungra
Bingara
Inverell
Gilgai
Tingha
Bundarra
Barraba
Guyra
Glen Innes
Emmaville
Deepwater
Ashford
Burren Junction
Goulburn River National Park
Wollemi National Park
Yengo National Park
Barrington Tops NP
Warrumbungle National Park
Pilliga Nature Reserve
Mt Kaputar National Park
Coolah Tops National Park
Oxley Wild Rivers National Park
Washpool National Park
Nymboida NP
Guy Fawkes River National Park
New England NP
Werrikimbe
Great Dividing Range
Produced for On The Road Magazine.
www.custommappingservices.com.au
Base map and data © Custom Mapping Services 2024
CUSTOM MAPPING SERVICES .COM.AU

New South Wales Map 2

New South Wales Map 3

New South Wales Map 4

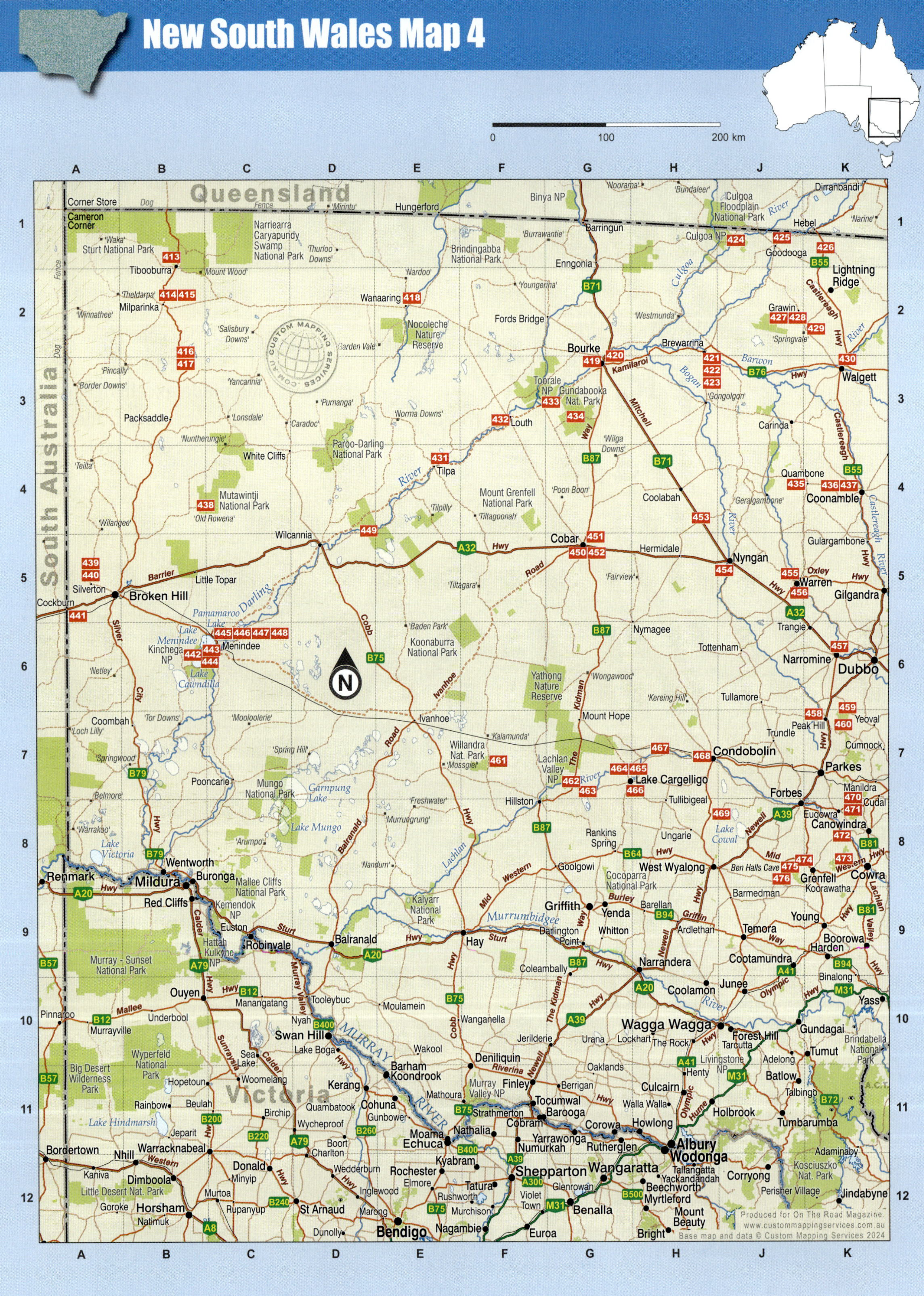

New South Wales Map 5

Going Off Grid In Style

Going off grid shouldn't mean going without. With the right onboard power, you can bring real comfort to the campsite, whether that is a morning coffee from your machine, an induction cooktop breakfast, or a laptop and projector for sunset movies. But, building a 12-volt system can be complex, and choosing the right brands, wiring up it correctly, and ensuring you have enough capacity can make or break your setup.

REDARC's new REDWorks power panels cut through the complexity. These power panels streamline off-grid power by taking the hassle out of choosing components and building a system from scratch. Pre-wired, pre-fused, and ready to install, REDARC's new REDWorks panels do the designing, wiring, and testing for you in one compact, integrated, and ready to install panel.

Designed to charge, control and distribute power through your vehicle, with a REDWorks panel on board you can power fridges, lights, compressors, tools and more through pre-wired genuine Anderson® outputs. Become the envy at every campsite and charge cameras, laptops and handheld devices, or power a projector and an induction cooktop.

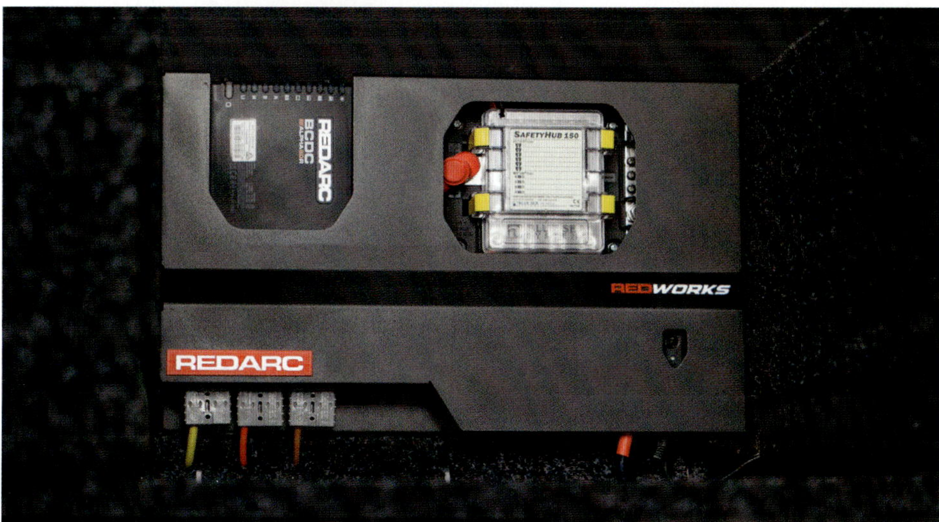

REDWorks manages the power between your start and secondary battery. While driving, REDWorks charges your secondary battery from your alternator. But when the sun is out, the in-built MPPT solar regulator means you can take advantage of free power from the sun. Thanks to Green Power Priority™, REDWorks will automatically prioritise solar first to reduce strain on your alternator.

Compatible with AGM, lead-acid, and lithium ($LiFePO_4$) batteries, including heated lithium, REDWorks will isolate your start battery to protect it from discharge when the engine is off, letting your secondary battery power your accessories while at camp.

Available in three models, Scout, Nomad and Pioneer, there's a REDWorks power panel for every adventure.

Perfect for powering a fridge, lights, and charging your phone and camera, the Scout is the perfect choice for minimalist touring setups or those diving into 12V for the first time. At the size of an A4 sheet, it fits neatly under a seat, behind drawers, or tucked into a canopy.

If you want to charge more gear and power more accessories, Nomad takes things to the next level. With an integrated fuse block, Nomad grows with your rig, allowing you to easily expand your off-grid set-up without any drastic re-wiring. Available in both 25amp and 50amp variants, Nomad is ready to handle bigger loads all while keeping things plug-and-play.

If it's a powerhouse on wheels that you're after, the flagship Pioneer is your answer. Featuring a 50amp DC to DC charger, Pioneer combines high-output charging and RedVision monitoring to deliver a system that puts you in charge. Monitor battery health, water tanks and system performance, all while controlling your devices like lights, fridges, and pumps through the RedVision App or Display. It delivers expedition grade convenience in a standard 4x4 setup, without the complexity or cost.

All REDWorks 50amp varieties are EV and hybrid-ready thanks to configurable input current limits. These panels also look after your start battery thanks to their Start Battery Charging and Start Battery Recovery features. So, no more strangers and no more jumper leads.

Australian Made and built for harsh conditions, REDWorks gives you the power to escape the everyday, to make anywhere home, to explore without limits.

Smarter power solutions backed by Australian engineering and industry leading support, push further and stay in control, no matter where the track leads.

To learn more about REDWorks, head to **redarcelectronics.com/redworks**

What Is the JackaMast?

The JackaMast is a Like-for-Like replacement of the Jayco 3 – stage telescopic mast. It is retrofittable across many windup camper manufacturers and build models. Stainless steel manufacturing, high-grade poly guides, thicker walls and round tube design provides strength where you need it most.

Our increased length overlapping poly guides, provide a total hands-off operation. No more broken poly guides, adjusting and guiding whilst lifting!!

The JackaMast is fully modular, with threaded and bolted components. Meaning it is fully serviceable. The JackaMast can be installed into campers that have both the JackaJay and manual lift system.

Our new and improved roof mount block, features a Roof Height adjustment mechanism, providing simple roof adjustments without the need to access the interior lifting system.

Safety Features include : Increased length high grade poly guides, provide stability and strength. The threaded design limits the ability for the sections to come apart. No more stress or nasty surprises when poly guides break and mast separates.

Increased Strength Features : Full stainless steel manufacturing, thicker upgrade walls material, round tube design, solid roof mount design.

Features / Benefits : Full stainless steel manufacturing, Built-In Roof height adjustment mechanism, extended poly guides for increased support, hands-off operation, 2-year warranty (domestic use), fully serviceable.

For more information visit **www.jackaindustries.com** or call 1300 052 252

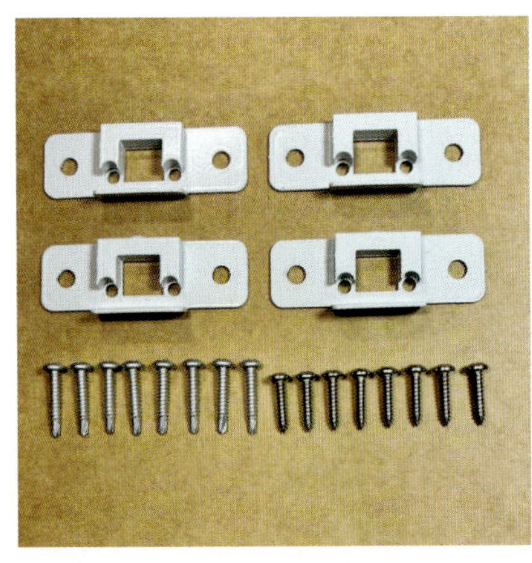

What Is Jackajay?

The complete 12V electrical roof lift system for all wind-up camper trailers. No longer struggle with winding your camper trailer roof up and down you just press a button with JACKAJAY.

The system is driven by a precision linear motor drive technology, with energy efficient direct drive lift which provides outstanding dependability.

Features & Benefits

- Power Source : 12V electric
- Retro fitted to older camper trailers
- DIY friendly
- Colour coded components for error free installation
- 5-year Warranty (domestic use)
- Live battery voltage monitoring
- Under voltage control
- Full colour LCD 4.3 inch touch screen
- Fault/obstruction detection
- Elimination of operator error
- Plug-n-play harnessing

There is no re-working of the structure or cabinetry within your camper trailer. JACKAJAY fits in exactly the same place as the old winch and cable system.

Simply remove the old system and install JACKAJAY – the easy way!

For more information visit www.jackaindustries.com or phone Stuart 0426 952 890 or Malcolm 0451 819 848

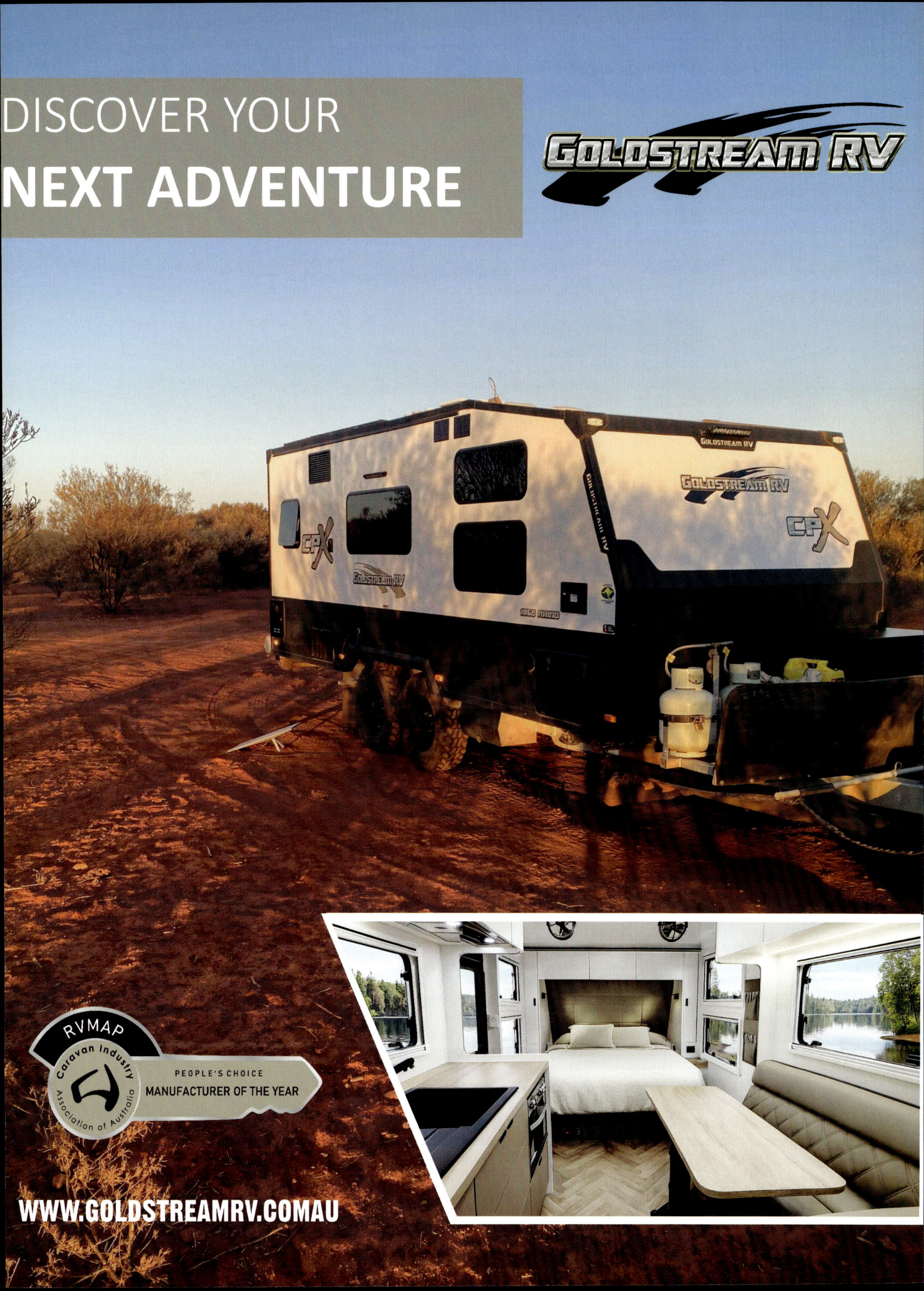
DISCOVER YOUR
NEXT ADVENTURE
GOLDSTREAM RV
RVMAP
Caravan Industry Association of Australia
PEOPLE'S CHOICE
MANUFACTURER OF THE YEAR
WWW.GOLDSTREAMRV.COMAU

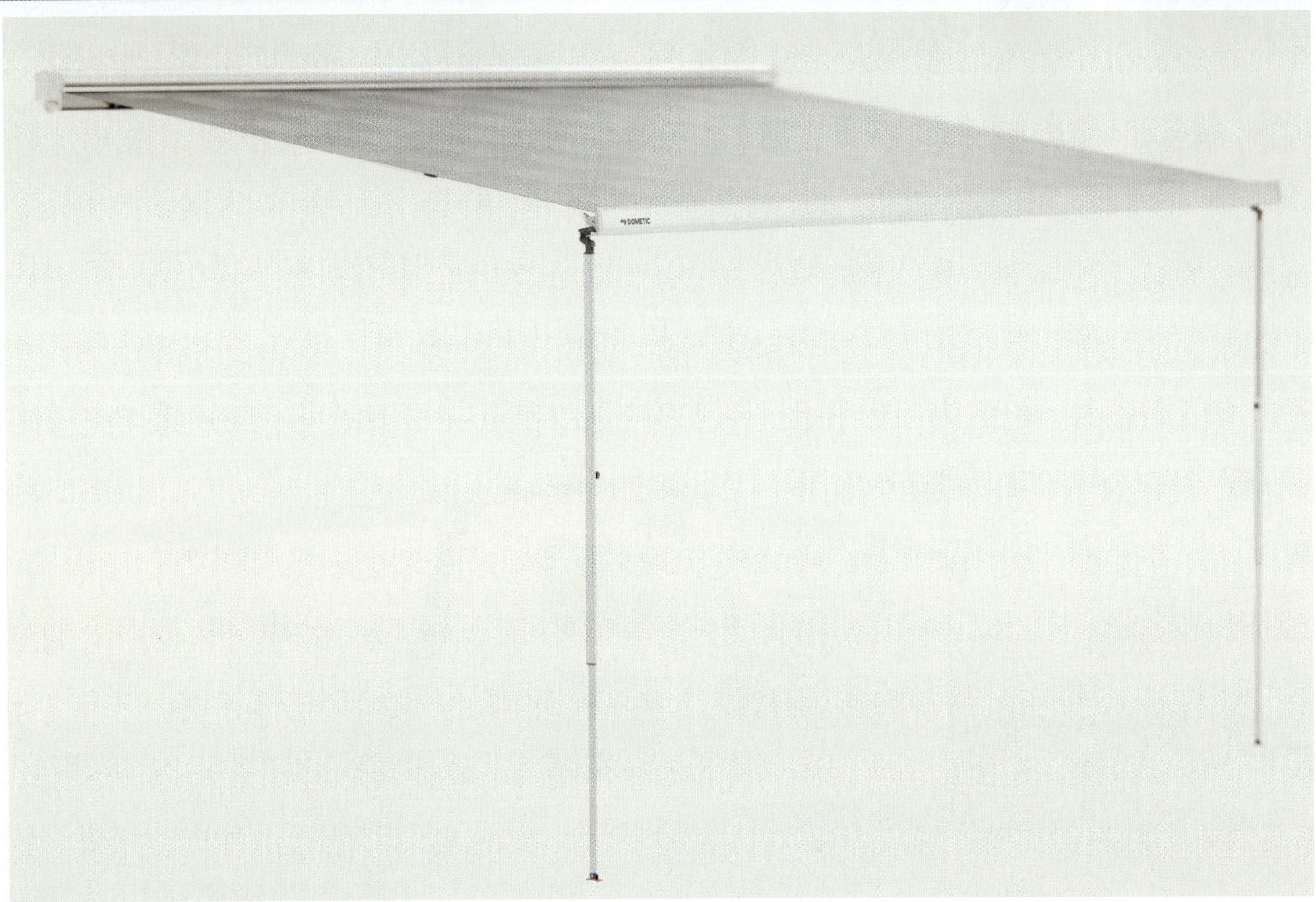

Make Friends with your Dometic Awning

Think of your Dometic caravan awning as your mobile veranda, providing shelter from sun and rain, a comfortable outdoor space to enhance your camping experience. The additional shade can also help keep your caravan cooler. Here are some handy hints for setup, maintenance, and overall use to help you get the most out of your caravan awning:

1. Practice Setup at Home - Familiarity: If you're using a new awning or setting it up for the first time, practice at home. This will help you understand the process and ensure you have all the necessary equipment.

2. Secure It Properly - Guy Ropes: Tension and adjust guy ropes correctly for added stability. Always stake them at a 45-degree angle for the best grip in the ground. It is also possible to secure Dometic awning legs to the vehicle with the appropriate brackets. Wind: Stow your awning in windy or stormy conditions to prevent damage or tearing. Angle: Set up the awning at an angle and with the correct tension to ensure rainwater runs off and prevents pooling on the vinyl. For longer awnings, a curved roof rafter will prevent pooling on the vinyl. If heavy rain is expected, it is safest to close the awning until it passes. Travelling: Before each trip, check that the awning is properly secured and locked closed to prevent it from opening while you're driving.

3. Use Flooring for Comfort - Breathable Mats: Use breathable mats where traditional groundsheets are not allowed, such as on grass. These mats help prevent damage to the covered area and allow water to drain through.

4. Keep the Awning Clean - Regular Cleaning: Clean the awning fabric with mild soap and water after each trip to remove dirt, mildew, and grime. Avoid using harsh chemicals that can damage the material. A teaspoon of dishwashing detergent in a bucket of warm water does the job. Dry Before Storing: Ensure the awning is completely dry before packing it away to prevent mould and mildew from forming during storage. This will help extend the life of the awning fabric.

5. Check for Repairs and Maintenance - Maintenance: Inspect your awning a couple of weeks before setting off on a trip for any cracks, rips, or delamination. This will allow time for repair or replacement. o Dometic Patch Kit: Carry a small repair kit for minor tears or punctures. Most kits include fabric patches, adhesives, and tools for a quick fix.

Conclusion Look after your awning and it will look after you, providing shade, shelter, and extra outdoor living space. Always ensure your awning is well-maintained and properly set-up to enhance your outdoor lifestyle. By following these suggestions, you'll ensure your awning remains in great condition and serves you well on all your caravan adventures.

What Dometic fridge suits your needs best?

Dometic Absorption vs. Compressor Fridge

The choice between a Dometic compressor or absorption caravan refrigerator depends on your travel style, power sources, and camping conditions.

Dometic Compressor Caravan Refrigerators

Compressor fridges operate like the one in your home, using a motor-driven compressor to circulate refrigerant and maintain cooling.

Key Benefits:

1. Fast, powerful cooling with reliable freezer performance, even in extreme heat
2. Highly energy-efficient on 12V/24V battery or 240V mains
3. No gas required – ideal for solar/ battery off-grid setups
4. Perfect for hot Australian climates and long off-grid trips

Best For:

Off-grid travellers using solar/battery systems who need strong cooling and freezing in high temperatures.

Dometic Absorption Caravan Refrigerators

Absorption refrigerators use heat to create a cooling effect through a migration and separation of chemicals.

This technology, though older, remains relevant in the RV market and is enhanced by modern electronics and internal fans (some models).

They can run on multiple power sources: 12V battery, mains electricity, or gas (LPG), although use on 12V is primarily for travelling due to high power consumption on DC. LPG is the most efficient power source.

Key Benefits:

1. Virtually silent operation (no compressor)
2. True 3-way flexibility: runs efficiently on LPG, 240V mains, or 12V (12V mainly while driving)
3. Preserves battery life by running on gas for days
4. Very few moving parts = high reliability and low mechanical failures
5. Excellent when mains power is unreliable or unavailable

Best for:

Caravanners who value silence, want gas-powered independence, or camp in areas with limited electricity

Comparison Summary :

Feature	Dometic Compressor Fridge	Dometic Absorption Fridge
Cooling Efficiency	Fast, reliable, and efficient in a wide range of temperatures	Slower cooling, works harder in extreme heat
Power Sources	12V/24V, 240V mains electricity	12V, 240V mains electricity, LPG gas
Energy Efficiency	Low power consumption, good for efficient solar/battery, faster cooling	Very efficient on gas but less on DC
Noise Level	Low-level compressor and fan can be reduced with silent function	Relatively silent with low fan noise, the which can be turned off if necessary
Maintenance	Periodic cleaning of the condenser system needed, especially after trips	Low maintenance but gas should be serviced regularly by a qualified technician
Off-Grid Suitability	Great for solar/battery setups	Ideal for gas-powered, off-grid camping
Durability	More mechanical parts, but long-mechanical lasting components	Long-lasting with very few failures

Which Fridge is Right for You?

• Dometic Compressor Fridge: Best for travellers who prioritise cooling efficiency, especially in hot climates, and those using solar panels or battery power for off-grid adventures. If you need a freezer, this is a better choice for high ambient conditions.

• Dometic Absorption Fridge: Ideal for caravanners seeking multi-power flexibility, particularly gas operation, and quiet operation in remote or off-grid locations. Great for places without reliable access to mains electricity.

Which filter system is right for you?

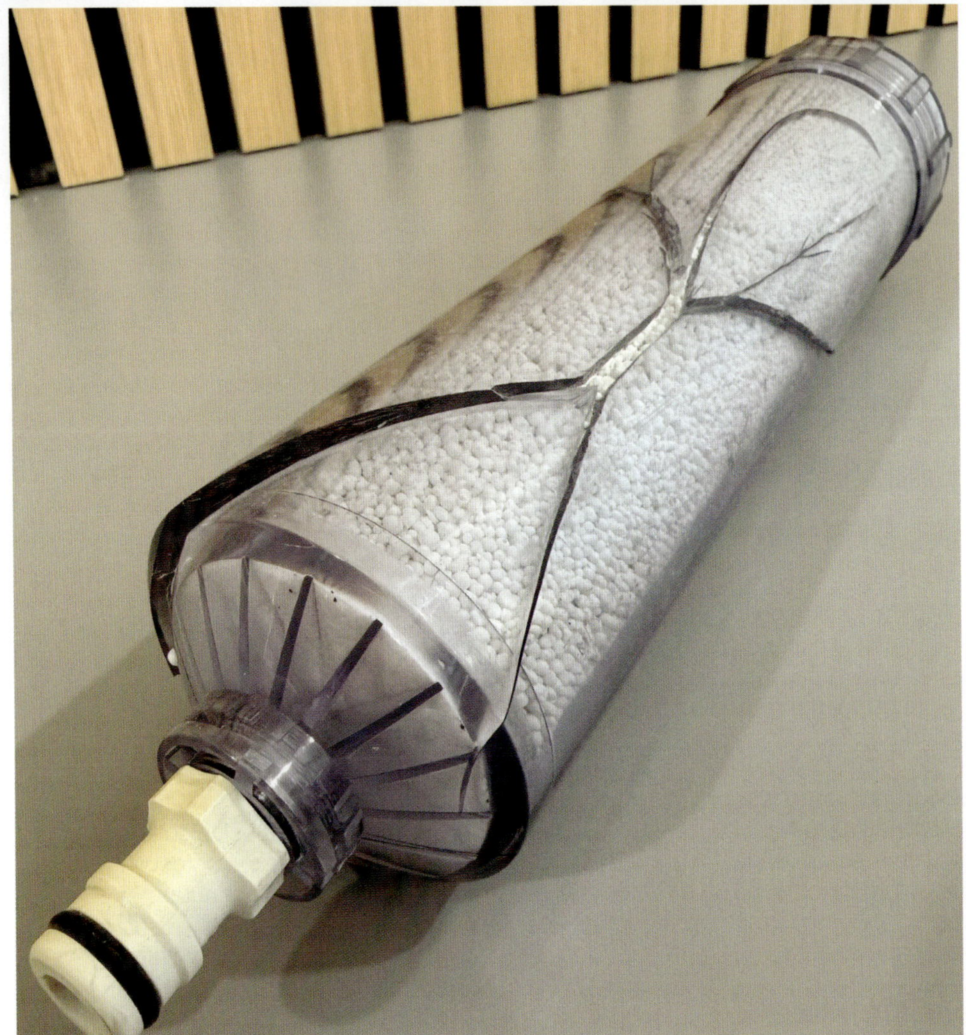

Twenty-two years ago, the Australian RV market had only one filter available. Now, there are many options, but which ones work and which ones aren't suitable? A problem for consumers is that the Australian WaterMark Standard doesn't cover the RV industry, leaving salespeople with the freedom to tell you anything and sell you anything without consequence. Therefore, it's important to listen carefully and be aware of what's not being said. Here are a few things to look out for:

Inlet size. If the filter has a small 1/4" inlet, it's probably a converted domestic filter. Domestic filters rely heavily on chlorine to stay bacteria-free, which is why you need to change them regularly, even if you haven't used them much.

Flow Arrow. If a filter has a 'direction of flow' arrow on it, the manufacturer is telling you not to back-flush it. Many people ignore this advice or are told by salespeople that they can back-flush them. However, this can cause the membranes, which are designed for water flow only in the direction of the arrow, to become dislodged, releasing carbon particles that block your inlet valves and taps on your van.

Pressure rating is important. Many imported filters are designed to meet the high American standard, but for low pressure. American water pressure is about half of what it is here in Australia, averaging around 600 kPa. Therefore, a water filter with a maximum pressure rating of 450 kPa could be the weakest link in your entire pumping system.

Self-sanitising. Silver-impregnated filters have been around since the 1970s, but their use can give consumers a false sense of confidence. These filters failed us back then and still do today. I've never seen a laboratory test report on any other silver-impregnated system. Furthermore, if you're told to dry the filter out and put it in the fridge when not in use, that's an indication that the system lacks the ability to kill bacteria. It's simply a way to control the growth of bacteria, but as you know, things still go off in the fridge.

These are just a few of the issues that led us to design Australia's B.E.S.T. RV Water Filter. Now, with over 150,000 units, all 100% Australian-made and hand assembled on the Gold Coast. All our testing has been undertaken by the Gold Coast City Council's Scientific Services, and it is pressure tested to 3100kPa.

Written by Colin Hopgood - Director and Creator of the B.E.S.T. Inline RV Water Filter

Mobile power made easy

When you hit the open road, it's not just about where you're going, it's about the freedom to go anywhere.

From the red heart of the outback to the lush coastal tracks, Australians share a common spirit of adventure. Yet one challenge unites every traveller, whether you're towing a caravan, setting up camp in the bush, or touring the country in your 4WD: keeping your power reliable when you're far from the grid.

That's where Enerdrive | Dometic comes in. For over a decade, Enerdrive has been at the heart of Australia's off-grid revolution, giving travellers the ability to take modern comforts wherever the road leads. Now, as part of the global Dometic family, the brand continues to set the benchmark in off-grid power technology, designed, assembled, and tested right here in Brisbane, for Australian conditions. Because out here, when the nearest power point is hundreds of kilometres away, you can't afford to take chances. You need power you can trust.

Enerdrive's story is uniquely Australian. Long before off-grid power became mainstream, the Enerdrive team recognised that travellers needed something better than modified marine or industrial systems. They needed something tougher, purpose-built for Australia's unpredictable climate and demanding terrain.

Enerdrive | Dometic canopy and power systems are designed and assembled locally by people who live and breathe off-grid travel. The engineers, technicians and support crew behind the brand understand the difference between theory and reality, between how something works in a lab, and how it performs after days on corrugated roads in 45°C heat. That's why every product undergoes rigorous testing to ensure it survives the harshest conditions Australia can throw at it, from blistering deserts to freezing alpine mornings. It's also why so many serious travellers, tradies, and adventure tourers won't trust their setup to anything else.

A great power system isn't just about the hardware, it's about the peace of mind that comes with knowing you're supported wherever you are. Enerdrive | Dometic backs every system with a five-year warranty and lifetime technical support from a local team who actually understand your setup. That means real help, from real people, when you need it most.

Whether you're installing a canopy power system, troubleshooting a charger,

or planning your next upgrade, support is only a phone call away. This level of service is rare in today's world, but it's one of the reasons Enerdrive has built such a loyal following among travellers, installers and industry professionals alike. Because when you're hundreds of kilometres from anywhere, confidence matters just as much as capability. Whether you're building a custom 4WD canopy setup, fitting out a touring caravan, or upgrading your camper trailer, Enerdrive offers a tailored solution that's ready for anything. Whether it is 12V and 24V batteries and chargers to inverters, solar, and monitoring systems, everything is built around reliability, efficiency, and ease of use. Here's how the key components work together to keep your power flowing, no matter how far off the beaten track you travel.

At the heart of any off-grid setup is the battery, and Enerdrive | Dometic's B-TEC Ultra lithium batteries feature IP67 marine-grade protection, internal steel reinforcement, and a lifespan of over 6000 charge cycles at 80% depth of discharge. That means years of dependable use, even under heavy loads and tough conditions. The advanced Bluetooth monitoring system lets you check your battery's health and performance from your phone, while our distinctive integrated cell heater ensures safe and efficient charging in sub-zero conditions ensuring you can charge your battery on a cold winters night. When it's time to store your setup, a simple on/off switch disconnects the system, preventing unnecessary drain allowing you to store your batteries for up to 6 months before checking on their state of charge. These aren't ordinary batteries, they're purpose-built power reserves for serious travellers who want performance that won't quit.

Enerdrive | Dometic's DC-DC and solar charging systems are designed for complete autonomy, intelligently switching between alternator and solar inputs as conditions change. When you're on the move, the DC-DC charger harnesses your vehicle's alternator to replenish your auxiliary battery. It uses a multi-stage charging process to maximise battery life and efficiency, ensuring you arrive at camp with your batteries topped up and ready to go. Once you're parked the solar controller takes over. It constantly adjusts voltage and current to make the most of available sunlight, delivering maximum energy even under partial shade or cloudy conditions. The result? Consistent, reliable charging from both your engine and the sun, so you're never left short on power.

Sometimes, solar and alternator power just aren't enough, especially if you're camped for long periods, travelling short distances, or dealing with days of poor sunlight. That's where AC battery chargers come in. Plugging into any 240V mains input, the AC charger efficiently recharges your battery system automatically adjusting output based on connected loads and battery condition, extending the life of your system.

Enerdrive | Dometic AC and DC chargers are unique in offering fan cooled devices ensuring your devices continue to work effectively in Australia's hot 45°conditions.

Enerdrive | Dometic inverters convert DC battery power into 230V AC, the same type of electricity you'd use at home. A 2000W inverter will comfortably power small appliances like coffee machines, TVs, microwaves, and laptops. For those who want to go all out, a 3000W inverter is capable of running high-demand appliances such as induction cooktops, kettles, air fryers, and even full-size hairdryers. Selected Enerdrive | Dometic have built-in RCD safety switches to protect both your battery and your devices in the event of a surge, while the AC transfer function automatically switches to mains power when it's available. That means seamless, safe operation whether you're plugged in or completely off-grid.

Every Enerdrive | Dometic product is designed with one goal in mind: dependability. When you're travelling through the outback, your power setup needs to just work, no fuss, no surprises. That's why Enerdrive's components are built with high-grade materials, intelligent thermal management, and heavy-duty protection. Battery chargers feature active cooling fans to maintain performance even in extreme temperatures, while inverters and controllers are engineered for efficient, low-heat operation. Every cable, fuse, and terminal is selected to meet or exceed Australian electrical standards. These are not generic imports, they're purpose-engineered systems, made to thrive in real Australian conditions.

Ultimately, Enerdrive | Dometic is about more than just volts and amps. It's about the freedom to live life on your own terms, to go further, stay longer, and experience the beauty of Australia without compromise. It's about waking up to a hot cuppa in the middle of nowhere. Keeping your food fresh after days on the road. Charging your camera as you capture that perfect sunset. It's about knowing that your power won't let you down when you're hundreds of kilometres from the nearest town. Because freedom isn't a destination, it's a way of life.

With Enerdrive | Dometic powering your adventure, you can make every journey your own. Silent. Cool. For more info visit **enerdrive.com.au**

Electric Windows from Linear Actuators

Linear Actuators Australia has been around for many years hiding in the backgrounds of a lot of projects but doing the heavy lifting none the less.

From humble beginnings in the window industry, opening and closing louvre windows we have carved a reputation for being able to take on the impossible projects and make them work.

These large Electric Servery Windows use two heavy duty linear actuators on each side to raise and lower the large glass panels with the press of the remote control.

And are a result of constant research and development to create a new product that has taken the market by storm.

After installing a number of these systems and constantly refining the installation processes we were left with a product that can easily be supplied for the DIYer to install.

When we had a number of customers with pop top vans wanting a way to raise and lower their van roofs, we set out to design a system that was up to the task.

We created a 12volt system that utilizes the vans 4 original gas struts so if there was ever an issue the roof could still be used without the electric system.

The four motors each have a lifting force of 100kg and work to lift the roof to the point where the gas struts take over and do the lifting.

When it comes to pack up time lowering the motors actually pulls against the struts and lowers the roof smoothly until the struts stop carrying the weight and revert back to the motors taking the load.

We then put the same type of thinking into the pop top systems and developed an easy to install 12volt roof lifter kit.

The kit will come with everything you need to fit the motors including brackets, cables with waterproof connections, switch, fixing screws, battery power cable and cable clips.

The instruction manuals are very simple with colour photos and no small print.

If you are considering purchasing a roof lifting kit and are unsure if you would be up to the task of installing it yourself.

Let us know and we can send you the installation instructions beforehand so you can have a look to see what is involved knowing you can call us for any questions you may have even during the install process.

We are based in Brisbane and have had a few customers want us to install the system for them which usually takes about 3 to 4 hours.

For more information : Address - Unit 1 / 30 Kingtel Place, Geebung. Phone - 07 32655771

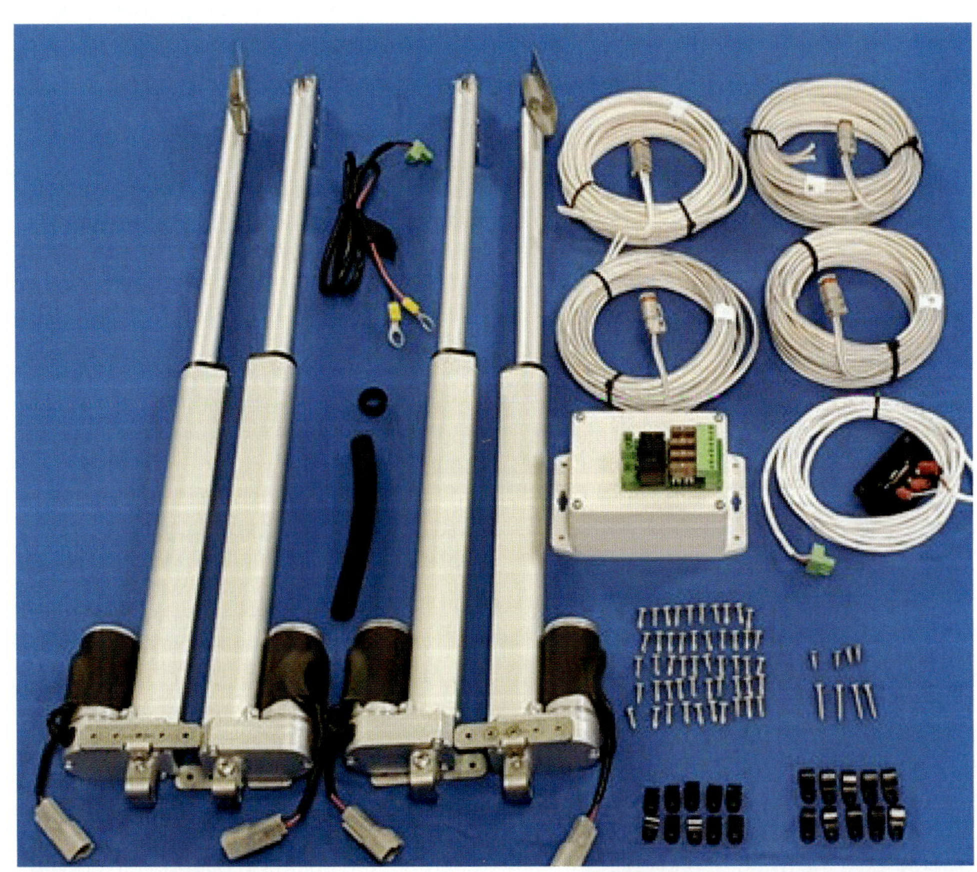

Vista RV Crossover XLE

Top of the line model for all your adventure travels

Vista RV has been the proud producer of a great range of camper trailers for nearly 20 years. Proudly designed and manufactured in Australia at their modern production facility in Bayswater Victora. The Crossover range of camper trailers comprise of 3 models, namely the Crossover Classic, the Crossover XLI and the top-of-the-line Crossover XLE. For this Spotlight we will focus on the Crossover XLE model.

The Crossover XLE is a fantastic offroad camper trailer with more than a touch of luxury. Light and manageable enough to get into those difficult but brilliant campsites and then the creature comforts make your stay one to enjoy.

Coming in at just under 2000kgs the tow vehicle options to partner with a Vista Crossover are many.

Among the many features found on the Crossover XLE include a spacious interior with queen size bed which converts easily to a four seater dinette plus under seat storage, a large slide-out kitchen with dual gas burners, a kitchen sink and wind break, easily assessable heavy duty slide for chest style fridge/freezer, an ensuite shower pod with vanity recess that sets up in quick time. Together with state-of-the-art Redarc total vehicle management system, 250 watt flexible solar panel and the quite outstanding MS Series Suspension it is smooth but tough with an amazing wheel travel of 330mms or 13 inches in the old scale.

A listing of the specifications, standard features are following.

Specifications Crossover XLE
Size : 5300 x 1900 x 2190
ATM : 1980kgs
TARE : 1300kgs
Payload : 680kgs
Ball Weight : 130kgs

Standard Features :
215 watt Mono Flexible Solar Panel, Ensuite/Shower Pod with vanity recess, Redarc Redvision TVMS, Redarc Manger 30 BMS 105AH AGM, Battery (x2), Water pump low noise IP4 Rated (x2), Hand pump for manual water retrieval, 240VAC Inlet and Outlets (x2), External slide out kitchen with sink, Front boot and nose cone storage, Spare wheel, 4.5kg Propane gas bottle (x2), 20L Jerry can storage (x4), Sirocco gimbal fans (x2), Inner Spring Mattress.

For more information visit **www.vistarv.com.au** or phone (03) 9729 1234.

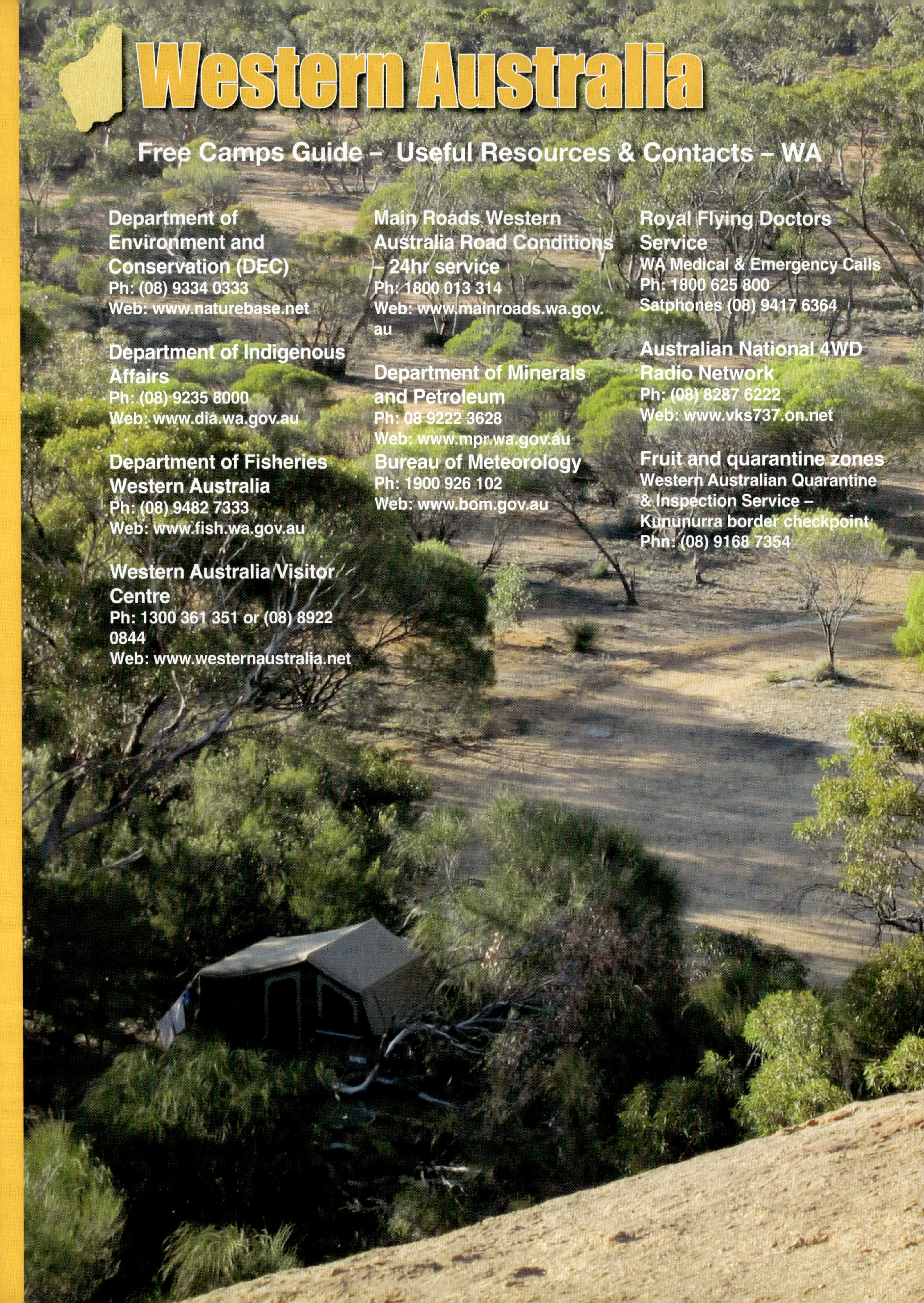

Western Australia

Free Camps Guide – Useful Resources & Contacts – WA

Department of Environment and Conservation (DEC)
Ph: (08) 9334 0333
Web: www.naturebase.net

Department of Indigenous Affairs
Ph: (08) 9235 8000
Web: www.dia.wa.gov.au

Department of Fisheries Western Australia
Ph: (08) 9482 7333
Web: www.fish.wa.gov.au

Western Australia Visitor Centre
Ph: 1300 361 351 or (08) 8922 0844
Web: www.westernaustralia.net

Main Roads Western Australia Road Conditions – 24hr service
Ph: 1800 013 314
Web: www.mainroads.wa.gov.au

Department of Minerals and Petroleum
Ph: 08 9222 3628
Web: www.mpr.wa.gov.au

Bureau of Meteorology
Ph: 1900 926 102
Web: www.bom.gov.au

Royal Flying Doctors Service
WA Medical & Emergency Calls
Ph: 1800 625 800
Satphones (08) 9417 6364

Australian National 4WD Radio Network
Ph: (08) 8287 6222
Web: www.vks737.on.net

Fruit and quarantine zones
Western Australian Quarantine & Inspection Service – Kununurra border checkpoint
Phn: (08) 9168 7354

Free Campsites in Western Australia

1. Punammi Unpuu (Mitchell Falls) camping area - Kimberley
Map Ref: MAP 1 G1 GPS: 14 49 12 S 125 43 06 E
Located at the western end of Mitchell Plateau Road, 88km W of Kalumburu Road within the Mitchell River NP. Ph: 08 9195 5500

2. Munurru camping area - Kimberley
Map Ref: MAP 1 G1 GPS: 14 53 03 S 126 12 09 E
King Edward River Crossing located on Mitchell Plateau Road, 8.km W of Kalumburu Road. Ph: 08 9195 5500

3. Mambi Island - Kimberley
Map Ref: MAP 1 H1 GPS: 15 34 55 S 128 28 22 E
From Kununurra head W for 18km on the Victoria Hwy and take signposted turnoff to Valentine Springs. Dry weather only. Ph: 08 9168 1177

4. Skull Rock camping area - Kimberley
Map Ref: MAP 1 J1 GPS: 15 31 42 S 128 37 10 E
Located 36km N of Kununurra. Access via Carlton Hill Road and Weaber Plains Road. Ph: 08 9168 1177

5. Halls Creek Camp Area
Map Ref: MAP 1 J2 GPS: 15 37 20 S 128 41 28 E
Camp spot on the Ord River 32kms NW of Kununarra. Turn N of Victoria Hwy 13kms W of Kununurra onto Valentine Spring Rd for 14km. Turn NE at T jcn for 4.5kms.

6. Buttons Crossing - Kimberley
Map Ref: MAP 1 J2 GPS: 15 46 10 S 128 38 70 E
Not far from Kununurra, camping area is 18km N of Victoria Hwy via the Harry Creek Rd. Dry weather only Ph: 08 9168 1177

7. Dampier Peninsula Bush Camp - Kimberley
Map Ref: MAP 1 F2 GPS: 16 43 31 S 122 54 09 E
Head east along Broome Rd for 10km and turn on to the Broome-Cape Leveque Rd. After 15km turn left on to Manari Rd and follow signs to camp of your choice stretched over the next 35km. Ph: 1800 883 777

8. Silent Grove camping area - Kimberley
Map Ref: MAP 1 G2 GPS: 17 03 59 S 125 14 58 E
Signposted access off Gibb River Road, 8km W of Imintji Roadhouse. A further 20km to camping area. Within King Leopold Conversation Park. Ph: 08 9195 5500

9. Barnett River Gorge - Kimberley
Map Ref: MAP 1 G2 GPS: 16 32 22 S 126 07 12 E
Via the Gibb River Rd signposted 40kms N of the Mount Barnett Roadhouse. www.kimberleytourism.com

10. Hann River
Map Ref: MAP 1 G2 GPS: 16 30 51 S 126 21 20 E
Camping 54km E of Mount Barnett Roadhouse

11. Russ Creek
Map Ref: MAP 1 H2 GPS: 16 02 53 S 126 42 04 E
Camping at Russ Creek on the N side of the road, E side of creek.

12. Prices Point camping area - Broome Region
Map Ref: MAP 1 E3 GPS: 17 29 25 S 122 08 59 E
Access track is 13km N of access track to Quondong Point camping area. Ph: 08 9191 3456

13. Quondong Point - Kimberley
Map Ref: MAP 1 E3 GPS: 17 35 35 S 122 10 10 E
7.5km N of Barred Creek. A number of camping areas off the Manari Rd. Ph: 08 9191 2222

14. Barred Creek camping area - Broome Region
Map Ref: MAP 1 E3 GPS: 17 39 59 S 122 12 06 E
Close to Broome with access track 9km N of Willie Creek Road, camping area along banks of Barred Creek. Ph: 08 9191 3456

15. Willie Creek camping area - Kimberley
Map Ref: MAP 1 E3 GPS: 17 45 33 S 122 12 39 E
Bush camping area close to the natural boat launch, 7.1km along Willie Creek Road, which is signposted 5.1km along Manari Road Ph: 08 9191 3456

16. Boab Quarry - Kimberley
Map Ref: MAP 1 G3 GPS: 17 54 42 S 125 17 45 E
54km NW of Fitzroy Crossing from Great Northern Hwy turn N on to Leopold Downs Rd (gravel) for 11km to a Y intersection. Take right hand fork for approx. 500m to numerous sites along the Limestone Range. Ph: 08 9191 0999

Mambi Island No 3

Lower Ord River, WA 70km north of Kununurra

Catherine Lawson & David Bristow

When the East Kimberley's famous Ord River was dammed in 1970, Lake Argyle soon filled to become the largest man-made lake in Australia. Below Argyle's dam wall, freshwater flows for 57km to Lake Kununurra where it's blocked by the diversion dam that secures a water supply for the town.

One of the best places to set up camp and launch a tinny is at Mambi Island on the Lower Ord River, 70km north of Kununurra. This grassy clearing on the river's shady, western bank is reserved for campers and anglers, with toilets and most importantly, a concrete boat ramp providing easy access to a wide stretch of the river.

Camping by the Lower Ord River.

It's a particularly scenic spot so arrive armed with supplies of drinking water and firewood, and remember to take away your rubbish. Pets are permitted, but because this is saltwater croc territory, dogs are best kept away from the water's edge.

You'll find Mambi Island on the back road between Kununurra and Wyndham, a 4WD route that is a trip in itself, following Parry Creek Road to a host of freshwater swimming holes at Valentine and Middle Springs, and Black Rock Falls.

About 30km north of Mambi Island in Parry Lagoons Nature Reserve, Marlgu Billabong attracts an astonishing variety of bird species, including migratory birds from as far away as Siberia.

Taking as its name the Aboriginal word for wild bird, Marlgu Billabong has boardwalks, a camouflaged bird hide and plenty of identification charts to help part-time twitchers distinguish between the vast flocks of whistling ducks, green pygmy geese, swamp hens, ibis and jabirus that congregate on the water.

If you can, catch a sunrise or set from Telegraph Hill that overlooks the billabong, where you can also stroll a short trail around ruins of the Wyndham Wireless Station, abandoned in 1921.

The unsealed roads to Mambi Island are accessible to 4WD vehicles. Off-road caravans and camper trailers are recommended for tackling the corrugated, rutted sidetracks that lead into Middle Springs and Black Rock Fall. Visit during the cool, dry season (May to September).

There are saltwater crocodiles in the area.

Just The Facts

Mambi Island

Getting there: Kununurra is located 40km west of the NT border. To reach Mambi Island, head 18km west of town on the Victoria Highway and take the signposted turnoff north to Valentine Springs. Accessing Parry Creek Road directly from Kununurra via Ivanhoe Crossing is possible very late in the dry season, but this wide crossing and the strong current will deter some travellers.

Facilities: Toilets.

Wheelchair Access: No.

Rates: Free.

Pets: Permitted.

Contact: Phone the Kununurra Visitor Centre on (08) 9168 1177 or head to **www.visitkununurra.com.** Check road conditions with Main Roads WA on 1800 013314 or visit **www.mainroads.wa.gov.au.**

Dampier Peninsula Bush Camps No 7

Broome, WA

60km north of Broome

Catherine Lawson & David Bristow

On the Kimberley coast north of Broome, a lonely stretch of red cliffs, pindan woodlands and white sand beaches have long lured fishers, campers and solitude seekers. But for now, the future of four free council camping reserves, located between 38 and 60 kilometres north of Broome, hangs in the balance as Woodside's proposed gas plant awaits Federal environmental approval. While reassurance is being given that access to the camps and fishing spots will remain, the same assurance doesn't apply to the pristine beaches and coral-fringed shores that will be devastatingly impacted by the construction of the plant.

For now, campers can choose sites at Willie Creek, Barred Creek, Quondong Point and James Price Point, the site of the proposed gas plant, all accessed off Manari Road. To get there, head east out of Broome and turn left onto the Broome-Cape Leveque Road. After 15km, turn left onto Manari Road and follow the signposts to your choice of camp, stretched out over the next 35km.

Travellers with conventional vehicles will have no trouble reaching the camps in the dry season. However, the sandy access tracks to the beach should intimidate vehicles without four-wheel-drive capability, and those who do hit the sand must be mindful of the local tides that have an enormous range.

The fishing in this part of the world varies with the seasons. During the dry season (May to September) when temperatures average 15 to 31 degrees Celsius, catch queenies or trevally off the beaches and mangrove jack up the creeks. According to locals, the threadfin salmon around at this time are good tasting fish that love a fight. Fish for them on an incoming tide and around creek mouths when the tide reaches full height. Boat fishing on a clear day offshore might snare you catches of blue bone groper, red emperor or northwest snapper around the reefs.

Driving on the sand should only be attempted in a 4WD.

When the warmer wet season comes around, barramundi are far easier to find but you'll have to enjoy the steamy conditions yourself and be aware that deadly irukandji and box jellyfish are around (November to April).

Willie and Barred creeks are popular barra hunting grounds and good places to retreat to when the winds blow onshore and make boating uncomfortable. To reach the Willie Creek camping area, drive 5km along Manari Road, and another 7km south along Willie Creek Road. With a natural boat ramp, fishers will enjoy this spot, but remember that if the fish are around, there's a good chance a crocodile will be, too.

Barred Creek camping area is another favourite fishing spot found 9km further up Manari Road and off a small clearing on the bank of the creek. The campsites that stretch for 3km along Quondong Point's red sea cliffs overlook a strip of white sand and the deep blue sea, and many are shaded by trees. You'll find this scenic spot signposted just over 7km up the track and a short drive towards the coast.

Another 13 kilometres north, the flat headland at James Price Point lacks shade but provides easy access to the beach, and it is this spot that might one day be engulfed by gas plant infrastructure.

Off the point, low tides reveal rocky pools teeming with soft corals and living shells, fish, octopus, small spotted rays and juvenile turtles. On our many stays at James Price Point we have snorkelled here, watched humpback whales cruising offshore and sea eagles and ospreys overhead.

Camping at the beach.

Just The Facts

Dampier Peninsula Bush Camps

Location: Head east along Broome Road and turn onto the Broome-Cape Leveque Road. After 15km, turn left onto Manari Road and drive another 5km to the turn-off for Willie Creek, 9km to the Barred Creek turnoff, 7.6km to Quondong Point and 13.4km more to reach James Price Point.

Facilities: No facilities are provided (pack out all rubbish). Maximum three-day stay.

Rates: Free.

Pets: Yes.

What to catch: Barramundi, mangrove jack, queenfish, trevally, blue bone groper, red emperor, threadfin salmon and more.

Contact: Broome Visitor Centre, 1800 883 777 visit www.broomevisitorcentre.com.au. For updates on the future of James Price Point, visit www.savethekimberley.com

Free Campsites in Western Australia

17. Ngumban Cliff - Kimberley
Map Ref: MAP 1 G3 GPS: 18 44 52 S 126 06 32 E
Located 96km SW of Fitzroy Crossing signposted off the Great Northern Hwy. Ph: 08 9191 5355

18. Caroline Pool
Map Ref: MAP 1 H3 GPS: 18 13 36 S 127 45 35 E
Camping spot 15km E of Halls Creek via Duncan Rd. Turn E 13km SE of Halls Creek, sandy track

19. Wolfe Creek Crater camping area - Kimberley
Map Ref: MAP 1 H3 GPS: 19 10 36 S 127 47 12 E
Access signposted along the Tanami Rd, 130km S of Halls Creek. Then drive E for 23km to the small camping area with little shade. Ph: 08 9168 4200

20. Cape Keraudren camping area - Pilbara
Map Ref: MAP 1 D4 GPS: 19 57 26 S 119 46 08 E
Signposted access off the Great Northern Hwy opposite Pardoo Roadhouse, 152km NE of Port Hedland. Continue 14km N direction along the unsealed road to camping area . Ph: 08 9175 8000

21. Three Mile Pool
Map Ref: MAP 1 B5 GPS: 21 45 44 S 114 57 05 E
Camping 5km S of Old Onslow. Turn W 64km N of Hwy 1 junction and travel 19km dirt rd.

22. Fortescue River Mouth Camping - Pilbara
Map Ref: MAP 1 B5 GPS: 20 59 59 S 116 08 23 E
Leave North West Coastal Hwy 80km S of Karratha. Signposted access 24km off hwy to the camp area. Ph: 08 9144 4600

23. Dampier Archipelago - Central West
Map Ref: MAP 1 C5 GPS: 20 27 46 S 116 51 40 E
From Karratha follow Dampier Rd, turn on to the Burrup Peninsula Rd and continue north to Withnell Bay. Ph: 08 9143 1488

24. Cleaverville Beach campsite - Pilbara
Map Ref: MAP 1 C5 GPS: 20 39 40 S 116 59 53 E
26km NW of Roebourne via North Coastal Hwy. Chemical toilet required to stay. Ph: 08 9186 8555

25. Coorinjinna Pool
Map Ref: MAP 1 C5 GPS: 20 43 22 S 117 48 00 E
Camping 20km N of Whim Creek. Turn N opposite hotel site and travel 14km, turn R opposite old gravel site and travel 1km to sites along the river. Dirt rd.

26. Balla Balla Inlet - Pilbara
Map Ref: MAP 1 C5 GPS: 20 43 21 S 117 48 04 E
River camping spots 20km N of Whim Creek. Turn N opposite Hotel for 15km, then R opposite old gravel pit onto track for 1km. Ph: 08 9144 4600

27. Sherlock River
Map Ref: MAP 1 C5 GPS: 20 56 41 S 117 36 41 E
Camping spot 56km E of Roebourne. Turn N 100m W of bridge.

28. Snake Creek camping area - Pilbara
Map Ref: MAP 1 C5 GPS: 21 20 37 S 117 14 37 E
Signposted access off the Roebourne-Wittenoom Road in Millstream-Chichester NP, access track is 2km E of Python Pool access track. Ph: 08 9184 5144

29. Murlamunyjunah Crossing Pool camping area - Pilbara
Map Ref: MAP 1 C5 GPS: 21 34 37 S 117 05 13 E
Within the Millstream-Chichester NP via Snappy Gum Drive which is signposted off the Millstream-Yarraloola Rd. Ph: 08 9184 5144

30. Pear Creek
Map Ref: MAP 1 D5 GPS: 20 50 24 S 119 36 38 E
89km SE of Great Northern Hwy.

31. Doolena Gorge Camp Spot
Map Ref: MAP 1 D5 GPS: 20 55 32 S 119 47 08 E
109kms SE of Great Northern Hwy or 34kms N of Marble Bar turn off. Turn S on dirt track on Port Hedland side of river and follow track for 1.5km. Overhanging trees.

32. Carawine Gorge - Pilbara
Map Ref: MAP 1 E5 GPS: 21 28 85 S 121 01 61 E
153km E of Marble Bar via Ripon Hills Rd then south on the Woodie Woodie Rd. Dry weather only. Ph: 08 9176 5900

Camp right where you are fishing.

Cape Keraudren Coastal Reserve

No 20

Pardoo, WA

1,632.2 km from Perth

John Clarke

Site-seeing between Broome and Port Headland is a little thin on the ground. Eighty Mile Beach is touted as a destination, but as one local put it to me, "At the end of the day, it's just a beach." The Great Northern Hwy sweeps inward from Broome running about 30-40klms inland from the coast so a dirt road run is guaranteed.

We had read about Cape Keraudren, and saw it as a possible 2-3 day stay on our way to Port Headland. It was the shortest distance between the highway and the ocean, so, if the road was as rough as bags, it would be mercifully short lived. Three hours later we arrived at the turnoff and cruised along a brand new stretch of bitumen, all the way to the Reserve entrance. The Reserve is one of those cash in the envelope deals, but of course, who carries cash these days? You can book on line, and there is internet at the check-in booth.

There were three main campgrounds to choose from. For your purposes, they are the creek site (Cootenbrand Creek), the beach site (Cape Keraudren) and the bay site (Boat Ramp Bay). We reckoned the sign posted beach site (the creek site) was the go. We couldn't see our destination till we rounded a small sand dune to be met by the irresistible combination of river, sand and ocean, and pretty much all to ourselves.

We set up on the creek bank, deciding not to un-hitch. This would prove fortuitous later that night. I caught sight of the high water mark on the opposite bank. It seemed a little higher than the area we had parked on. As benign as the creek looked in the early afternoon sunshine, we had heard about the extraordinary tides on the WA north coast.

My internal alarm went off just after 11pm and I took a look outside. Yes the creek was up and the volume of water zipping by was disconcerting. Of course everything seems disconcerting in the middle of the night. In the space of twenty minutes the level had risen another half a metre, lapping at the very rim of the river bank. Still an hour till full tide. In the end, we decided to move twenty metres to slightly higher ground.

.

The headland site looks straight out onto the Indian Ocean and is definitely for the park and view set. Easy access to the beach and extended rock shelves.

The Boat Ramp Bay site is probably the pick of the three. Acres of space, and of course, a boat ramp. Vans were lined up like ships at anchor at the pick of the locations. Stunning views, a steady breeze and a walk out across the sandy bay to the reef at low tide, with fishing and snorkelling recommended here. You would be trading off a little privacy, but probably worth it.

All three sites have toilets with the headland site also having a dump point. There is no fresh water and its BYO fire wood. There is no shade at any of the locations, but the constant sea breezes more than compensate. All three sites have something unique to recommend them, so try and spend time at each one if you can.

Spectacular sunsets are a feature of the area.

33. Eel Pool - Pilbara
Map Ref: MAP 1 E5 GPS: 21 41 07 S 121 07 33 E
The Gorge camping area is approx. 180km E of Marble Bar on the Oakover River. Access track is 34km S of the Woodie Woodie - Telfer - Ripon Hills Road junction Ph: 08 9176 5900

34. Running Waters camping area
Map Ref: MAP 1 E5 GPS: 21 41 07 S 121 07 33 E
From the Carawine Gorge access track proceed S along Woodie Woodie Rd for 29km then W on to Skull Springs Rd. Continue for 12km to track to east which leads to bush camping beside the David River. Ph: 08 9176 5900

35. Skull Springs - Pilbara
Map Ref: MAP 1 E5 GPS: 21 52 25 S 121 00 20 E
108kms E of Nullagine which is 1200kms N of Perth via the Great Northern Hwy. Ph: 08 9175 2888

36. Burrel Bore camping area
Map Ref: MAP 1 F5 GPS: 21 01 19 S 123 20 27 E
Camping area surrounding the bore, 300m SE of Wapet Rd, 330km SE of Great Northern Hwy. Must be self-sufficient traveller. Ph: 08 9176 9040

37. Razorblade Bore camping area
Map Ref: MAP 1 F5 GPS: 21 33 12 S 123 21 40 E
Bush camping near the bore amongst a small grove of trees on the Wapet Rd 207km NW of Kunawarritji. Must be self-sufficient traveller. Ph: 08 9176 9040

38. Tjingkulatjatjarra Pool camping area - Pilbara
Map Ref: MAP 1 E5 GPS: 22 30 29 S 122 04 47 E
Bush camping on the S side of the river. Access off main park track. Ph: 08 9143 1488

39. Desert Queen Baths bush camping - Pilbara
Map Ref: MAP 1 F5 GPS: 22 27 59 S 122 15 58 E
287km SE of Marble Bar via Ripon Hills and Telfer Rds. Camping area is 18km SE of main track part of the Karlamilyi NP previously named Rudall River National Park. Ph: 08 9143 1488

40. White Gum Bore camping area - Pilbara
Map Ref: MAP 1 F6 GPS: 22 50 15 S 122 09 15 E
Bush camp at White Gum Bore, 9km N of Talawana Track Ph: 08 9143 1488

41. Jupiter Well camping area - Pilbara
Map Ref: MAP 1 H5 GPS: 22 52 59 S 126 36 04 E
Located on Gary Junction Road, 157km E of Gary Junction. Ph: 08 8950 1711

42. Cape Range National Park - Central West
Map Ref: MAP 1 A6 GPS: 22 01 21 S 113 55 17 E
Head north from Exmouth and follow coast for 36km to the national park. Ph: 08 9949 2808

43. Hamersley Gorge Camp
Map Ref: MAP 1 C5 GPS: 22 14 34 S 117 57 34 E
67km N of Tom Price. Take Bingarra Rd N for 25kms then turn R onto Nanaturra Rd and travel 41kms to campsite on L. Ph: 08 9189 8121

44. Dales campground - Pilbara
Map Ref: MAP 1 D6 GPS: 22 28 30 S 118 33 04 E
Within the Karijini NP. From Karijini Drive take the Eastern access road into the park, and then a further 18kms to the camping area. Ph: 08 9189 8157

45. The Blowholes camping area - Pilbara
Map Ref: MAP 1 A7 GPS: 24 29 16 S 113 24 44 E
Turn off the North West Coastal Hwy 24km N of Carnarvon and continue 50km to the coast. Campground is located 1km south. Ph: 08 9941 0000

46. Bush Bay - Central West
Map Ref: MAP 1 B7 GPS: 25 07 50 S 113 45 14 E
Take the signposted turn off the North West Coastal Hwy 33km S of Carnarvon and continue along the dirt track for 8km to Bush Bay. Ph: 08 9941 0030

47. New Beach - Central West
Map Ref: MAP 1 B7 GPS: 25 09 25 S 113 47 55 E
Located 41km S of Carnarvon. Turn 91km N of Wooramel Roadhouse. Dry weather only Ph: 08 9941 0030

48. Temple Gorge camping area - Pilbara
Map Ref: MAP 1 B7 GPS: 24 39 38 S 115 10 56 E
Located in Kennedy Range NP. From Gascoyne Junction proceed N along the signposted Ullawarra Road for 49km to the signposted access to the park. Ph: 08 9943 0988

Featured Campsite

Brought to you by

Cape Range National Park No 42

Cape Peron, WA
36km southwest of Exmouth

Catherine Lawson and David Bristow

At WA's Cape Range National Park, sealed roads lead straight to more than 100 beachfront campsites where self-sufficient travellers spend as little as $5.50 per night to swim, snorkel and fish on Australia's largest and most accessible, fringing coral reef.

Together, Cape Range National Park and Ningaloo Marine Park protect a rare paradise of rugged red canyons and turquoise lagoons on 260km-long Ningaloo Reef. On any day you might spot green turtles, stingrays, reef sharks and a mesmerising procession of up to 500 reef fish species that flourish amongst the coral bombies.

The adventure begins just metres from your choice of 13 campgrounds that might overlook prime snorkelling sites or provide access to boat ramps, walking trails and excellent fishing zones.

For great snorkelling, try the shady camps at Lakeside or North Mandu (no generators, no fishing), and for fishing access, choose Neds Camp, Tulki or Yardie Creek.

Be aware that generators are not welcomed at North Mandu, Kurrajong, Osprey Bay and Bungurra camps, and if you need access to a wheelchair-friendly toilet, head to Neds Camp, Lakeside or Kurrajong.

There's so much to do in Cape Range National Park that you might well stretch your stay to the 28-day limit. The mass spawning of corals along the reef every March and April lures whale sharks - the world's largest fish - along with manta rays and migrating humpbacks that linger until November when nesting green, loggerhead, hawksbill and flatback turtles return to their birth places in the dunes.

Ancient rock pools are great to explore or just sit at and watch the sea.

Snorkelling is easily the most popular thing to do at Cape Range, and top sites include the Drift Dive located at the southern edge of Turquoise Bay, Lakeside and the Oyster Stacks. Anglers with boats can launch at the Tantabiddi boat ramp located just north of the park boundary, but be aware that important animal sanctuaries within the marine park prohibit or restrict fishing, so check with the visitor centre for details before heading out.

Away from the sea, the Mandu Mandu Gorge Walk (3km, 2hrs) provides a scenic leg-stretcher to lofty lookouts, while in Yardie Creek Gorge you can join a leisurely one-hour boat ride, paddle your own canoe or hike a trail in search of black-footed rock wallabies (500m, 20mins).

Facilities across the national park are limited to picnic tables and toilets, a bore for drinking water, and a visitors centre with interpretive displays, park brochures and maps, and a small shop for cold drinks and treats.

The best time to visit is during the cool winter months, outside of the busy WA school holiday period. Some campsites can be booked in advance (pay online at parkstay.dpaw.wa.gov.au); the rest are assigned on a first-come-first-served basis at the park entrance so arrive early during peak holiday periods.

Crystal clear water for kayaking.

Spectacular sand dunes.

Just The Facts

Cape Range National Park

Getting there: Head north of Exmouth and follow the coast for 36km to the national park. Entry costs $12/vehicle or $6 for concession card holders (including seniors). A WA national parks holiday pass permits free entry for four weeks ($44).

Facilities: Picnic tables, toilets and bore water, no fires, BYO drinking water. Maximum stay 28 days.

Rates: $7.50/adult, $5.50 for concession card holders and $2.20/child.

Wheelchair Access: To the toilets at Neds Camp, Lakeside and Kurrajong.

Pets: No

Contact: Phone the national parks Milyering Visitors Centre (08) 9949 2808 or visit www.dpaw.wa.gov.au. For information on the region phone the Exmouth Visitors Centre on (08) 99491176 or head to www.visitningaloo.com.au or www.australiascoralcoast.com

Free Campsites in Western Australia

49. Bilung Pool Camp Spot
Map Ref: MAP 1 C7 GPS: 25 42 22 S 115 59 09 E
Located 152kms N of Murchison Roadhouse or 147km SE of Gascoyne Junction. Turn W at sign S of Bilung Creek, follow track 200m to pool.

50. Bilyun Pool
Map Ref: MAP 1 D7 GPS: 25 54 15 S 118 39 47 E
Located 88km N of Meekatharra. Turn W 74km N of Meekatharra onto Ashburton Downs Rd. On left after Murchison River. Travel 14km on track to sites.

51. 25 Mile Well
Map Ref: MAP 1 D8 GPS: 26 15 54 S 118 39 31 E
Located 41km N of Meekatharra.

52. Geraldton Bore - Goldfields
Map Ref: MAP 1 G7 GPS: 25 10 46 S 124 40 04 E
Access along Gunbarrel Hwy, 208km E of Carnegie Station, and 33km W of Everard Junction, near the Len Beadell blazed tree. Ph: 08 9080 5555

53. Camp Beadell - Goldfields
Map Ref: MAP 1 G7 GPS: 25 33 04 S 125 20 02 E
Access along Gunbarrel Hwy, 95km E of Geraldton Bore, and some 63km SE of Everad Junction. Ph: 08 9080 5555

54. Yarla Kutjarra Campsite - Gibson Desert
Map Ref: MAP 1 H7 GPS: 25 36 38 S 127 13 13 E
Follow the Great Central Rd 95km NE of Warburton or 136km SE of Warakurna. Dry weather only.

55. Rock Holes Camp
Map Ref: MAP 1 H7 GPS: 26 11 52 S 126 23 03 E
Camp are 20kms SE of Warburton

56. Mananytja Rock Hole
Map Ref: MAP 1 G8 GPS: 26 50 10 S 125 39 29 E
Camping 122km N of Tjukayirla Roadhouse. Turn N 100m W of Rockhole and follow track. Ph: 1800 013 314

57. Camp Paradise
Map Ref: MAP 1 G8 GPS: 26 57 55 S 125 24 43 E
Camping 92km N of Tjukayirla Roadhouse. Turn N off road. Ph: 1800 013 314

58. South Gregories Camp Area
Map Ref: MAP 1 B8 GPS: 25 34 43 S 113 27 55 E
Located 44kms N of Denham. Turn L from Dampier Rd onto Monkey Mia Rd 3kms then L onto Peron Rd for 39km camp site on L. 4WD only. Ph: 08 9219 9000

59. Shark Bay - Central West
Map Ref: MAP 1 B8 GPS: 26 04 39 S 113 34 49 E
Turn off the North West Coastal Hwy 830km N of Perth. Camping areas are located between 19km and 36km SE of Denham off Shark Bay Rd. Ph: 1300 367 072

60. Gladstone camping area - Pilbara
Map Ref: MAP 1 B8 GPS: 25 57 08 S 114 14 42 E
Access signposted off the NW Coastal Hwy 145km S of Carnarvon and 55km N of Overlander Roadhouse. Continue 6km west direction to the camping area. Ph: 08 9941 0000

61. Stock Well 9 Camp Spot
Map Ref: MAP 1 C8 GPS: 27 20 40 S 115 53 41 E
53km S of Murchison Settlement or 148km N of Mullewa. Turn E and follow track to well.

62. Ballinyoo Bridge
Map Ref: MAP 1 C8 GPS: 27 31 35 S 115 46 29 E
Camping area 132km N of Mullewa. Camping along the river. Dirt rd.

63. Garden Rock
Map Ref: MAP 1 D8 GPS: 27 29 21 S 118 01 36 E
16km SE from Cue on Cue-Sandstone Rd. Dirt Rd.

64. Lake Mason camping area - Mid West
Map Ref: MAP 1 E8 GPS: 27 35 16 S 119 31 13 E
Within Lake Mason Conservation Park 56km N of Sandstone. Camping area is in the homestead precinct on Sandstone-Wiluna Rd. Ph: 08 9080 5555

Featured Campsite

Brought to you by

Shark Bay No 59

Denham, WA

830km from Perth

Catherine Lawson and David Bristow

A thin strip of squeaky white sand separates Shark Bay's watery wilderness from the rust red sand cliffs. Walking on the edge of translucent blue seas, eagle rays and shovel-nosed sharks shoot by in the shallows, and in deeper waters, green sea turtles and dugongs feed on the largest seagrass banks in the world.

This extraordinary World Heritage Area also harbours Monkey Mia's world-famous dolphins and the magnificent 4WD-only Francois Peron National Park that provides sanctuary for rare bilbies, woylies, malas and malleefowls. Abundant stromatolites flourish in the hypersaline waters at Hamelin Pool, rare marine colonies that exist in only one other place on earth.

And to top it all off, there's a great range of low-cost beachfront campsites from just $10/site. The Shires' once-free camping areas at Goulet Bluff, Whalebone Bay, Fowlers Camp and Eagle Bluff are legendary for their incredible cliffside locations on the edge of Denham Sound.

But in order to protect the pristine nature of the camps and optimise the enjoyment of visitors, the shire now restricts the number of vehicles allowed at each of the camping areas to just four. That means you'll need to phone ahead or drop into the Shark Bay World Heritage Discovery & Visitor Centre on Denham's foreshore to secure your one-night-only camping permit and pay an administration fee of $10/vehicle.

Signposted off Shark Bay Road between 36 and 19km south of town, the camping areas provide no facilities, but dogs are permitted and the well-graded roads are fine for conventional vehicle and rigs except after wet weather. You can use your generator but no open fires are permitted, and rubbish (including toilet paper) must be bagged up and taken into town for disposal.

Chose Goulet Bluff for access to Shell Beach, Whalebone Bay for its flat, caravan-friendly sites, Fowlers for beach fishing and protection from the wind for tent-based campers, and Eagle Bluff to snorkel and watch the ospreys and sea eagles overhead.

There has been a walkway installed along the clifftops.

Camping has been limited to one night only and a restriction on visitors.

The crystal clear waters tempt swimmers and the fishing is reputedly very good, either from the beaches or off boats out in the bay. One tip for visitors to this area: BYO plenty of drinking water or be prepared to buy it from Denham's desalination plant.

One night is not nearly long enough to explore Shark Bay but the great news is that you can move on to one of five low-cost campgrounds in nearby Francois Peron National Park. These provide free gas barbecues, toilets and picnic tables for travellers with high-clearance 4WD vehicles and the camping fees are modest too: $5.50/night for seniors and other concession card holders, $2.20 for kids and $7.50 per adult, payable via self-registration booths on site.

Highlights of a visit to Francois Peron National Park include the 1.5km Wanamalu walking trail to Skipjack Point, and a long soak in old Peron Homestead's hot tub, overflowing with 44-degree artesian bore water. Staying in Shark Bay is most pleasant from June to October, and after winter rains which paint the peninsula's sandy plains with Shark Bay daisies, white myrtles, yellow wattles and purple peas.

Just The Facts

Shark Bay

Getting there: Turn off the North West Coastal Highway 830km north of Perth. The four camping areas are located between 19km and 36km southeast of Denham, off Shark Bay Road. The entrance to Francois Peron National Park is located 4km north of Denham.

Facilities: Only Francois Peron National Park provides camping facilities: picnic tables, free gas barbecues and toilets.

Rates: The Shark Bay camps attract an administration charge of $10/vehicle. In Francois Peron National Park, nightly camping fees of $5.50 (concessions, including seniors), $2.20 (kids) and $7.50 (adults) are payable via self-registration on site.

Wheelchair Access: No

Pets: Permitted at the Shark Bay Camps but not in Francois Peron National Park.

Contact: Phone or visit the Shark Bay World Heritage Discovery & Visitor Centre on Denham's main street (1300 367 072, (08) 9948 1590) to obtain a camping permit and pay fees. For information on the region head to www.sharkbayvisit.com or www.dpaw.wa.gov.au.

Free Campsites in Western Australia

65. Wanjarri Shearing Shed camping area - Goldfields
Map Ref: MAP 1 E8 GPS: 27 24 06 S 120 38 53 E
From Leinster take the Goldfields Hwy for 50km to the signposted road on the E to Yacka, and then a further 16.5km E to the camping area. Access road can be rough and is for use in dry weather only. Ph: 08 9080 5555

66. Wanjarri Nature Reserve Shearing Shed camping area
Map Ref: MAP 1 E8 GPS: 27 24 07 S 120 38 53 E
From Leinster take Goldfields Hwy for 58kms to the signposted road on the east to Yacka. Drive through mining leases and follow signs to reserve after 16.5km. Dry weather only Ph: 08 9080 5555

67. Giles Breakaway
Map Ref: MAP 1 F8 GPS: 28 18 49 S 122 42 03 E
Camping spot 50km N of Laverton. At Outback Way sign turn S onto track to Breakaway. Ph: 1800 013 314

68. Yeo Lake Homestead camping area - Goldfields
Map Ref: MAP 1 G8 GPS: 28 04 59 S 124 19 10 E
213km NE of Laverton on the Anne Beadell Highway. Ph: 08 9080 5555

69. Neale Junction camping area - Goldfields
Map Ref: MAP 1 H8 GPS: 28 18 18 S 125 48 58 E
At the junction of the Anne Beadell and Connie Sue Highways which is 166km E of Yeo Homestead. Ph: 08 9080 5555

70. Plumridge Lakes Nature Reserve bush camp
Map Ref: MAP 1 G9 GPS: 29 50 59 S 125 40 19 E
The reserve is SE of Laverton and accessed via the Rason Lake Rd off Merolia Rd. Access track on Connie Sue Hwy. Ph: 08 9080 5555

71. Forrest Airport
Map Ref: MAP 1 J10 GPS: 30 50 53 S 128 06 30 E
Camp area at Forrest Airport, Forrest-Mundrabilla Rd, 122km NW of Eucla. Ph: 08 9022 6403

72. Newman Rock - Goldfields
Map Ref: MAP 1 F10 GPS: 32 06 07 S 123 10 40 E
Newman Rock is 1km N of the Eyre Hwy, 142km E of Norseman or 50km W of Balladonia.

73. Caiguna Blowhole
Map Ref: MAP 1 G11 GPS: 32 16 36 S 125 25 52 E
Camp spot 5km W of Caiguna, 199km E of Balladonia, GPS on entry.

74. Caiguna East
Map Ref: MAP 1 H10 GPS: 32 14 42 S 125 32 24 E
Camp spot 6km E of Caiguna, 59km W of Cocklebiddy, GPS on entry 500m S of hwy.

75. Nuytsland Nature Reserve
Map Ref: MAP 1 H10 GPS: 32 01 19 S 126 11 10 E
Camp spot 7.5km E of Cocklebiddy. GPS at hwy turn off, take track S of hwy, past big sinkhole, turn R before the sinkhole, L at intersection, W of cave. 4WD recommended.

76. The Old Quarry
Map Ref: MAP 1 H10 GPS: 31 54 33 S 126 49 46 E
Camp spot 19km W of Madura or 81km E of Cocklebiddy. GPS at Hwy turn off, sites about 1km from hwy.

77. Dunn Rocks
Map Ref: MAP 1 F11 GPS: 33 55 34 S 122 20 23 E
Camp spot 58km E of Esperance via Merivale Rd for 33km, turn R into Dunn Rock Rd for 12km, turn R for 4km. Must be self sufficient. Ph: 08 9219 9000

78. Membinup Beach
Map Ref: MAP 1 F11 GPS: 33 53 26 S 122 38 58 E
Camp area 90km E of Esperance via Merivale Rd & Daniels Rd. 12km dirt road. Suitable for 4WD & offroad vans only. Ph: 08 9083 1555

79. Alexander Bay
Map Ref: MAP 1 F12 GPS: 33 53 06 S 122 44 53 E
Camp area 105km E of Esperance via Merivale Rd & Alexander Rd. 16kms dirt road. 4WD recommended Ph: 08 9083 1555

80. Deralinya Ruins - Esperance
Map Ref: MAP 1 G11 GPS: 33 03 15 S 123 23 20 E
Camp area is located 7km W of Mt Ragged track. Access is via track 12.5km S of junction of Balladonia & Mt Ragged track. Ph: 08 9083 2100

Featured Campsite

Brought to you by

Giles (Jindalee) Breakaway No 67

Outback, WA

50km northeast of Laverton

Colin and Prue Kerr

Promoted as Australia's longest shortcut, the Great Central Road, from Laverton (WA) to Winton (Qld) is an increasingly popular outback trail cutting off several thousand kilometres for those travelling directly across the country.

With Government promises for a progressive upgrade of what is, today, a mostly gravel roadway, this splendid outback travel experience has opened up some previously very remote and difficult to access desert country to a wide range of travellers. 4WD high clearance vehicles are recommended for this journey and you'll also need permits (2) to travel through some of the Aboriginal country that this trail traverses. Along the way, there are currently over 30 interpretive panels containing outback stories and specific site information on the wide variety of places and geological features found in this ever-changing landscape.

For those with time on their hands, visitors can enjoy fossicking for gemstones, wander through indigenous art and craft centres, check out a remote meteorological station and witness some splendid natural sights, including Uluru (Ayers Rock), Kata Tjuta (the Olgas) and some quite spectacular breakaway country along the way.

Out here travellers have a variety of accommodation options including motel, cabin and caravan park facilities at roadhouses at some communities, or for those set up for independent camping, there are many bushland camping spots just off the road.

Spectacular rock cliffs and wildflowers.

One of the most appealing and scenically beautiful of those is at the Giles Breakaway, around 50 km northeast of Laverton in the Great Victoria Desert.

Here, the very basic picnic and camping ground has no facilities, apart from a table and chair set up in the shade. With cleared space able to accommodate a number of units without camping on top of each other, this scenic spot overlooks an extensive and very colourful canyon-like gorge lined with beautiful breakaway cliffs which are quite spectacular, especially in the late afternoon or early morning sunlight.

A really great spot to sit on the edge of the cliff overlooking the valley below and enjoy a morning coffee or a few quiet drinks at happy hour watching the local birdlife and the ever changing colours on the cliff faces.

Formed by erosion over millions of years, the cliffs and caves are the result of the hard caprock at the top levels protecting the softer strata beneath. The cliff top edges here are quite unstable and visitors are warned to take care when walking around the area. 

The campsite is a place to relax amonst the red dust.

Just The Facts

Giles Breakaway Campsite

Location: On Great Central Road 50 km northeast of Laverton. The campsite overlooking breakaway cliffs is approximately 400 metres off (and out of sight of) the road.

Facilities: Picnic table and chairs. No other facilities apart from nice level campsites, some with shade. There is also an information panel here on the Breakaway. Take all rubbish away with you.

Rates: Free

Pets: Yes, allowed.

Disabled: Nothing specific

Contact: For information: Great Beyond Visitor Centre, Augusta Street, Laverton - phone: (08)9031.1361 – email: greatbeyond@laverton.wa.gov.au – web: www.laverton.wa.gov.au

Free transit permits to cross Aboriginal lands are available on line. Visit www.ngaanyatjarra.org.au/ngaanyatjarra-council/permits (WA section) and www.clc.org.au/articles/cat/application-for-a-transit-permit/ (NT section).

For further travel information, check www.outbackway.org.au

Free Campsites in Western Australia

81. Balbinya Ruins - Esperance
Map Ref: MAP 1 G11 GPS: 33 05 30 S 123 34 10 E
12.5km S of junction of Mt Ragged track & Balladonia Rd. Ph: 08 9083 2100

82. Israelite Bay - Esperance
Map Ref: MAP 1 G11 GPS: 33 37 35 S 123 51 98 E
Some 200km E of Esperance . Access through the Cape Arid NP .
Campground located at end of Fisheries Rd. Ph: 08 9071 0666

83. Point Malcolm camping area - Esperance
Map Ref: MAP 1 G11 GPS: 33 47 55 S 123 45 22 E
Signposted access off Fisheries Road, 60km E of the signposted Poison Creek turn off. Ph: 08 9075 0055

84. Tenindewa Pioneer Well - Central West
Map Ref: MAP 2 A3 GPS: 28 36 41 S 115 21 41 E
Located on the Geraldton - Mt Magnet Rd 80km E of Geraldton. Dry weather only Ph: 08 9961 1500

85. Breakaway camping area - Mid West
Map Ref: MAP 2 B3 GPS: 28 57 01 S 115 32 23 S
Located 35km N of Mingenew in Coalseam Conservation Park. Continue along Coalseam Road to the signposted access to the camping area. Ph: 08 9921 5955

86. Miners Camp Camping area - Mid West
Map Ref: MAP 2 B3 GPS: 28 57 29 S 115 33 15 S
Located 36km N of Mingenew in Coalseam Conservation Park. From Mingenew follow Coalseam Road to the parks Southern Boundary. Ph: 08 9921 5955

87. Gutha Hall Camp Area
Map Ref: MAP 2 B3 GPS: 28 59 32 S 115 56 53 E
74kms SE of Mullewa at 216 Evaside Rd. Take Mullewa Wubin Rd for 69kms and turn L onto Gutha W Rd for 3.5kms turn R onto Evaside Rd.

88. Kalanooka Springs
Map Ref: MAP 2 C3 GPS: 29 11 25 S 116 14 19 E
Camping spot 30km E of Morowa. Travel 16km on dirt rd.

89. Paynes Find Camp
Map Ref: MAP 2 D3 GPS: 29 09 55 S 117 42 22 E
12kms N of Paynes Find turn W 1.2kms before parking area, several access tracks. Various campsites.

90. Lake Ballard - Goldfields
Map Ref: MAP 2 H3 GPS: 29 27 48 S 120 36 33 E
Signposted off the Goldfields Hwy 57km NW of Menzies. Ph: 08 9024 2702

91. Malcolm Dam - Goldfields
Map Ref: MAP 2 J2 GPS: 28 52 42 S 121 26 48 E
10kms E of Leonora on the Laverton-Leonora Rd and take signposted turnoff to Malcolm Dam for 3km. Ph: 08 9037 7016

92. Niagara Dam - Goldfields
Map Ref: MAP 2 J3 GPS: 29 24 25 S 121 25 55 E
60kms NE of Menzies or 191kms N of Kalgoorlie via the Goldfields Hwy. Ph: 08 9024 2041

93. Cliff Head Campsite - Perth Region
Map Ref: MAP 2 A4 GPS: 29 30 54 S 114 59 50 E
Cliff Head is a beach and tiny settlement of shack off the Indian Ocean Drive 50km N of Leeman. Ph: 08 9927 1404

94. Camel Soak & John Forrest Lookout - Central West
Map Ref: MAP 2 C4 GPS: 29 24 00 S 116 36 34 E
39kms E of Perenjori. Take the Perenjori-Rothsay Rd and S on to the Rabbit Proof Fence Rd. Ph: 08 9973 1105

95. Caron Dam Reserve
Map Ref: MAP 2 C4 GPS: 29 33 56 S 116 18 57 E
Camping spot 65km N of Wubin. Turn W at Caron Dam sign.

96. Bunjil Rocks
Map Ref: MAP 2 C4 GPS: 29 39 50 S 116 22 18 E
Camping spot 57km N of Wubin. Turn W at signpost travel for 1km. Dirt track on right.

Featured Campsite

Tenindewa Free camp No 84

Mullewa, WA
82 km east of Geraldton

Jill Harrison

A great overnight stop when exploring Western Australia's wildflower country through the mid-west is Tenindewa, located on the 115 kilometre northern loop of the Mullewa wildflowers and historic interpretive loop trail. The northern trail features 13 interpretive sites including three at Tenindewa.

Located in the Wolya Reserve, about 17 kilometres west of Mullewa just off the Geraldton to Mt Magnet Road, we had seen this campsite on our map on a previous trip but hadn't stopped to take a look. This year we were ready to find a camp around 3pm and Tenindewa suited our plans perfectly.

The bush reserve is surrounded by farmland. There are no facilities, but there are plenty of places to set up camp away from the road and the setting surrounded by wildflowers in spring more than make up for the lack of facilities. Check local fire bans before lighting a campfire. We drove in a short way and found a quiet place to set up camp. You might like to scout around on foot, as we did, to locate the perfect spot for you. Some areas offer some shade.

Not far from where we camped is a small dam and Wolya Well which is Site #3 on the Mullewa Northern Loop Trail. The first eastward road from Geraldton passed through here to Mullewa and then north to the Murchison sheep stations. Aboriginal people had used Wolya Soak for hundreds of years before the small dam was built. The well was sunk in the late 1880s, fitted with a windlass and bucket, and was invaluable to people trekking to the goldfields during the gold rush years.

Old stone causeway across the lake to the school

Tenindewa old school site

Exploring wildflower country – old Tenindewa store-post office in the background

Located next to the railway line on Griffiths Road just off the Geraldton-Mt Magnet Road, is Site #1 on the trail, the old Tenindewa Stock yards, part of the old rail bridge and the Store-Post Office-Telephone Exchange. These are all that remain of a once thriving community built around the siding and the railway gangs.

The Geraldton to Mullewa railway line was constructed in 1894 and the railway station opened in 1908. Originally named 55 Mile Siding, its name was changed to the aboriginal name for a nearby gully, Kockatea, and later to Tenindewa, also an aboriginal word, but the meaning is now unknown.

Most properties in the area ran cattle and sheep as well as growing grain. Stock were brought to the stock yards, sometimes driven overland, and loaded onto trains bound for Perth or Geraldton.

There are two signposted Mullewa drive loop trails suitable for 2Wdrive vehicles, and featuring interpretive panels and steel sculptures. Some have picnic tables and fire rings. Collect a map from the Mullewa Visitor Information Centre.

Just The Facts

Tenindewa Campsite

Where is it: 28.61006, 115.36348
Located at Wolya Reserve. 82 kilometres east of Geraldton and 17 kilometres west of Mullewa. Turn north off the Geraldton-Mt Magnet Road, onto Yuna-Tendinewa Road. The turnoff is about 1.5kms along. Suitable for caravans, motorhomes, camper trailers and tents.

Facilities: None. Take your rubbish away with you.
Be aware of current fire bans, and bring your own firewood.
Please keep your pet on a lead.

More information:
Mullewa Visitor Information: https://visitmullewa.com.au/
Tenindewa Town: https://tenindewa.com/about/

Brought to you by

kokodacaravans.com.au

Cliff Head Campsite

No 93

Cliff Head, WA

38km south of Dongara
Keith and Susan Hall

The Indian Ocean Drive is a popular route for those travelling between Perth and Geraldton to the north. This relatively new coastal road is very scenic and mostly free of truck traffic. But even though the road passes by several large national parks along the way, there are not many beach or bush camping options.

One great free camping site can be found at the northern end of the Indian Ocean Drive. Although the campground is only about 50m off the main road, it is not signposted and is very easy to miss. Look for tracks going off on the west side of the road at about 50km north of Leeman or about 6km south of the turnoff from the Brand Highway.

If coming from the north, the first track which accesses the northern end of the campsite is a short, flat, but unsealed road leading to a parking area with a toilet and some large bins for rubbish. From this main parking area, sandy tracks go north and south parallel to the beach. There are campsites either side of the long sandy track that stretches south for more than half a kilometre along the beach. On one side of the track the sites are only 10m from the water's edge, while on the other side they are more sheltered by a low limestone cliff.

Other popular sites are tucked under the cliff at the southern end of the beach, which gives the location its name. From this end of the beach there are alternative tracks that give access back to the main road, but they have a steep incline.

The southern end of the camp ground has a collection of fishermen's shacks and a small private jetty. This is definitely more of a fishing spot than a swimming and sunbathing beach, because during our visit the white sand was almost invisible under a layer of seaweed. Maybe the seaweed disappears in the summer months though.

The beach at Cliff Head may not be at its best in spring, but the wildflowers are pretty and you can enjoy watching a pair of Ospreys in their nest high up on a pole above the little jetty. Ospreys, sometimes called Sea Hawks, are large birds with a hooked beak, powerful legs and sharp talons which they use, feet first, to catch fish in the ocean. When they have a fish safely grasped in their talons, you may see them flying high overhead on their way back to the nest with food for their chicks.

There are no signs to say so, but according to Dongara Visitor Information Centre, free camping is allowed at Cliff Head for up to 72 hours. Previous campers have constructed fireplaces from rocks and scraps of corrugated iron, but no fires are allowed from October to April. Dump points are available at the two caravan parks at Port Denison, Dongara's port town, and can be used for a fee. There is also a free dump point at the Arrowsmith rest area on the Brand Highway, 50km south of Dongara.

Sheltered sites under the cliff at the southern end of the Cliff Head camping area.

Osprey nest at Cliff Head.

Yellow Tail Flower adds colour to the bush at Cliff Head in the spring.

Just The Facts

Tenindewa Campsite

Where is it: 28.61006, 115.36348
Located at Wolya Reserve. 82 kilometres east of Geraldton and 17 kilometres west of Mullewa. Turn north off the Geraldton-Mt Magnet Road, onto Yuna-Tendinewa Road. The turnoff is about 1.5kms along. Suitable for caravans, motorhomes, camper trailers and tents.
Facilities: None. Take your rubbish away with you.
Be aware of current fire bans, and bring your own firewood.
Please keep your pet on a lead.
More information:
Mullewa Visitor Information: https://visitmullewa.com.au/
Tenindewa Town: https://tenindewa.com/about/

Free Campsites in Western Australia

97. Comet Vale
Map Ref: MAP 2 J4 GPS: 29 56 53 S 121 07 05 E
Camping 101km N of Kalgoorlie at old town site

98. Goongarrie Homestead camping area - Goldfields
Map Ref: MAP 2 J4 GPS: 29 58 56 S 121 02 42 E
Signposted access along the Goldfields Hwy, 90km N of Kalgoorlie. Camping in vicinity of the homestead. Ph: 08 9080 5555

99. Rowles Lagoon camping area - Goldfields
Map Ref: MAP 2 J4 GPS: 30 25 35 S 120 51 51 E
68km N of Coolgardie along Coolgardie N Road. Then 6.5km NE to the camping area. On the eastern shore of Rowles Lagoon Ph: 08 9080 5555

100. Credo Station camping area - Goldfields
Map Ref: MAP 2 J5 GPS: 30 27 55 S 120 49 38 E
75kms NW of Coolgardie via Coolgardie Northern Rd. Camping in the vicinity of the homestead. Ph: 08 9080 5555

101. Lake Indoon
Map Ref: MAP 2 A5 GPS: 29 51 37 S 115 09 17 E
Camping spot 12km SW of Eneabba

102. Apex Camp Jurien Camp Area
Map Ref: MAP 2 A5 GPS: 30 18 09 S 115 02 40 E
Camp at 15 Bashford St, Jurien Bay. From Brand Hwy take Jurien Bay Rd for 38km then L onto Indian Ocean Drive for 27kms then L. Ph: 08 9652 1010

103. Buntine Rocks
Map Ref: MAP 2 C5 GPS: 29 58 12 S 116 35 07 E
Camping spot 18km NW of Wubin via Buntine East Rd.

104. Wubin Rocks
Map Ref: MAP 2 C5 GPS: 30 03 51 S 116 40 31 E
Camping spot 8km NE of Wubin. Turn NW onto Manuel Rd 6km E of Wubin.

105. Jibberding Rock
Map Ref: MAP 2 D5 GPS: 30 00 09 S 116 49 29 E
Camping spot 22km NE of Wubin.

106. Petrudor Rock
Map Ref: MAP 2 D5 GPS: 30 25 30 S 116 58 00 E
Camping spot 31km E of Pithara. Turn S off Pithara East Rd onto Petrudor Rd and travel 8km dirt rd.

107. Newcarlbeon Rock Camp Area
Map Ref: MAP 2 D5 GPS: 30 39 59 S 117 25 05 E
Located 20km N of Koorda via Koorda-Kulja Rd on Newcarlbeon Rd. Signposted.

108. Koorda Native Flora Reserve
Map Ref: MAP 2 E5 GPS: 30 44 25 S 117 33 10 E
Camp area 16kms N of Koorda via Koorda-Mollerin Rd on Mulji Rd. Signposted.

109. Mollerin Rock Camp Area
Map Ref: MAP 2 E5 GPS: 30 32 19 S 117 33 57 E
Situated 45kms N of Koorda via Koorda-Mollerin Rd on Kulja-Mollerin Rd. Signposted.

110. Billiburning Rock Camp Area
Map Ref: MAP 2 E5 GPS: 30 10 20 S 117 55 04 E
34km N of Beacon via Ingleton Rd & White Rd, 18kms dirt road.

111. Datjoin Well & Rock Reserve
Map Ref: MAP 2 E5 GPS: 30 27 44 S 118 04 07 E
Camp spot 5km W of Wialki on Buralin-Wialki Rd. Signposted.

112. Beringbooding Rock - North Eastern WA Wheatbelt
Map Ref: MAP 2 F5 GPS: 30 33 31 S 118 29 36 E
70km NE of Mukinbudin near the intersection of the Beringbooding & Cunderin Rds.

113. Elachbutting Rock - North Eastern WA Wheatbelt
Map Ref: MAP 2 F5 GPS: 30 35 36 S 118 36 53 E
100km N of Westonia and 70km NE of Mukinbudin. www.westonia.wa.gov.au

114. Jaurdi Station Homestead - Goldfields
Map Ref: MAP 2 H5 GPS: 30 48 58 S 120 09 43 E
Located on Ryans Find Road which is accessed off Mt Walton (Heath) Road via Great Eastern Hwy. Ph: 08 9080 5555

115. Wallaroo Rock Camp Area
Map Ref: MAP 2 H6 GPS: 31 03 29 S 120 17 53 E
Situated 103kms W of Coolgardie. Turn N off Hwy 64kms W of Coolgardie at the Old Woolgangie Township sign. Travel 38km 4WD track to rock. Ph: 08 9080 5555

116. Lake Douglas Recreation Reserve
Map Ref: MAP 2 J5 GPS: 30 56 38 S 121 23 35 E
Camping spot 12km SW of Kalgoorlie. Turn S and follow signs for 3km. Dirt rd, limited stay.

117. Minnivale Campsite - Perth Region
Map Ref: MAP 2 D6 GPS: 31 08 19 S 117 11 07 E
Minnivale is a tiny settlement on a side road off the Nungarin-Wyalkatchem Rd. Minnivale is 16km E of Dowerin and the township is 5km from the main road. Ph: 08 9631 1202

118. Marshall Rock camping area - Perth Region
Map Ref: MAP 2 E6 GPS: 30 50 30 S 117 54 22 E
Some 270km NE of Perth and 10km SE of Bencubbin. Signposted access on Marshall Rock South Road. Ph: 08 9685 1202

119. Danberrin Rock
Map Ref: MAP 2 E6 GPS: 31 16 51 S 118 03 08 E
Camp spot 15km S of Nungarin via Danberrin Rd, Baird Rd West. Signposted.

120. Eaglestone Rock
Map Ref: MAP 2 E6 GPS: 31 04 00 S 118 13 49 E
Camping spot 21km NE of Nungarin towards Lake Brown.

121. Weira Reserve
Map Ref: MAP 2 F6 GPS: 30 59 40 S 118 23 13 E
Camp spot 13kms R of Mukinbudin via Kooda-Bullfinch Rd. Signposted/

122. Baladgie Rock - Goldfields
Map Ref: MAP 2 F6 GPS: 30 57 20 S 118 52 05 E
43km NE of Westonia, 30km W of Bullfinch. Turn north from the Koorda Bullfinch Rd and follow for approx. 4km to camp area. Track in follows edge of lake and could be boggy when wet.

123. Weowanie Rock - Goldfields
Map Ref: MAP 2 G6 GPS: 31 04 25 S 119 27 18 E
Approx 21km NE of Yellowdine. Turn north off the Great Eastern Highway onto the Marvel Lock Yellowdine Rd. 13km to Duladgin Rock then 8km to Weowanie. Track in follows edge of salt lake and could be boggy when wet.

124. Karalee Rock & Dam campsite - Goldfields
Map Ref: MAP 2 G6 GPS: 31 15 04 S 119 50 25 E
Karalee is 420km E of Perth, access on unsealed road from Great Eastern Hwy. Ph: 08 9049 1001

125. Thursday Rock - Holland Track - Goldfields
Map Ref: MAP 2 H6 GPS: 31 31 10 S 120 37 32 E
Located 21km from the Victoria Rock Rd. 4WD only section of the Holland Track is 170km and runs in a NE direction from 56km E of Hyden on the Hyden-Norseman Rd to Victoria Rock Rd 78km S of Coolgardie.

126. Victoria Rock - Goldfields
Map Ref: MAP 2 J6 GPS: 31 17 30 S 120 55 50 E
Signposted off Victoria Rock Rd 45km SW of Coolgardie. Ph: 08 9080 5555

127. Burra Rock - Goldfields
Map Ref: MAP 2 J6 GPS: 31 23 36 S 121 12 01 E
Burra Rock is 60kms S of Coolgardie via the Burra Rock Rd. Ph: 08 9080 5555

128. Cave Hill Nature Reserve - Goldfields
Map Ref: MAP 2 J6 GPS: 31 39 60 S 121 13 60 E
Located 96kms from Coolgardie via Hyden. Dry weather only. Ph: 08 9080 5555

Minnivale Campsite

No 117

Minnivale, WA

21km east of Dowerin

Keith and Susan Hall

Facilities at Minnivale include a dump point and a cold shower.

The WA wheatbelt is a perfect touring destination, especially in the spring when the wildflowers are in bloom. A vast network of good roads crisscross the region and road traffic is sparse. Most of the small towns welcome tourists with accommodation in inexpensive caravan parks, but free camping options are uncommon.

The central wheatbelt region does have a free camping site at Minnivale, east of Dowerin, where stays of up to seven days are allowed. Situated in a tiny settlement with a railway siding, wheat bin and a couple of private residences, the Minnivale campsite is on open ground, with expansive views of the surrounding countryside. Just behind the campsite is a large nature reserve which is a wildflower hotspot in the spring.

Minnivale was originally known as 36 Mile Post on the rabbit proof fence. It became a more established settlement when a railway siding was built in 1911. The wheat bin was constructed in 1963, but is no longer in use.

The campsite at Minnivale seems to be a productive reuse of the town's former recreation area. The old tennis courts are still there, but the old toilets are now part of the campsite, with one being converted into a cold shower cubicle. The shire of Dowerin has added a dump point, picnic tables and a tourist information board in a wildflower garden. There is also an outdoor tap and a clothesline. The nearest fuel and supplies are at Dowerin which is 21 km east of Minnivale.

A donation box next to the wildflower garden is a good way to pay for water that you might have used or to make a contribution to maintaining the facilities. The notice board details some of the flowers you can see in the surrounding bush. During our visit in early September, we were delighted to find lots of small Donkey Orchids. On the road coming into the campsite, we stopped to admire the spectacular Pink Spiked Hakea.

Minnivale is on the tourist route known as the Wheatbelt Way, a drive trail that takes in nine towns in the north eastern Wheatbelt. The trail starts at Dowerin and the second stop is Minnivale, followed by Naaning Well. Historic Naaning Well is on the main road, 16km from Dowerin and near the turn off to Minnivale.

From a parking area which has a picnic table and toilet, there is a short walk though the bush to the well. At least we came to what looked like a depression in the ground with some old farm carts nearby, although this didn't look like the photo on the notice board at the car park.

In 1869, explorer John Forrest camped at Naaning Well and in the late 1880s the well provided water for travellers to the goldfields further east. When gold was discovered near Southern Cross in 1887, the best route for travellers was from Perth to Northam by train and then by horse drawn wagon or on foot to Goomalling and on through what is now Dowerin to Wyalkatchem and beyond.

For touring information on the Wheatbelt Way, visit www.wheatbeltway.com.au. Another tourist route from Dowerin to Merredin is called the Pioneers' Pathway, www.pioneerspathway.org.au

Donkey Orchids flower in spring in the surrounding bush.

Old farm wagon at Naaning Well.

Just The Facts

Minnivale Campsite

Location: Minnivale is a railway siding and tiny settlement on a side road off the Nungarin-Wyalkatchem Road. The turnoff to Minnivale is 16km east of Dowerin and the township is 5km from the main road on a sealed but narrow road.

Facilities: Picnic tables, cold shower, toilet and dump point

Wheelchair access: No special facilities

Rates: Free

Pets: No restrictions indicated

Contact: Shire of Dowerin, (08) 9631 1202, www.wheatbelttourism.com/where-to-stay/dowerin/dowerin-accommodation/

Free Campsites in Western Australia

129. Walyunga Campground
Map Ref: MAP 2 C7 GPS: 31 43 59 S 116 03 09 E
Situated 10kms S of Bullsbrook. From Great Northern Hwy turn L to Walyunga Rd. Signposted. Ph: 08 9219 9000

130. Kwolyin camping area
Map Ref: MAP 2 E7 GPS: 31 53 01 S 117 42 06 E
The Kwolyin campsite is located 7kms W of Shackleton on the Bruce Rock-Quairading Road, 25km S of Kellerberrin and the Great Eastern Highway, 40kms west of Bruce Rock, and 229kms E of Perth. Ph: 08 9061 1377

131. Roe Dam Camp Area
Map Ref: MAP 2 F7 GPS: 31 59 50 S 118 48 55 E
Situated 54km N of Hyden. Follow Hyden-Mt Walker Rd for 46km via Mt Walker Rd for 4km then Roe Dam Rd for 4 kms and Yeomans Rd 600m.

132. Anderson Rock Camping Area
Map Ref: MAP 2 F7 GPS: 32 10 08 S 118 51 04 E
Camp spot 40kms N of Hyden. Travel Hyden-Mt Walker Rd for 36kms then turn R into Anderson's Rock Rd for 2.5km & R again for 2kms. Off Road vans only

133. The Breakaways - Goldfields
Map Ref: MAP 2 H7 GPS: 32 16 34 S 120 15 46 E
Located 137km of Hyden and 143km W of Norseman on the Hyden to Norseman Rd. Access is signposted and on the south side of the road.

134. Boondi Rock Campground - Goldfields
Map Ref: MAP 2 H7 GPS: 31 60 59 S 120 23 10 E
Located in the Goldfields Woodlands NP 80kms W of Coolgardie via Great Eastern Hwy. Ph: 08 9080 5555

135. McDermid Rock campsite -Goldfields
Map Ref: MAP 2 J7 GPS: 32 01 19 S 120 44 21 E
192km from Hyden. Ph: 08 9039 1071

136. Lake Johnston - Goldfields
Map Ref: MAP 2 J7 GPS: 32 00 55 S 120 47 10 E
Lake Johnson is located 135kms W of Norseman along the Hyden-Norseman Rd. Ph: 08 9039 1071

137. Disappointment Rock Camp
Map Ref: MAP 2 J7 GPS: 32 07 48 S 120 55 44 E
Camp area 87kms W of Norseman on the Hyden-Norseman Rd. Narrow access and limited spaces.

138. Lake Cowan Camp Area
Map Ref: MAP 2 K7 GPS: 32 02 28 S 121 40 43 E
23kms N of Norseman, travel along Coolgardie-Esperance Hwy for 23km then turn off on R.

139. Norseman East Rest Area - Goldfields
Map Ref: MAP 2 K7 GPS: 32 06 34 S 121 54 10 E
Located 16km E of the town of Norseman on the northern side of the Eyre Hwy. Ph: 08 9039 1071

140. Dundas Rocks - Goldfields
Map Ref: MAP 2 K7 GPS: 32 23 26 S 121 46 23 E
The Dundas Coach Rd Heritage Trail starts 1.5km from Norseman with a 50km circuit returning to town.

141. Bromus Dam - Goldfields
Map Ref: MAP 2 K7 GPS: 32 27 30 S 121 41 04 E
32km S of Norseman. 200m s of parking area is the road to the dam where there is a large shady area, great for overnight.

142. Willow Springs camping area - South West
Map Ref: MAP 2 C8 GPS: 32 02 52 S 115 55 22 E
Turn off the Brockman Hwy 25km W of Bridgetown on to Gold Gully Rd for 5km to camp. Ph: 08 9731 6232

143. Pumphreys Bridge Lions Park
Map Ref: MAP 2 D8 GPS: 32 39 45 S 116 54 17 E
Camping spot at Pumphreys Bridge 43km N of Narrogin beside CWA building.

144. Lions Dryandra Camp Area
Map Ref: MAP 2 D8 GPS: 32 47 03 S 116 58 19 E
Take Stevens Rd S of Dryandra for 4kms then turn R into Wandering-Narrogin Rd for 6kms then R into Kawan Rd for 3km turn L 850m.

Featured Campsite

Brought to you by

Kwolyin Campsite

No.130

Western Australian central wheatbelt

By Jill Harrison

Picnic tables, a shelter, BBQ and Toilets.

The Western Australian Wheatbelt has very few opportunities for bush camping, but one worth considering is the Kwolyin campsite located on the Bruce Rock-Quairading Road about 60 kilometres south of Kellerberrin and the Great Eastern Highway.

The Kwolyin camp ground located at the old Kwolyin townsite was created in the last few years to replace the former Kokerbin Rock campsite, nine kilometres to the north, which, as locals put it, had been "loved to death".

The campsite has been established on the old football and cricket grounds and you can still see the 1930s cricket pitch. The town was originally named Koarin, but was thought to be too close to the pronunciation of another town, Kauring, so the name was changed to Kwolyin. Wheat farming began in the area in 1908 and the first Kwolyin town lots were sold in 1913. Lack of water caused growth problems for the town before its final demise was sealed in 1992 when the Kwolyin Hotel was destroyed by fire. All that remains of the town today is the Catholic Church opened in 1955.

The campsites scattered through the scrubby bushland are suitable for tents, caravans and camper trailers. There is a large picnic shelter with gas BBQ adjacent to a camp kitchen which is closed in on three sides sheltering gas hotplates, benches and sink with water. The tent area also has a picnic shelter and a wood fired BBQ built by the Bruce Rock Men's Shed. Please be aware there are fire bans October to March.

The flushing toilets have hand basins and are wheelchair friendly.

There are four loop walks accessible from the campsite: 1.2km Granite Garden walk, 2km Cathedral Rocks walk, and the 2.2km Railway walk across nearby Coarin Rock, or take a walk around the old town site. Please refer to signage at the camp for information on the walks, wear sturdy boots, a hat and sunscreen and carry water with you. Depending on when you visit, insect repellent and a fly net could be a must!

Walkers are asked to keep to the marked trails to protect the fragile plant communities. An information board identifying 99 local wildflowers, including orchids, is located at the main BBQ area. During spring you may also see fruiting Sandalwood and Quandong trees which were an important food source to early inhabitants.

From Kwolyin it is an easy day trip to Kokerbin Rock, only nine kilometres to the north. Covering nine hectares, Kokerbin Rock is the third largest monolith in Australia and bush walkers will enjoy exploring this 122 metre high rock, caves, woodland and historic sites. A track skirts the base of the rock and it is worth walking to the top to enjoy the 360 degree panoramic views of the surrounding grain and sheep country.

Granite outcrops, like Kokerbin are a feature of the central Wheatbelt. Kokerbin is an important cultural traditional site for the Noongar aboriginal people both ceremonially and as a resource for water, stone and wildlife. Granite outcrops were used by early explorers, surveyors and sandalwood cutters to camp, take their bearings and water their horses. A community annual Boxing Day picnic commencing in 1911 was held at Kokerbin Rock.

With less than 10% of the Wheatbelt's original native vegetation remaining, nature reserves and granite outcrops provide a valuable habitat for wildlife and flora. Kokerbin's boulder formations, sheoak, sandalwood and eucalypt woodlands are home to a diversity of wildlife including echidnas and the threatened black-flanked rock wallaby.

You can also follow the sixty kilometre Granite Way drive trail which includes Kokerbin Rock, Mt Stirling and Mt Caroline, all of which have picnic areas. Mt Stirling and Mt Caroline were named by explorer Ensign Dale in 1830.

Basic supplies can be purchased at Shackleton, where you can see Australia's smallest bank. Operating between the 1930s and 1997, this three by four metre weatherboard building was used as an aircraft observation post during World War 2.

Free camping at Kwolyin makes this a great spot to stop if you are travelling through the central Wheatbelt.

Just The Facts

Kwolyin Campsite

Location: The Kwolyin campsite is located 7kms west of Shackleton on the Bruce Rock-Quairading Road, 25km south of Kellerberrin and the Great Eastern Highway, 40kms west of Bruce Rock, and 229kms east of Perth.

Facilities: Flushing toilet with wash basin (recommend you bring your own toilet paper), camp kitchen with gas hotplates and sink, picnic tables and shelter, gas BBQ, rubbish bins, information shelter.

Wheelchair Access: Yes.

Rates: Free.

Pets: Dogs allowed on leash.

Campfires: Prohibited October to March. Please bring your own firewood.

Best time to visit: Winter and spring.

Walks: Please refer to the information board for distances, estimated walk times and degree of difficulty.

For more information on the area: www.brucerock.wa.gov.au

Free Campsites in Western Australia

145. Gorge Rock Pool - Perth Region
Map Ref: MAP 2 E8 GPS: 32 27 28 S 117 59 39 E
Follow the Brookton Hwy 20km E of Corrigin to reach the signposted campground. Ph: 08 9063 2203

146. Orange Resort
Map Ref: MAP 2 G8 GPS: 32 37 35 S 119 21 27 E
Camp area 67km N of Lake King. Follow Hyden-Lake King Rd for 66kms.

147. Peak Charles National Park - Goldfields
Map Ref: MAP 2 J8 GPS: 32 52 60 S 121 10 35 E
107kms N of Esperance via Lake King Norseman Rd then Peak Charles Rd. Ph: 08 9083 2100

148. Marrinup - South West
Map Ref: MAP 2 C8 GPS: 32 42 10 S 116 01 35 E
Located 5km W of Dwellingup on Grey Rd. Ph: 08 9538 1108

149. Herron Point camping area - Perth Region
Map Ref: MAP 2 C9 GPS: 32 44 28 S 115 42 38 E
Located 23km S of Pinjarra. Turn right off the South Western Hwy on to Old Bunbury Hwy, right on to Herron Point Rd and continue to campsite. Ph: 08 9531 7777

150. Martin's Tank Lake campground - Perth Region
Map Ref: MAP 2 C9 GPS: 32 50 44 S 115 40 02 E
Within the Yalgorup NP 74km N of Bunbury off Bunbury Hwy on to Preston Beach Rd. Ph: 08 9303 7750

151. Belvidere Camping Ground - South West
Map Ref: MAP 2 C9 GPS: 33 14 07 S 115 41 48 E
Within the Leschenault Peninsula Conservation Park. From the Old Coast Road take the signposted Buffalo Road for approx. 7kms to campsites. Ph: 08 9735 1988

152. Hoffman Mill camping area - Perth Region
Map Ref: MAP 2 C9 GPS: 33 00 14 S 116 04 59 E
Camp area located 22kms E of Yarloop access via Logue Brook Dam which is signposted off the Sth Western Hwy. Ph: 08 9735 1988

153. Stockton Lake Rec Area - West Entrance - South West
Map Ref: MAP 2 D9 GPS: 33 23 10 S 116 13 50 E
Old mine site 8km E of Collie via Piavanini Rd off the Coalfields Hwy. Ph: 08 9734 1988

154. Norring Lake Camp Area
Map Ref: MAP 2 E9 GPS: 33 26 50 S 117 17 04 E
20kms SW of Wagin. From Hwy take Beaufort St via Umbra St for 7kms turn L onto Norring Rd for 7km, slight R for 3km & turn L staying on Norring Rd for 1km. Self contained vehicles only.

155. Queerarrup Lake
Map Ref: MAP 2 E9 GPS: 33 30 55 S 117 13 27 E
Camping 28km N of Woodanilling. Turn N off Robinson Rd 18km W of Woodanilling. Ph: 08 9823 1506

156. Phillips River Crossing
Map Ref: MAP 2 H9 GPS: 33 36 10 S 119 53 06 E
Camping spot 25km W of Ravensthorpe.

157. Munglinup Beach camping area - South East
Map Ref: MAP 2 J9 GPS: 33 51 50 S 120 47 51 E
Located 109km W of Esperance via Sth Coast Hwy then Doyle Rd to signposted Springdale Rd and then 7km along Muglinup Beach Rd. Ph: 08 9071 2330

158. Glen Mervyn Dam bush camping
Map Ref: MAP 2 C10 GPS: 33 29 55 S 116 05 51 E
From Collie proceed south along Collie-Mumballup Rd for 17km to signposted Best Rd continue on Best Rd for 1km to a gravel track which leads to numerous tracks that lead to camp sites. Ph: 08 9734 2051

159. Ironstone Gully Falls camping area - South West
Map Ref: MAP 2 C10 GPS: 33 39 11 S 115 42 12 E
Signposted access along Goodwood Road, 11km SE of Capel and 18km SW of Donnybrook. Ph: 08 9727 0222

160. Ironstone Gully Falls
Map Ref: MAP 2 C10 GPS: 33 39 12 S 115 42 12 E
Camping area 18km SW of Donnybrook. Ph: 08 9727 0222

Featured Campsite

Brought to you by

Martins Tank Lake Campsite No.150

Yalgorup National Park, WA

112km south of Perth

Jill Harrison

Approximately 112kms south of Perth, midway between Mandurah and Bunbury in Western Australia's south west, is Martin's Tank campground. Its proximity to the metropolitan area makes it a convenient weekend getaway destination.

Martins Tank Lake is one of ten salt lakes within the 12,888 hectare Yalgorup National Park on the western edge of the Swan Coastal Plain, squeezed between the Indian Ocean and the Old Coast Road. Aboriginal people inhabited this area for 40,000 years before Europeans first visited here around 1829. The Park was formally established in the 1970s to protect the coastal lakes, swamps and tuart woodlands.

Martins Tank campground is accessed off Preston Beach Road about 11 kilometres along a sand and limestone road which is suitable for 2WD but may be wet during winter. There are 30 individual campsites: five suitable for tents only; 16 for tents or smaller campervans and nine can accommodate caravans, camper trailers and large campervans. There are also four `open` camping areas (without individual sites) each of which can accommodate four tents and has parking for larger vehicles.

A campground upgrade completed in 2013 included a camp kitchen with gas BBQs, gas burner, sinks, tables and benches. There are also open-air gas BBQs. It is recommended that you bring your own drinking water, as the quality of the water in the water tank cannot be guaranteed and should only be used for washing. Please be aware of fire restrictions and bring a fuel stove. During busy months there is a campground host.

A short walk from the camp takes you to the edge of the lake, which is only around 1.5 metres deep. Swimming, canoeing and fishing are prohibited.

The Yalgorup wetland system is a haven for birdwatchers and internationally recognised on the Ramsar List as an important habitat for migratory waterbirds including the Red Knot which breeds around the Arctic Circle.

View the birdlife, particularly during summer, from the bird hide on the edge of Lake Pollard. Black swans arrive here in large numbers from October to March to graze on the musk grasses.

There is a large camp kitchen.

The six kilometre (approximately 2-3 hours) Lake Pollard loop trail begins at the entrance to the Martins Tank campground – about one kilometre from the camp ground itself. The walk track is clearly marked, flat and easy going and follows a sandy vehicle access track, through jarrah, tuart, peppermint, bull banksia and Christmas trees, particularly during spring when purple climbing wisteria, red cocky's tongues and yellow hibbertias make a splash of colour through the bush.

Turn right about two kilometres along the track at the sign-posted T-junction. A short way along a side track takes you through paperbark trees to the wooden bird hide on the lake's edge.

From the bird hide you can either retrace your steps along the flatter route, or continue on the steeper loop trail which follows a fire break and a private property fence before continuing along Preston Beach Road back to the campsite.

There is a day use area at Lake Hayward. Not far along Preston Beach Road is the 4.5 kilometre Healthlands walk trail which takes you to the edge of Lake Preston. From the limestone ridgeline there are sweeping views over Lake Preston to Myalup and you may see rare Limestone and Fremantle mallees.

Of the ten lakes in the park, Lake Clifton is the most unique due to its population of 2000 year old thrombolites. These are the largest known example of living non-marine microbialites in the Southern Hemisphere, and one of only a few places in WA where living thrombolites survive. The thrombolites are extremely fragile so a walkway has been erected at an observation point accessed via Mt John Road off the Old Coast Road. The five kilometre Lakeside Loop limestone walk trail begins at the information shelter and runs parallel to the lake edge before looping back to the car park.

Martins Tank campground is about 8.7 kilometres from Preston Beach where you can refuel or buy supplies from the general store. There is a children's playground at the picnic ground adjacent to the beachfront and 4WD beach access. The beach is popular for fishing and 4WD beach driving, but strictly no camping.

Just The Facts

Martins Tank Lake Campsite

Getting there: 112kms south of Perth via the Forrest Highway, the Old Coast Road, and Preston Beach Road. 40km from Mandurah, 65km from Bunbury.

GPS: GPS: -32.8461, 115.6689

Fees: Payable into the honour box at the campground information board or to the camp host. $10/adult/night, $2.20/child 6-15 years, $6.60/valid concession card holder, Companion card – accompanying carer camps free.

Facilities: Drop toilet, rainwater tank, picnic tables, camp kitchen.

Disabled facilities: Nothing specific.

Campfires are usually permitted in two communal fire pits between April 1 and November 30 but fire restrictions may be imposed at any time and without notice. Bring your own firewood.

Generators are permitted except in the individual tent-only campsites.

Restrictions: No pets. No swimming, canoeing or fishing.

Suggested: Bring a fuel stove and drinking water and take your rubbish away with you. Look out for snakes and bring insect repellent as mosquitoes can be an issue.

Activities: Camping, bush walking, photography and bird watching. Preston Beach offers 4WDriving, fishing and swimming.

When to go: Spring and Autumn. The campground is popular during school holidays and weekends from October to April, particularly public holiday weekends.

For more information: Department of Parks & Wildlife WA: http://parkstay.dpaw.wa.gov.au/camp-finder/viewproperty/martins-tank/92/

Telephone: DPAW Swan Coastal District (08) 9303 7700.

Free Campsites in Western Australia

161. Grimwade Dam - South West
Map Ref: MAP 2 C10 GPS: 33 42 10 S 116 03 02 E
Located 11km NE of Balingup via Grimwade Rd. Ph: 08 9764 1818

162. Wattle Ridge Vineyard
Map Ref: MAP 2 C10 GPS: 33 49 45 S 116 04 16 E
Camping spot 2km E of Greenbushes on Boyup Brook Rd. Ph: 08 9764 3595

163. Greenbushes Sportsground
Map Ref: MAP 2 C10 GPS: 33 50 13 S 116 02 49 E
Camp area 2km N of Greenbushes near northern exit to Greenbushes. Max 7 days.

164. Lake Ewlyamartup Camp Area
Map Ref: MAP 2 E10 GPS: 33 41 31 S 117 44 12 E
Situated 19km E of Katanning. Travel for 15km on Katanning-Nyabing Rd then R into Langaweira Rd for 1km. Camp area left 120m on left side.

165. Borden Recreation Ground
Map Ref: MAP 2 F10 GPS: 34 04 22 S 118 15 31 E
Camping at Borden.

166. Gordon Inlet Camping Area - Albany Region
Map Ref: MAP 2 H10 GPS: 34 17 16 S 119 29 01 E
Located at Gordon Inlet Road which is accessed off Gairdner Road, 20km NE of Bremer Bay. 4WD access only. Ph: 08 9835 1022

167. House Beach camping area - Albany Region
Map Ref: MAP 2 H10 GPS: 34 21 46 S 119 31 11 E
4WD access off Gordon Inlet Road signposted and accessed off Gairdner Road, 43km NE of Bremer Bay. Ph: 08 9835 1022

168. Boranup Forest campground - South West
Map Ref: MAP 2 B11 GPS: 34 10 41 S 115 04 04 E
Within the Leeuwin-Naturaliste NP 35km SW of Margaret River via Caves Rd and Boyanup Drive. Ph: 08 9757 7025

169. Greens Island Camping area - South West
Map Ref: MAP 2 C11 GPS: 34 11 58 S 115 56 45 E
From Manjimup head W on Graphite Rd, turn right onto Donnelly Drive then Greens Rd for 1km to camp. Ph: 08 9771 7988

170. Big Brook Arboretum - South West
Map Ref: MAP 2 C11 GPS: 34 24 14 S 116 00 13 E
Camp area 10km N of Pemberton via signposted Golf Links Road and then Mullineaux Road. A further 7km to the signposted access to the arboretum. Ph: 08 9776 1207

171. River Road Bridge Camp Area
Map Ref: MAP 2 D11 GPS: 34 30 35 S 116 06 09 E
Camp spot on E & W side of River Rd Bridge, 17km SE of Pemberton via Burma & Spring Gully Rds to River Rd for 16kms. Ph: 08 9219 9000

172. Fish Creek - South West
Map Ref: MAP 2 D11 GPS: 34 40 23 S 116 22 34 E
Located in D'Entrecasteaux NP. Signpost off Fish Creek track 13km S of Chesapeake Rd. Ph: 08 9776 1207

173. Moores Hut - South West
Map Ref: MAP 2 D12 GPS: 34 52 03 S 116 13 03 E
Located in D'Entrecasteaux NP. 40km SE of Northcliffe via Chesapeake Rd. Ph: 08 9776 1207

174. Coodamurrup Beach - South West
Map Ref: MAP 2 D12 GPS: 34 52 03 S 116 13 03 E
Located in D'Entrecasteaux NP. Bush camping at Coodamurrup Beach along beach and behind dunes. Located 3km S of Moores Hut. Ph: 08 9776 8393

175. Mouth of Gardner - South West
Map Ref: MAP 2 D12 GPS: 34 50 41 S 116 07 19 E
Located in D'Entrecasteaux NP. Camping beside the Gardner River. Access track from Windy Harbour Rd. Ph: 08 9776 1207

176. Fernhook Falls camping area - South West
Map Ref: MAP 2 D11 GPS: 34 49 01 S 116 35 28 E
Within the Mt Frankland South NP. From Walpole W along the South Western Hwy 34kms then along signposted Beardmore Rd for further 36km. Ph: 08 9840 0400

Featured Campsite

Brought to you by

Sunrise over the misty water of Grimwade Dam.

Grimwade Dam No 161

Balingup, WA

70km southeast of Bunbury

Western Australia's fashionable southwest corner has long been a magnet for city dwellers escaping south on cottage getaways to unwind over boutique wines.

This makes Grimwade Dam – located just 11km north of Balingup - an unexpected find for campers in search of a laidback freebie.

Once a timber mill settlement, Grimwade Dam is today surrounded by working pine plantations and nature is slowly reclaiming the old mill site. Foundations are all that remain of small shacks, and pathways lead past rusting mill machinery, winches and rail tracks beneath the blackberry bushes.

In the autumn, beautiful deciduous trees create a carpet of yellow and amber leaves that make taking a stroll irresistible.

Caravan-friendly campsites are spread throughout the natural forest that fringes the plantation pines, and none is more keenly sought than those on the edge of Grimwade's stunning, sapphire-hued dam.

With access to the water for swimming and fishing, we always manage to secure a waterfront spot under the trees and indulge in warming campfires in winter and cool swims over the hot summer months.

Grimwade Dam provides no facilities, but there are no time limits either and pets, generators and campfires are permitted. Just pile some timber into one of the existing fire rings at day's end, stoke it up and watch the black cockatoos feeding in the treetops as the sun goes down. Remember to bring drinking water and firewood and take your rubbish away with you.

Armed with a licence you can snare marron in the dam, but you'll need to time your visit well. The WA marron season typically lasts just 28 days, beginning in early January. Get a licence online at www.fish.wa.gov.au.

While in Balingup, don't miss a visit to WA's largest arboretum, the 60-hectare Golden Valley Tree Park. Walking trails at this heritage-listed park lead around the Golden Valley Homestead (circa 1890) where the oldest trees thrive, and through an oak grove, bamboo and conifer forests, and the Australian collection of oil mallees, sandalwood, wattles, arid woodland trees and kurrajongs.

This park is free to visit and dogs on leads are welcome (as are donations).

During autumn the trees are spectacular.

The deciduous international tree collection was particularly vibrant on our autumn visit, and a gentle climb to Yungerup Springs and Pear Tree Lookout provided clear views over a valley carpeted with the gold, amber and red leaves.

Signposted off the South Western Highway 2km south of Balingup, Golden Valley is open every day and provides wood barbecues, a picnic shelter, toilets and walking maps (www.goldenvalleytreepark.org.au).

Just The Facts

Martins Tank Lake Campsite

Getting there: To reach Grimwade Dam, turn onto Grimwade Road, 11km northeast of Balingup and look for a gravel road on your left, about 1km after the Grimwade Road junction (to Kirup). The unsealed roads are accessible to conventional vehicles.

Facilities: None.

Wheelchair Access: N/A.

Rates: Free.

Pets: Permitted.

Contact: Phone the DEC office in Kirup on (08) 9731 6232 or Balingup Visitor Centre on (08) 9764 1818 or visit www.balinguptourism.com.au.

Free Campsites in Western Australia

177. Centre Road Crossing Camp
Map Ref: MAP 2 D12 GPS: 34 54 37 S 116 37 20 E
Camp area 30km NW of Walpole. Travel 28kms on SW Hwy turn R onto Centre Rd for 5km. 4WD only. Ph: 08 9840 0400

178. Lake Poorrarecup - South West
Map Ref: MAP 2 E11 GPS: 34 25 10 S 117 14 10 E
Lake is located 13km E of Frankland along the Frankland-Cranbrook Rd. Ph: 08 9826 1008

179. Boat Harbour - South West
Map Ref: MAP 2 E12 GPS: 35 02 07 S 117 04 59 E
Take South Coast Hwy 107km E of Albany then Boat Harbour Rd for 20km to beach. Ph: 08 9841 1088

180. Parry Beach Recreation area -South West
Map Ref: MAP 2 E12 GPS: 35 02 26 S 117 09 42 E
From Denmark proceed W along the South Coast Hwy for 23km to the signposted Parry Beach Road then a further 6km to the signposted access road to the camping area. Ph: 08 9848 0300

181. Cosy Corner East - South West
Map Ref: MAP 2 E12 GPS: 35 03 45 S 117 38 52 E
15kms W of Albany via Cosy Corner Rd off Lower Denmark Rd. Ph: 08 9841 9290

182. Torbay Inlet - South West
Map Ref: MAP 2 F12 GPS: 35 02 20 S 117 40 45 E
Located 28km W of Albany via Lower Denmark & Tobay Inlet Rds. Ph: 08 9841 9290

183. Two Peoples Bay camping area - South West
Map Ref: MAP 2 F11 GPS: 34 56 17 S 118 10 46 E
52km NE of Albany on Two People Bay along Betty's Beach Road. From South Coast Hwy take Homestead Road then Betty's Beach Rd. Ph: 08 9847 3088

184. East Bay camping area
Map Ref: MAP 2 F11 GPS: 34 56 17 S 118 10 47 E
Located at Two Peoples Bay from Albany follow the South Coast Hwy north easterly for 37km to Homestead Rd then take East Bay Rd for 700m to site. Ph: 08 9841 9290

185. Bettys Beach camping area
Map Ref: MAP 2 G11 GPS: 34 56 13 S 118 12 30 E
From Albany follow the South Coast Hwy north easterly for 37km to Homestead Rd. Continue for 115km to Bettys Beach Ph: 08 9841 9290

186. Norman's Beach - South West
Map Ref: MAP 2 G11 GPS: 34 55 26 S 118 12 52 E
From Albany head NE on the South Coast Hwy for 36km, turn right on to Homestead Road and continue for 9km to Normans Beach Rd. Continue for 2km on unsealed track to campsite. Ph: 08 9841 9333

187. Cape Riche camping area - South West
Map Ref: MAP 2 G11 GPS: 34 35 52 S 118 44 56 E
From Albany follow the South Coast Hwy for 98km to signposted Sandalwood Rd. Then 18.5km to camping area. Bring you own firewood Ph: 08 9847 3088

188. Millers Point Reserve - South West
Map Ref: MAP 2 G11 GPS: 34 27 14 S 118 52 42 E
From Bremer Bay take the Borden-Bremer Bay Road for 47km to Millers Point Rd to camping area on Beaufort Inlet. Ph: 08 9835 1022

Featured Campsite

Brought to you by

Normans Beach

No.186

Two Peoples Bay, WA

47km west of Albany

Catherine Lawson and David Bristow

The mouth of the river flows into Normans Beach.

Known as the birthplace of Western Australia, the City of Albany is a stately waterfront town of weathered stone buildings and heritage sights that hark back to 1827 when a garrison then known as Frederickstown was established on the shores of King George Sound.

Today, the city's dedication to preserving and commemorating its history is almost as admirable as its conservation of surrounding wild places where you can camp for free at a string of quiet, waterfront camps.

A favourite spot that provides easy access for campers keen to float their boats, Normans Beach is located a 30-minute drive east of Albany on the shores of a paperbark-fringed inlet. The beach is named to remember the pioneering Norman brothers - Arthur, Percy and John Jnr – whose family were some of first European settlers in the area.

It's a cosy camp nestled amongst stunted coastal heathlands of sheoak, peppermint trees and bull banksia and overlooks a deep, tannin-hued pool. Here you can launch a kayak to paddle past elegant flocks of black swans and explore the edge of Mount Many Peaks Nature Reserve across the water. From camp, a short walking trail leads to Norman's long, nearby beach, following the edge of the inlet that is mostly closed to the sea behind the dunes.

Normans Beach rates as one of Albany Shire's smaller free campgrounds with space for a half-dozen, modest-sized rigs at most. The bare basic facilities are limited to a pit toilet and rubbish bins, but this camp scores big points for its immensely picturesque waterfront location and the fact that you can stay as long as you like.

Because it borders a nature reserve and provides habitat for waterbirds, dogs are not permitted, and the Shire of Albany no longer allows campfires so come prepared to cook in your rig. When it's time to move on, there are another two free camps located a few minutes' drive away.

Just past the turnoff to Normans Beach, the track continues to another magnificent white sand beach on the shores of Two Peoples Bay and a great little camping spot at Bettys Beach bookcased by giant granite boulders that glow golden with orange lichen at sunset.

On sunny days, nothing beats a leisurely stroll from the river outlet at Normans Beach and along the white sand that arcs around to the tiny blue cove at Bettys Beach. The pods of dolphins frequently spotted fishing the shallows offshore are a good sign that the fishing is good, and from Bettys, anglers with a 4WD vehicle can access the beach to launch a tinny at low tide.

Normans Beach arcs around to the tiny blue cove of Bettys Beach.

The nature reserve is a great habitat for water birds.

Just The Facts

Normans Beach

Getting there: From Albany head north east on the South Coast Highway for 36km, turn right onto Homestead Road and continue for 9km to Normans Beach Road. You'll find the camp 2km along this unsealed track, navigable by conventional vehicles.

Facilities: A pit toilet and rubbish bins.

Rates: Free

Wheelchair Access: No

Pets: No

Contact: Visit www.rainbowcoast.com.au or www.albany.asn.au to find out about other free camps in the area. Alternatively, phone the Albany Visitor Centre on (08) 9841 1088 or head to www.amazingalbany.com.au. For boat fishing permits and bag limits visit www.fish.wa.gov.au.

Free Campsites in Western Australia Index

Western Australia Map 1

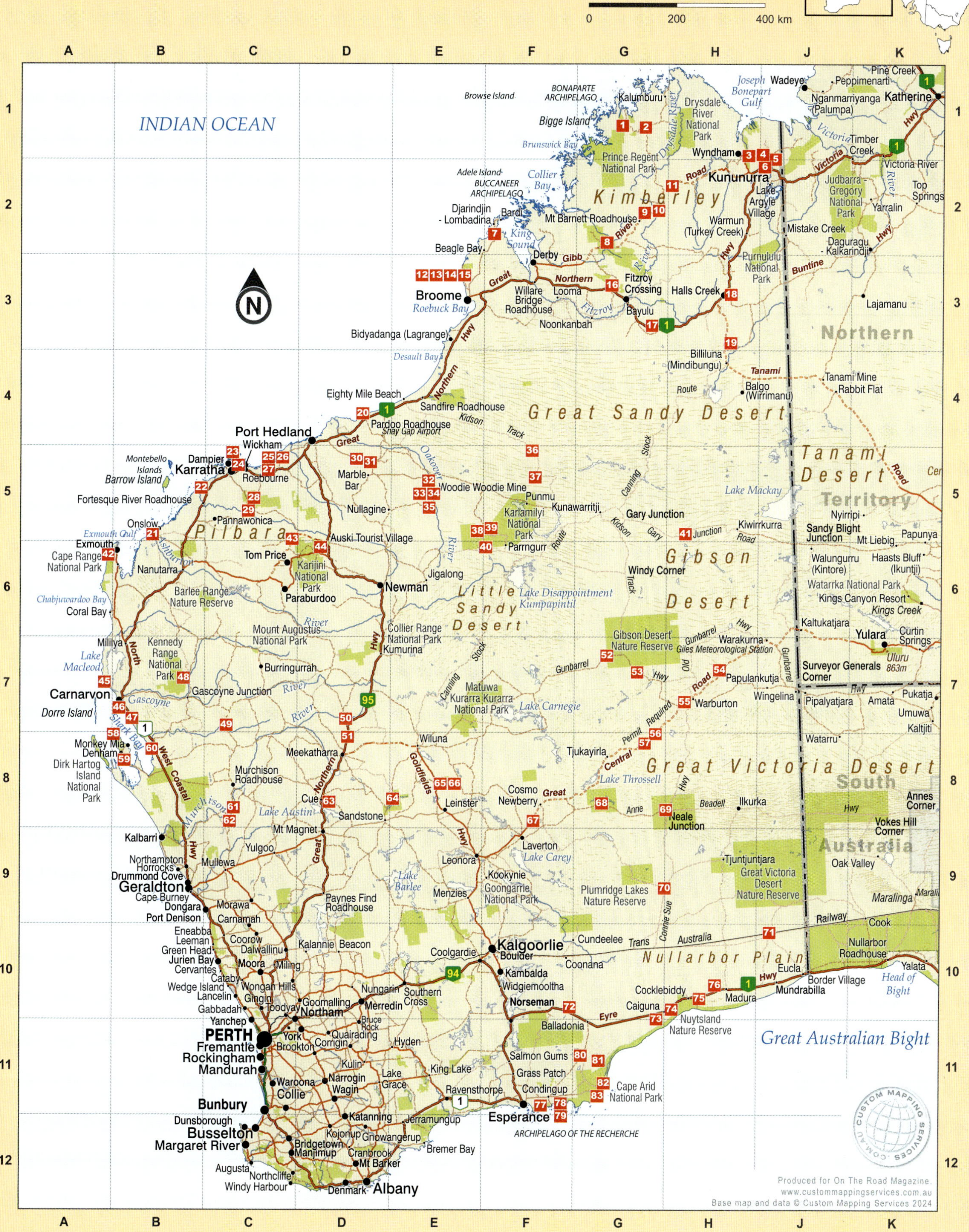

Western Australia Map 2

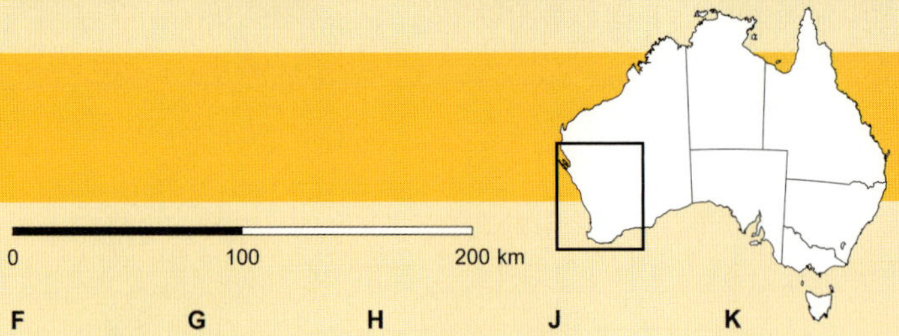

0 100 200 km

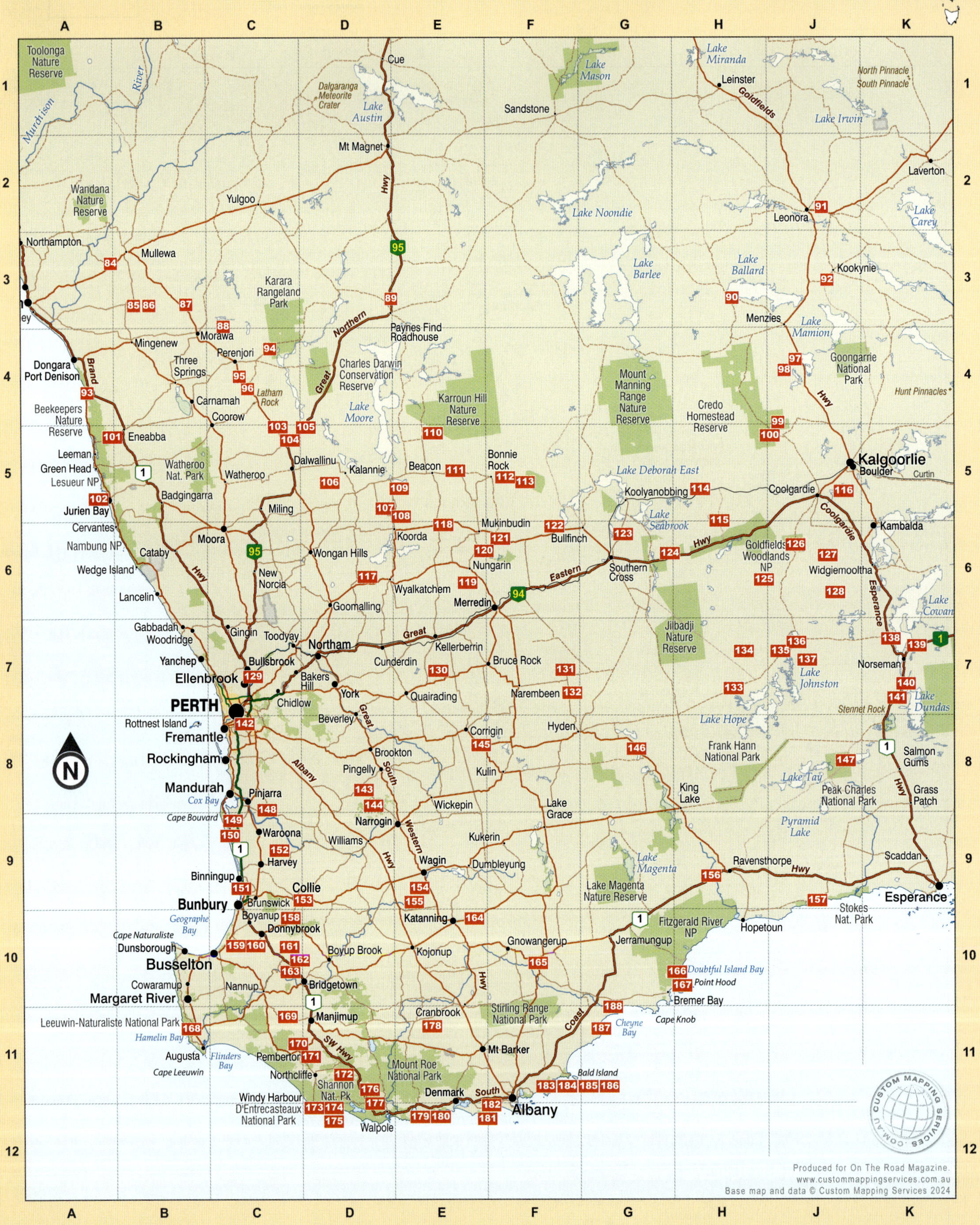

A B C D E F G H J K

1 2 3 4 5 6 7 8 9 10 11 12

Toolonga Nature Reserve
Murchison River
Cue
Dalgaranga Meteorite Crater
Lake Austin
Lake Mason
Lake Miranda
Leinster
Goldfields
North Pinnacle
South Pinnacle
Sandstone
Lake Irwin
Mt Magnet
Laverton
Hwy
Wandana Nature Reserve
Yulgoo
Lake Noondie
91
Leonora
Lake Carey
Northampton
95
Lake Barlee
Lake Ballard
Kookynie
84
Mullewa
Karara Rangeland Park
89
92
85 86
87
88
Morawa
Northern
Paynes Find Roadhouse
90
Menzies
Lake Mamion
Mingenew
Perenjori
94
Great
Charles Darwin Conservation Reserve
Mount Manning Range Nature Reserve
97
98
Goongarrie National Park
Dongara
Port Denison
Brand
Three Springs
95
Latham Rock
Karroun Hill Nature Reserve
Hunt Pinnacles
93
96
Carnamah
Lake Moore
Credo Homestead Reserve
Hwy
Beekeepers Nature Reserve
Coorow
103
105
99
104
110
100
101
Eneabba
Bonnie Rock
Kalgoorlie
Boulder
Curtin
Leeman
Green Head
Lesueur NP
1
Watheroo Nat. Park
Watheroo
Dalwallinu
Kalannie
Beacon
111
112
113
Lake Deborah East
106
109
Koolyanobbing
114
Coolgardie
116
Badgingarra
102
Jurien Bay
Miling
107
108
Lake Seabrook
115
Coolgardie
Kambalda
Cervantes
Mukinbudin
118
122
Nambung NP
Moora
Koorda
121
Bullfinch
123
126
Cataby
95
Wongan Hills
120
124
Hwy
Goldfields Woodlands NP
127
Nungarin
Southern Cross
Widgiemooltha
Wedge Island
Hwy
New Norcia
117
Eastern
125
119
Wyalkatchem
Merredin
94
Esperance
128
Lake Cowan
Lancelin
Goomalling
Jilbadji Nature Reserve
Gabbadah
Woodridge
Gingin
Toodyay
Great
138
139
1
Northam
Kellerberrin
136
Yanchep
Bullsbrook
Cunderdin
134
135
137
Bruce Rock
Norseman
131
Ellenbrook
129
Bakers Hill
130
Lake Johnston
140
York
133
PERTH
Chidlow
Quairading
Narembeen
132
Lake Dundas
141
Stennet Rock
Rottnest Island
142
Beverley
Great
Hyden
Lake Hope
Fremantle
Corrigin
Frank Hann National Park
146
1
Salmon Gums
145
Rockingham
Brookton
South
Albany
Pingelly
Kulin
147
Lake Tay
Mandurah
Cox Bay
Pinjarra
143
Peter Charles National Park
Grass Patch
Hwy
King Lake
Lake Grace
148
144
Wickepin
Cape Bouvard
Narrogin
Pyramid Lake
149
Western
Waroona
Williams
Kukerin
150
152
1
Hwy
Wagin
Lake Magenta
Ravensthorpe
Hwy
Scaddan
Harvey
Dumbleyung
Binningup
156
Esperance
151
Collie
154
Lake Magenta Nature Reserve
Bunbury
153
Brunswick
155
157
Stokes Nat. Park
Geographe Bay
Boyanup
158
Katanning
164
1
Fitzgerald River NP
Hopetoun
Cape Naturaliste
Donnybrook
Dunsborough
159
160
161
Boyup Brook
Kojonup
Gnowangerup
Jerramungup
Busselton
162
165
163
Hwy
166
Doubtful Island Bay
Cowaramup
Nannup
Bridgetown
167
Point Hood
Margaret River
1
Bremer Bay
Stirling Range National Park
188
Leeuwin-Naturaliste National Park
169
Manjimup
Cranbrook
Cape Knob
Coast
168
Hamelin Bay
178
187
Cheyne Bay
SW Hwy
170
Mt Barker
Augusta
Flinders Bay
Pemberton
171
Northcliffe
Mount Roe National Park
Bald Island
Cape Leeuwin
172
Shannon Nat. Pk
176
Denmark
South
183
184
185
186
Windy Harbour
D'Entrecasteaux National Park
173
174
177
182
Albany
175
179
180
181
Walpole

Custom Mapping Services .com.au

taking it easy, has never been so easy.
KOKODA
STRENGTH • PASSION • PRIDE
2025
CARAVAN OF THE YEAR
SPONSORED BY
CARAVAN
Winner
MOST INNOVATIVE & HIGHEST X-FACTOR
KOKODA

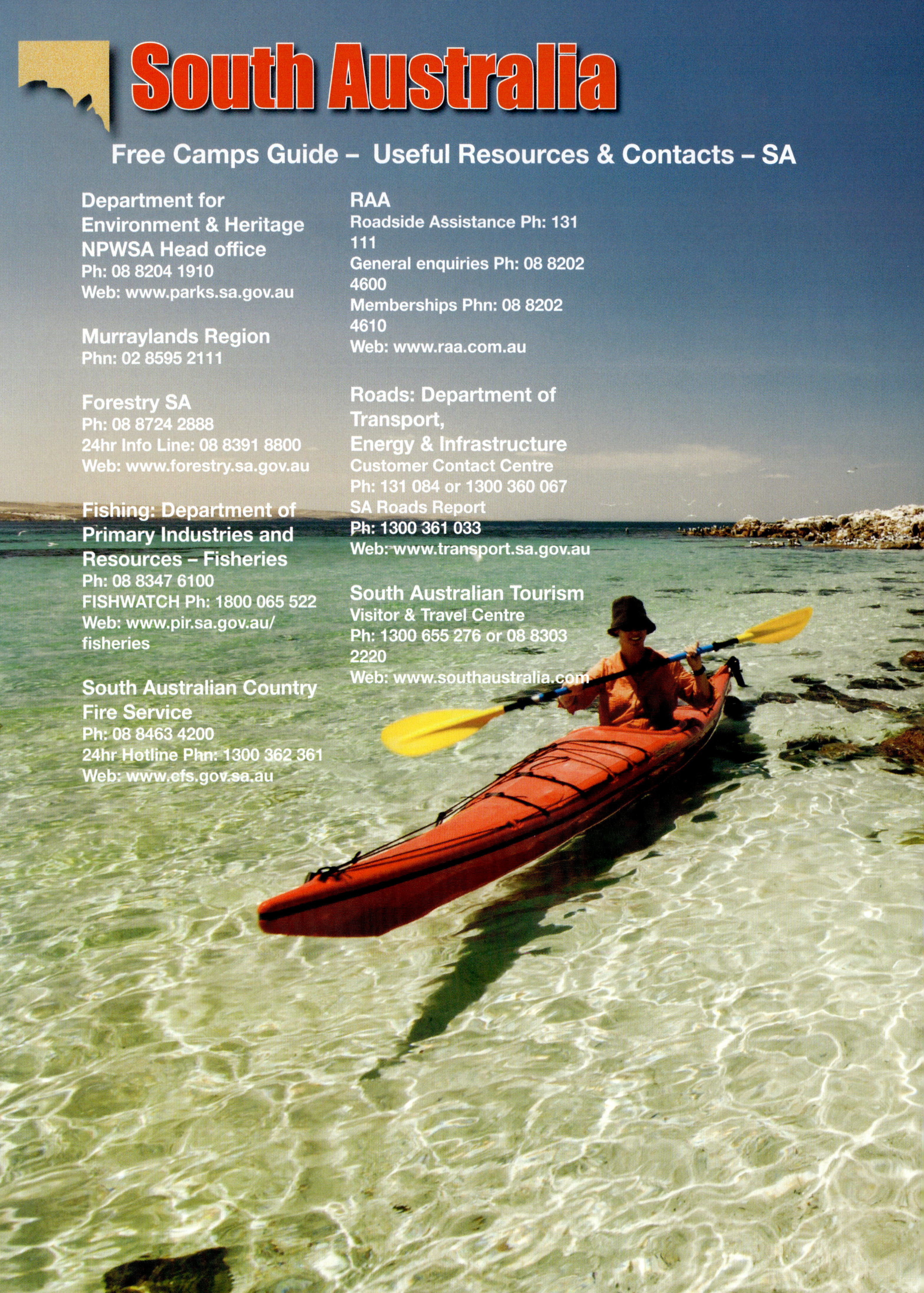

South Australia

Free Camps Guide – Useful Resources & Contacts – SA

Department for Environment & Heritage NPWSA Head office
Ph: 08 8204 1910
Web: www.parks.sa.gov.au

Murraylands Region
Phn: 02 8595 2111

Forestry SA
Ph: 08 8724 2888
24hr Info Line: 08 8391 8800
Web: www.forestry.sa.gov.au

Fishing: Department of Primary Industries and Resources – Fisheries
Ph: 08 8347 6100
FISHWATCH Ph: 1800 065 522
Web: www.pir.sa.gov.au/fisheries

South Australian Country Fire Service
Ph: 08 8463 4200
24hr Hotline Phn: 1300 362 361
Web: www.cfs.gov.sa.au

RAA
Roadside Assistance Ph: 131 111
General enquiries Ph: 08 8202 4600
Memberships Phn: 08 8202 4610
Web: www.raa.com.au

Roads: Department of Transport, Energy & Infrastructure
Customer Contact Centre
Ph: 131 084 or 1300 360 067
SA Roads Report
Ph: 1300 361 033
Web: www.transport.sa.gov.au

South Australian Tourism
Visitor & Travel Centre
Ph: 1300 655 276 or 08 8303 2220
Web: www.southaustralia.com

Free Campsites in South Australia

1. Mount Dare Homestead camping area -Outback
Map Ref: MAP 1 F1 GPS: 26 04 13 S 135 30 10 E
Located 105km SE of Finke via Kulgera on the Stuart Hwy. Access is signposted. Ph: 08 8670 7835

2. Eringa Waterhole - Oodnadatta Track
Map Ref: MAP 1 E2 GPS: 26 17 57 S 134 43 10 E
45kms S of the SA/NT border on the Hamilton to Mt Dare Rd. Dry weather only. Ph: 08 8670 7835

3. Perdirka Ruins - Outback
Map Ref: MAP 1 F2 GPS: 26 39 21 S 135 12 44 E
Camping near ruins beside Ghan Railway. Access N of Oodnadatta via Oodnadatta Track signposted to Mt Sarah and Hamilton for 91km to the PAR. Then E for 16km to site. Ph: 1800 816 078

4. Kathleen Creek - Outback
Map Ref: MAP 1 E2 GPS: 27 01 17 S 134 45 13 E
Camping spot 89km NW of Oodnadatta. Tracks along the creek

5. Olarinna Creek - Outback
Map Ref: MAP 1 E2 GPS: 27 09 48 S 134 37 09 E
Camping spot 104km NW od Oodnadatta. Track on W side of creek to site.

6. Marla Travellers Rest - Outback
Map Ref: MAP 1 D2 GPS: 27 18 15 S 133 37 21 E
Located at the signposted junction of the Oodnadatta Track and Stuart Hwy 211km west of Oodnadatta or 233km north of Coober Pedy. Ph: 08 8670 7001

7. Tippipila Creek Camping area - Outback
Map Ref: MAP 1 J2 GPS: 26 59 43 S 139 00 57 E
Bush camping 13km N of Mungerannie Hotel access road. And 184km S of Birdsville with camping only on Birdsville side of creek. Ph: 07 4656 3300

8. Cadelga Ruins - Outback
Map Ref: MAP 1 K1 GPS: 26 05 13 S 140 24 39 E
Camp area 155kms SE of Birdsville on Cordillo Rd, Innamincka

9. Arckaringa Station
Map Ref: MAP 1 E3 GPS: 27 56 12 S 134 44 18 E
Located on Painted Desert Rd, Oodnadatta Area. Station Stay 140km N of Coober Pedy. Ph: 08 8670 7992

10. Goorikiana Creek - Oodnadatta Track
Map Ref: MAP 1 E3 GPS: 27 54 20 S 134 49 10 E
145km N of Coober Pedy or 80km SW of Oodnadatta. Dry weather only

11. North Creek - Outback
Map Ref: MAP 1 F3 GPS: 27 44 15 S 135 36 15 E
Camping spot 28km S of Oodnadatta on N side of road beside the old railway bridge.

12. Algebuckina Campsite - Oodnadatta Track
Map Ref: MAP 1 F3 GPS: 27 55 05 S 135 48 59 E
On the Oodnadatta Track 55kms S of Oodnadatta. Dry weather only. Roadhouse 1800 802 074

13. Old Peake Telegraph Station
Map Ref: MAP 1 F3 GPS: 28 04 36 S 135 54 22 E
Bush camping 15km NE of Oodnadatta Track at the ruin.

14. The Peake bush camp
Map Ref: MAP 1 F3 GPS: 28 04 36 S 135 54 22 E
16km NE of track at the site of Old Peake Telegraph 112km W of William Creek. Ph: 08 8670 7822

15. Ski Beach
Map Ref: MAP 1 K3 GPS: 27 45 52 S 140 41 06 E
Within Innamincka Regional Reserve, camp area SW of Innamincka on Fifteen Mile Track, Innamincka area. Drive 6km turn R to Ski Beach. 5 day limit. Pre-book. 4WD only. Ph: 08 8648 5328

16. Innamincka Town Common camping area - Outback
Map Ref: MAP 1 K3 GPS: 27 45 05 S 140 43 38 E
Located beside Coopers Creek 800m SW of the hotel and store. Ph: 08 8675 9900

Eringa Waterhole Campsite No 2

Outback, SA

About 180km north of Oodnadatta

Helmut & Elizabeth Mueller

The dusty banks of Eringa Waterhole make for an idyllic outback bush camp. The waterhole is quite extensive and it holds a fair bit of water, except during extended drought years. It's no surprise that this bounty attracts animals as well as travellers, and on our last visit the bird life was particularly plentiful and outnumbered even the flies.

Eringa is on Hamilton Station and public access is via the Hamilton-Mt Dare road, which runs north from the Oodnadatta Track about 18km north of Oodnadatta, just about where the Oodnadatta Track makes a dogleg west toward Marla. The Hamilton-Mt Dare road is gravel and suitable for four-wheel-drive vehicles, traversing low red dunes of the Pedirka Desert as well as many hard, rocky sections. It's not a terribly tough track to tackle, but like any outback road, drivers need to take care and drive to the conditions. Travellers and campers also need to be aware that Hamilton is a private station so the area should be treated with respect.

Facilities equate to exactly nil at Eringa, which is perfect for a bush camp. Informal sites are located on either side of the tree-lined waterhole and, depending on the number of travellers set up at the time, the age-old trees also offer a little privacy. Activities are also low-key, and it's a place suitable for the serious recreations of relaxing, soaking up the sun in winter and admiring the millions upon millions of stars that highlight an outback sky.

The area does have a bit of history to explore – the original Eringa holding is said to be one of Cattle King Sidney Kidman's first holdings, while outback legend R.M. Williams worked at the station for a short time. An easy walk from the waterhole is the scattered remains of a few homestead buildings, though only the thatch meat house retains enough form to reckon its purpose.

Despite being roughly in the middle of nowhere, Eringa is far from lonesome or desolate. In the right season, the surrounding gibber country is softened by small and obviously hardy low shrubs and herbage that offer a smear of floral colour – no doubt in preparation for a bumper crop of burrs. Over a number of visits to this waterhole we've been lulled or otherwise by cattle camping out, taunted by yabbies on the water's edge, and heard other travellers scream from the cold when taking a dip in Eringa's waters.

But by far it's the bird life that dominates the beauty of the waterhole. On a mid-winter visit, the avian squatters carried on as though spring had arrived and took full advantage of warm days that followed near-freezing nights. The variety was amazing and ultimately entertaining. In the highest trees, whistling kites preened and hacked beak-fulls from fresh-caught fish, while squadrons of darters practised fly-bys and small grebes dipped and paddled. Ringnecked parrots danced for each other while inspecting prospective nesting holes, and tiny honeyeaters combed gum leaves for lerps in between snatching sips of Eringa water.

If you've ever had a thought of carrying out a thorough investigation on which is the most raucous bird – galah or little corella – Eringa waterhole is the place to do it. One particularly bad-bellied bird kept the piercing, grating, cacophonous din up all night. Perhaps the racket was just all about keeping this special place to themselves.

Early morning reflections can be colourful and striking.

White-plumed honeyeater is a busy little bird.

Ruins near the waterhole.

Just The Facts

Eringa Waterhole Campsite

Getting there: 45km south of the SA/NT border (on the Hamilton to Mt Dare road). Access is signposted as suitable for four-wheel-drive vehicles. (26 17 57 S, 134 42 99 E)

Facilities: Nil. Travellers must be self-sufficient in everything, and take out what they take in. Mt Dare, about 72km northwest, is the closest place for basic supplies. Timber is at a premium, so BYO if you're set on having a campfire. Wheelchair access. Nothing specific. This is a natural bush setting with no development.

Rates: Free

Pets: Okay, but Eringa is on a station property and the waterhole is used for watering cattle, so pets should be restrained at all times.

Contact: For road conditions contact 1300 361 033, www.dpti.sa.gov.au/OutbackRoads. For area details contact (08) 8670 7835, www.mtdare.com.au

Free Campsites in South Australia

17. Policemans Camping Area - Outback
Map Ref: MAP 1 K3 GPS: 27 45 31 S 140 42 17 E
Within Innamincka Regional Reserve signposted access 1.9km along Fifteen Mile Track then 1.2km to camping area.Fifteen Mile Track is signposted off the Strzelecki Track 1.4km south of Innamincka. Bring water & firewood. Ph: 08 8675 9909

18. Burkes Grove Camp Area
Map Ref: MAP 1 K3 GPS: 27 43 22 S 140 46 43 E
Within Innamincka Regional Reserve on Adventure Way, Innamincka. Camp area 11km NE of Innamincka. Take Innamincka-Nappa Merrie Rd E from Innamincka then turn N for 7km. 21 day limit. 4WD only. Ph: 08 8675 9909

19. Cullyamurra Waterhole
Map Ref: MAP 1 K3 GPS: 27 42 07 S 140 50 20 E
Within Innamincka Regional Reserve on Innamincka-Nappa Merrie Rd, Innamincka. Camp area 14km N from road. Pre-book. 4WD only. Ph: 08 8648 5328

20. Hutchison Memorial
Map Ref: MAP 1 E4 GPS: 29 04 30 S 134 51 12 E
Parking area on Stuart Hwy, Coober Pedy 240 N of Glendambo or 12km S of Coober Pedy.

21. ABC/Halligan Bay camping area -Outback
Map Ref: MAP 1 G4 GPS: 28 45 49 S 136 56 23 E
On the western shores of Lake Eyre 71km E of William Creek off the Oodnadatta Track. Ph: 1800 816 078

22. Beresford Bore - Outback
Map Ref: MAP 1 G4 GPS: 29 14 16 S 136 39 27 E
Bush camping in vicinity of railroad siding and bore which is signposted along the Oodnadatta Track 22.1km west of Coward Springs or 50km south east of William Creek. Then 600m to siding. Bring water & firewood.

23. Coward Springs Campground - Outback
Map Ref: MAP 1 G4 GPS: 29 24 14 S 136 48 44 E
132km W of Marree off the Oodnadatta Track. Ph: 08 8675 8336

24. Curdimurka Railway Siding - Oodnadatta Track
Map Ref: MAP 1 G4 GPS: 29 28 59 S 137 05 10 E
102km W of Marree & 30km E of Coward Springs. Ph: 08 8675 8336

25. Marree Hotel - Outback
Map Ref: MAP 1 H4 GPS: 29 38 54 S 138 03 52 E
Camping area at Marree Hotel. Fee for showers. Ph: 08 8675 8344

26. Lake Harry - Outback
Map Ref: MAP 1 H4 GPS: 29 26 03 S 138 14 46 E
Camping area 32km NE of Marree.

27. Clayton Wetlands campsite - Outback
Map Ref: MAP 1 H4 GPS: 29 16 31 S 138 22 16 E
Access on the Birdsville Track, 53km NE of Marree. Ph: 08 8675 8311

28. Cooper Creek camping area - Outback
Map Ref: MAP 1 H4 GPS: 28 37 25 S 138 42 36E
Signposted along the Birdsville Track, 83km N of Clayton Wetlands CS. Ph: 08 8675 8317

29. Blanchwater
Map Ref: MAP 1 J4 GPS: 29 33 01 S 139 27 01 E
Camping at ruins 156km NE of Lyndhurst N side of creek and E side of road.

30. Montecollina Bore Camping Area - Strzelecki Track
Map Ref: MAP 1 J4 GPS: 29 24 03 S 139 59 21 E
On the Strzelecki Track 220km NE of Lyndhurst. Dry weather access only. Ph: 08 8675 9909

31. Kingoonya camping area
Map Ref: MAP 1 F5 GPS: 30 54 41 S 135 18 51 E
43km W of the Stuart Hwy with access signposted off the hwy N 500m N of Glendambo. Located west of hotel building. Ph: 1800 816 078

32. Roxby Downs
Map Ref: MAP 1 G5 GPS: 30 32 50 S 136 56 24 E
Camp spot 1.8km E of Roxby Downs & Andamooka turnoff. Large open bush area with many tracks.

Free Campsites in South Australia

33. Andamooka Campground - Outback
Map Ref: MAP 1 G5 GPS: 30 27 04 S 137 09 46 E
Camp ground 1km W of Andamooka. Donation. Ph: 08 8672 7023

34. Farina Campgrounds - Flinders Ranges
Map Ref: MAP 1 H5 GPS: 30 03 41 S 138 16 22 E
Signposted access off the Lyndhurst-Marree Road, 25km N of Lyndhurst and 53km S of Marree, then drive in 2km to the camping area. Ph: 08 8648 4714

35. Lyndhurst Hotel Camping Area - Flinders Ranges
Map Ref: MAP 1 H5 GPS: 30 17 17 S 138 21 05 E
Located 33km north of Leigh Creek at the start of the Strzelecki Track. Camping area beside hotel. Ph: 08 8675 7781

36. Nuccaleena Mine - Flinders Ranges
Map Ref: MAP 1 H6 GPS: 30 57 10 S 138 30 49 E
Located on Public Access Route No.3 42km NE of Parachilna via Moolooloo Rd off Glass Gorge Rd. Ph: 1800 678 447

37. Patawarta Gap - Flinders Ranges
Map Ref: MAP 1 H6 GPS: 30 57 10 S 138 41 20 E
42km NW of Blinman via Public Access Route No 5. Camping area located on Moolooloo Homestead Station. Dry weather only Ph: 08 8648 4861

38. Artimore Ruins - Flinders Ranges
Map Ref: MAP 1 H6 GPS: 30 59 59 S 138 43 04 E
Take the road to Arkaroola which is 2.8km S of Blinman Hotel. Follow signposted road to Narrina then follow track 12km to the ruins. Do not camp close to ruins. Ph: 1800 678 447

39. Parachilna Gorge - Flinders Ranges
Map Ref: MAP 1 H6 GPS: 31 08 05 S 138 31 48 E
Numerous sites with access via Parachilna Road 11km E of Parachilna. Ph: 08 8648 4022

40. Alpana Station
Map Ref: MAP 1 H6 GPS: 31 08 25 S 138 41 04 E
Camp area 55km N of Wilpena Pound on Wilpena Rd, Blinman. Fee for ensuite. Ph: 08 8648 4626

41. Chambers Gorge Campground - Outback
Map Ref: MAP 1 J5 GPS: 30 57 12 S 139 12 53 E
Camping area 27km NE of Wirrealpa. 4WD recommended

42. Mulga View Bush camping - Flinders Ranges
Map Ref: MAP 1 J6 GPS: 30 54 57 S 139 10 04 E
Sheep & cattle property along the Blinman-Arkaroola Rd, 67km NE of Blinman. Ph: 08 8648 4859

43. Mt Chambers Gorge bush camping - Flinders Ranges
Map Ref: MAP 1 J6 GPS: 30 56 59 S 139 09 30 E
Signposted access from Blinman-Arkaroola Rd, 63km NE of Blinman. Private property and camp in designated areas. Ph: 1800 777 880

44. Bunda Cliffs - Nullarbor
Map Ref: MAP 1 B6 GPS: 31 36 26 S 129 46 33 E
On the Eyre Hwy 75km E of Border Village and 109km W of Nullarbor Roadhouse. www.nullarbornet.com.au

45. Murrawijinie Caves - Nullabor
Map Ref: MAP 1 B6 GPS: 31 21 59 S 130 52 41 E
Signposted just west of Nullarbor Roadhouse the dirt track leads for 10.4km to the caves.

46. Whitewell Tank
Map Ref: MAP 1 C6 GPS: 31 25 17 S 131 03 00 E
Parking area on Head of Bight Rd, 2km SW of Eyre Hwy, Yalata.

47. Gilgerabbie Hut - Nullabor
Map Ref: MAP 1 B6 GPS: 31 32 29 S 130 47 17 E
Camp area 190kms E of Eucla or 313kms W of Ceduna on Eyre Hwy at Gilgerabbie.

48. Mexican Hat Campground
Map Ref: MAP 1 C7 GPS: 32 00 57 S 132 20 23 E
Located within Fowlers Bay Conservation Park via Coorabie Rd, Fowlers Bay. Two camp spots on Mexican Hat Rd W of Fowlers Bay. 5 day limit. Pre-book. Ph: 08 8625 3144

Featured Campsite

Brought to you by

kokodacaravans.com.au

Bunda Cliffs Lookout

No 44

Nullarbor National Park, SA

75km east of Border Village

Catherine Lawson & David Bristow

Camp right where you are fishing.

Stretching beyond view for 200km between the blue bush fringe of Nullarbor National Park and the Great Australian Bight Marine Park, the Bunda Cliffs drop 80 vertigo-inducing metres into the wild Southern Ocean.

Dramatically undercut, these crumbling cliffs on the edge of what rates as the world's largest, flattest, limestone plateau, provide incredible views from lookouts signposted along the Eyre Highway between Border Village and Bunda Cliffs Scenic Lookout, 75km east.

These lookouts and pull-offs provide especially scenic spots to spend a night, and to watch the sun set and rise from your high point above Bunda's sea-ravaged cliffs.

Camped here at the end of a hot summer's day plagued by flies, we kicked back as a storm passed overhead, triggering arcing rainbows to the east and sending lightning bolts to illuminate the sea below.

Not only did the storm bring a magical end to the day, but the change of weather sent temperatures tumbling and by first light we were up and ready to explore the rest of Nullarbor National Park. Protecting the largest semi-arid karst (cave) landscape in the world, the national park harbours around 20 large caves, some with underground lakes and passages.

Within easy reach of most travellers is Murrawijinie Caves, signposted near the Nullarbor Roadhouse, 110km east of Bunda Cliffs Lookout, where you can climb down into a series of three sinkholes and discover galleries of ochre hand stencils.

Nullarbor National Park's 2.8 million hectares of low-lying saltbush and bluebush also provide sanctuary for Australia's largest population of southern hairy-nosed wombats, but you're more likely to spot southern right whales over its cliffs during the winter months.

These enormous, endangered creatures that can grow to the size of a bus, reach the safety of the Great Australian Bight Marine Park in May or June each year to socialise and mate, so that by August, calves are spotted swimming alongside their mothers.

Lured by the warm water flowing east in the Leeuwin Current, around half of Australia's estimated 2400 southern right whales (eubalaena australis) are believed to gather at the head of the Great Australian Bight each winter. Humpbacks make the journey from sub-Antarctic feeding grounds too, adding to the tally of up to 63 calves born in the marine park each season.

We've been lucky enough to spot whales right below Bunda Cliffs, spy-hopping and rolling around on the surface as they mate. For an interpretive experience and access to great whale watching vantage points with wheelchair access, visit Head of Bight, 14km east of the Nullarbor Roadhouse ($12/adult & $5/child).

For me, the Bunda Cliffs are the most dramatic and breathtaking on the Great Australian Bight that rates as the longest line of sea cliffs in the world (International Hydrographic Bureau, 1953), stretching from WA's West Cape Howe all the way to Tassie's Cape Grim. It's also an incredibly scenic place to wake up.

Spectacular sunsets are a feature of the area.

Just The Facts

Town Common

Highway 75km east of Border Village and 109km west of Nullarbor Roadhouse. Scenic viewpoints are located right along this stretch of coastline.

Facilities: None.

Wheelchair Access: N/A.

Rates: Free.

Pets: Permitted.

Contact: check out www.nullarbornet.com.au. For information on Nullarbor National Park and whale watching, head to www.environment.sa.g

49. Scotts Beach Campground
Map Ref: MAP 1 C7 GPS: 32 00 15 S 132 23 05 E
Camp spot on Scotts Bay Rd, Fowlers Bay 13km W of Fowlers Bay via Corrabie Rd then S for 6.5km, W end behind dunes, sand tracks. 5 day limit. 4WD only. Ph: 08 8688 3111

50. Fowlers Bay bush camping - Eyre Peninsula
Map Ref: MAP 1 C7 GPS: 32 00 18 S 132 23 12 E
Within the Fowlers Bay CP via Scotts Bay Road, off the Fowlers Bay-Corrabie Road. Ph: 08 8625 3144

51. Rushys Balcony
Map Ref: MAP 1 D6 GPS: 31 49 27 S 132 25 10 E
Camp area on Eyre Hwy, Coorabie, 24km W of Bookabie.

52. Point Bell Camping Area - Eyre Peninsula
Map Ref: MAP 1 D7 GPS: 32 10 06 S 133 08 44 E
Located in Point Bell Conservation Park 87km west of Ceduna. From Ceduna follow the Denial Bay Rd west for 36km to unsignposted Point Bell Rd. 4WD recommended. Bring water & firewood. Ph: 08 8625 3144

53. Davenport Creek camping area - Nullabor
Map Ref: MAP 1 D7 GPS: 32 10 59 S 133 26 22 E
41kms W of Ceduna on Eyre Hwy. Signposted on Denial Bay Rd to un-signposted Davenport Rd. Continue along for 16.5 km to Davenport Creek. Dry weather only Ph: 08 8625 2780

54. Laura Bay Campground - Eyre Peninsula
Map Ref: MAP 1 E7 GPS: 32 14 32 S 133 49 48 E
Located 21km south east of Ceduna. Signposted access off the Eyre Hwy 19km south east of Ceduna then drive 2.4km to camp area. Bring water & firewood. Ph: 08 8625 3144

55. Point Brown Campground
Map Ref: MAP 1 E7 GPS: 32 31 53 S 133 51 35 E
Camp spot 30kms S of Smoky Bat via Flinders Hwy & Pt Brown Rd. 20kms dirt road.

56. Old Perlubie School Site
Map Ref: MAP 1 E7 GPS: 32 24 48 S 134 24 07 E
Located 13km W of Wirrulla.

57. Wirrulla Camp & Rec Ground
Map Ref: MAP 1 E7 GPS: 32 24 16 S 134 31 57 E
Camp area at Walker Tce, Wirrulla opposite town centre reserve. Pay & shower at general store or hotel. Ph: 08 8626 7033

58. Perlubie Beach - Streaky Bay - Eyre Peninsula
Map Ref: MAP 1 E7 GPS: 32 39 45 S 134 17 46 E
21kms west of Streaky Bay on the Flinders Hwy. Signposted to the beach. Ph: 08 8626 7033

59. Tractor Beach
Map Ref: MAP 1 E7 GPS: 32 52 13 S 134 06 47 E
Camp area on Westall Way, Streaky Bay 17km SW of Streaky Bay. Dirt road. Display permit. Honesty box. Ph: 08 8626 7033

60. Eyres Waterhole
Map Ref: MAP 1 E7 GPS: 32 49 05 S 134 14 46 E
Rest area located on Flinders Hwy, Streaky Bay 5km SE of Streaky Bay.

61. Speeds Point Camping Area - Eyre Peninsula
Map Ref: MAP 1 E7 GPS: 32 55 51 S 134 07 45 E
Located 16km south of Streaky Bay at Yanerbie Beach. Signposted access 900m along Speeds Point Rd which is signposted 3.3km along Yanerbie Rd. Drive south along Westall Way Scenic Drive for 4.3km to signposted Yanerbie Rd. Self-sufficient campers. Bring water. Ph: 08 8626 1001

62. Pildappa Rock - Gawler Ranges - Eyre Peninsula
Map Ref: MAP 1 F7 GPS: 32 45 10 S 135 13 50 E
16kms north of Minnipa via McKenzie and Pildappa Rds. Ph: 08 8680 2969

63. Tcharkuldu Rock
Map Ref: MAP 1 F7 GPS: 32 50 50 S 135 11 45 E
Camp area 6km E of Minnipa via Brockelberg Rd, Minnipa. Dirt Road. 7 day limit. Donation box. Ph: 08 8680 2969

64. Waltumba Camping Area
Map Ref: MAP 1 F7 GPS: 32 07 20 S 135 53 46 E
Located within Gairdner NP on Mount Station Rd, Mount Ive. Camp area 30km NW of Mt Ive Station on E side of lake. 4WD only. Ph: 08 8648 1817

Featured Campsite

Brought to you by KOKODA STRENGTH • PASSION • PRIDE kokodacaravans.com.au

Perlubie Beach No.58

Streaky Bay, SA

717km from Adelaide
Catherine Lawson & David Bristow

A rainbow illuminates Perlubie Beach.

SA's Eyre Peninsula provides so many free and cheap campgrounds that most travellers are hard-pressed to discover them all. Our night at lovely Perlubie Beach was shared with just one other campervan (and a couple of mice – it was grain harvest season after all).

Located 21km north of Streaky Bay and signposted off the Flinders Highway, Perlubie Beach is a beachfront freebie that makes an ideal base camp for anyone spending time exploring the region. There are eight coastal conservation parks to discover: Acraman Creek to the north, Olive, Eba and Pigface Islands just offshore, and south of Streaky Bay, Calpatanna Waterhole, Venus and Sceale Bays, and the sea lion sanctuary at Point Labatt.

Despite its broad expanse of sandy shoreline, Perlubie Beach campground is a small site with a tight turning circle for big rigs and enough room for only six to eight vehicles. There are good facilities, though – toilets, an outdoor shower, drinking water and, on the beach, big shade shelters and a cool swing for kids (of any age).

The hard sand beach is excellent for long sunset walks and the fishing is said to be excellent (this is South Australia…). If you know your tackle, expect catches of salmon, King George whiting, trevally, tommy ruffs, snapper and blue swimmer crabs in season. The Streaky Bay jetty is a popular spot to fish for snapper from October to December. Some say the catches can reach 20kg. If the fishing fails, local outlets sell fresh catches of oysters, abalone, crayfish and scallops.

Custom-made for beach holidays, Streaky Bay is a small, friendly spot with a small supermarket and good public facilities including boat ramps, foreshore barbecues, picnic shelters and a swimming enclosure. Navigator Matthew Flinders named the town in 1802 for the streaked appearance of its sea, a result of the oily kelp growing in the bay, and not as Flinders speculated, the presence of a river.

Explorer Edward John Eyre crossed the peninsula in search of this phantom river, establishing a camp at " Cooeyanna" (Eyre's Waterhole) 3km east of town, which can be visited within the Calpatanna Waterhole Conservation Park.

More about the town's history is revealed at the National Trust Museum on Montgomerie Terrace. Travellers who visit during April might catch the annual Eyre Peninsula Farmer and Fishermen's Market held on the Streaky Bay foreshore, while the locals celebrate New Years Day with a picnic on Perlubie Beach itself.

If you arrive to find Perlubie Beach campground full, continue north to the scenic community campground at Haslam.

Space is at a premium at this small coastal camp.

Just The Facts

Perlubie Beach

Getting there: Follow the Flinders Highway 21km west of Streaky Bay and take the signposted turn-off to the beach.
Facilities: Toilets, outdoor coldwater shower, drinking water, beach shelters, kids' swing, and mobile phone reception.
Wheelchair access: No.
Rates: Honesty box $5pn
Pets: Yes.
Contact: Phone the Streaky Bay Tourist Centre on (08) 8626 7033 or visit www.streakybay.com.au.
For information on local conservation parks, visit www.parks.sa.gov.au

Free Campsites in South Australia

65. Kooma View Old Farmhouse
Map Ref: MAP 1 F7 GPS: 33 08 58 S 135 48 37 E
Camp area on Eyre Hwy, Koongawa, 65km W of Kimba or 24km E of Kyancutta. Ph: 0488 943 900

66. The Gums
Map Ref: MAP 1 F7 GPS: 33 08 31 S 136 25 11 E
Rest area at Kimba on the Eyre Hwy. Ph: 08 8627 2026

67. Kimba Recreation Reserve
Map Ref: MAP 1 F7 GPS: 33 08 04 S 136 24 54 E
Camp area at Buckleboo Rd, ext of North Terrace. Entry through Kimba Pioneer Memorial archway. Coin shower. 5 day limit. Honesty box Ph: 08 8627 2026

68. Kimba East Parking Area
Map Ref: MAP 1 G7 GPS: 33 02 56 S 136 46 09 E
Parking area 35km E of Kimba on Eyre Hwy, Kimba.

69. Lakes Edge camping area - Eyre Peninsula
Map Ref: MAP 1 G7 GPS: 33 02 04 S 136 36 59 E
Signposted access off the Eyre Hwy, 68km W of Iron Knob and 17km E of Kimba. Then 9km to the Lake's Edge. Ph: 08 8688 3111

70. Iron Knob West Park Area
Map Ref: MAP 1 G7 GPS: 32 57 50 S 136 53 16 E
Parking area 37km SW of Iron Knob on Eyre Hwy, Iron Knob. Ph: 1300 872 677

71. Shingles Beach Ridges
Map Ref: MAP 1 G7 GPS: 32 55 17 S 137 44 57 E
Camp Area at Fitzgerald Bay, turn E off B100 on to Port Bonython Rd 8km N of Whyalla then N after 16km to end of bitumen. 2km dirt rd. Signposted. Ph: 08 8645 7900

72. Fitzgerald Bay Bush Camp - Eyre Peninsula
Map Ref: MAP 1 G7 GPS: 32 55 20 S 137 45 10 E
65kms south of Port Augusta take Fitzgerald Bay Rd then signposted to Fitzgerald Bay. At end of bitumen turn left and follow 204km to find camp spot. Ph: 1800 088 589

73. Willow Waters Bush Camping - Flinders Ranges
Map Ref: MAP 1 H6 GPS: 31 54 04 S 138 36 50 E
Signposted off Wilpena-Blinman Rd 13km NE of Hawker. Ph: 1800 777 880

74. Cradock Hotel
Map Ref: MAP 1 H7 GPS: 32 04 10 S 138 29 36 E
Parking area at Cradock. RM Williams Way 27kms SE of Hawker. Free camp with patronage, fee for showers. Ph: 08 8648 4107

75. Warren Gorge - Flinders Ranges
Map Ref: MAP 1 H7 GPS: 32 10 57 S 138 00 26 E
Located 21km N of Quorn, via Arden Vale Rd. Ph: 08 8648 6419

76. Horseshoe Top-End Station Stay
Map Ref: MAP 1 H7 GPS: 32 22 49 S 138 22 49 E
Station Stay 11kms N of Moockra on 1133 Horseshoe Rd. Book ahead. Ph: 0448 048 836

77. Waukaringa Ruins camping area - Flinders Ranges
Map Ref: MAP 1 J7 GPS: 32 18 10 S 139 26 32 E
Signposted off the Yunta-Arkaroola road, 34km N of Yunta. Ph: 08 8650 5099

78. Mambray Creek Campground - Yorke Peninsula
Map Ref: MAP 1 H7 GPS: 32 50 26 S 138 02 14 E
Within the Mt Remarkable NP. Signposted access off the Princess Hwy, 45km N of Port Pirie. Then 4.5km E to the campground. Ph: 08 8634 7068

79. Ippinitchie Campground - Yorke Peninsula
Map Ref: MAP 1 H7 GPS: 33 04 01 S 138 13 59 E
Camp area 6km SW of Wirrabara via Wirrabara Forest Rd. Ph: 08 8668 4163

80. Appila Springs camping area - Mid North
Map Ref: MAP 1 H7 GPS: 33 00 11 S 138 28 59 E
8km NE of Appila off the Appila-Tarcowie Road. Central to several historic towns. Ph: 08 8666 2014

81. Charlies Camp
Map Ref: MAP 1 E8 GPS: 33 14 43 S 134 44 53 E
Camp area 72kms S of Streaky Bay on Flinders Hwy S of Venus Bay Rd.

82. Coodlie Park Farm - Eyre Peninsula
Map Ref: MAP 1 E8 GPS: 33 16 15 S 134 47 18 E
Signposted access along the Flinders Hwy, 45km N of Elliston and 20km S of Port Kenny. Ph: 08 8687 0411

83. Sheringa Coastal camping area - Eyre Peninsula
Map Ref: MAP 1 F8 GPS: 33 51 57 S 135 10 37 E
Located 51km S of Elliston. Signposted access along Sheringa Beach Road which is signposted off the Flinders Hwy. Ph: 08 8687 9200

84. Carappee Hill bush camping - Eyre Peninsula
Map Ref: MAP 1 F8 GPS: 33 25 56 S 136 16 20 E
Within the Carappee Hill Conservation Park, 8km NE of Darke Peak via Carappee Hill Rd. Ph: 08 8688 3111

85. Wharminda Soaks Picnic Area
Map Ref: MAP 1 F8 GPS: 33 55 51 S 136 09 47 E
Picnic area 10km W of Wharminda, signposted at railway crossing. Dirt rd and small vehicles only, low trees 4WD recommended.

86. Carrow Wells Campground
Map Ref: MAP 1 F8 GPS: 34 08 39 S 136 20 01 E
Camping area 4km S of Port Neill via coast road. Dirt road.

87. Lipson Cove camping area - Eyre Peninsula
Map Ref: MAP 1 F8 GPS: 34 15 59 S 136 15 59 E
From Tumby Bay follow the Lincoln Hwy N for 17km then signposted turn-off for 8km to Lipson Cove. Ph: 08 8688 2101

88. Cowleys Beach Campground
Map Ref: MAP 1 G8 GPS: 34 11 50 S 136 17 56 E
Camping area 11km S of Port Neill via coast road.

89. Cleve Showgrounds
Map Ref: MAP 1 G8 GPS: 33 42 03 S 136 29 26 E
Camp area cnr Rudall Rd & West Tce, Cleve on W side of town, N of Hwy. Honesty box. Ph: 0428 827 749

90. Yeldulknie Weir
Map Ref: MAP 1 G8 GPS: 33 41 35 S 136 32 39 E
Picnic area on Yeldulknie Weir Rd, Cleve, 37km W of Cowell or 5km E of Cleve. Travel via Cowell Rd then N to Yeldulknie Rd. Ph: 08 8628 2004

91. Cowell RV Park
Map Ref: MAP 1 G8 GPS: 33 41 40 S 136 55 20 E
Camp area on Beach Rd, Cowell S end of town via Wellington Rd. 14 day limit. Display permit. Ph: 08 8629 2019

92. Port Gibbon Foreshore Campsite - Eyre Peninsula
Map Ref: MAP 1 G8 GPS: 33 48 06 S 136 48 06 E
From Cowell take the Lincoln Hwy S for 7kms to Elbow Hill then take signposted road to Point Gibbon. Dry weather only. Ph: 08 8621 4444

93. Cliff Top Camp
Map Ref: MAP 1 G8 GPS: 33 48 02 S 136 48 41 E
Camp area on Beach Rd, Port Gibbon 23km S of Cowell, E of Port Gibbon. Permits from council office or Beach Rd. 14 day limit. Ph: 08 8629 2019

94. The Knob Camping Area - Eyre Peninsula
Map Ref: MAP 1 G8 GPS: 33 48 05 S 136 50 58 E
16km S of Cowell & 4km E of Port Gibbon along Beach Rd. Signposted tourist drive for 14km to camping area along foreshore. 4WD beach access. Ph: 08 8629 2019

95. Tiparra Rocks - Yorke Peninsula
Map Ref: MAP 1 G8 GPS: 34 17 12 S 137 29 58 E
Camp area 6km from Balgowan off Tiparra West Rd. Dirt road. Ph: 08 8832 0000

96. The Bamboos Campground - Yorke Peninsula
Map Ref: MAP 1 G8 GPS: 34 15 12 S 137 30 10 E
9km N of Balgowan. Take Tiparra West Rd. District Council of Yorke Pen 08 8832 0000

Free Campsites in South Australia

97. The Gap Campground - Yorke Peninsula
Map Ref: MAP 1 G8 GPS: 34 14 06 S 137 30 10 E
11km N of Balgowan. Take Tiparra West Rd. District Council of Yorke Pen 08 8832 0000

98. The Acreage
Map Ref: MAP 1 H8 GPS: 34 01 42 S 137 51 41 E
Camp spot 4km W of Paskeville cnr New Holland & Paskeville Rds. Signposted. Self contained vehicles only. Donations appreciated. Ph: 0428 272 083

99. Tickera North
Map Ref: MAP 1 G8 GPS: 33 45 37 S 137 43 49 E
Parking area 4.5km N of Tickera on the Coast Road. Turn W to beach.

100. Clements Gap Old School
Map Ref: MAP 1 H8 GPS: 33 29 45 S 138 05 04 E
Camp spot 19.5km NE of Port Broughton or 10.5kms SW of Merriton in old school grounds close to Clements Gap Conserv Park.

101. Yackamoorundie Park
Map Ref: MAP 1 H8 GPS: 33 34 06 S 138 26 43 E
Camp area N side of town on cnr Main North Rd & North Tce, Yacka on Broughton River. Ph: 0407 574 475

102. Gulnare Sportsground
Map Ref: MAP 1 H8 GPS: 33 28 05 S 138 26 25 E
Camp area 350m S of Post Office, 18-20 View St, Gulnare. Ph: 0408 841 451

103. Mundoora Museum Camping Park
Map Ref: MAP 1 H8 GPS: 33 35 46 S 138 05 04 E
Camp area on East Tce, Mundoora 13km W of August Hwy via Ingram Gap Rd. Honesty box. Ph: 0423 488 450

104. White Cliffs Reserve - Mid North
Map Ref: MAP 1 H8 GPS: 33 35 35 S 138 23 50 E
Located on Yacka Rd 6km E of Koolunga alongside Broughton River. Dry weather only Port Pirie Regional Tourism 08 8633 8700

105. Curnow's Hut Camping Area - Mid North & Yorke Peninsula
Map Ref: MAP 1 H8 GPS: 33 19 21 S 138 33 25 E
From Jamestown proceed south along signposted RM Williams Way, after 8.5km turn into signposted Springs Rd/Bundaleer Forest. C=Follow Springs Rd for 1.5km to Springs Rd/Bundaleer Gardens then veer left for 4km to gate entrance. Locked gate access. Ph: 08 8668 5000

106. Spalding Recreation Ground
Map Ref: MAP 1 H8 GPS: 33 29 56 S 138 36 22 E
Camp area 250m W of Post Office on RM Williams Way, Spalding. Ph: 08 8845 2017

107. Terowie camping area - Mid North
Map Ref: MAP 1 H8 GPS: 33 09 00 S 138 55 14 E
22kms S of Peterborough. Ph: 08 8892 0100

108. Old Shed Main Camp
Map Ref: MAP 1 J8 GPS: 33 26 52 S 139 08 27 E
Access along Caroona Rd off Eastern Rd, 9.3 km E of junction with B64 hwy. Take Caroona Rd N for 27km to park entrance then 1km to camp area. Ph: 08 8892 3025

109. Convention Beach camping area
Map Ref: MAP 1 E9 GPS: 34 16 39 S 135 21 10 E
Popular fishing and surfing spot located behind sand dunes. 36km N of Wangary along Ulina Lane off Flinders Hwy N of Wangary. Ph: 1300 788 378

110. Greenly Beach camping area
Map Ref: MAP 1 E9 GPS: 34 21 15 S 135 21 33 E
29km N of Wangary along Greenly Beach Rd, then Coles Point Rd off Flinders Hwy, 15km N of Wangary. Ph: 1300 788 378

111. Coles Point camping area
Map Ref: MAP 1 F9 GPS: 34 22 10 S 135 21 13 E
27km N of Wangary, accessed 10.6km along Coles Point Rd off the Flinders Hwy, 15km N of Wangary. Ph: 1300 788 378

112. Little Yangie Bay camping area - Eyre Peninsula
Map Ref: MAP 1 E9 GPS: 34 38 24 S 135 21 43 E
Located on the Coffin Bay NP on the Coffin Bay NP access road, 15km W of the ranger headquarters. Ph: 08 8688 3111

Free Campsites in South Australia

113. Big Yangie camping area - Eyre Peninsula
Map Ref: MAP 1 F9 GPS: 34 37 03 S 135 22 22 E
On the Coffin Bay NP access road 1km N of the temporary closure gate. Ph: 08 8688 3111

114. Fishery Bay camping area
Map Ref: MAP 1 F9 GPS: 34 54 41 S 135 40 43 E
32km SW of Port Lincoln along Fishery Bay Rd off Proper Bay Rd, 20km S of Port Lincoln. Ph: 1300 788 378

115. Wauraltee Beach - Yorke Peninsula
Map Ref: MAP 1 G9 GPS: 34 35 20 S 137 30 32 E
Camp area 17km S of Port Victoria and 4km W of Wauraltee. 4km dirt road. Ph: 1300 764 227

116. Port Minlacowie
Map Ref: MAP 1 G9 GPS: 34 49 58 S 137 27 35 E
Camp area 17km SW of Minlaton on Beegoodye Wells Rd via Minlacowie Rd, 650m N of Minlacowie Rd intersection. Permit applies. Ph: 1800 202 445

117. Barkers Rocks camping area
Map Ref: MAP 1 G9 GPS: 34 42 52 S 137 29 14 E
Camping area on the W coast of the Peninsula, 12km NW of Minlaton via Bluff Beach Road/Port Rickeby to the signposted road to Barkers Rocks and follow it for 3kms to camping area. Permits are required Ph: 08 8832 0000

118. Port Julia Camping Area - Mid North & Yorke Peninsula
Map Ref: MAP 1 G9 GPS: 34 39 45 S 137 52 37 E
Located in the village of Port Julia on the east coast of the Peninsula.From Port Lincoln proceed north on Yorke Hwy to signposted Julia Rd. Proceed for 1.4km to signposted Osprey St where camping area is on the left in Reichenbach Memorial Park.Bring firewood. Ph: 1800 202 445

119. Swincers Rocks
Map Ref: MAP 1 G9 GPS: 34 58 15 S 136 58 14 E
Camp area 13km SW of Corny Point on Wurlie Rd, dirt road. Permit applies. Ph: 1800 202 445

120. Gravel Bay
Map Ref: MAP 1 G9 GPS: 34 55 55 S 136 59 57 E
Camp areas 18km W of Corny Point on Lighthouse Rd on coastal reserve at bottom of cliff not in Berry Bay carparks. Permit applies. 4WD only. Ph: 1800 202 445

121. Gleesons Landing Camping Area - Mid North & Yorke Peninsula
Map Ref: MAP 1 G9 GPS: 35 00 22 S 136 57 57 E
Located on the west coast of the foot, 19kms south west of Corny Point. Signposted access off Corny Point-Marion Bay Rd/Scenic Drive. Bring firewood & water. Ph: 1800 202 445

122. Burners Beach
Map Ref: MAP 1 G9 GPS: 34 54 00 S 137 14 38 E
Camp area 12km W of Point Turton on Point Souttar Rd, Point Turton. Permit applies. Ph: 1800 202 445

123. Warooka Camp Ground
Map Ref: MAP 1 G9 GPS: 34 59 32 S 137 23 53 E
Camp area at Warooka Oval cnr Oval Ave & Fifth St, Warooka. Donation envelopes in cylinder on site. 5 day limit. Ph: 08 8854 5004

124. Stenhouse Bay Camping - Mid North & Yorke Peninsula
Map Ref: MAP 1 G9 GPS: 35 16 26 S 136 56 30 E
Located 1.1km south of Innes NP visitor centre. Signposted access off Stenhouse Bay Rd. Bring firewood. Ph: 08 8854 3200

125. Harveys Return Camp
Map Ref: MAP 1 G10 GPS: 35 45 04 S 136 38 16 E
Location in Flinders Chase NP, Cape Borda Rd, Cape Borda. Camp area 137km W of Penneshaw, 4km E of Cape Borda lighthouse. Ph: 08 8553 4444

126. Western River Cove
Map Ref: MAP 1 G10 GPS: 35 40 40 S 136 58 18 E
Camp area 29km W of Parndana on Western River Rd, Western River. Dirt road, steep in places. Small vehicles only. Permit applies. Self registration. Ph: 08 8553 4500

127. Stokes Bay
Map Ref: MAP 1 G10 GPS: 35 37 30 S 137 12 23 E
Camp area 38km W of Kingscote on North Coast Rd, Stokes Bay. Via Stokes Bay Rd travel 4km W of Parndana. Behind café, check-in and pay at café. Ph: 08 8553 4500

128. Rocky River camping area - Kangaroo Island
Map Ref: MAP 1 G10 GPS: 35 57 11 S 136 44 08 E
Within the Flinders Chase NP, located 300m S of Flinders Chase Visitor Information Centre. Ph: 08 8559 7235

Free Campsites in South Australia

129. Murray Lagoon camping area - Kangaroo Island
Map Ref: MAP 1 G10 GPS: 35 54 20 S 137 27 11 E
Within the Cape Gantheaume Conservation Park. Via South Coast Rd then Seagers Rd. Ph: 08 8553 8233

130. Brown Beach Campground
Map Ref: MAP 1 H10 GPS: 35 47 38 S 137 51 27 E
Camp area at Browns Bay on Hog Bay Rd, Dudley West. Permit applies. Self registration. Fee for shower. Ph: 08 8553 4500

131. Antechamber Bay East camping area - Kangaroo Island
Map Ref: MAP 1 H10 GPS: 35 47 12 S 138 04 00 E
Signposted along Cape Willoughby Rd, 19km SE from Penneshaw. Various sites along the Chapman River. Ph: 08 8553 2381 Reservations necessary

132. Long Point Camping Area - South East
Map Ref: MAP 1 H10 GPS: 35 41 43 S 139 09 46 E
From Meningie on the Princes Hwy take signposted Narrung Rd for 19.8kms to signposted Long Point Rd. This leads 4.6km to Long Point Rd then 1.1km to camping area. Ph: 08 8575 1200

133. Pelican Campground
Map Ref: MAP 1 J10 GPS: 35 53 49 S 139 24 05 E
Located in Coorong NP 28kms S of Meningie, 3km dirt road. Book online. Ph: 08 8735 1177

134. Messent Bush Camping - South East
Map Ref: MAP 1 J10 GPS: 36 06 34 S 139 42 29 E
From Princes Hwy at Salt Creek take signposted Salt Creek Rd which leads for 6.2km to a track to the north signposted to the Messent Conservation Park. Continue 1km to park entrance then 4WD access to camp. Ph: 08 8735 1177

135. 42 Mile Crossing
Map Ref: MAP 1 J10 GPS: 36 17 15 S 139 42 42 E
Camp area 69km N of Kingston SE. Turn W 66km N of Kingston SE, 3km dirt road. 5 day limit. Ph: 08 8735 1200

136. Lake Indawarra
Map Ref: MAP 1 J10 GPS: 35 53 16 S 140 03 28 E
Camp area 34kms NW of Keith, SW off Dukes Hwy at Tintinara to Woods Well Rd, SE to Kings Rd.

137. Mount Monster
Map Ref: MAP 1 J10 GPS: 36 12 03 S 140 19 15 E
Camp area 15km S of Keith on the Riddoch Hwy.

138. Willalooka Tavern
Map Ref: MAP 1 J10 GPS: 36 23 35 S 140 21 01 E
Located at 3449 Riddoch Hwy, Willalooka, 34km S of Keith. Register at bar. Patrons only. Ph: 08 8757 8242

139. Pertendi Hut Camping Area - South East
Map Ref: MAP 1 K10 GPS: 35 38 23 S 140 46 45 E
Signposted access on the Pinnaroo-Bordertown Rd 44km south of Pinnaroo. Pinnaroo-Bordertown Rd is signposted off the Dukes Hwy 11km west of Bordertown. 140m to historic hut and camping area. Bring firewood & water. Ph: 08 8580 1800

140. Poocher Swamp camping area - South East
Map Ref: MAP 1 K10 GPS: 36 18 07 S 140 40 41 E
Located on Cannawigara Road, 8.4km West of Bordertown. Ph: 08 8762 3412

141. Jimmys Waterhole camping area - South East
Map Ref: MAP 1 K10 GPS: 36 21 10 S 140 41 34 E
Located in the small town of Mundulla just off the Dukes Hwy with access off Rowney Rd. Suitable for self-sufficient campers. Bordertown Visitor Info Centre 08 8752 0700

142. Creecoona Waterhole
Map Ref: MAP 1 K10 GPS: 36 18 49 S 140 48 02 E
Rest area on Dukes Hwy, Bordertown 5km E of Bordertown.

143. Wolseley Hotel
Map Ref: MAP 1 K10 GPS: 36 21 53 S 140 54 18 E
Located on Railway Terrace, Wolseley 15km S of Bordertown off Dukes Hwy into Ridgeway Rd then W to Railway Tce. Register at bar. Ph: 08 8753 2239

144. The Granites - Coorong - South East
Map Ref: MAP 1 J11 GPS: 36 39 30 S 139 51 20 E
17km north of Kingston SE. Signposted turnoff to the Granites and continue for 3km to the coast.

Free Campsites in South Australia

145. Kingston SE Campsites
Map Ref: MAP 1 J11 GPS: 36 49 34 S 139 51 37 E
44kms from Robe. SE end of Encounter Bay and the Coorong. Ph: 08 8767 2033

146. Mount Scott Conservation Park
Map Ref: MAP 1 J11 GPS: 36 46 49 S 140 03 17 E
Camping area 24km NE of Kingston SE. turn off Desert Camp Rd and travel 19km. Dirt road.

147. Padthaway bush camping - South East
Map Ref: MAP 1 J11 GPS: 36 34 50 S 140 30 45 E
Within the Padthaway Conservation Park access via the Padthaway-Bordertown Rd 3km NE of the Riddoch Hwy at Padthaway. Ph: 08 8762 3412

148. Cockatoo Lake Reserve - South East
Map Ref: MAP 1 J11 GPS: 36 44 59 S 140 34 58 E
Lake is accessed along Grubb Rd which is signposted from Padthaway. Ph: 08 8766 2002

149. Farirview bush camping - South East
Map Ref: MAP 1 J11 GPS: 36 49 01 S 140 24 41 E
Within the Fairview Conservation Park. Access via Woolumbool Road via the Riddoch Hwy 15km N of Naracoorte. Ph: 08 8762 3412

150. Mullinger Swamp
Map Ref: MAP 1 K11 GPS: 36 50 57 S 140 58 11 E
Located in Kybybolite Rec Reserve on Mullinger Rd, Kybybolite. Camp area N side of park. Travel E off Riddoch Hwy to Wimmera Hwy then N to Frances Rd then E to Mullinger/Butterworth Rd then S to camp. Ph: 08 8762 1399

151. Naracoorte Showground
Map Ref: MAP 1 K11 GPS: 36 57 16 S 140 44 48 E
Camp area on cnr Smith St & Cadgee Rd, Naracoorte. Enter beside Bowls Club. 7 day limit. Ph: 0414 453 360

152. Bool Lagoon Campground - South East
Map Ref: MAP 1 J11 GPS: 37 06 20 S 140 43 17 E
Access to reserve is signposted off the Riddoch Hwy 18km south of Naracoorte.Campground is signposted access 6.4km west of Riddoch Hwy then 500m to reserve entrance then further 2.5km to Bool Lagoon. No fires. Ph: 08 8760 1201

153. Wrights Bay Campground
Map Ref: MAP 1 J11 GPS: 37 02 31 S 139 44 33 E
Camp area 19km N of Robe on Wrights Bay Rd, Mount Benson. See caretaker. Ph: 0427 007 006

154. Long Gully Campground
Map Ref: MAP 1 J11 GPS: 37 15 17 S 139 48 03 E
Located in Little Dip CP. Camp area 14kms S of Robe via Nora Creina Dr, 6km dirt road. Book online. Ph: 08 8735 1177

155. Three Mile Bend camping area - South East
Map Ref: MAP 1 J11 GPS: 37 27 09 S 139 59 31 E
Camp area 5km N of Beachport within the Beachport Conservation Park. Access via Five Mile Rd. Ph: 08 8735 1177

156. Lucindale Showground
Map Ref: MAP 1 J11 GPS: 36 58 08 S 140 21 59 E
Caravan Park in showgrounds next to Yakka Park on Oak Ave, Lucindale. Ph: 08 8766 2038

157. Kotgee camping area -South East
Map Ref: MAP 1 J11 GPS: 37 34 18 S 140 07 18 E
Within the Canunda NP 3km SE of Southend. Access via Bevilaqua Ford Track off the Boozy Gully access road. Ph: 08 8735 1177

158. CMCA Penola RV Park
Map Ref: MAP 1 J11 GPS: 37 22 20 S 140 50 23 E
Camp area at MacCorquindale Sports Grounds on John St, Penola. Ph: 02 4978 8788

159. Greenrise Lake Campsite - South East
Map Ref: MAP 1 K11 GPS: 37 23 48 S 140 50 09 E
Penola is located 388km SE of Adelaide. Greenrise Lake is 1km S of town on western side of Riddoch Hwy.

160. Lake Leake
Map Ref: MAP 1 J11 GPS: 37 36 42 S 140 35 34 E
Camp area 14km W of Kalangadoo via Kangaroo Flat Rd & Lake Leake Rd.

Free Campsites in South Australia

161. Tantanoola Campsite - South East
Map Ref: MAP 1 J12 GPS: 37 41 48 S 140 27 21 E
Tantanoola is 15km SE of Millicent. Camp area is across from hotel in Tantanoola.

162. Cape Banks Lighthouse
Map Ref: MAP 1 J12 GPS: 37 53 51 S 140 22 37 E
Located in Canundra NP. Camp area 5km NW of Carpenter Rocks via Cape Banks Rd. Ph: 08 8735 1177

163. Little Blue Lake - South East
Map Ref: MAP 1 J12 GPS: 37 55 46 S 140 40 44 E
13km S of Mt Gambier turn right onto the Mt Salt Rd opposite Bellum Hotel. Travel 3km to site.

164. Mount Schanck Campsite - South East
Map Ref: MAP 1 J12 GPS: 37 56 32 S 140 43 44 E
15km S of Mt Gambier beneath the western wall of the Mt Schanck crater.

165. Mount Gambier Showgrounds
Map Ref: MAP 1 J12 GPS: 37 50 16 S 140 47 51 E
Camp area on Pick Ave Mount Gambier. Caretake on site, max 28 day stay. Ph: 0408 492 182

166. Allendale East Memorial Park - South East
Map Ref: MAP 1 J12 GPS: 38 00 23 S 140 42 30 E
22km S of Mt Gambier on the Riddoch Hwy or 4km N of Port MacDonnell.

167. Finger Point - South East
Map Ref: MAP 1 J12 GPS: 38 03 06 S 140 38 55 E
When entering Port MacDonnell, 27km S of Mt Gambier, turn right along the foreshore for 2.5km. Travel to end of road.

168. Burra Showgrounds
Map Ref: MAP 1 B9 GPS: 33 40 05 S 138 55 28 E
Camp area at Lot 4 Hall Tce, Burra North via Young St. Ph: 0447 938 152

169. Mallee camping area - Red Banks Conservation Park -Mid North
Map Ref: MAP 1 B9 GPS: 33 40 21 S 139 06 03 E
Signposted access along Eastern Road, 15km E of Burra. Ph: 08 8892 3025 or Burra Visitor Centre 08 8892 2154

170. Redbanks Conservation Park
Map Ref: MAP 1 C9 GPS: 33 39 53 S 139 05 37 E
Camp area 17kms E of Burra, via Burra to Morgan Rd, via Eastern Rd. 11km dirt road. Ph: 08 8892 3003

171. Burra Creek Gorge camping area
Map Ref: MAP 1 B9 GPS: 33 49 48 S 139 02 48 E
26km S of Burra signposted access along Worlds End Hwy off the Goyder Hwy, 15km E of Burra. Ph: 08 8892 2154

172. Port Parham Foreshore - Gulf of St Vincent
Map Ref: MAP 1 A10 GPS: 34 25 44 S 138 15 28 E
Take the A1 from Adelaide and turn W 1km N of Dublin for a further 9km to the foreshore camp. District of Mallala 08 8527 2006

173. Parham Camping Ground
Map Ref: MAP 1 A10 GPS: 34 25 34 S 138 15 20 E
Camp area on The Esplanade, Port Parham. 5 tonne limit. Self register onsite. 14 day limit. Cassette only DP. Ph: 08 8527 0200

174. Greenock Centenary Park
Map Ref: MAP 1 B10 GPS: 34 27 32 S 138 55 43 E
Camp area at oval on Martin St, Greenock, via Murray St. 7 day limit. Register & pay at entry. Ph: 0409 177 657

175. Hogwash Bend Camping Area - Riverland & Central Murray
Map Ref: MAP 1 C10 GPS: 34 05 05 S 139 51 18 E
20km NW of Waikerie on the Morgan-Waikerie Rd. 17km E of Morgan ferry. Great riverside camping. Ph: 08 8541 2332

176. Ramco Point - Riverland & Central Murray
Map Ref: MAP 1 C10 GPS: 34 10 05 S 139 55 59 E
On the Ramco Point Rd 5km W of Waikerie. Boat ramp and riverside camping. Dry weather only. Ph: 08 8541 2077

Featured Campsite

Brought to you by

Tantanoola Free Campsite No.161

Across the road from the Tantanoola Tiger Hotel

John Mainwaring

Part of the large free campsite across the road from the famous Tantanoola Hotel.

This large and grassy free campsite suits rigs of all sizes. There are many sheltering trees in the long campsite which runs along between the old, now disused, railway line and the road. The local council, Wattle Range Council, is moving to have all the towns within its boundaries registered as RV Friendly. To this end the council is improving and building toilet facilities and installing Blackwater dump sites wherever it can. Tantanoola now has a new toilet block with dumpsite, undercover BBQs and children's playground.

Being just across the road from the hotel the security is good and counter meals are available on most days. The hotel also has on display the famous Tantanoola Tiger that terrorized the district back in the late 1890's. In August 1895 an animal was shot by local man Thomas John Donovan, which was believed to have been the mysterious predator. The animal turned out to be more like a wolf than a cat. Later, it was determined to be an Assyrian wolf, although how it arrived in South Australia has been the subject of a number of theories. The most popular, and most likely was that the wolf was a survivor from one of the many shipwrecks along the nearby coast.

There are some fascinating things to do in the Tantanoola district. There is the huge wind farm only a few km away along the coast with self drive driving tours that you can take. Some of the views along the way are quite spectacular.

Only a short drive away on the Princes Highway is the fascinating Tantanoola Caves. These breathtaking caves are known for their scenic beauty, pink dolomite caverns and an array of unusual speleothems. The Tantanoola Caves is one of the renowned and most-visited destinations in South Australia. This cave is the only wheelchair accessed cave near Mount Gambier.

The Tantanoola Caves is somewhat like a huge chamber of 30m width and 8m overall height. However, it is one of the smallest caves in South Australia that has numerous stunning speleothems and several helictites. The cave is a limestone cave that was formed when the sea retreated leaving a low coastal cliff overlooking the now coastal plains. This cave is well worth a look even if you're not camping nearby.

Also close by is Canunda National Park where great sea views can be found from the cliffs and beaches. There are also several walking tracks and four wheel driving tracks for enthusiasts who wish to get to those out of the way spots.

The town of Millicent is only 15km away where you can find a full range of services including supermarkets. Mt Gambier, a city of 23,000 with crater lakes, caves and great shopping can be found only 32km south of Tantanoola.

Tantanoola free campsite is a great place to base yourself while exploring all there is to do in this fascinating district, thanks to the district council of Wattle Range who had the foresight to establish and maintain it.

The incredibly beautiful Tantanoola Caves.

Just The Facts

Tantanoola Free Campsite

Where: Tantanoola can be found in the lower South East of South Australia 15km south east of Millicent or 32km northwest of Mt Gambier. The town is several km off the Princes Highway in a quiet rural location.

The camping area is a long level grassed area with ample room for rigs of all sizes and plenty of shade if required.

Amenities: Toilets with disabled access, dump site, playground, water and undercover BBQ,

Phone & TV: Excellent reception for both.

Pets: OK on a lead.

Free Campsites in South Australia

177. Hart Lagoon/Ricciuto Creek camping area
Map Ref: MAP 1 C10 GPS: 34 09 42 S 139 57 46 E
3.5km W of Waikerie camping along the river. 1.7km along Ricciuto Rd off the Morgan-Waikerie Rd. Ph: 08 8541 2332

178. Maize Island Lagoon
Map Ref: MAP 1 D10 GPS: 34 09 59 S 140 00 41 E
This conservation park has numerous campsites located only a few kilometres from Waikerie. Dry weather only Ph: 08 8595 2111

179. Holder Bend Reserve & Boat Ramp - Riverland & Central Murray
Map Ref: MAP 1 C10 GPS: 34 11 10 S 140 00 59 E
From the Sturt Hwy approx. 4km E of Waikerie take Holder Top Rd and then Holder Bottom Rd to camping area located on river bank.

180. Lowbank Landing - Riverland & Central Murray
Map Ref: MAP 1 D10 GPS: 34 11 04 S 140 04 12 E
Signposted off the highway 6.6km E of Waikerie at the end of Low Bank Rd. Many spots along river. Dry weather only

181. Herons Bend
Map Ref: MAP 1 D10 GPS: 34 09 07 S 140 20 26 E
Camp at Overland Corner 1.2km W of Overland Corner Hotel. GPS at entry from road then follow track to the river.

182. Overland Corner Conservation Reserve - Riverland & Central Murray
Map Ref: MAP 1 D10 GPS: 34 09 30 S 140 20 20 E
Signposted off the B64 Goyder Hwy. 1km W of Overland Corner Hotel. Camping by river. Dry weather only

183. Lake Bonney Reserve - Riverland & Central Murray
Map Ref: MAP 1 D10 GPS: 34 11 42 S 140 25 38 E
Dispersed camping 10km NW Barmera, access via Queen Elizabeth Drive on eastern shore of Lake Bonney. Ph: 08 8582 1922

184. Sugarloaf Campground - Riverland & Central Murray
Map Ref: MAP 1 D10 GPS: 34 13 22 S 140 22 43 E
Once in Loch Luna Reserve access is signposted via Nappers Bridge entrance track. From information station follow track to south signposted to Sugarloaf then 5.5km to camping area at end of track. Ph: 08 8580 1800

185. Cobdogla Pump Station
Map Ref: MAP 1 D10 GPS: 34 15 45 S 140 24 02 E
Camp 2km S of Cobdogla. Turn S onto Park Tce from Shueard Rd then Schell Rd for 2km. Turn W over causeway to Pump Station. Camp N & S of Station.

186. Chowilla Creekside Camps
Map Ref: MAP 1 E9 GPS: 33 57 06 S 140 51 00 E
Dispersed camping 48km N of Renmark via Old Wentworth Rd, Renmark. Pre-book. 5 day limit. Loose gravel and potholes. Check website for hunting open season. Ph: 08 8595 2111

187. Little Gums Campground
Map Ref: MAP 1 E10 GPS: 34 00 32 S 140 51 25 E
Located in Chowilla Game Reserve on Old Wentworth Rd, Renmark area. Camp area 32km NE of Renmark. Turn S to signposted road to park entry, dirt road. 2WD in dry conditions only. Permit applies. Ph: 08 8595 2111

188. Border Cliffs camping area - Riverland & Central Murray
Map Ref: MAP 1 E10 GPS: 33 58 22 S 140 57 28 E
Located in the Chowilla Game Reserve at the end of Murtho Road, 32km NE of Parina. Ph: 08 8595 2111

189. Murtho Forest Landing - Riverland & Central Murray
Map Ref: MAP 1 E10 GPS: 34 03 59 S 140 46 58 E
16km N of Renmark signposted off the Paringa-Murtho Rd. Riverside camping. Ph: 08 8586 6704

190. TM Price Rotary RV Park
Map Ref: MAP 1 D10 GPS: 34 12 23 S 140 42 10 E
Camp area 6km W of Renmark on cnr Sturt Hwy & 28th St, Renmark area. Pre-book. Ph: 1300 661 704

191. Plushs Bend - Riverland & Central Murray
Map Ref: MAP 1 E10 GPS: 34 13 10 S 140 45 10 E
Located close to Renmark, take Twenty-Third St off Sturt Hwy. Riverside camping. Ph: 08 8586 6704

192. Colligans Campground - Riverland & Central Murray
Map Ref: MAP 1 E10 GPS: 34 14 57 S 140 39 09 E
Located at the western end of Lyrup Flats section 7km north east of Berri. From the Sturt Hwy take signposted road to Lyrup Flats 2.2km east of Sturt Hwy and B201 junction. Follow this road south for 2km to track on the east signposted Lyrup Flats. Continue on track for 300m to information and self-registration station then 200m to signposted access track to camp. Bring firewood. Ph: 08 8580 1800

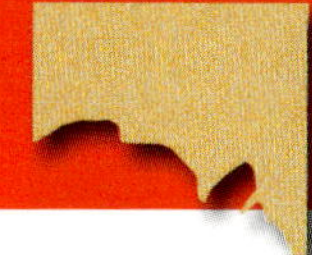

Free Campsites in South Australia

193. Martins Bend Campground - Riverland & Central Murray
Map Ref: MAP 1 E10 GPS: 34 17 28 S 140 37 59 E
Camp Area 3km E of Berri, via Riverview Rd. Large camping area beside river. Ph: 08 8582 5511

194. Lyrup Flats Section
Map Ref: MAP 1 E10 GPS: 34 14 57 S 140 39 07 E
Numerous campsites located in Murray River NP, Berri. Camp area 1.5km N of Lyrup. Turn S 9km SW of Renmark. Enter next to ferry crossing, 500m dirt road. Ph: 08 8595 2111

195. SS Ellen RV Park
Map Ref: MAP 1 E10 GPS: 34 15 14 S 140 38 52 E
Rest area at Lyrup S side of river, W of ferry crossing. Numbered sites in carpark area. Pre-book. 7 day limit. Ph: 1300 661 704

196. Rilli Reserve camping area
Map Ref: MAP 1 D10 GPS: 34 23 36 S 140 35 03 E
Bush camping beside the river along Briers Rd. 8km N of Loxton signposted off Bookpurnong Rd (Berri Rd) then 2.1km to reserve. Ph: 08 8584 8071

197. Milichs Landing camping area
Map Ref: MAP 1 D10 GPS: 34 26 43 S 140 30 07 E
6km W of Loxton off Moorook Rd and 24km SE of Moorook, access road is opposite the Swan Reach turn-off. Campsites near boat ramp and suitable for overnight. Ph: 08 8584 8071

198. Thiele's Sandbar - Riverland & Central Murray
Map Ref: MAP 1 D10 GPS: 34 26 14 S 140 34 28 E
Access via Tower Drive off the Bookpurnong Rd, Loxton. Dirt track to large sandy beach beside river. Dry weather only.

199. Rocky Paddock Campground - Close to Adelaide
Map Ref: MAP 1 B11 GPS: 34 43 05 S 138 56 26 E
Situated in Mount Crawford Forest 1hour from Adelaide CBD. Access off Warren Road then Tower Rd which is 400m south of Mount Crawford Forest Info Centre. 750m along Tower Rd take road to Sailers Gully picnic area for 500m to signposted track to camping area. Ph: 08 8521 1700

200. Hettner Landing - Riverland & Central Murray
Map Ref: MAP 1 B11 GPS: 34 45 10 S 139 33 29 E
Located 50m from the Walker Flat General Store which is 49k E of Mt Pleasant. Dry weather only Ph: 08 8569 0100

201. John S Christian Reserve camping area - Murray
Map Ref: MAP 1 C11 GPS: 34 42 10 S 139 29 19 E
25km S of Swan Reach signposted access along the Black Hill-Shell Hill Road. Ph: 08 8569 0100

202. Bolto Reserve camping area - Riverland & Central Murray
Map Ref: MAP 1 C11 GPS: 34 55 10 S 139 19 08 E
Located on the eastern bank of the river, 60k S of the Mannum ferry. Large area well shaded camping sites. Ph: 08 8569 1303

203. Haythorpe Reserve camping area - Riverland & Central Murray
Map Ref: MAP 1 C11 GPS: 34 54 55 S 139 19 41 E
On the road to Bowhill in Mannum just 400m N of the ferry. Ph: 08 8569 1303

204. Swan Reach Conservation Park
Map Ref: MAP 1 C10 GPS: 34 34 29 S 139 28 44 E
Camp area 16km E of Sedan or 14km W of Swan Reach. 2km of dirt road S of Hwy. Ph: 08 8576 3690

205. Tenbury - Hunter Reserve camping area - Riverland & Central Murray
Map Ref: MAP 1 C10 GPS: 34 33 59 S 139 36 10 E
A few hundred 100m W of Swan Reach ferry on the Swan Reach Sedan Rd. Riverside camping Ph: 08 8569 0100

206. Ridley Bush Camping - Riverland & Central Murray
Map Ref: MAP 1 C11 GPS: 34 36 06 S 139 35 15 E
Northern boundary of Ridley Conservation Park is 8km south of Swan Reach. Signposted access along the Swan Reach-Mannum Rd. Numerous tracks lead off to campsites. Self-sufficient campers and bring firewood. Ph: 08 8576 3400

207. Wongulla Campground
Map Ref: MAP 1 C11 GPS: 34 42 03 S 139 34 32 E
Camp area 53km S of Blanchetown on Cliff View Dve, Wongulla.

208. Walker Flat Boat Ramp Reserve & Camping area - Riverland & Central Murray
Map Ref: MAP 1 C11 GPS: 34 45 16 S 139 33 59 E
3okm N of Mannum on southern side of Walker Flat village. Ph: 08 8570 8050

Free Campsites in South Australia

209. Greenways Landing
Map Ref: MAP 1 C11 GPS: 34 39 18 S 139 39 32 E
Camp area on Greenways Shack Rd, Nildottie 3km W of Nildottie. Turn off just N of Nildottie, follow road to river campsites. Ph: 08 8569 0100

210. Sunnydale Boat Ramp
Map Ref: MAP 1 C11 GPS: 34 41 08 S 139 36 50 E
Camp area 44km S of Blanchetown at end of Christians Rd, Sunnydale. 5 day limit. Ph: 08 8569 0100

211. Caurnamont Reserve - Riverland & Central Murray
Map Ref: MAP 1 C11 GPS: 34 51 21 S 139 36 50 E
Located at ferry crossing 29km NE of Mannum. Boat ramp access.

212. Purnong Riverside Reserve Camping area - Riverland & Central Murray
Map Ref: MAP 1 C11 GPS: 34 51 30 S 139 37 10 E
Located at Purnong ferry landing on Purnong Rd which is 38km E of Mannum. Ph: 08 8569 1303

213. Bakara bush camping - Riverland & Central Murray
Map Ref: MAP 1 C10 GPS: 34 30 11 S 139 55 07 E
Within the Bakara Conservation Park 32km E of Swan Reach access via the Swan Reach-Loxton Rd. Then turn in to Martin Rd. Ph: 08 8576 3690

214. Paruna Camping Park
Map Ref: MAP 1 E11 GPS: 34 43 11 S 140 43 44 E
Camp area 34km S of Loxton on cnr Railway Terrace & First St, Paruna. Honesty box and sign for key. Ph: 08 8587 3003

215. Billiatt Bush Camping - Riverland & Central Murray
Map Ref: MAP 1 D11 GPS: 35 01 23 S 140 29 28 E
Located in Billiatt Conservation Park 37km north of Lameroo. Access along the Lameroo-Alawoona Rd with numerous access tracks to bush camping areas. Self-sufficient campers. Ph: 08 8576 3400

216. Peebinga Bush Camping - Riverland & Central Murray
Map Ref: MAP 1 E11 GPS: 34 57 13 S 140 50 09 E
Located in Peebinga Conservation Park 65km south of Loxton or 31km north of Pinnaroo. From the Pinnaroo-Loxton Rd take the signposted road to Kringin 13. Follow this road west towards Kringin for 3km to crossroad. The road on the south leads to park. Contact ranger for directions to camping spots. Bring firewood. Ph: 08 8576 3400

217. Karte Bush Camping - Riverland & Central Murray
Map Ref: MAP 1 E11 GPS: 35 05 25 S 140 44 12 E
Karte Conservation Park is situated 26km north west of Pinnaroo or 5km south of Karte. Signposted access along Karte Rd. From Pinnaroo take signposted Homburg Terrace off the Mallee Hwy to signposted Foster Rd. Then follow to junction with signposted Karte Rd. Camping area is 250m off Karte Rd. Ph: 08 8580 1800

218. Rockleigh Bush Camp
Map Ref: MAP 1 B11 GPS: 35 01 06 S 139 05 48 E
Camp area 25km NE of Murray Bridge on South Eastern Fwy, N to Ferries McDonald & Schenscher Rds then W to Thile Rd then N to Peach Rd then N to 380 Critchley Rd, Rockleigh. Call ahead as gates locked. Ph: 0417 833 640

219. Chookarloo Campground
Map Ref: MAP 1 B12 GPS: 35 12 10 S 138 42 51 E
Camp area 5km SW of Meadows on Brookman Rd, Kuitpo in Kuitpo Forest Reserve. Permit from Info Centre form Apr-Nov. Ph: 08 8391 8800

220. Murray Bridge Showgrounds
Map Ref: MAP 1 C11 GPS: 35 06 49 S 139 18 13 E
Camp area 3km from Post Office at 113 Old Princes Hwy, Murray Bridge. Entry via gate 2, 7 day limit. Ph: 0400 880 578

221. Coles Crossing bush camping area - Close to Adelaide
Map Ref: MAP 1 B12 GPS: 35 19 42 S 138 42 30 E
Situated 17km NW of Mt Compass via Nagikta Rd onto Enterprise Rd then Mt Magnificent Rd to the Coles Crossing Rd. Campsite beside the Finniss River. Ph: 08 8552 3677

222. Eagle Dell
Map Ref: MAP 1 B12 GPS: 35 25 24 S 138 43 58 E
Camp area 13km N of Goolwa at 453 Frome Rd, Currency Creek. Pre-book as gates locked. GPS at turnoff. Closed in summer. Ph: 0439 832 804

223. Frank Potts Reserve - South East
Map Ref: MAP 1 B12 GPS: 35 18 01 S 139 02 28 E
Approx. 1km S of Langhorne Creek about 10 minutes from Strathalbyn on the Wellington Rd.

224. Rapid Bay Campground - Close to Adelaide
Map Ref: MAP 1 A12 GPS: 35 31 29 S 138 11 30 E
Along the foreshore at Rapid Bay along Essington Lewis Dve. Ph: 08 8598 3003

Picnic tables, a shelter, BBQ and Toilets.

Frank Potts Res No.223

Langhorne Creek SA

This free campsite is one of the prettiest and most comfortable you will find in a day's drive. Most of the large campsite area is level but the upper slope is not steep and most rigs can be easily levelled to account for the slope. The sloped area is only about a quarter of the total campsite so it isn't of concern unless the park is crowded.

The campsite has plenty of shade from the many trees, most of which are younger, more vigorous trees with lots of leafy canopy. Along the side furthest from the road there is the river that waters the vineyard on its further side. There is just enough seepage from this stream to give the campsite a nice green tinge even two thirds of the way through the summer.

The single toilet is maintained by the local council and the times we have visited it has been clean with good supplies of toilet paper and no smell. The several rubbish bins in the campsite are emptied regularly by the council thus preventing any smell from them.

Langhorne Creek is one of Australia's premium winery districts and when camped here you are surrounded by grape vines and wineries. The town of Langhorne Creek is just a few minutes walk away with one of the larger wineries, Bleasdale only a km in the other direction. The town is small but it does have a hotel and a few shops. The district population in 2011 was 1,198.

Langhorne Creek has a wine history dating back to 1850. Traditionally a red wine growing district widely known for its production of outstanding Cabernet Sauvignon and Shiraz grape varieties. These two red wine grape varieties constitute approximately 70% of the total vineyard plantings in the region. Over recent years considerable experimentation has occurred and a wide range of grape varieties is now grown. The vineyards harvest from early March to late April. At this time you may have some noise from harvest machinery and also encounter some itinerate workers camped at the reserve.

The town is on the banks of the Bremer River which flows into Lake Alexandrina. In winter, the river frequently floods across the vineyards, contributing to the terroir of the region.

Visitors can easily keep themselves busy for a couple of days visiting the many wineries' cellar door sales and sampling the wide varieties of wines available. When we camped overnight last time we bought a bottle of Frank Potts Sparkling Shiraz from the hotel for $25.00 and found it to be a truly good buy.

Each year Langhorne Creek holds its "Love Langhorne Creek" festival to give the opportunity for wine lovers to discover wines and experience a wine region with a difference.

The festival, which is held annually over the Valentine's weekend in February, is a favourite for those who love the Langhorne Creek Wine Region. There is even a chauffeur driven bus "The Creek Cruiser" to pick you up, take you to the cellar doors and drop you home again. Enquiries and bookings can be made on 08 8537 3316.

The Frank Potts Reserve is a great place to spend a day or two so please look after the campsite by doing the right thing at all times.

Just The Facts

Frank Potts Reserve

WHERE: Frank Potts Reserve can be found about 1km south of Langhorne Creek Township on the Wellington Road. There is a smaller campsite just across the bridge beside the Bremer River but this has no facilities. Langhorne Creek is about a 50 minute drive from Adelaide and 10 minutes from Strathalbyn.

FACILITIES: Toilet only but with disabled access.

RATES: Free.

PETS: Yes as long as they are on a lead. Takes rigs of all sizes.

Stringybark Campground No.225

Deep Creek Conservation Park SA

Glenys Gelzinis

Camping amongst the gumtrees.

Stringybark Campground is one of five campgrounds in Deep Creek Conservation Park, and is the pick of the bunch if you're looking for the luxury of flushing toilets and hot showers when you're camping. As its name suggests, this campground is surrounded by a Stringybark forest and is very shaded and sheltered from any wind.

All roads in this park are unsealed and easy for all vehicles to negotiate, but you will have more fun if you have a 4WD to discover some spectacular beaches and coastal scenery.

Deep Creek is at the southern tip of the Fleurieu Peninsula and only around 100 kilometres from Adelaide. The popularity of Deep Creek for caravan and camping enthusiasts is due to its huge amount of dense natural forest and the many Xanthorrhoea, or grass trees throughout the park. The bush is also thick with ferns and the environment is green and lush.

There is a lot of wildlife to find in the forest area and surrounding scrub including western grey kangaroos, echidnas, deer and a wide variety of birds. The kangaroos are regular visitors to the campgrounds and aren't too bothered by people sharing their environment.

The campsites in all of the campgrounds are numbered and have to be booked and paid for online before your visit. Mobile phone coverage is limited in most areas of the park. The campgrounds suit various set ups from tents to caravans and everything in between but three of the campgrounds, Cobbler Hill, Trigg and Stringybark, are more suited for caravans. When you book online you can select a campsite according to the number of people in your group and space needed.

From Stringybark Campground there are a few walking trails to take which vary in distance and the length of time it takes to complete them. An easy walk for the whole family is the forest circuit loop which takes you on a track through the forest over a slightly undulating track for around 2.6 kilometres and back to the campground. There is also a spring wildflower walk which takes around two and a half hours to complete the almost five kilometre walk.

Stringybark Campground has 16 numbered campsites, some of which can accommodate small groups, and there is plenty of space between sites. Each of the sites also has a fire pit to use with firewood that you bring in.

There are walking trails throughout the forest.

Just The Facts

Deep Creek Conservation Park

Where: Deep Creek Conservation Park is around 100 kilometres south of Adelaide on the Fleurieu Peninsula.

There are 5 campgrounds, 4 are drive-in and 1 is walk-in only.

Sites have to be booked and paid for online with National Parks and Wildlife Service SA and fees vary depending on which campground you stay in.

Stringybark sites start at $28.50 per night.

Stringybark Campground has flushing toilets and hot showers, fire pits and non-potable water available.

There is a couple of 4WD only tracks in the park which involve tackling steep and rocky terrain that lead to Boat Harbour Beach, and Blowhole Beach.

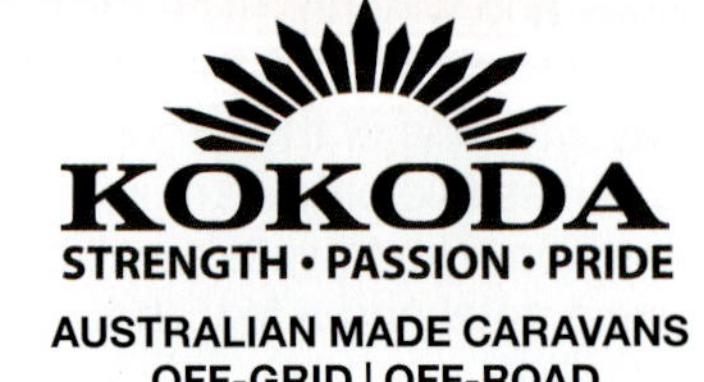

Free Campsites in South Australia

225. Stringybark Campground - Close to Adelaide
Map Ref: MAP 1 A12 GPS: 35 36 24 S 138 14 26 E
Within Deep Creek Conservation Park signposted access along Tapanappa Rd 9kms south west of Range Road and 1.4km east of Three Bridges Rd. Proceed 400m to camping area. Bring water & firewood. Ph: 08 8598 0263

226. Cobbler Hill Campground - Close to Adelaide
Map Ref: MAP 1 A12 GPS: 35 38 49 S 138 10 27 E
Within the Deep Creek Conservation Park. Access via Blowhole Creek Rd off Tent Rock Rd. Ph: 08 8598 0263

227. Trig Campground - Close to Adelaide
Map Ref: MAP 1 A12 GPS: 35 38 51 S 138 12 57 E
Within the Deep Creek Conservation Park, signposted access along Tent Rock Rd 4km S of its junction with Three Bridges Rd. Ph: 08 8598 0263

228. Waitpinga Campground - Close to Adelaide
Map Ref: MAP 1 A12 GPS: 35 37 41 S 138 29 59 E
Within the Newland Head Conservation Park 17km SE of Victor Harbour. Access via Waitpinga Rd. Ph: 08 8552 3677

229. Narrung Jetty Reserve Camping Area - South East
Map Ref: MAP 1 B12 GPS: 35 30 50 S 139 11 10 E
Located at ferry crossing 2km west Narrun Village from Meningie take the signposted Narrung Rd for 40km. Overlooking the water. Ph: 08 8575 1008

230. Baan Hill - South East
Map Ref: MAP 1 D12 GPS: 35 30 10 S 140 26 20 E
Signposted access on Baan Hill Rd 23km S of Lameroo. Southern Mallee District Council 08 8576 3002

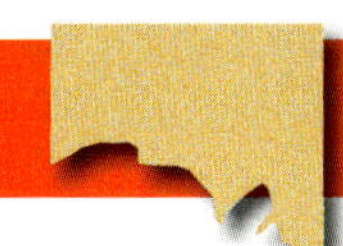

Free Campsites in South Australia Index

Free Campsites in South Australia Index

South Australia Map

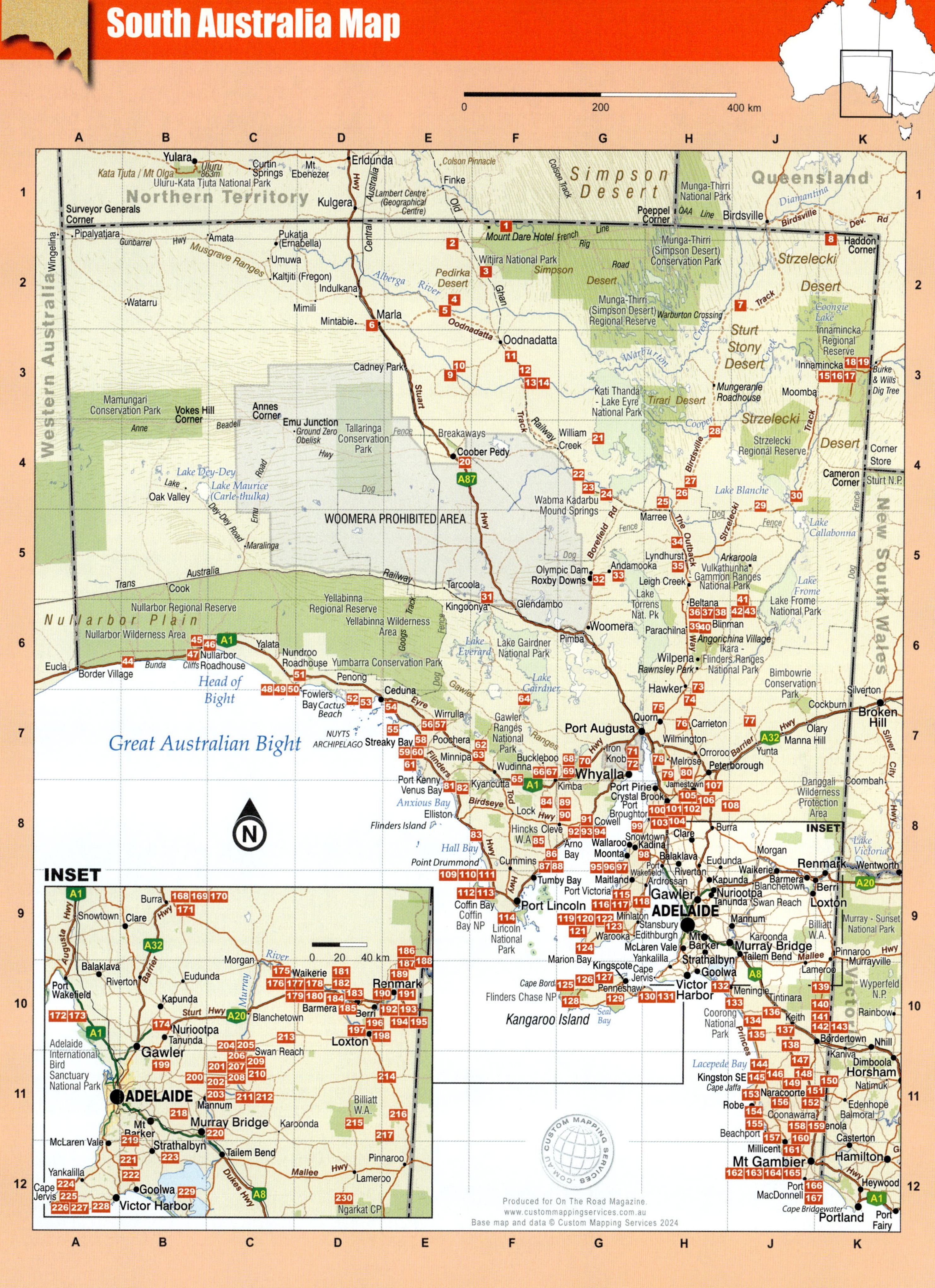

Northern Territory

Free Camps Guide – Useful Resources & Contacts – NT

Parks & Wildlife Commission
Darwin Phn: (08) 8999 4555
Katherine Phn: (08) 8973 8888
Alice Springs Phn: (08) 8951 8250
Permits office, Palmerston
Phn: (08) 8999 4814
Web: www.nt.gov.au/nreta/parks

Department of Resources-
Primary Industry, Fisheries and Resources
Phn: (08) 8999 2144
Web: www.nt.gov.au/d/Fisheries

Department of Resources
Minerals & Energy
Fossicking enquiries
Phn: (08) 8999 5322

Bushfires NT
Phn: (08) 8922 0844
Web: www.nt.gov.au/d/Minerals_Energy

AANT
Roadside assistance
Phn: 131 111
Web: www.aant.com.au

Department of Construction and Infrastructure – Road Report
Phn: 1800 246 199
Web: www.ntlis.nt.gov.au/roadreport

Northern Land Council
Phn: (08) 8920 6211
Web: www.clc.org.au

Central Land Council
Phn: (08) 8951 6211
Web: www.clc.org.au

Tourism NT
Phn: (08) 136 768
Web: www.travelnt.com

Visitor Information Centres
Tourism Top End
Phn: 1300 138 886
Web: www.tourismtopend.com.au

Katherine Region Tourism, Visitor Information Centre
Phn: 1800 653 142
Web: www.visitkatherine.com.au

Central Australia Tourism, Visitor Information Centre
Phn: 1800 645 199
Web: www.centralaustraliatourism.com.au

Bureau of Meteorology
Phn: 1900 926 102
Web: www.bom.gov.au

Royal Flying Doctors Service
NT After Hours Emergency Calls
Phn: (08) 8952 5733

Australian National 4WD Radio Network
Phn: (08) 8287 6222
Web: www.vks737.on.net

Free Campsites in Northern Territory

1. Leaders Creek Fishing Base camping area - Close to Darwin
Map Ref: D2 GPS: 12 13 26 S 131 05 33 E
Signposted access along Gunn Point Road, 43km N of Howard Springs. Then Drive in NE direction for 6.6km to camping area entrance and the boat ramp. Ph: 08 8983 5009

2. Finniss River Crossing - Close to Darwin
Map Ref: C2 GPS: 12 58 02 S 130 45 35 E
Camp Spot 53kms SW Berry Springs or 95kms NW Batchelor via Litchfield Park Rd. 4WD recommended.

3. Litchfield Park Road Camp Spot - Close to Darwin
Map Ref: C2 GPS: 13 00 09 S 130 44 34 E
58kms SW Berry Springs or 92kms NW of Batchelor via Litchfield Park Rd. 4WD recommended.

4. Wangi Falls camping area - Close to Darwin
Map Ref: C2 GPS: 13 09 44 S 130 40 50 E
Signposted access off Litchfield Park Road, 66km W of Batchelor within the Litchfield NP. Over 30 campsites. Ph: 08 8976 0282

5. Buley Rockhole camping area - Close to Darwin
Map Ref: C2 GPS: 13 06 46 S 130 47 11 E
Within Litchfield NP 42kms SW of Batchelor. Twelve numbered campsites, well shaded and very popular. Ph: 08 8976 0282

6. Shady Camp camping area - Close to Darwin
Map Ref: D2 GPS: 12 28 58 S 131 43 31 E
Off the Arnhem Hwy in to Point Stuart Rd and then Harold Knowles Rd. Within the Mary River NP. Ph: 08 8999 4555

7. Hardies Lagoon bush camping area Close to Darwin
Map Ref: D2 GPS: 12 47 02 S 131 36 37 E
Large lagoon on western bank of Mary River. Access is along Arnhem Hwy 6km E of Corroboree Park Tavern and Roadhouse.Then drive north eat for 9km to entrance grid fenced camping area. Camp away from water. Ph: 1800 246 199

8. Four Mile Hole camping area - Kakadu Region
Map Ref: E2 GPS: 12 34 17 S 132 13 10 E
Along Arnhem Hwy 2km E of Kakadu NP Visitor Display. From highway drive N for 8km to signposted access track to Two Mile Hole. Keep right take signposted turn to Four Mile for 26km then take signposted turn for 4km to site. Ph: 08 8938 1120

9. Two Mile Hole Camping Area - Kakadu Region
Map Ref: D2 GPS: 12 41 30 S 132 09 04 E
Follow the sign from Arnhem Hwy, 55km E of Bark Hut, for 12km. Ph: 08 8938 1120

10. Alligator Billabong camping area - Kakadu Region
Map Ref: E2 GPS: 12 52 10 S 132 26 17 E
Reached via the track to Red Lily Billabong by 4WD, this campsite is 26km S of the Arnhem Hwy. Ph: 08 8938 1120

11. Bucket Billabong camping area - Kakadu Region
Map Ref: E2 GPS: 12 51 16 S 132 27 25 E
2km past Red Lily Billabong camping area. 4wd Access only. Ph: 08 8938 1120

12. Red Lily Billabong - Kakadu Region
Map Ref: E2 GPS: 12 51 06 S 132 29 40 E
Dispersed camping 60kms SW Jabiru or 160kms E Humpty Doo. S off Arnhem Hwy 2km W of Aurora Kakadu Resort onto bush track for 18kms. Ph: 08 8938 1120

13. Black Jungle Springs camping area - Kakadu Region
Map Ref: E2 GPS: 13 02 53 S 132 09 52 E
4WD ACCESS ONLY. On the Old Jim Jim Road, which links the Arnhem Hwy to the Kakadu Hwy, 18km E of Bark Hut Inn. Composting Toilets only. Ph: 08 8938 1120

14. Rocky Bottom Creek Crossing camping area - Arnhem Land
Map Ref: G2 GPS: 12 54 40 S 135 17 38 E
On the N Side of the road, on the east side of the crossing, this small site with no facilities is on the Central Arnhem Rd, 60km N of the Ramingining Rd Junction. Ph: 08 8971 9899

15. Flat Rock Creek Crossing camping Area - Arnhem Land
Map Ref: G2 GPS: 12 43 22 S 135 35 30 E
Small site no facilities on the Central Arnhem Rd, 108km N of the Ramingining Rd Junction. It is to the east of the road, on the south side of the creek crossing. Ph: 08 8971 9899

16. Giddy River Crossing - Arnhem Land
Map Ref: H2 GPS: 12 21 31 S 136 42 24 E
River crossing signposted along Central Arnhem Rd 46km S of Nhulunbuy. Suitable for overnight. Ph: 08 8971 9899

Free Campsites in Northern Territory

17. Burrell Creek Camp Spot - Kakadu Region
Map Ref: D3 GPS: 13 26 32 S 131 10 04 E
Camp spot 27kms S of Adelaide River or 69kms NW of Emerald Springs Roadhouse. Turn W off Stuart Hwy on Dorat Rd.

18. Adelaide River Crossing Camp Spot - Kakadu Region
Map Ref: D3 GPS: 13 28 59 S 131 05 52 E
31kms SE of Adelaide River or 73kms NW of Emerald Springs Roadhouse. Turn W off Stuart Hwy on Dorat Rd then W into Saly River Rd for 10kms.

19. Douglas Hot Springs camping area - Kakadu Region
Map Ref: D3 GPS: 13 45 53 S 131 26 21 E
Access via Oolloo Road, which is accessed off the Scenic Route (Old Stuart Hwy). Very large camping area with some shaded sites. Ph: 08 8976 0282

20. Daly River Esplanade bush camping area - Kakadu Region
Map Ref: D3 GPS: 14 00 01 S 131 14 01 E
Signposted access on Oolloo Road, 28.8km SW of Douglas Daly Tourist Park. Then in 900m to the locked gate, track leads 250m to first campsite. Bookings required. Phone prior for refundable deposit for key. Ph: 08 8976 0282

21. Oolloo Crossing - Katherine Region
Map Ref: D3 GPS: 14 04 10 S 131 15 05 E
Camp sites along the banks of the Daly River 37km S of Douglas Daly Tourist Park on Oolloo Rd. Dry weather only Ph: 08 8976 0282

22. Umbrawarra Gorge camping area - Katherine Region
Map Ref: D3 GPS: 13 57 56 S 131 41 52 E
Access off Stuart Hwy 3km S of Pine Creek within the Umbrawarra Gorge NP. Small, camping area located beside the road which can get dusty. Ph: 08 8976 0282

23. Leliyn (Edith Falls) Camping Ground - Katherine Region
Map Ref: E3 GPS: 14 10 48 S 132 11 17 E
Signposted access along the Stuart Hwy 42km NW of Katherine. Proceed 20km to camping area. Bring firewood. Ph: 08 8972 1886

24. Lorrungurl Campground - Katherine Region
Map Ref: D4 GPS: 14 45 29 S 131 35 46 E
Signposted along the Victoria Hwy 87.5kms west of Stuart Hwy at Katherine. Proceed 46km to campground. Bring firewood. Ph: 08 8973 8888

25. Flora River National Park - Katherine Region
Map Ref: D4 GPS: 14 45 28 S 131 35 43 E
Follow the Victoria Hwy W of Katherine for 86km,take signposted turn-off and continue N for 36km on unsealed access rd. Ph: 08 8973 8888

26. Gurrandalng campground - Timber Creek
Map Ref: B5 GPS: 15 52 31 S 129 03 05 E
Within the Keep River NP. Signposted access along the park entrance road, 15km N of the Victoria Hwy. Ph: 08 9167 8827

27. Jarnem campground - Timber Creek
Map Ref: B4 GPS: 15 45 44 S 129 05 57 E
Signposted access along the park entrance road, 16km N of Gurrandalng access road, and 31km N of the Hwy within the Keep River NP. Ph: 08 9167 8827

28. Big Horse Creek campground - Timber Creek
Map Ref: C4 GPS: 15 36 44 S 130 24 09 E
Signposted access along Victoria Hwy, 11km W of Timber Creek Roadhouse within the Gregory NP. Camping area set above the Victoria River. Ph: 08 8975 0888

29. Escarpment Lookout - Timber Creek
Map Ref: C4 GPS: 15 38 30 S 130 27 10 E
Located in Gregory NP. Signposted access along Broadarrow Track 53km S of East Baines CA. Dry weather only Ph: 08 8975 0888

30. Victoria River Roadhouse - Timber Creek
Map Ref: D4 GPS: 15 36 57 S 131 07 38 E
Located above the Victoria River along the Victoria Hwy 92km E of Timber Creek. Ph: 08 8975 0744

31. Sullivan Creek campground - Timber Creek
Map Ref: D4 GPS: 15 35 13 S 131 16 30 E
Located in Gregory NP. Signposted access along Victoria Hwy, 1.5km E of the Victoria River Roadhouse. Ph: 08 8975 0888

32. Jalmurark Campground - Katherine Region
Map Ref: E4 GPS: 14 57 18 S 133 13 09 E
From the Stuart Hwy take the signposted Homestead Road which is 2km S of Mataranka. Continue to John Hauser Dve for further 13km to large camping area with some well shaded sites. Ph: 08 8975 4560

Flora River Nature Park No 25

122kms west of Katherine

Catherine Lawson & David Bristow

Walking along the river you discover some beautiful places to relax.

Attracting anglers and paddlers and providing generously for campers, Flora River Nature Park protects a 25km-long stretch of the spring-fed Flora River, along with its surrounding floodplain and savannah woodland. With walking trails, a boat ramp for canoes and travel-sized tinnies, and the opportunity to spot crocs, birdlife and catch barramundi, this destination could occupy adventurers for days.

This excellent Top End camp is found 122km southwest of Katherine, 36km off the Victoria Highway at the end of a gravel track that conventional vehicles can access without drama in the dry season. The spacious Djarrung Campground provides shady unpowered sites with picnic tables and fire pits, and easy access to a central amenities block where you can indulge in a hot shower and collect drinking water.

From the camp, short walking trails lead to Djarrung and Kathleen Falls, two dynamic spots where the Flora River is channeled over limestone tufa dams that span the river, sending the water tumbling into swirling, jade-coloured spas. Feeding on the cool mist, pandanus and paperbark trees stretch their limbs out over the stream that ebbs away past freshwater crocodiles hunting barramundi in impossibly translucent pools.

A 3km-long stretch of the Flora River is reserved for powerboats and fishing, while paddlers can tackle a daylong adventure downstream, portaging around three areas to protect the fragile tufa dams. The Northern Territory's usual fishing bag limits apply, but only line fishing with lures is permitted in the Flora River to prevent the capture of turtles, especially the rare pig-nosed turtle, found in only a few locations across the NT.

Camping under the stars.

Paddling up the Flora River.

Free Campsites in Northern Territory

33. WW11 Gorrie Airfield - Katherine Region
Map Ref: E4 GPS: 15 29 25 S 133 11 41 E
Camp spot at Old Airfield. Turn off Hwy 66kms S of Mataranka onto signposted track. Go for 1km, turn R at Y intersection & then R again where hubcap on tree, follow to runway. GPS at entrance. Day use.

34. Tomato Island campground - The Gulf
Map Ref: F4 GPS: 14 44 46 S 134 41 28 E
Signposted access just off the road along the Savannah Way 44km E of the turn off to Roper Bar. Located in Limmen NP. Very popular site. Ph: 08 8975 9940

35. Yurrlmungji (Bullshark) Campground - The Gulf
Map Ref: G4 GPS: 14 45 36 S 134 47 13 E
Camp area 57kms E of Roper Bar or 281kms N of Cape Crawford Ph: 08 8975 9940

36. Towns River Crossing campground - The Gulf
Map Ref: G4 GPS: 15 02 06 S 135 13 10 E
From Mataranka head E on the Roper Hwy for 173km to Roper Bar. From here backtrack to the hwy and turn left towards Limmen NP and Towns River camp for 117km to SE. Ph: 08 8975 9940

37. Cox River - The Gulf
Map Ref: G4 GPS: 15 19 19 S 135 20 42 E
Camping spot 155km SE of Roper Bar.

38. Limmen River Fishing camp - The Gulf
Map Ref: G4 GPS: 15 15 55 S 135 30 05 E
Signposted access along Nathan River Road/Savannah Way 200m N of the causeway crossing of the Cox River within the Limmen NP. Ph: 08 8975 9940

39. Limmen Crossing campground - The Gulf
Map Ref: G4 GPS: 15 28 33 S 135 24 24 E
Within the Limmen NP. Signposted access along the Savannah Way, 13km S of the access road to Limmen River Fishing Camp. 19km N of Butterfly Springs. Ph: 08 8975 9940

40. Butterfly Springs - The Gulf
Map Ref: G4 GPS: 15 37 34 S 135 27 32 E
From Mataranka take the Roper Hwy to Roper Bar then a further 180kms to Butterfly Springs. Dry weather only. Ph: 08 8975 9940

41. Southern Lost City - The Gulf
Map Ref: G4 GPS: 15 48 33 S 135 27 21 E
Turn W off Carpentaria Hwy 26km S of Borroloola and drive 50km before turning N. Continue for 67kms to Southern Lost City turn-off then 4km to camp. Ph: 08 8975 9940

42. Lorella Springs - The Gulf
Map Ref: G4 GPS: 15 43 15 S 135 38 26 E
Camping are 265 SE of Roper Bar. Turn E off The Great Top Rd and travel 3okm to entrance. Ph: 08 8975 9917

43. Negri River Camp Spot - Katherine Region
Map Ref: B5 GPS: 17 04 35 S 129 00 10 E
Near NT/WA border 300kms SW Timber Creek via Buntine Hwy. S into Duncan Rd from Victoria Hwy, travel for 133kms. 4WD recommended.

44. Drovers Rest - Timber Creek
Map Ref: C5 GPS: 15 53 30 S 130 12 10 E
Situated in Gregory NP. Signposted access 40km along the Bullita Stock Route. Then drive west 11km to the camping area above Barrabarrac Creek. Dry weather only Ph: 08 8975 0888

45. Baines Campsite - Timber Creek
Map Ref: C5 GPS: 15 58 30 S 130 17 59 E
Located in Gregory NP. Campground is 450m N of the East Baines river crossing on the Bullita Stock Route. Dry weather only Ph: 08 8975 0888

46. Spring Creek Yard - Timber Creek
Map Ref: C5 GPS: 16 05 12 S 130 20 40 E
Signposted access 13km along the Bullita Stock Route in Gregory NP. Great site beside waterhole. Dry weather only Ph: 08 8975 0888

47. Bullita Homestead campground - Timber Creek
Map Ref: C5 GPS: 16 06 47 S 130 25 25 E
Located 100m W of the Gregory NP access road, along the Bullita Stock Route. Gregory NP access road is signposted along Victoria Hwy 10km SE of Timber Creek. Ph: 08 8975 0888

48. Fig Tree Yard - Timber Creek
Map Ref: C5 GPS: 16 14 38 S 130 25 38 E
Signposted access along Humbert Track, 20km from the Gregory NP access road and the 4WD track information board and visitor book. Drive in a NE direction for 1.2km to Fig Tree Creek. Dry weather only Ph: 08 8975 0888

Featured Campsite

Brought to you by

Southern Lost City

No.41

Limmen National Park, NT

148km northwest of Borroloola

Catherine Lawson and David Bristow

The amazing Southern Lost City rises out of the spinifex plains.

Appearing suddenly on this remote national park's southern outskirts, a dramatic sandstone escarpment carved with towering pillars tempts walkers to lose themselves deep inside the Southern Lost City. Following a meandering track that disappears into slender rock chasms, walkers squeeze between rounded domes and crane their necks skyward at the buttresses that glow golden, tangerine and fiery red at sunrise and sunset.

Above it all atop a ridge peppered with the hot pink blooms of turkey bushes and flowering woollybutt trees, viewpoints on the edge of a deep, wide valley provide expansive views of the rocky escarpments beyond. To the west as the crow flies, little-visited Nathan (Western) Lost City lures even more determined travellers along a rugged 28km-long 4WD track to discover Aboriginal rock art and excellent vistas over the O'Keefe Valley from the top of the range.

Following finches back down onto the Southern Lost City's spinifex flats, the hour-long walking trail returns to a spacious campground that provides big sites with unbeatable views and easy access into the Lost City at dusk and dawn when it glows in true splendour. The campsites don't provide much middle-of-the-day shade, but if you arrive at day's end in time to explore at sunset, this won't be a problem. Alternatively, wind out or string up a good awning and spend time in search of the short-eared rock-wallabies that take refuge from the heat on rock ledges.

Rough corrugations and flooded causeways make the route a challenge.

Minimal overnight camping fees of $3.30/adult, $1.65/child (aged 5-15 years) or $7.70/family have now been introduced at four bush camps in Limmen National Park – Southern Lost City, Butterfly Falls, Towns River and Limmen River campgrounds. The rates at the very popular Munbililla (Tomato Island) Campground on the Roper River are higher due to the provision of new facilities that include hot showers ($10/person/night or $20/family).

The basic facilities at Southern Lost City include wheelchair-accessible toilets, picnic tables and fireplaces, and there are no time limits on your visit. You'll need to bring your own drinking water and take your rubbish away with you, but you can use generators.

After a long walk through the Lost City, walkers keen to cool off might gravitate 25km north to the shady waterhole beneath Butterfly Falls. Nestled in a sheer rocky amphitheatre, this tranquil oasis is Limmen's only safe swimming hole and provides a campground that might very well be the next stop on your adventure through the national park. Other highlights include the enormous Lomarieum Lagoon behind St Vidgeon Ruins for its incredible birdlife, and Munbililla (Tomato Island) where you can launch a boat and wrangle barramundi on the Roper River.

Declared a national park in July 2012 and protecting an amazing 935,400 hectares of woodlands, wetlands and deep, emerald rivers, Limmen National Park provides an ideal escape for off-road ready travellers happy to swap creature comforts for idyllic waterfront camps and superb fishing and birdwatching opportunities.

If you go, time your trip for the winter dry season and be aware that Limmen Bight Fishing Camp provides the only fuel and basic supplies on the 338km stretch between Roper Bar and Cape Crawford. Freshwater and estuarine crocodiles inhabit Limmen National Park's waterways so avoid swimming except at Butterfly Falls.

Just The Facts

Southern Lost City

Getting there: Turn west off the Carpentaria Highway 26km south of Borroloola and drive 50km before turning north. Continue for 67km to the Southern Lost City turnoff and another 4km to camp. Rough, corrugated roads and flooded causeways make this route suitable for 4WD vehicles and sturdy off-road camper trailers and caravans. It may become impassable anytime during the November to March wet season.

Facilities: Wheelchair-accessible toilets, picnic tables and fire pits.

Rates: $3.30/adult, $1.65/child (aged 5-15 years) or $7.70/family.

Wheelchair Access: To toilets

Pets: No

Contact: Phone the Limmen Ranger Station on (08) 8975 9940 or head to www.parksandwildlife.nt.gov.au. Get an NT road report at www.ntlis.nt.gov.au (phone 1800 246 199).

Free Campsites in Northern Territory

49. Top Humbert Yard - Timber Creek
Map Ref: C5 GPS: 16 26 40 S 130 27 50 E
Located in Gregory NP. Signposted access along Humbert Track 28km south of the signposted access to Fig Tree Yard, just S of the Humbert River crossing. Dry weather only Ph: 08 8975 0888

50. East Baines camping area - Timber Creek
Map Ref: C5 GPS: 16 38 17 S 130 27 02 E
This site, on the Broadarrow track is 30km W of Camel Point on the East Baines River. 4WD access only. Ph: 08 8975 0888

51. Camel Point - Timber Creek
Map Ref: C5 GPS: 16 38 29 S 130 27 04 E
Located in Gregory NP. Signposted access along Broadarrow Track 28km W of Wickham Track. Dry weather only Ph: 08 8975 0888

52. Depot Creek - Timber Creek
Map Ref: C5 GPS: 16 38 25 S 130 27 10 E
Located in Gregory NP. About 45km from the Buntine Hwy. Through private property. Dry weather only Ph: 08 8975 0888

53. Fish Hole Yard - Timber Creek
Map Ref: C5 GPS: 16 42 50 S 130 40 10 E
Camp area on the Wickham River on private property just outside Gregory NP. Signpost access along Gibbie Track. Dry weather only Ph: 08 8975 0888

54. Paperbark Yard - Timber Creek
Map Ref: C5 GPS: 16 52 10 S 130 36 40 E
Located in Gregory NP. Signposted access along Gibbie Track 20km S of the junction of Gibbie and Wickham track. Dry weather only Ph: 08 8975 0888

55. Jasper Gorge camping area - Timber Creek
Map Ref: C5 GPS: 16 01 52 S 130 48 07 E
Signposted access 55km along the Buchanan Hwy. From the Victoria Hwy take the signposted Buchanan Hwy which is 27km E of Timber Creek within the Gregory NP. Ph: 08 8975 0888

56. Charlies Crossing - Katherine Region
Map Ref: D5 GPS: 16 01 51 S 130 48 10 E
Camping site 56km S of Victoria Hwy on Buchanan Hwy. Dirt road.

57. Dashwood Crossing East - Katherine Region
Map Ref: D5 GPS: 16 20 01 S 131 06 52 E
Camp spot on Buchanan Hwy 86kms NW of Top Springs. Tracks on East side of river. Small vehicles. 4WD only.

58. Dashwood Crossing West - Katherine Region
Map Ref: D5 GPS: 16 20 02 S 131 06 45 E
Camp spot on Buchanan Hwy 85kms NW of Top Springs. 4WD only.

59. Illawarra Creek - Katherine Region
Map Ref: D5 GPS: 16 35 19 S 131 51 10 E
Camp spot 200 W of Dunmara on Buchanan Hwy. 7kms E of Top Springs on both sides of road and E side of creek.

60. Hiway Inn Roadhouse camping area - Tennant Creek
Map Ref: E5 GPS: 16 18 26 S 133 23 09 E
Roadhouse and caravan park located along the Stuart Hwy at the junction with Carpentaria Hwy. 272km S of Katherine. Ph: 08 8975 9925

61. Dunmarra Wayside Inn camping area - Dunmarra - Tennant Creek
Map Ref: F5 GPS: 16 40 47 S 133 24 44 E
Located on the Stuart Hwy, 8km S of the Buchanan Hwy and 350km N of Tennant Creek. Ph: 08 8975 9922

62. Little River - The Gulf
Map Ref: G5 GPS: 16 42 10 S 135 38 14 E
259kms E of Daly Waters and 120kms SW of Borroloola on the Carpentaria Hwy. Ph: 0400 156 685

63. Heartbreak Hotel Camping Area - The Gulf
Map Ref: G5 GPS: 16 41 01 S 135 43 21 E
Located in the Cape Crawford area at the junction of the Carpentaria and Tablelands Hwy 270km east of the Stuart Hwy. Boil the water or treat first. Ph: 08 8975 9928

64. Borroloola Boat & Fishing Club Camping Area - The Gulf
Map Ref: H5 GPS: 15 56 07 S 136 28 43 E
King Ash Bay is 42km north east of Borroloola beside the McArthur River. Signposted access along the road to Bing Bong Station 21km north east of Borroloola. Bring water & firewood. Ph: 08 8975 9800

Little River Rest Area No.62

Carpentaria Hwy, NT

10km west of Cape Crawford

Catherine Lawson & David Bristow

Travellers on the NT's Carpentaria Highway tend to be a hardy, self-sufficient bunch, bound for fishing adventures in Borroloola or an off-road journey across the Gulf on the Savannah Way.

And when you've got everything you need on board and can do without creature comforts, any scenic spot becomes the perfect place to camp.

Little River Rest Area is just that: a basic bush camp stretched along the water's edge providing nothing more than shady sites and great views as the sun sets west, silhouetting trees across the plains.

Waterbirds and campers congregate here as the day cools down, the wildlife in fortunately far greater numbers.

On our recent wintertime visit we shared the camp with just two other vehicles: a handful of backpackers in a campervan and a couple in a old motorhome who made themselves forever memorable because they quarrelled their way through happy hour before the husband peeled off his clothes and proceeded to strut naked around camp.

Kicking back with ice-cold supplies picked up at Cape Crawford's Heartbreak Hotel, 10km away, the spectacle became just another one of those weird things you experience living life on the road.

Given that it sells the only beer and hot food for 380km, the Heartbreak Hotel is a difficult spot to pass by. And if you're not tackling an off-road adventure into Limmen National Park's lost cities, a helicopter operation at Cape Crawford will fly you over them.

But you don't have to spend a cent to experience the region's spectacular sandstone wilderness in miniature at Caranbirini Conservation Reserve, about 65km east of Little River.

Located right on the Carpentaria Highway, Caranbirini protects fascinating sandstone spires resembling organ pipes that tower over the spinifex and woodland plains, and a waterhole that sustains a host of bird species year-round.

The area is spectacular.

Hidden inside the park's hide we spotted brolgas, green pygmy geese and pacific black ducks, and once we hit the easy Barrawulla Walk trail, flocks of tiny double-barred finches that rose up from the grasslands.

This short walk (2km/1hr return) leads past pillars of purple-hued sandstone, through narrow rock alleyways and shady rocky tunnels where we sat in silence watching butterflies flit about and fig trees twisting up towards the light.

In the open spaces between the fat rock buttresses burning bright orange in the midday sun, gum trees and palms stretch out in the sunshine, clumps of spinifex sprouting at their feet.

Time spent on the longer Jagududgu Walk that loops for 5km through the park might improve your chances of spotting rare Carpentarian grasswrens or the tiny Borroloola gecko, found only in this amazing Gulf region.

Just The Facts

Little River Rest

Getting there: You'll find Little River Rest Area 259km east of Daly Waters and 120km southwest of Borroloola on the sealed Carpentaria Highway.

Facilities: Bins.

Wheelchair Access: N/A.

Rates: Free.

Pets: Yes.

Contact: Little River Rest Area is a recommended stop on the Savannah Way (www.savannahway.com.au). For more information on Caranbirini Conservation Reserve head to www.nt.gov.au/nreta/parks or phone (08) 8975 8792.

Free Campsites in Northern Territory

65. Wearyan River - The Gulf
Map Ref: H5 GPS: 16 10 01 S 136 45 22 E
Camp area 55kms SE of Borroloola or 223km NW of Wollogorang. Tracks along both sides of river.

66. Foelschhe River Crossing Camp Spot - The Gulf
Map Ref: H5 GPS: 16 12 39 S 136 53 01 E
Camp spot 70kms E of Borroloola on Carpentaria Hwy on both sides of hwy on E side of River. 4WD recommended.

67. Calvert River - The Gulf
Map Ref: H5 GPS: 16 56 02 S 137 21 28 E
On the Savannah Way 175kms E of Borroloola.

68. Robinson River Crossing - The Gulf
Map Ref: J5 GPS: 16 56 01 S 137 21 29 E
Camp spot 105km Se of Borroloola. Track on NW side of river.

69. Banka Banka Station Camping Area - Tennant Creek
Map Ref: F7 GPS: 18 47 32 S 134 01 05 E
Signposted access on the Stuart Hwy 100km north of Tennant Creek. Ph: 08 8964 4511

70. Warrego Gold - Tennant Creek
Map Ref: F7 GPS: 19 19 32 S 133 51 55 E
Camp spot 70kms NW of Tennant Creek via Stuart Hwy 1.5km N to Warrego Rd turnoff. Turn L along bitumen rd for 45.5kms to turnoff on right. Take track N for 14km to old mine. Self contained only.

71. The Pebbles - Tennant Creek
Map Ref: F7 GPS: 19 31 56 S 134 10 08 E
Signposted off the Stuart Hwy 16kms N of Tennant Creek. Ph: 1800 500 879

72. Barkly Homestead camping area - Tennant Creek
Map Ref: G7 GPS: 19 42 38 S 135 49 39 E
Signposted access along the Barkly Hwy 187km E of the Stuart Hwy. Ph: 08 8964 4549

73. Wauchope Hotel camping area - Tennant Creek
Map Ref: F8 GPS: 20 38 26 S 134 13 20 E
Located on the Stuart Hwy 114km S of Tennant Creek at Wauchope. Ph: 08 8964 1963

74. Devils Marbles camping area - Tennant Creek
Map Ref: F8 GPS: 20 34 05 S 134 15 51 E
Camp area 104km S of Tennant Creek signposted off the Stuart Hwy. Ph: 08 8962 4599

75. Whistleduck Creek camping area - Tennant Creek
Map Ref: F8 GPS: 20 38 11 S 134 46 46 E
Camp area 87km S of Tennant Creek via Kurundi Rd. Ph: 08 8962 4599

76. Old Police Station Waterhole - Tennant Creek
Map Ref: G8 GPS: 20 45 15 S 135 11 12 E
Camp area 87km S of Tennant Creek. Turn E onto Kurundi Rd for 119km then turn S for 43km. Dir rd 4WD essential. Ph: 08 8962 4599

77. Frew River Camping Area - The Gulf
Map Ref: G8 GPS: 20 45 45 S 135 11 36 E
Located in the Davenport Ranges NP and signposted off the Stuart Hwy. Take the signposted Old Police Station Waterhole turnoff. Follow access road to park 44.3km north of Barrow Creek. Unsealed road to 74km to road junction. Turn left proceeding north east to park then 70km to Frew River 4WD Loop. Campsites beside waterhole. Bring water & firewood. Ph: 08 8962 4599

78. Renehans Bore bush camp - Tennant Creek
Map Ref: D9 GPS: 21 16 39 S 130 50 58 E
Along the Tanami Rd 160km NW of Yuendumu turn-off and 100 s of the Granites Gold Mine. Ph: 1800 246 199

79. Barrow Creek WW11 Stagins Area - Tennant Creek
Map Ref: F9 GPS: 21 18 07 S 134 03 07 E
Camp spot 28km N of Barrow Creek. Signposted 1km off Hwy. GPS at entrance.

80. Annas Reservoir - Alice Springs Region
Map Ref: E10 GPS: 22 41 40 S 133 22 25 E
Located 30km W of Stuart Hwy in Annas Reservoir Conservation Reserve. Access track is 5km S of Aileron through private property, permission required from Aileron Station (08 8956 9706) Ph: 08 8951 8250

The Pebbles No. 71

Stuart Highway, NT

16km north of Tennant Creek
Catherine Lawson & David Bristow

Informal trails lead around the Pebbles.

When it comes to scenic NT destinations, the mini-sized Pebbles prove that size is not always everything. A scenic sight worthy of the short detour off the Stuart Highway, the Pebbles provides a spacious camping area that is perfect for oversized rigs and travellers keen to stretch out and enjoy some outback solitude.

Widely compared with the more famous Devils Marbles to the south, the Pebbles are great boulders in miniature form (interestingly, Uluru means great pebble). For those tackling the remote run through the Red Centre, the Pebbles makes an excellent overnight stop and you'll find it 16km north of Tennant Creek.

The campground facilities are limited to barbecues, picnic shelter and toilet, but that won't bother the self-sufficient travellers who arrive in time to watch the setting sun ignite the red rocks in hues of gold and fiery crimson.

Informal trails lead around the great piles of glinting orbs, some seemingly running away across the open spinifex plains.

Walking is best reserved for the cooler hours of the day when the emus are more active, too. Known as "Kunjarra", the Pebbles are significant to the local Warumungu women as a dancing place for munga munga (women's corroboree), a vital expression of traditional indigenous culture.

A few minutes' drive away, Tennant Creek provides supplies, creature comforts and a host of tourist spots, including the lovely Mary Ann Dam. This is a great place to picnic, watch the waterbirds and take a dip when the water level is high, and the great day-use facilities include picnic shelters, barbecues, toilets and even hot water showers.

The largest town between Katherine and Alice Springs, historic Tennant Creek is a bit of a rough diamond but has plenty to interest travellers with time enough to explore.

The creek itself was discovered and named by explorer John McDouall Stuart in 1860, and the town sprung up later around its Overland Telegraph repeater station, preserved as an historical reserve for selfguided tours 11km north of town.

The site of Australia's last great gold rush and third richest goldfield, Tennant Creek has three local mines to tour and an interpretive tourism site – the Battery Hill Mining Centre.

The Pebbles is a particularly hot destination to visit during summer, but from April to October the temperatures become bearable and the nights comfortably chilly. Don't be deterred by the six kilometres of unsealed track that lead into the Pebbles, as the road is easily navigated by all kinds of rigs with care.

Many travellers dash through this region en route to bigger rocks further south, but the Pebbles makes a great overnight stop for those keen to catch as many spectacular sunsets and rises as they can.

Just The Facts

The Pebbles

Getting there: Signposted off the Stuart Highway, 16km north of Tennant Creek. The final 6km is via an unsealed, graded track, suitable for all rigs with care.
Facilities: BBQs, toilet and picnic shelter.
Wheelchair access: Nothing specific.
Rates: Free.
Pets: Yes.
Contact: Freecall the Tennant Creek Visitor Information Centre on 1800 500 879 or visit www.barklytourism.com.au

The Pebbles satisfies self-sufficient and big-rig travellers.

Free Campsites in Northern Territory

81. Mud Tank Zircon Field bush camping - Alice Springs Region
Map Ref: F10 GPS: 23 00 32 S 134 16 00 E
7.8km E of Gemtree. South of the Plenty Hwy and signposted. Zircons found here and camping is possible along the main track from the fossicking field. Fossickers permit required. Ph: 08 8999 5322

82. John Hayes Rockhole campground - Alice Springs Region
Map Ref: F10 GPS: 23 32 24 S 134 21 18 E
Access to the park is signposted along the Ross Hwy 67km E of the Stuart Hwy. Then drive a further 4km in a N direction to 4WD access track. Ph: 08 8951 8250

83. Gorge campground - Alice Springs Region
Map Ref: F10 GPS: 23 31 18 S 134 23 48 E
Within Trephina Gorge NP. Access to the park is signposted along the Ross Hwy 67km E of the Stuart Hwy. Then a further 8km in a N direction to the camping area. Ph: 08 8951 8250

84. Trephina Gorge Nature Park Ross River - Alice Springs Region
Map Ref: F10 GPS: 23 32 47 S 134 22 37 E
Follow the sealed Ross Highway E of Alice Springs for 76km, turn N and travel 9km to Trephina Gorge NP. Ph: 1800 645 199

85. Panorama Campground - Alice Spring Region
Map Ref: F10 GPS: 23 31 20 S 134 23 49 E
Camp are 85km E of Alice Springs. Turn N onto Trephina Gorge Nature Park 76km E of Alice Springs, 10km to camp spot, 5km dirt rd. Ph: 08 8951 8250

86. N'Dhala Gorge camping area - Alice Spring Region
Map Ref: F10 GPS: 23 38 20 S 134 27 47 E
Camping area is 85km E of Alice Springs via the Ross Hwy. Final 2km is unsealed and requires 4WD. Ph: 08 8951 8250

87. Spotted Tiger Bore - Alice Springs Region
Map Ref: G10 GPS: 23 02 21 S 134 55 04 E
Campground 8km S of Harts Range Police Station. Turn S 500m W of police station and travel 8km to site. Ph: 08 8956 9722

88. Mac & Rose Chalmers Conservation Reserve - Alice Springs Region
Map Ref: G10 GPS: 22 28 08 S 135 05 01 E
Camp at Tower Rock 75kms N of Plenty Hwy, turn N 20kms R of Harts Range Police Station 75kms to campground. 4WD only. Ph: 08 8956 9097

89. Tower Rock - Alice Springs Region
Map Ref: G10 GPS: 22 28 03 S 135 05 04 E
300kms NE of Alice Springs. Access rd off the Plenty Hwy about 230km from the junction with the Stuart Hwy. Ph: 08 8952 5800

90. Jervois Station camping area - Alice Springs Region
Map Ref: G10 GPS: 22 57 04 S 136 08 39 E
Signposted access along the Plenty Hwy, 277km E of the Stuart Hwy and 223km W of the NT/QLD border along the banks of the Marshall River. Ph: 08 8956 6307

91. Arthur River Camp Spot - Alice Springs Region
Map Ref: H10 GPS: 22 40 11 S 136 37 51 E
60 kms NE of Jervois Station. Tracks beside creek. Dirt road.

92. Mount Guide Camp Spot - Alice Springs Region
Map Ref: H10 GPS: 22 35 36 S 136 57 30 E
100kms NE of Jervois Station. Tracks on N side of road.

93. Mount Pozieres Camp Spot - Alice Springs Region
Map Ref: H10 GPS: 22 26 01 S 137 25 38 E
67kms W of NT/QLD border on S side of road, tracks to gravel area.

94. Ridgetop Camping Area - Alice Springs Region
Map Ref: E10 GPS: 23 34 58 S 132 30 52 E
Camp area 24km NW of Glen Helen. Small vehicles only Ph: 08 8956 7799

95. Woodland Camping Area - Alice Springs Region
Map Ref: E10 GPS: 23 35 25 S 132 30 46 E
Camp area 23km NW of Glen Helen. Turn N for 5km off Namatjira Dve. Ph: 08 8956 7799

96. Ormiston Gorge - Alice Springs Region
Map Ref: E10 GPS: 23 37 57 S 132 43 29 E
Camp area 12km NE of Glen Helen in West MacDonnell NP. Turn N 4km E of Glen Helen. Ph: 08 8956 7799

Featured Campsite

Brought to you by

Trephina Gorge No. 84

East MacDonnell Ranges, NT
85km east of Alice Springs

Catherine Lawson & David Bristow.

Standing sentry outside Trephina Gorge for more than 300 years, the largest ghost gum in the East MacDonnell Ranges towers 33 metres above the plains, an astonishing beauty that dwarfs the stunted gums we discover clinging to fractured rock faces within Trephina Gorge itself.

Early risers watch the sunrise from the other side of Trephina Gorge too where a two kilometre-long circuit dips and climbs along the rim's teetering stacks of red quartzite (1hr). Down slopes dotted with hakeas and acacias, the walking trail drops into the gorge, following the sandy creek downstream beneath towering rock faces and red river gums, the tallest of which were logged in the 1950s and turned into sleepers for the Ghan rail line.

The spectacular colours of the Gorge.

After all the action that takes place in and above the gorge, Trephina's free-range camp provides ample rest with shady, caravan-friendly sites and walk-in areas for tent campers too. The facilities are excellent for such a remote spot and include wheelchair-accessible toilets, free gas barbecues with burners, picnic tables and rainwater tanks. Access to the camp is sealed, but those with 4WD vehicles and off-road rigs can access a more secluded campground at nearby John Hayes Rockhole (BYO water).

Winter's mild daytime temperatures (20-27°C) make April to September the best time to visit Trephina Gorge, but you'll need to prepare for nights that frequently dip to zero degrees. Stock up on food, fuel and other supplies before leaving Alice Springs.

The sunrise lights up the Gorge.

Just The Facts

Trephina Gorge

Location: Follow the sealed Ross Highway east of Alice Springs for 76km, turn north and travel 9km to Trephina Gorge Nature Park.
Facilities: Free gas barbecues and burners, toilets, picnic tables and rainwater tanks.
Rates: \$3.30/adult, \$1.65/child (5-15 years) and \$7.70/family (2 adults and up to 4 kids).
Wheelchair Access: To toilets
Pets: No
Contact: For more information phone the Parks & Wildlife Service NT in Alice Springs on (08) 8951 8250 (www.parksandwildlife.nt.gov.au) or contact the Central Australian Tourism (Ph: 1800 645 199, www.discovercentralaustralia.com).

Free Campsites in Northern Territory

97. Serpentine Chalet - Alice Springs Region
Map Ref: E10 GPS: 23 45 01 S 132 54 56 E
Bush camping in West MacDonnell Ranges 108km W of Alice Springs. 4WD only, no caravans. Ph: 08 8956 7799

98. Serpentine Chalet Bush - Alice Springs Region
Map Ref: E10 GPS: 23 45 10 S 132 55 10 E
Located in West McDonnell NP 108km W of Alice Springs. Access is signposted along Namatjira Drive. Dry weather only Ph: 08 8956 7799

99. Birthday Waterhole camping area - Alice Springs Region
Map Ref: E10 GPS: 23 43 50 S 133 20 59 E
Owen Spring Reserve is 50km out of Alice Springs, with this camping ground located 5km SE of Stuart's Pass. Access track is along Namatjira Drive. Ph: 08 8951 8250

100. Reedy Hole Waterhole - Alice Springs Region
Map Ref: F10 GPS: 23 46 10 S 133 20 46 E
Situated in the West McDonnell NP. Campsites on the Reedy Hole Waterhole on the Hugh River. Access track is along Namatjira Drive. Ph: 08 8951 8250

101. Hugh River Bush camping areas - Alice Springs Region
Map Ref: F10 GPS: 23 48 59 S 133 23 12 E
The Hugh River trail begins on Namatjira Drive with the turn-off being 50km SW of Alice Springs. Sandy trail. Ph: 08 8951 8250

102. Ntaria Campground - Alice Springs Region
Map Ref: E11 GPS: 23 56 33 S 132 46 50 E
Camp area at Hermannsburg. Collect keys & pay at supermarket opposite. Ph: 08 8956 7480

103. Ellery Creek Big Hole - Alice Springs Region
Map Ref: E11 GPS: 23 46 48 S 133 04 22 E
Camp area 80km W of Alice Springs in West MacDonnell NP. Dirt road small vehicles only. Ph: 08 8956 7799

104. Palm Valley camping area - Alice Springs Region
Map Ref: E11 GPS: 24 03 29 S 132 44 49 E
147km W of Alice Springs via Larapinta Dve off the Hermannsburg signposted access road. Ph: 08 8951 8250

105. Finke River bush camping - Alice Springs Region
Map Ref: E11 GPS: 24 05 39 S 132 50 53 E
Bush camping is permitted within the river bed alongside the Finke River. Generators not permitted.Must be self-sufficient. Ph: 08 8951 8250

106. Boggy Hole camping area - Alice Springs Region
Map Ref: E11 GPS: 24 08 09 S 132 51 40 E
Within the Finke Gorge NP, on Finke River 4WD track 33km S of Larapinta Dve. Ph: 08 8951 8250

107. Lawrence Gorge - Alice Springs Region
Map Ref: F11 GPS: 23 59 58 S 133 26 10 E
Within the Owen Springs Reserve in the Gregory NP. Access is via the Owen Springs Reserve Tourist Drive 20k N of Redbank Gorge. Camping is permitted along some 5km of the Hugh River. Ph: 08 8951 8250

108. Stuarts Well Roadhouse Camping Area - Alice Springs
Map Ref: E11 GPS: 24 20 24 S 133 27 32 E
Located on the Stuart Hwy 93km south of Alice Springs. Bring firewood. Ph: 08 8956 0808

109. Rainbow Valley camping area - Alice Springs Region
Map Ref: F11 GPS: 24 19 51 S 133 37 57 E
Follow the Stuart Hwy 75km S of Alice Springs, take the signposted turn-off to the east and follow unsealed road for 22km to park. Ph: 08 8951 8250

110. Redbank Waterhole - Alice Springs region
Map Ref: F11 GPS: 24 08 59 S 133 28 10 E
Located in the Owen Springs Reserve in the Gregory NP. Enter the park from Stuart Hwy along Owen Springs Reserve Tourist Drive for 4km then left for a further 2km to the camping area along the banks of the Hugh River. Ph: 08 8951 8250

111. Henbury Meteorites camping area - Alice Springs Region
Map Ref: E11 GPS: 24 34 16 S 133 08 35 E
Signposted access along the Ernest Giles Road, 11km W of the Stuart Hwy within the Henbury Meteorites Conservation area. Ph: 08 8951 8250

112. Rodinga Ruins - Alice Springs Region
Map Ref: F11 GPS: 24 33 07 S 134 05 10 E
Camp area 106km SE of Alice Springs. Turn off Stuart Hwy 11km S Alice onto Roger Vale Rd, immediate S onto Maryvale Rd for 94 kms. Turn E 500m to camp.

Rainbow Valley Conservation Reserve No.109

The Red Centre, NT
97km south of Alice Springs

Catherine Lawson and David Bristow

The spectacular glow at Rainbow Valley.

Camped upon 'Wurre', one of the last hunting and gathering grounds of the Southern Arrernte people, travellers wait all day to watch the sun go down over the aptly-named Rainbow Valley. Casting crimson, tangerine and golden light across a jagged ridge of weathered sandstone, the setting sun transforms this arid landscape creating one of Australia's most vibrant desert spectacles.

Rainbow Valley's campground is scenically located on the edge of a shimmering white claypan to provide the best views of the range, and it's far easier to access than you might imagine. You'll find it 22km off the Stuart Highway, just over an hour's drive south of Alice Springs, but bear in mind that a 4WD vehicle is recommended to navigate the sandy patches beyond the highway turnoff.

The park provides pit toilets, picnic shelters and free gas barbecues, and the roomy campsites with firepits mean you can stoke up a campfire to ward off the chill of below-zero winter temperatures. During the popular winter travel season the best campsites are occupied long before sunset, sending latecomers over the dunes to a spacious overflow area.

Close to the main camp, an information shelter helps you tune into your surroundings and put a name to a host of hardy plants: succulents such as samphire and parakeelya that magnificently carpet the reserve's claypans after heavy rains, the hardier desert raisin and bush tomatoes, and bright clumps of everlasting and poached egg daisies that linger late into the dry season.

Foot trails lead across the spinifex sand plains through the archway of magnificently sculpted Mushroom Rock where tiny fairy martins build mud nests beneath the rock's enormous weathered sandstone overhangs. Lured by the howls of dingoes echoing off the range, we ventured beyond, following dry creekbeds through a grove of desert oaks to some easily climbed outcrops that afforded incredible vistas across the James Range, an important bush tucker dreaming site.

The Upper Southern Arrernte people returned to Rainbow Valley after annual rains that triggered the lush bloom of vegetation and guaranteed a rich bounty of food. During this time they conducted sacred ceremonies and adorned caves and rock faces with paintings and petroglyphs.

When European settlement of the Red Centre in the late 1800s began forcing traditional people off their lands, Rainbow Valley was one of the last places where they could hunt and gather. More than 100 years on, evidence of their occupation remains and thousand-year-old artifacts - grinding stones, stone tool fragments and charcoal - have been discovered atop dunes and beneath rock overhangs.

Comprised of fragile 350-million-year-old Hermannsburg sandstone, Rainbow Valley's weathered bluffs and ridges throw off great boulders and crumble into sandy slopes, providing habitat and hideouts for black-flanked (or black-footed) rock wallabies and dingoes. Outside of the brief rainy season, little wildlife bares its head but the spinifex grasslands support dense populations of lizards - up to 440 per hectare.

Plenty of space and facilities.

Every sunset at Wurre is incredibly memorable and a full moon rising here is a sight to behold. A rare photographic moment occurs when rain fills Rainbow Valley's claypan, reflecting its vibrant cliffs and triggering the bloom of bright purple parakeelya that carpet the desert.

Just The Facts

Rainbow Valley Conservation Reserve

Getting there: Follow the Stuart Highway 75km south of Alice Springs, take the signposted turnoff to the east and follow this unsealed road for 22km to the park. A 4WD vehicle is recommended.

Facilities: Gas barbecues, pit toilets, an interpretive area and picnic shelters (no rubbish bins, no generator use permitted, no firewood collection inside the park).

Rates: \$3.30/adult, \$1.65/child (5-15 yrs) and \$7.70/family (2 adults, 4 kids), payable on site.

Wheelchair Access: To toilets.

Pets: No

Contact: For more information phone the Parks & Wildlife Service NT in Alice Springs on (08) 8951 8250 (www.parksandwildlife.nt.gov.au) or contact the Central Australian Tourism (Ph: 1800 645 199, www.discovercentralaustralia.com).

Free Campsites in Northern Territory

113. Chambers Pillar camping area -Alice Springs Region
Map Ref: F11 GPS: 24 52 29 S 133 49 29 E
Camp area 164km S of Alice Springs on the Old Ghan Railway Track. Ph: 08 8951 8250

114. Bundooma Siding - Alice Springs Region
Map Ref: F11 GPS: 24 53 34 S 134 15 34 E
Located 151 S of Alice Springs on the Old Ghan Track.

115. Docker River Community camping area - Alice Springs Region
Map Ref: C11 GPS: 24 51 54 S 129 03 38 E
Signposted access along Tjukaruru Road, 800m W of Docker River Community. Close to WA border. Ph: 08 8956 7337

116. Curtin Springs Roadhouse - Alice Springs Region
Map Ref: D12 GPS: 25 19 00 S 131 45 21 E
Free unpowered sites at this roadhouse. On Lasseter Hwy, 85km E of the Entrance to the Uluru-Kata Tjuta NP. Dry weather only Ph: 08 8956 2906

117. Mt Ebenezer Roadhouse camping area - Alice Springs Region
Map Ref: E12 GPS: 25 10 44 S 132 40 36 E
Located on the Lasseter Hwy, 57km W of the Stuart Hwy. Ph: 08 8956 2904

118. Lamberts Centre - Alice Springs Region
Map Ref: F12 GPS: 25 36 36 S 134 21 17 E
Access track is 145kms E of Kulgera which is 21km W of Finke. Ph: 08 8952 5800

Free Campsites in Northern Territory Index

Northern Territory Map

Tasmania

Free Camps Guide – Useful Resources & Contacts – TAS

Parks & Wildlife Service
Ph: 1300 135 513
Web: www.parks.tas.gov.au

Forestry Tasmania
Ph: (03) 6233 8203
Web: www.forestrytas.com.au

Hydro Tasmania
Ph: 1300 360 441
Web: www.hydro.com.au

Inland Fisheries
Phn: (03) 6261 8050 or
1300 INFISH
Web: www.ifs.tas.gov.au

Department of Primary Industries, Parks, Water & Environment – Sea Fishing & Aquaculture Recreational Fisheries Enquiries
Ph: (03) 6233 7042
Web: www.fishing.tas.gov.au

Tasmania Fire Service
Ph: 1800 000 699 or
(03) 6230 8600
Web: www.ract.com.au

Tourism Tasmania
Ph: 1300 827 743
Web: www.discovertasmania.com.au

Bureau of Meteorology
Ph: 1900 926 102
Web: www.bom.gov.au

Spirit of Tasmania Information and Reservations
Ph: 1300 368 550
Web: www.spiritoftasmania.com.au

Free Campsites in Tasmania

1. North East River camping area - Flinders Island
Map Ref: J2 GPS: 39 45 32 S 147 57 39 E
Near Stanley Point northern end of Flinders Island. Off the NE Road which is 15km E of Killercrankie. Ph: 03 6359 5002

2. Allports Beach camping area - Flinders Island
Map Ref: J2 GPS: 40 00 39 S 147 53 18 E
On the west coast of Flinders Island 21km N of Whitemark. Access to Allport Beach is off Port Davies Road, SW of Emita. Ph: 03 6359 5002

3. Lillies Beach camping area - Flinders Island
Map Ref: J3 GPS: 40 01 15 S 147 52 19 E
Camping area on the beach off Port Davies Road, SW of Emita, west coast Flinders Island. Ph: 03 6359 5002

4. Trousers Point camping area
Map Ref: J3 GPS: 40 13 02 S 148 01 40 E
Strzelecki NP SE corner of Flinders Island. Camping area along the C806 road, 15km S of the Lady Barron Rd. The C806 road is signposted off the Lady Barron Road S of Whitemark and NW of Lady Barron. Ph: 03 6359 2217

5. Yellow Beaches Coastal Reserve camping area - Flinders Island
Map Ref: K3 GPS: 40 12 41 S 148 14 47 E
Located 2km E of Lady Barron southern end of Flinders Island. From Lady Barron head 1km E along Franklin Pde, which becomes Pot Boil Rd. The campsite is 500m along on the right. Ph: 03 6359 5002

6. Greens Point Campground - North West Coast
Map Ref: B4 GPS: 40 54 34 S 144 40 42 E
Marrawah is located at the end of the Bass Hwy (A2) 186km W of Devonport. South of Marrawah an off-road section of the Western Explorer Rd continues across Arthur River to Corinna. Ph: 1300 138 229

7. Murrawah - Green Point
Map Ref: B4 GPS: 40 54 33 S 144 40 47 E
Beach camping 3km W of Marrawah via Green Point Rd.

8. Montagu Camping Ground - North West
Map Ref: C4 GPS: 40 44 40 S 144 58 45 E
Located 4km N of Montagu along Old Port Road, which is signposted off the C215 road. 1km E of Montagu locality. Camping open Nov-May. Ph: 0428 5824 843

9. Smithton Esplanade
Map Ref: C4 GPS: 40 50 18 S 145 07 14 E
Area on West Esplanade, Smithton. Limited stay.

10. Tall Timbers Hotel
Map Ref: C5 GPS: 40 51 22 S 145 07 12 E
Camp at hotel on Scotchtown Rd Smithton. Limited stay. Ph: 03 6452 4800

11. Black River camping area - North West
Map Ref: D4 GPS: 40 50 36 S 145 19 08 E
Located 8.8km E of the Stanley turn-off (B21) and 2.2km W of Peggs Beach turn-off. Drive in 700m to the campsite. Ph: 03 6452 4998

12. Peggs Beach camping area - North West
Map Ref: D4 GPS: 40 51 04 S 145 21 10 E
Located 2.2km E of Black River turn-off and 42km W of Wynyard. Ph: 03 6452 4998

13. Manuka Campground - North West
Map Ref: B5 GPS: 41 02 41 S 144 40 04 E
Located along Arthur River in the Arthur Pieman CA, 200m N of Arthur River Ranger base. Ph: 03 6457 1225

14. Peppermint Campground
Map Ref: B5 GPS: 41 02 51 S 144 40 05 E
Camping area at Arthur River within the Arthur-Pieman CA next to ranger station. Ph: 03 6457 1225

15. Prickly Wattles Campground - North West
Map Ref: B5 GPS: 41 03 36 S 144 40 45 E
Within the Arthur Pieman CA, located along Arthur River Road, 2km S of the Arthur River ranger base. Ph: 03 6457 1225

16. Nelson Bay
Map Ref: B5 GPS: 41 07 37 S 144 40 21 E
Camping spot at Nelson Bay 15km S of Arthur River in Arthur-Pieman CA. Beach side of rd. Ph: 03 6457 1225

Free Campsites in Tasmania

17. Julius River Forest Reserve - North West Coast
Map Ref: C5 GPS: 41 09 15 S 145 01 40 E
46km S of Smithton. Camp area located 9km E of Kanunnah Bridge. 700m E of picnic area. Main attraction is the magnificent rainforest. Ph: 03 6452 4900

18. Wynyard Showgrounds
Map Ref: E5 GPS: 40 59 11 S 145 43 39 E
Camping spot on Jackson St, Wynyard N side of town. Limited stay. Ph: 03 6442 3079

19. Cooee Point - North West
Map Ref: E5 GPS: 41 02 19 S 145 52 37 E
Cooee Point is 3km W of Burnie which is 50km W of Devonport. Ph: 03 6430 5831

20. Halls Point - Sulpher Creek - North Coast
Map Ref: E5 GPS: 41 05 38 S 146 01 39 E
10kms E of Burnie, beachfront camp at Sulphur Creek. www.discovertasmania.com

21. Midway Point
Map Ref: E5 GPS: 41 05 46 S 146 02 27 E
Camping spot 1km E of Sulphur Creek off Preservation Dve. Limited stay.

22. Koybaa Camping Area - North East
Map Ref: F5 GPS: 41 09 35 S 146 33 52 E
Located in Narawntapu NP 40km east of Devonport. Access to park is signposted along the C740 road which is signposted off the B71 Hwy south east of Devonport. Signposted access along main park rd 4km west of Ranger Station. Bring water. Ph: 03 6428 6277

23. Springlawn camping area - North East
Map Ref: F5 GPS: 41 08 52 S 146 36 10 E
Located along park road in Narawntapu NP, 1km from park entrance just past ranger station. Ph: 03 6428 6277

24. Bakers Point camping area - North East
Map Ref: F5 GPS: 41 09 44 S 146 34 02 E
Access along main park road, 4km W of the Ranger Station in Narawntapu NP. Ph: 03 6428 6277

25. Horse Yards camping area - North East
Map Ref: G5 GPS: 41 09 14 S 146 36 31 E
Camp area 13kms N of the B71/C740 in the Narawntapu NP 40kms E of Devonport. Ph: 03 6428 6277

26. Herbies Landing camping area - Midlands & The North
Map Ref: H4 GPS: 40 50 12 S 147 39 01 E
Access along Homestead Rd in the Waterhouse Conservation area. Beach boat launch. Ph: 03 6352 6421

27. Village Green Camping Area
Map Ref: H4 GPS: 40 49 35 S 147 39 39 E
Camp Area 41km NE of Bridport. Turn N off the B82, 27km NE of Bridport onto Homestead Rd, then L after 12.4km for 1.6km. 14km dirt road. Maximum stay 1 month. Ph: 03 6356 1173

28. Waterhouse Point camping area - North East
Map Ref: J4 GPS: 40 49 49 S 147 40 24 E
Via a track off Homestead Rd, 1.4km E of the Herbies Landing turn-off. About 1km in, the track splits; camping is in this area as well as along a track heading east. Ph: 03 6352 6421

29. Brads camping area - Waterhouse Conservation Area - The North
Map Ref: H5 GPS: 40 49 58 S 147 40 41 E
Signposted access via track to Waterhouse Point, 1.4km E of Herbies Landing. Beach boat launch. Ph: 03 6352 6421

30. Mathers Camping area - Midlands & The North
Map Ref: H5 GPS: 40 49 58 S 147 40 14 E
Campsite within the Waterhouse Conservation area. Access via the signposted access track to Waterhouse Point. Ph: 03 6352 6421

31. Casuarina Hill camping area - Midlands & The North
Map Ref: J5 GPS: 40 50 21 S 147 41 11 E
Located in the Waterhouse Conservation area some 24km E of Bridport. Camping area is accessed along Homestead Road. Dry weather only Ph: 03 6352 6421

32. Ransons Beach Camping Area - Midlands & The North
Map Ref: J5 GPS: 40 50 41 S 147 41 14 E
Located 41km NE of Bridport access via Homestead R. Dry weather only Ph: 03 6356 1173

Featured Campsite

Brought to you by

Cooee Point

No 19

Burnie, Tasmania
3 kms west of Burnie

John Mainwaring

A handy spot along Tasmania's northern coast can be found just 3 kilometres west of Burnie's town centre. Opposite Burnie Mazda, about 100 metres west of the Cadbury factory you will see Cooee Point Road and that will take you to the local council's free campsite that encourages you to stay a while and enjoy all the many things Burnie has to offer.

Now before this you will need to duck into the Information Centre at "The Makers' Workshop" which is hard to miss as you pass through Burnie. There you can get your 5 day permit to free camp if you have a self-sufficient van with self-contained ablutions. This is a nice seaside location with a free water supply, a couple of bins and a dump point for toilets. It is next door to the old, closed down abattoir so pretty quiet and from what I have seen on my many visits through Burnie, it seems to be quite popular year round. Council people call in occasionally to make sure visitors are abiding by the rules, which sadly includes no dogs at this site due to the numerous penguins in the area. But this is one of those intelligent councils that does what it can to be attractive to the passing RV dollar and hopes to entice you to stay a while.

Camp right on the edge of the sea.

Burnie is a good spot to explore the locality. It has all the necessary services and some pretty good shopping as well, so the provisions for your travels are no problem. Just a few kilometres further west is the turn off to Cradle Mountain and on down to Zeehan, Waratah and Strahan. You should also pick up the pamphlet "Created From Chaos" from the local visitors centres in the north coast area and check out some of the fascinating volcanic and geological history laid out along the coast between Devonport and Wynyard. You can see similar evidence of the forces that formed this area from your window as you lounge around at Cooee Point as well.

There is also a whiskey distillery in town worth a visit and the local penguin rookery is just behind The Makers' Workshop so pretty close to the town centre. This is a great spot to collect yourself, stock up and then head off on a trip down the Western Explorer or perhaps contemplate life in general before driving the last 50 kms to Devonport to catch the boat back to the mainland. Burnie is friendly and like many Tassie towns, very welcoming to the RV fraternity so well worth a dalliance.

Just The Facts

Cooee Point

Getting there: Cooee Point is 3 kms west of Burnie's town centre, which is 50 kms west of Devonport on Tasmania's north coast.

Facilities: Rubbish collection, RV dump point and fresh water. No toilets so campers must be self-contained.

Wheelchair Access: The area is a flat, hard packed surface so no issues with access for wheelchairs.

Rates: Free with a limit of 5 consecutive nights.

Pets: Not permitted.

Contact: Burnie Information Centre 03 6430 5831, 9am to 5pm, 7 days.

The town of Burnie is right there for your needs.

Free Campsites in Tasmania

33. South Croppies Point camping area - North East
Map Ref: H5 GPS: 40 51 57 S 147 35 43 E
From Homestead Rd turn left 2km N of the Big Waterhouse Lake track, then take the right for 2km. Track conditions can vary so best to check before travel. Ph: 03 6352 6421

34. Big Waterhouse Lake Camp Area - Waterhouse Con Area - The North
Map Ref: H5 GPS: 40 53 42 S 147 36 59 E
Located 34km NE of Bridport. Homestead Rd, accessed off Waterhouse Rd (B82) 27km from Bridport. Boat ramp nearby. Ph: 03 6356 1173

35. Blackmans Lagoon Camp Area - Waterhouse Con Area - The North
Map Ref: H5 GPS: 40 54 44 S 147 35 51 E
Located 26.5km NE of Bridport. Access off B82, 24 km from Bridport. Camping among pine trees. 4WD access to beach. Ph: 03 6356 1173

36. Petal Point Campground - The North
Map Ref: J5 GPS: 40 46 48 S 147 56 45 E
Situated 21km along the C83 N of Gladstone, via Cape Portland Rd. Numerous sites close to beach. Ph: 03 6352 6421

37. Little Musselroe Bay - Musselroe Bay Con Area - East Coast
Map Ref: J5 GPS: 40 45 55 S 148 02 10 E
Access via Cape Portland Road 27km from Gladstone. Vehicle access restricted between Christmas and Easter. Other times walk-in only. Ph: 03 6376 1550

38. Musselroe Bay - Musselroe Bay Conservation Area - East Coast
Map Ref: K5 GPS: 40 50 10 S 148 10 45 E
Some 24km NE of Gladstone, via C843, C845 & Forester Kangaroo Drive. Dirt road. Oceanfront campsites. Boat ramp nearby. Dry weather only Ph: 03 6356 1173

39. Top Camp Campground - North East
Map Ref: K5 GPS: 40 52 34 S 148 12 14 E
Within the Mt William NP 27kms NE of Gladstone along the C845. Ph: 03 6376 1550

40. Stumpy's Bay Campsites - North East
Map Ref: K5 GPS: 40 52 17 S 148 13 18 E
Located within Mt William NP and signposted access 7.9km along the Forester Kangaroo Drive which starts 1.1km north of the park information board. Bring water & firewood.

41. Deep Creek camping area - North East
Map Ref: K5 GPS: 40 58 11 S 148 18 45 E
Located in the Mt William NP. Site 37km E of Gladstone along the C846. Ph: 03 6376 1550

42. Policemans Point Campground
Map Ref: K5 GPS: 41 03 52 S 148 17 32 E
40km from Gladstone. Turn at South Ansons Bay Rd. Mostly dirt road. Ph: 03 6376 1550

43. Bay of Fires - Bay of Fires Conservation Area
Map Ref: K5 GPS: 41 07 15 S 148 15 57 E
Take Binalong Bay Rd (C850) NE of St Helens, turn on to The Gardens Rd and 9.5km from St Helens turn E and continue for 300m then right turn to Grants Lagoon, first of many camps. Ph: 03 6376 1550

44. Waratah camping ground - North West
Map Ref: D6 GPS: 41 26 44 S 145 31 57 E
Located on Smith St in Waratah behind the council offices. Ph: 03 6439 7100

45. Lake Kara Campsite - North West
Map Ref: E6 GPS: 41 15 45 S 145 50 41 E
Self contained vehicles only. Off Ridgeley Hwy to Upper Natone Rd at Hampshire then S to Osborns Rd & Lake Kara Rd.

46. Upper Natone Forest Reserve - North West
Map Ref: E5 GPS: 41 15 08 S 145 51 45 E
Camping area at Hampshire on Blythe Rd, E off Ridgeley Hwy off Upper Natone Rd.

47. Riana Pioneer Park camping ground - North West
Map Ref: E5 GPS: 41 12 56 S 145 59 56 E
Camp area 2kms S of Riana via Pine Road. Ph: 03 6111 4779

48. Wings Wildlife Park
Map Ref: E6 GPS: 41 15 49 S 146 02 43 E
Camp area 2km NW of Gunns Plains on Winduss Rd. Ph: 03 6429 1151

Bay Of Fires Conservation Area

No 43

St Helens, Tasmania

10km northeast of St Helens

Catherine Lawson & David Bristow

Freycinet's arc of impossibly white quartz sand curled around a shimmering blue sea has long lured travellers to Tassie's magnificent west coast.

But what many travellers don't realise is that this incredible coastline continues north beyond Bicheno and St Helens where the highway heads inland, to the Bay of Fires.

Named by Captain Tobias Furneaux in 1773 for the indigenous campfires he spotted burning ashore as he sailed past, Bay of Fires Conservation Area stretches from Binalong Bay to Eddystone Point at the southern tip of Mt William National Park.

This landscape of calm lagoons nestled behind long stretches of white sand beach, and tiny coves tucked between sculpted granite outcrops that spill out onto an emerald sea, excites all kinds of outdoor aficionados – fishers, paddlers, walkers, swimmers and especially photographers.

There's also a huge choice of free campgrounds offering just the basics – toilets, tables and fire pits – that prove perfect for self-sufficient nature-lovers who set up at beachfront sites for stays of up to four weeks.

Choose between camps with boat ramps and endless strips of sand for walking and fishing, campsites tucked in quiet coves for calm sea swims, or protected spots alongside the lagoons where you can launch a boat, go paddling and watch the birds.

Camping by this beautiful coastline.

The coastal rocks are spectacular.

Access to the conservation park is from St Helens, where you can pick up supplies, including firewood, and top up your fuel and water. From town, head north on Binalong Bay Rd (C850) and The Gardens Rd (C848) and follow the signposts to your preferred camp.

Closest to town and with a boat ramp, Grants Lagoon is favoured by campers keen to fish and launch small boats and sailing dinghies. The grassy campground is free-range, making it suitable for all sizes of rigs, and the nearby day-use area provides access to the ocean beach.

The secluded camps nestled at the northern end of Jeanneret Beach accommodate even big rigs, and provide opportunities to swim, paddle, fish and access the Binalong Bay Coastal Walk. Another bonus here is that the toilets are wheelchair-accessible.

Next up is Swimcart Beach, famed for its surf fishing, but its small, sandy sites best accommodate camper trailers, tents or small campervans. There are toilets and a picnic area to the north beside the lagoon and you'll get mobile reception from camp.

Cosy Corner has both secluded and more spacious beachfront campsites located at both ends of the beach, making this one spot suitable for all kinds of rigs, with toilets and mobile reception too.

North of Cosy Corner, the snug campsites at another four locations suit small rigs and tent campers: Sloop Reef, Sloop Lagoon, Big Lagoon and Policemans Point. There are no toilets here, so BYO.

Set up camp overlooking Sloop Reef's amazing white sand beach, or settle in between Sloop Lagoon and the sea and take a 30-minute return stroll along the Sloop Rock Tramway.

Big Lagoon provides calm water access too, but my pick is the isolated camp at Policemans Point on the southern side of Ansons Bay (via Ansons Bay Road (C843) and The Priory). This enormous grassy camp with plenty of quiet waterfront nooks on the inlet for tents, provides no facilities, but you can walk to the beach, launch a boat and on our visit we had the entire camp to ourselves.

Just The Facts

Hall Point

Getting there: Take Binalong Bay Road (C850) NE of St Helens, turn onto The Gardens Road and 9.5km from St Helens, turn east, follow this road for 300m before taking a right-hand turn to reach Grants Lagoon, the first of the camps.

Facilities: Toilets (at some camps) picnic tables and fire pits. Launch boats at The Gulch at Binalong Bay, The Gardens, Eddystone Point and Policemans Point.

Wheelchair Access: To toilets at Jeanneret Beach.

Rates: Free.

Pets: On leads.

Contact: Parks & Wildlife Service (St Helens office) by phone: (03) 6376 1550 or visit www.parks.tas.gov.au.

49. Leven Canyon Reserve - The North
Map Ref: E6 GPS: 41 24 10 S 146 01 59 E
42km south of Ulverstone in central northern Tasmania. www.centralcoast.tas.gov.au

50. Lake Barrington West Camping area - North West
Map Ref: E6 GPS: 41 22 40 S 146 13 06 E
Camp sites just off Lake Barrington Rd, 8km S of Lower Wilmot. Ph: 03 6491 1036

51. Kentish Park - North Coast
Map Ref: F6 GPS: 41 22 56 S 146 13 20 E
South of Devonport on the east shore of Lake Barrington 6km W of West Kentish. Ph: 03 6491 1036

52. Lake Gairdner - North Coast
Map Ref: E6 GPS: 41 28 58 S 146 03 50 E
Located 5km W of Moina. Turn W off C132, 1km S of Moina. Beside lake. Dirt road access. Ph: 03 6271 6221

53. O'Neils Creek Reserve - North West
Map Ref: E6 GPS: 41 28 00 S 146 13 11 E
Located along the C136 road in Gowrie Park, 14km S of Sheffield. Ph: 03 6491 1036

54. Lilydale Falls - North Coast
Map Ref: H6 GPS: 41 13 55 S 147 12 32 E
From Launceston take A8 N then right in to Golconda Rd for a further 22kms to Lilydale. Falls are 2km N of town. www.lilydaletas.net

55. Underwood Bridge
Map Ref: H6 GPS: 41 17 30 S 147 12 18 E
Camp area on Glenform Farm Rd, turn E off East Tamar Hwy from Launceston towards Georgetown. Take Lilydale Rd exit to Underwood Bridge. Must be self-sufficient.

56. Myrtle Park Recreation Ground - North East
Map Ref: H6 GPS: 41 18 31 S 147 21 56 E
Located off the A3 Hwy, 30km S of Scottsdale and 30km NE of Launceston. Ph: 1800 651 827

57. Nabowla
Map Ref: H5 GPS: 41 09 41 S 147 23 39 E
Camp spot at 200 Borth Blumont Rd Nabowla, NW from Scottsdale on William St, left to Golconda Rd through Lietinna. Must be self-sufficient.

58. Northeast Park camping area - North East
Map Ref: H6 GPS: 41 09 55 S 147 31 22 E
Signposted access on the A3 Hwy, 1km SE of Scottsdale. Ph: 03 6352 6520

59. Branxholm camping ground - North East
Map Ref: J6 GPS: 41 10 06 S 147 44 15 E
Located beside the Ringarooma River on the Tasman Hwy in Branxholm. Ph: 03 6354 6168

60. Weldborough Hotel Camping Ground - North East
Map Ref: J6 GPS: 41 11 39 S 147 54 17 E
Located on Tasman Hwy in Weldborough 21km south east of Derby and 42km north west of St Helens. Bring water & firewood and fire bin. Ph: 03 6354 2223

61. Big Lagoon - East Coast
Map Ref: K6 GPS: 41 12 34 S 148 16 42 E
Numerous tracks off Gardens Rd 2km N of the bridge over Sloop Lagoon. Ph: 03 6376 1550

62. Sloop Lagoon camping area - East Coast
Map Ref: K6 GPS: 41 12 32 S 148 16 43 E
Behind the S End of Taylors Beach, between Sloop Lagoon and the sea. Access is 2.5km along Old Gardens Rd. Ph: 03 6376 1550

63. Sloop Reef - Bay Of Fires Conservation Area - East Coast
Map Ref: K6 GPS: 41 12 58 S 148 16 57 E
Accessed off Gardens Road, 7.5km from Binalong Bay Road. Small camping area overlooking the water and beach. Ph: 03 6376 1550

64. Cosy Corner Campground - Bay of Fires Conservation Area - East Coast
Map Ref: K6 GPS: 41 13 20 S 148 16 59 E
15km NE from St Helens, via Binalong Bay Rd & Gardens Rd. Beachfront. Ph: 03 6376 1550

Featured Campsite

Brought to you by

Leven Canyon Campsite No 49

Leven Canyon Reserve, Tas

42km south of Ulverstone
Jim Foster

Upper campsite area at Leven Canyon.

LEVEN Canyon is a free campsite within the Leven Canyon Reserve, 42km south of Ulverstone in northern Tasmania. There is a sealed parking area for day-trippers, a barbecue, flush toilets, picnic tables and a shelter shed. There are also some outdoor fireplaces to enable you to safely have your own fire – subject to fire restrictions, of course.

The camping areas consist of the upper and lower areas, with the upper being most suitable for small to medium motorhomes and vans, with room for only about five or six rigs. The lower site is well grassed and more suitable for campervans, trailers, tents and for those hardy souls swagging it.

Leven Canyon is one of those rare places in Australia where you can camp free within a temperate rainforest. But as it is at a fairly high altitude and low latitude, you should expect that even in summer the nights at Leven Canyon to be fairly cool. We visited in late summer when the nights were quiet, clear and cool. In these southern climes the clear, crisp air shimmered with the light of myriad stars and a waxing moon loomed large and clear as it sailed overhead. The mornings sparkled with heavy dew, and fog shrouding the surrounding mountaintops lent them a dramatic air. The morning air was as sweet and crisp as a good Tassie riesling, and just as intoxicating.

The surrounding forest is mostly old growth, with an amazing amount of flora and fauna. Shy pademelons and wallabies come out in the evening to graze on the lush grasses, while bats and owls flash overhead on the hunt. But to enjoy the closeness of these wild creatures you must be quiet, move slowly and be careful not to blind them with a torch, especially the new and extremely bright LED torches now so popular. During the day, tiny wrens and finches flit amongst the bushes while parrots and other birds fill the trees with chatter.

The roads down from the northern coast are sealed but narrow and winding, so care should be taken. And to drive slowly allows you to better see the amazing views and sights. If, like us, you visit in late summer you will find wild apple trees laden with fruit here and there along the roads. And sweet and juicy wild blackberries can be freely picked from where they cover many roadside fences.

There is much to see and do near Leven Canyon. There is a 45-minute round trip walk that takes in the amazing lookout over Leven Canyon, the stairs and fern walk. For those not able or willing for the more strenuous round trip, the easy walk up to Cruickshank Lookout is well worth the effort.

Just down the road, near the bridge over the Leven River at Taylor's Flat, the fishing is reputed to be good, while a quick glance at your map of Tasmania will show you that Cradle Mountain is only about 45km away.

Or you can simply relax and enjoy being in one of the most beautiful spots on the planet.

Smaller rigs suit the lower sites.

Just The Facts

Leven Canyon Campsite

Getting there: 42km south of Ulverstone in central northern Tasmania.
Facilities: Picnic tables, shelter shed, fireplaces, flushing toilets. No power or drinking water. The main track to Cruickshank Lookout is classed as easy and is wheelchair-accessible. Other tracks require good walking shoes and you should carry drinking water. Campsites are not suitable for big rigs. Up to medium sized motorhomes such as seven or eight metres or caravans to the same are okay.
Wheelchair access: Toilets have access.
Rates: No camping fees.
Pets: I could find nothing about pets but as the area is a wilderness where wildlife is partly tame I would not recommend bringing any dogs or cats into the camp area.
Contact: www.centralcoast.tas.gov.au

Free Campsites in Tasmania

65. Jeanneret Beach Campground - Bay of Fires Conservation Area - East Coast

Map Ref: K6 GPS: 41 14 10 S 148 17 20 E
12km NE from St Helens, via Binalong Bay Rd off Gardens Rd. Great beachfront. Ph: 03 6376 1550

66. Swimcart Beach Campground - Bay of Fires Conservation Area - East Coast

Map Ref: K6 GPS: 41 13 58 S 148 17 06 E
13km NE from St Helens, via Binalong Bay Rd & Gardens Rd. Beachfront. Ph: 03 6376 1550

67. Grants Lagoon - Bay of Fires Conservation Area - East Coast

Map Ref: K6 GPS: 41 15 20 S 148 17 28 E
10km NE from St Helens, via Binalong Bay Rd & Gardens Rd. Near lagoon. Ph: 03 6376 1550

68. Moulting Bay - Humbug Point Nature Recreation Area - East Coast

Map Ref: K6 GPS: 41 16 56 S 148 17 01 E
Signposted off Binalong Bay Rd 8km N of St Helens. Then 1km dirt road to camping area. Boat beach launching possible. Ph: 03 6376 1550

69. Dora Point Camping Area - East Coast

Map Ref: K6 GPS: 41 16 40 S 148 19 45 E
13km NE from St Helens, via Binalong Bay Rd. Sites behind dunes. Beside the bay. Cold showers available. Ph: 03 6376 1550

70. Ben Lomond camping area - Ben Lomond NP - The North

Map Ref: H6 GPS: 41 30 20 S 147 36 56 E
Ben Lomond Road, 13km S of Upper Blessington. Camping area located 1km inside park boundary. Six sites only. Ph: 03 6336 4397

71. Griffin Park - Midlands & The North

Map Ref: J6 GPS: 41 28 10 S 147 51 10 E
Situated on the South Esk River. Signposted along the Griffin Rd, N of Mathinna. Ph: 03 6374 2102

72. South Esk River picnic & camping area

Map Ref: J6 GPS: 41 27 50 S 147 53 26 E
Beside the South Esk River at the junction of C423 and Griffin Rd, 1.7km N of Nathinna and the B43. Ph: 03 6352 6466

73. Diana's Basin - East Coast

Map Ref: K6 GPS: 41 22 24 S 148 17 18 E
9km S from St Helens or 4km N from Beaumaris. Beach access. Ph: 03 6376 1550

74. Paddys Island Campground - East Coast

Map Ref: K6 GPS: 41 23 59 S 148 17 32 E
Signposted off the A3 highway 2.5km NE of Beaumaris. Beachfront. Ph: 03 6376 1550

75. Scamander Forest Reserve - East Coast

Map Ref: K6 GPS: 41 26 22 S 148 13 59 E
11km W from Beaumaris access on Trout Creek Rd from Skyline Drive. Ph: 03 6374 2102

76. Trout Creek camping area - Scamander Conservation Area - East Coast

Map Ref: K6 GPS: 41 26 22 S 148 13 59 E
Turn off A3 at Beaumaris along Skyline Rd then take Eastern Creek Rd in to Trout Rd. Good fishing. Ph: 03 6352 6466

77. Shelly Point - Scamander Conservation Area - East Coast

Map Ref: K6 GPS: 41 26 08 S 148 16 40 E
2km S of Beaumaris off A3. 500m into camp area. Parking on beach is day access only. Ph: 03 6376 1550

78. The Bridge at Savage River - Corinna - West Coast

Map Ref: C6 GPS: 41 37 26 S 145 04 51 E
5kms north of Corinna.

79. Corinna Wilderness Experience - North West

Map Ref: C7 GPS: 41 39 03 S 145 04 40 E
Access via Savage River or Smithton from the N and via Zeehan from the South by barge. Bookings essential. Ph: 03 6446 1170

80. Reece Dam - North West

Map Ref: C7 GPS: 41 43 48 S 145 08 24 E
Reece Dam is 34km W of Rosebury and 58km W of Tullah.

Featured Campsite

Brought to you by

kokodacaravans.com.au

The Bridge At Savage River No 78

5kms north of Corinna

John Mainwaring

The Bridge over the Savage River.

On a recent excursion down the Western Explorer we were surprised to find just how few casual camp sites there were along this iconic drive. Currently there does not seem to be a lot of encouragement to extend your stay in this fascinating piece of northwest Tasmania. It seems the expectation is that you will cruise all the way between Arthur River and Corinna without much more than a coffee break by the roadside. That is a shame in such a magnificent and unique piece of country, and one that is relatively far off the beaten track. But down at the southern end of this tourist route we found a couple of nice spots at one of the river crossings that travellers will want to consider. Chatting to the ranger at Arthur River we were able to determine that camping at Lindsay River Bridge and Donaldson River Bridge was frowned upon and park fees were payable, and even up around Temma there is greater control being exercised now with pay sites the norm. But the bridge crossing at Savage River down towards Corinna is outside the park boundaries, so there appears to be no problem with setting up there for a freebie overnighter. We have met people who have overnighted at Donaldson River and Lindsay River but strictly speaking these are pay sites in the protected area so a ranger will extract payment if they happen upon you.

At either end of the bridge at Savage River there are some clear spaces for around half a dozen campsites. If these are taken there is a track off the side of the road at the southern end into the gloom of the thick forest where there are another dozen or so spots but personally I prefer the brighter areas out of the forest. There are no facilities to speak of at this site so tread lightly.

An interesting point about the Savage River site is that it was used as a camping spot by protesters during the construction of the Western Explorer and a number of these people claim that they heard the calls of the thylacine during their stay. Good for keeping the legend alive, but it also adds some interest to this particular location and maybe will spur you to keep the camera handy. Well, you never know. The forest around here is very, very thick and while you are there you can keep an eye out for Elvis as well.

There is a nice walk from this bridge to Corinna which can be done as an overnighter. If you are heading south and you arrive here and the sites have been snapped up then you might need to carry on to Corinna and pay for a spot by the river, but it does not fill up often in this remote area. My last visit was February, nominally peak season in Tassie and we shared it with just a couple of other campers.

If you are in this area, you are probably doing the Western Explorer between Stanley and Strahan. You will be focused on Corinna as a highlight of the drive and just generally absorbing the fantastic surrounds of the Arthur Pieman Protected Area which is so unlike any other part of Australia. But an overnighter at Savage River is very pleasant and won't cost you a cent.

Camping is off the road near the bridge.

Just The Facts

Savage River, Tasmania

Location: About 5 kms north of Corinna.

Facilities: No facilities other than a fireplace at the northern end.

Wheelchair Access: You will be pleasantly surprised to find some firm (in fact quite solid) sandy surfaces that are flat and appropriate for wheeled transport in the vicinity of the bridge.

Rates: Completely free.

Pets: Allowed.

Free Campsites in Tasmania

81. Granville Harbour - West Coast
Map Ref: C7 GPS: 41 48 29 S 145 02 16 E
From C249 it is around 9km to Granville Harbour coastal town, then follow track N to several camps amongst the tea trees.

82. Trial Harbour - West Coast
Map Ref: C7 GPS: 41 55 40 S 145 10 24 E
Located 1km N of Zeehan on the C249. A 20km track along a narrow and windy road to the coast.

83. Lake Mackintosh camping area - North West
Map Ref: D7 GPS: 41 41 07 S 145 39 23 E
Limited tent sites camping better suited for caravans, motorhomes or camper trailers. Adjacent to town of Tullah and N of the dam wall via Mackintosh Dam Road, 6.3km N of Tullah. Ph: 03 6271 6221

84. Lake Roseberry Foreshore
Map Ref: D7 GPS: 41 45 37 S 145 37 10 E
Parking area 12km E of Roseberry. Turn W 50m N of Murchison Bridge. Camp 200m off hwy. Limited stay.

85. Lake Parangana Recreation Area - Central Highlands
Map Ref: E7 GPS: 41 38 54 S 146 13 40 S
Situated 29km SW of Mole Creek. Along the C171 road 1km S of dam wall, via picnic area. Beside lake. Ph: 03 6271 6221

86. Mersey White Water Forest Reserve
Map Ref: E7 GPS: 41 41 59 S 146 13 04 E
Camping area 36km SW of Mole Creek, 9km S of dam wall, beside river.

87. Lake Rowallan Bridge - Central Highlands
Map Ref: E7 GPS: 41 43 23 S 146 13 09 E
25kms S of Liena via the B12 and then Mersey Forest Road. www.discovertasmania.com

88. Lake MacKenzie bush camping - Midlands & The North
Map Ref: F7 GPS: 41 40 59 S 146 22 58 E
Access via Lake MacKenzie Rd off the C171. 22km to this camping area is via unsealed and rough winding road. Sometimes snow covered. Dry weather only Ph: 1300 360 441

89. Andy's Motorhome Park - North East
Map Ref: G6 GPS: 41 31 34 S 146 50 44 E
Located in Westbury along the Meander Valley Rd 16km east of Deloraine behind Andy's Bakery CafÃ©. Self contained units only. Ph: 03 6393 1846

90. Quamby Corner
Map Ref: F7 GPS: 41 37 35 S 146 42 39 E
Camping 16km S of Deloraine. From Highlands Lakes Rd turn E onto "Golden Valley Rd then 150m to entrance. Ph: 03 6369 5156

91. Lower Liffey Reserve - Central Highlands
Map Ref: G7 GPS: 41 40 58 S 146 46 56 E
From the A5, 47km north of Miena turn east on to the C513. Ph: 03 6363 2678

92. Mt Blackwood Lookout - Central Highlands
Map Ref: G7 GPS: 41 49 03 S 146 53 21 E
70km N of Bothwell turn right on o B51 and continue for 30km past Arthurs and Great Lake to Mount Blackwood. Just below the summit on the descent to Poatina a signposted road to your right leads to the lookout and parking area. Ph: 1300 655 145

93. Fingal Bay
Map Ref: J7 GPS: 41 38 17 S 147 58 06 E
Parking area behind toilet block in Talbot St, Fingal. Limited stay.

94. St Mary's Sportsground
Map Ref: J7 GPS: 41 35 05 S 148 11 02 E
Camping are in St Mary's on Harefield Rd. Limited stay.

95. Little Beach Campground -Little Beach Conservation Area - East Coast
Map Ref: K7 GPS: 41 37 40 S 148 18 59 E
Camp Area 17km S of A3/A4 Junction or 5.5km N of Chain of Lagoons. Just off hwy. Walk to beach. Ph: 03 6256 7000

96. Lagoons Beach - North East
Map Ref: K7 GPS: 41 38 58 S 148 17 52 E
20km S of A3/A4 junction and 21k from St. Marys. Coastal location. Beachfront. Ph: 03 6256 7000

Featured Campsite

Brought to you by

kokodacaravans.com.au

Lower Liffey Res No.91

Central Highlands, Tas

47 kms north of Miena.

Gordon & Pamela May

Liffey Falls are a standout attraction.

A fellow traveller's enthusiastic account of waterfalls, rainforest and a camp with good facilities encouraged us to visit Liffey Falls and Lower Liffey Reserve (Tas) on our way north from Miena on the Lakes Highway (A5). He explained the falls are in a national park, but that Lower Liffey Reserve is a free camping area about eight kilometres further on.

About 47km north of Miena the turn-off east (C513) to Liffey Falls was clearly signposted and the gravel access road, though undulating, was reasonably wide. At a T-junction, we turned right to the falls, to do our sightseeing first. The Liffey Falls road was narrow and winding and signposted as not suitable for buses or caravans

A series of lookouts built along the steep sealed Falls walk provides views of Liffey River as it cascades over rocky rapids between a gorge heavily timbered with temperate rainforest trees of sassafras, myrtle and leatherwood. Framing the walk are arches of tree ferns or "manferns" as they are called in Tasmania.

Liffey Falls is a scenic standout and well worth the short hair-raising drive and steep walk. The natural beauty of the spot justifies its 1989 inclusion as a Tasmanian Wilderness World Heritage Area. After absorbing some of this soul food, it was time for the return walk. We could, instead, have walked straight ahead down to Lower Liffey campground – if only someone had driven our vehicle around the road for us!

Lower Liffey Reserve camping grounds, also located on the C513, required some back tracking. Getting lost was always a possibility!

However we followed the C513 and found the delightful forest reserve campgrounds set between two swiftly flowing streams. The campgrounds comfortably accommodated 20 camp sites or more. We found an open grassy site set among the eucalypts. Tasman parrots cheerily animated the branches. Fellow campers included families of tent campers, caravanners and motorhomers. Camp fires were permitted, other than during fire restriction periods.

Lower Liffey Reserve is controlled by Tasmania Forestry Service, which provides picnic tables, campfires and toilets with disabled facilities. Access to the falls is a two hour walk which starts off following the old timber hauling tramway, with a sharp uphill bit at the end. We were told it was more strenuous than the downhill walk from the Liffey Falls car park.

To us, relaxing between walks at an idyllic free camp seemed like a better alternative.

Happy camper at Lower Liffey reserve.

Just The Facts

Lower Liffey Reserve

Where: From the A5, 47km north of Miena turn east onto the C513. Hema map 73 C12, GPS coordinates 41 40 58 S, 148 46 54 E.

Facilities: Picnic tables, campfires, toilets with disabled access.

AUSTRALIAN MADE CARAVANS
OFF-GRID | OFF-ROAD

Free Campsites in Tasmania

97. Douglas-Apsley National Park - East Coast
Map Ref: J7 GPS: 41 51 50 S 148 11 20 E
11km NW from Bicheno off Rosedale Road. Short walk to camp area. Beautiful river location. Ph: 03 6256 7000

98. Macquarie Heads camping area - South West
Map Ref: C8 GPS: 42 13 16 S 145 13 44 E
Located at the end of the C251 (Macquarie Heads Road), 14km S of Strahan via an unsealed access road which can be rough at times. Ph: 03 6471 7382

99. Hells Gate - Strahan - West Coast
Map Ref: D8 GPS: 42 12 05 S 145 15 49 E
Drive 12km S of Strahan following signs to Hells Gate on Macquarie Heads Rd. A number of good quality 2WD tracks lead in to a pine plantation and a number of small clearings to camp. Ph: 03 6471 7622

100. Lake Burbury camping area - South West
Map Ref: D8 GPS: 42 05 47 S 145 40 28 E
Located along the A10 Hwy, 21km E of Queenstown and 86km W of Derwent Bridge. Ph: 03 6472 2762

101. Thureau Hills camping area - South West
Map Ref: D8 GPS: 42 08 38 S 145 39 01 E
Limited tent sites, campsites best for camper trailer, caravans and motorhomes. Access along A10 Hwy, 15km E of Queenstown. Then Dve 3.6km S to site. Ph: 03 6471 4700

102. Collingwood River Reserve
Map Ref: E8 GPS: 42 09 42 S 145 55 36 E
45K W of Derwent Bridge on the Lyell Highway (A10) Starting point for most Franklin River trips camping area next to bridge. Ph: 03 6471 7122

103. Lake King Williams camping area - South West
Map Ref: E8 GPS: 42 08 50 S 146 13 04 E
Accessed from the Lyell Hwy A10, 5km W of Derwent Bridge. Ph: 1300 360 441

104. Laughing Jack Lagoon bush camping - South West
Map Ref: F8 GPS: 42 10 59 S 146 20 10 E
20km E of Derwent Bridge on A10 via C602 road. Many sites either side of dam wall. Ph: 1300 360 441

105. Bronte Lagoon camping area - Central Highlands
Map Ref: F8 GPS: 42 11 11 S 146 28 40 E
Signposted access off the A10 Hwy, 200m S of its junction with the B11 Hwy. Travel 2km to boat ramp. Ph: 1300 360 441

106. Bradys Lake camping area - South East
Map Ref: F8 GPS: 42 14 02 S 146 29 56 E
North of Tarraleah, off A10 highway. Two access tracks, one south and one north of the canal. Numerous lakeside campsites. Ph: 1300 360 441

107. Lake Binney camping area -South East
Map Ref: F8 GPS: 42 15 34 S 146 28 56 E
Off the A10 hwy, 3km S of Bradys Lake. Camping area is located beside the highway near the boat ramp. Ph: 1300 360 441

108. Little Pine Lagoon Lakeside Reserve camping area - Central Highlands
Map Ref: F8 GPS: 41 59 57 S 146 36 44 E
Camp area 10kms SW of Miena or 24kms NE of Bronte Park via B11. Ph: 03 6259 8148

109. Pumphouse Bay camping ground - Central Highlands
Map Ref: G8 GPS: 41 59 05 S 146 51 42 E
Located 6km N of the A5 Junction and 36km S of Poatina in Arthurs Lake RA. Then drive in 800m to the camping area. Ph: 03 6259 5503

110. Jonah Bay camping ground - Central Highlands
Map Ref: G8 GPS: 41 57 31 S 146 54 10 E
Located 4km N of the Pumphouse Bay access road and 32km S of Poatina in Arthurs Lake RA. Drive in 3.1km to road junction, turn right and follow for 1.7km to the camping area. Ph: 03 6259 5503

111. Penstock Lagoon Campground
Map Ref: G8 GPS: 42 04 58 S 146 46 05 E
Access is via Waddamana Rd 5km S of Shannon. Ph: 03 6230 5111

112. Lagoon of Islands bush camping
Map Ref: G8 GPS: 42 06 42 S 146 56 05 E
Located in Central Plateau region via the Interlaken Rd off the A5 hwy. Signposted access and campsites around lakes edge. Ph: 1300 360 441

Hells Gate No 99

Near Strahan, TAS
13 kms south of Strahan
John Mainwaring

For travellers to Strahan in Tasmania's west, the camping area at Hells Gate is fairly well known. This is a council site at the tip of this peninsula where the sites are a pretty reasonable $6 per night. But not so many folks know that in the pine forest areas just prior to the camping ground, there is also free camping permitted and if you make your way along some of the tracks that wind their way through this pine plantation, there are a few pretty nice spots that give access to the Ocean Beach where you can park up and roll out the swag.

The attractions to this location generally include the amazing Hells Gate entry to Macquarie Harbour and the long stretch of Ocean Beach with its crashing surf and fishing opportunities. I have always been a bit paranoid on this particular beach having heard a few stories of big waves that come out of nowhere and sweep the beach right up to the high sand hills. That big old southern ocean can throw some surprises every now and again according to the locals so it pays to keep an eye out.

The camping areas, both pay and free, are around 15 kms from town and you can get all the supplies you will need in Strahan. It is the local tourist centre for the west coast with plenty to see and do. If fishing is your thing then the ocean beach is one option, but if the roaring forties are more than you can take then the relatively calm Macquarie Harbour is on the other side of the peninsula that takes you out to Hells Gate. In there you might even get lucky with escaped Ocean Trout and Atlantic Salmon from the large fish farming enclosures scattered round the harbour.

You are close to Strahan township.

The lighthouse into Macquarie Habour

The weather out near Hells Gate can be interesting at times. It can be fabulous or absolutely vile, either one at any time of the year. But if you are snuggled away into the pine forest you would be pretty nicely protected. If free camping is what you have in mind in the area then check out some of the pine forest nooks near Ocean Beach and if you don't mind parting company with a few dollars, the council camp area right at the end of the peninsula has some beaut grassy hideaways in the coastal scrub.

There access onto the Ocean Beach where you can park and camp

Just The Facts

Hells Gate

Getting There : Drive 12 kms south of Strahan following the signs to Hells Gate on Macquarie Heads Road. A number of good quality 2WD tracks lead into the pine plantation and lead to a number of small clearings where you can free camp.
Facilities : None.
Charges : None
Contact : Strahan Visitor's Centre (03) 6471 7622
Pets : Yes. Note too that pets are permitted at the pay site at Macquarie Heads.

Free Campsites in Tasmania

113. Woods Lake bush camping - Central Highlands
Map Ref: G8 GPS: 42 04 10 S 147 01 00 E
Numerous campsites along the lake foreshore from the B51 highway take Arthurs Lake Rd (C525) for 8.5km to the Woods Lake access track. Keep right and travel 12km to boat ramp & campsites. Ph: 1300 360 441

114. Dago Point camping area - Central Highlands
Map Ref: G8 GPS: 42 07 57 S 147 10 06 E
Camp area 26kms E of Steppes or 2km W of Interlaken. Lakeside camping sites with boat ramp. Ph: 03 6259 8148

115. Lake Leake Campground
Map Ref: J8 GPS: 42 00 44 S 147 48 02 E
Camp area 39km NW of Swansea via Lake Leake Rd, 4km dirt road. Limited space. Ph: 03 6381 1319

116. Tooms Lake Camping Ground
Map Ref: J8 GPS: 42 12 48 S 147 46 56 E
Camp area at Tooms Lake, 42km SE of Ross via C305, 20km dirt road. Ph: 03 6255 5228

117. Mayfield Bay Campground
Map Ref: J8 GPS: 42 14 21 S 148 00 45 E
Located in Mayfield Bay Conservation Area 16km S of Swansea. Beachfront. Gold coin donation Ph: 03 6256 7000

118. Friendly Beaches Campground
Map Ref: K8 GPS: 41 59 27 S 148 17 15 E
Located within Freycinet NP. Camping area 13km S of Hwy. Turn E 9km S of Hwy then travel 3km on dirt road to beach front sites. Ph: 03 6256 7000

119. Isaacs Point Campground - Freycinet NP East Coast
Map Ref: K8 GPS: 41 59 32 S 148 17 20 E
Freycinet NP lies 194km from Hobart or 173km from Launceston. Turn off the Tasman Hwy (A3) on to Coles Bay Rd 12km S of Bicheno. After 9km turn left to Friendly Beaches and follow gravel rd for 5km. Ph: 03 6256 7000

120. River and Rocks Campground - East Coast
Map Ref: J8 GPS: 42 05 16 S 148 14 10 E
Located 19km S of A3/C302 junction or 7.4km N of Coles Bay. Plenty of shade. Ph: 03 6256 7000

121. Whitewater Wall camping area - Freycinet NP - East Coast
Map Ref: K8 GPS: 42 06 29 S 148 20 31 E
Access via Cape Tourville Rd, then 2km along rough track into small sheltered camping area. Ph: 03 6256 7000

122. Richardsons Beach Campground - South East
Map Ref: K8 GPS: 42 07 26 S 148 17 46 E
Within the Freycinet NP via Coles Bay Rd off A3 Hwy, 11km south of Bicheno. Access is 300m north of the Visitor Information Centre along Freycinet Drive. Ph: 03 6256 7000

123. Honeymoon Bay camping area - South East
Map Ref: K8 GPS: 42 08 13 S 148 17 57 E
Signposted access on Freycinet Dve in Freycinet NP, 1.6km S of the park visitor information centre. Ph: 03 6256 7000

124. Bothwell Camping Ground - South West
Map Ref: G9 GPS: 42 22 58 S 147 00 29 E
Located in Market Place, Bothwell, there are 10 powered sites and 5 unpowered sites. Ph: 03 6259 5503

125. Oatlands Campsite - East Coast
Map Ref: H9 GPS: 42 18 10 S 147 22 40 E
Located beside Lake Dulverton, Oatlands on a tiny detour from the Midland Heritage Hwy. Watch for Oatlands sign 30km NE of Melton Mowbray. Ph: 03 6254 1212

126. Lake Dulverton Camping Area - South East
Map Ref: H9 GPS: 42 18 03 S 147 22 34 E
Signposted access along The Esplanade in Oatlands. Self contained units only. Ph: 03 6254 5000

127. Lake Repulse Bush Camping - South West
Map Ref: F9 GPS: 42 30 20 S 146 37 02 E
Within Repulse SF. Take the Ellendale Rd from A10 Hwy 6.7km south of Ouse then Dawson Rd 2.7km west of Hwy. Continue for 11.4km to forest entrance. The track on right leads to numerous bush campsites on lake foreshore. Steep tracks. Bring water & firewood. Ph: 03 6235 8100

128. Bethune Park - South East
Map Ref: F9 GPS: 42 32 16 S 146 43 58 E
Access via gate on Ellendale Rd (C608) just W of Dunrobin Bdg only 2km from Lyell Hwy. On Lake Meadowbank f'shore. Boat ramp. Ph: 03 6286 3202

Oatlands Campsite

No 125

Oatlands, TAS
30 kms NE of Melton Mowbray
Gordon and Pam May.

Back to the past is a blast at Oatlands (Tas). This tiny town boasts the greatest concentration of Georgian era stone buildings in Australia, a wind powered flour mill in operational order, and a waterbird-watchers nirvana beside a roomy free camp.

The camp is right next to town and set beside the Lake Dulverton overflow - a breeding ground for numerous waterbirds - particularly black swans. Wood barbecues, picnic tables, water and flush toilets are provided, visitors can stay 72 hours and dogs on leads are permitted. Waterfowl interpretative boards help those of us who can't tell a grebe from a gannet.

Dominating Oatlands skyline is Callington Mill (restored to full working order) where the entire process is demonstrated of how wheat was turned into flour in the 1800s. The mill tour requires a moderate degree of mobility, as it ascends steep steps to the top. Visitors must don helmets and hair nets and photography inside the mill is prohibited. The resident master miller guides visitors through the intricacies of wooden machinery and pulleys which allow the mill's enormous sails to power the grindstones. Delicious samples of Callington mill flour products are available at the township's bakery.

Developed as a garrison town during the 1820s, Oatlands has preserved the atmosphere of a pioneer regional centre. The original Supreme Courthouse tour is a 'must do'. Guides with a passion for history tell of felons and unfortunates who stood before the dock and served time in the nearby jail or laboured on construction of the Launceston-Hobart road. Parts of the jail wall and a large stone building occupy almost a street block.

Other guided tours include the Executioner's Trail and Oatlands Town Tour. All tours are available from the Oatlands Heritage Highway Visitors Centre. Alternatively, armed with a brochure from the centre, visitors can take self-guided walking tours of the township.

Visitors ready for the Callington Mill tour.

Swans at Lake Dulverton.

The historic Callington Windmill

Streets are lined with charming stone cottages. Some have flowers in window boxes, one has a stork sculpture topping the chimney and all are well maintained. Surprisingly, most of the cottages are still occupied by local residents.

A popular walk starts at the free camp and circles Lake Dulverton. Evening is an extra good time for spotting the aquatic activity – but then, it's also a good time to relax with fellow travellers and reminisce about Oatlands and the living history which has been so well preserved.

Just The Facts

Oatlands Campsite

Where: Beside Lake Dulverton, Oatlands on a tiny detour from the Midland Heritage Highway (A1). Watch for Oatlands sign 30km N-E of Melton Mowbray.

Facilities: Wood barbecues, tables, water, flush toilets, dogs permitted, 72 hour stay.

Further details: Oatlands Heritage Highway Visitor Centre, Mill Lane, Oatlands, Tas 7210. Phone: 03 6254 1212, heritage@southernmidlands.tas.gov.au

Free Campsites in Tasmania

129. Hamilton Camping Ground
Map Ref: G9 GPS: 42 33 31 S 146 49 52 E
Camping area at Hamilton beside the river at west end of town. Ph: 03 6286 3202

130. Land of the Giants campground - South West
Map Ref: F10 GPS: 42 41 04 S 146 42 57 E
Within the Mt Field NP the NP visitor centre along the Lake Dobson Road (C609), 7.6km W of Westerway, which is situated on the B61 road, 29km NW of New Norfolk. Ph: 03 6288 1526

131. Kimberley Cottage
Map Ref: H9 GPS: 42 33 46 S 147 34 02 E
Camp area at 1077 Woodsdale Rd N off Tasman Hwy at Runnymede. Ph: 0400 310 810

132. Teds Beach Campground - South West
Map Ref: E10 GPS: 42 47 13 S 146 03 38 E
Located 38km W of Scotts Peak Dam Road and 3km E of Strathgordon, overlooking Lake Pedder on Strathgordon Road (B61). Ph: 03 6288 1149

133. Huon Campground - South West
Map Ref: E10 GPS: 43 02 24 S 146 18 09 E
Access along the Scott's Peak Dam Rd (C607) 6km past Edgar Campground. Boat ramp nearby at Scott's Peak Dam. Ph: 03 6288 1149

134. Edgar Dam Campground - Lake Pedder - South West
Map Ref: F10 GPS: 43 01 58 S 146 20 45 E
About 2 hours drive from Hobart. Ph: 03 6288 1149

135. Eldee Camp Area
Map Ref: H10 GPS: 42 51 19 S 147 39 20 E
Camp area 2.5km E of Carlton via Josephs Rd. Ph: 0418 135 647

136. Derford Farm
Map Ref: J10 GPS: 42 48 08 S 147 50 08 E
Camp area at 285 Bream Creek Rd. At Copping turn off Arthur Hwy into Marion Bay Rd then N into Bream Creek Rd. Ph: 03 6253 5294

137. Lime Bay Camp Ground
Map Ref: H10 GPS: 42 57 27 S 147 42 16 E
16km N of Premaydena or NW of Koonya. Dirt road. Ph: 03 6250 2135

138. Fortescue Bay Campground
Map Ref: J11 GPS: 43 08 30 S 147 58 02 E
Locates within the Tasman NP 17km E of Port Arthur on Fortescue Bay Rd. Bookings required. Ph: 03 6250 2433

139. Arve River Picnic Ground camping area - South West
Map Ref: F11 GPS: 43 09 30 S 146 48 24 E
12km W of Geeveston at the Arve River Streamside Reserve. Ph: 03 6295 7111

140. Gordon Foreshore - Hobart Region
Map Ref: G11 GPS: 43 15 42 S 147 14 33 E
Gordon Foreshore Reserve lies 55kms S of Hobart via the Channel Hwy. www.discovertasmania.com

141. The Neck Campground - Bruny Island
Map Ref: G11 GPS: 43 17 56 S 147 19 50 E
26km S of ferry terminal located on Lutregala Rd. Ph: 03 6293 1419

142. Esperance Camping - South West
Map Ref: G11 GPS: 43 17 57 S 146 54 42 E
Located 7.7km along Esperance River Rd which is signposted off the A6 Hwy at Strathblane 4.4km south of the Dover Hotel. Camping on north side of river. Ph: 03 6295 7111

143. Lune River Crossing
Map Ref: G12 GPS: 43 25 15 S 146 54 25 E
Camp area on Lune River Rd via Hastings.

144. Ida Bay Railway camping area - South West
Map Ref: G12 GPS: 43 26 37 S 146 54 14 E
Located adjacent to the railway station along the C636 rd 7km S of the A6 highway. Ph: 03 6298 3110

Free Campsites in Tasmania

145. Jetty Beach Camp Area - Bruny Island
Map Ref: G12 GPS: 43 27 32 S 147 09 11 E
57km S of ferry terminal on the Old Jetty Road off Lighthouse Rd. Ph: 03 6293 1419

146. The Pines camping area - South East
Map Ref: G12 GPS: 43 26 16 S 147 14 48 E
Located 9km S of Lunawanna along Cloudy Bay Road in South Bruny NP. Ph: 03 6293 1419

147. Cloudy Bay Corner Beach Campground - Bruny Island
Map Ref: G12 GPS: 43 27 54 S 147 15 10 E
Located in South Bruny NP. 50km S of ferry terminal. Last 3km is beach access requiring 4WD and checking tides. Dry weather only Ph: 03 6293 1419

148. Gilhams Beach Campground - South West
Map Ref: F12 GPS: 43 32 40 S 146 53 20 E
Signposted off Cockle Creek Rd (C636) which is signposted off A6 highway 3km N of Southport. Located within the Recherche Bay Nature Recreation Area. Ph: 03 6264 8460

149. Finns Beach Campground
Map Ref: G12 GPS: 43 32 50 S 146 53 16 E
Signposted off Cockle Creek Rd (C636) which is signposted off A6 highway 5km N of Southport. Located within the Recherche Bay Nature Recreation Area. Ph: 03 6264 8460

150. Catamaran camping area
Map Ref: G12 GPS: 43 33 16 S 146 53 16 E
Site along Cockle Creek Road, 1.1km S of Finns Beach access track Ph: 03 6264 8460

151. Cockle Creek Campground - South West
Map Ref: G12 GPS: 43 34 45 S 146 53 18 E
2 hours drive south of Hobart via Dover on the Huon Hwy. Ph: 03 6264 8460

152. Boltons Green camping area
Map Ref: G12 GPS: 43 34 57 S 146 53 42 E
Located on Cockle Creek Road on South side of bridge at Cockle Creek, 20km S of Lune River. Ph: 03 6288 1149

Featured Campsite

Brought to you by

Cockle Creek Campsite

No 151

Two hours' drive south of Hobart

John Mainwaring.

Cockle Creek is certainly a destination to check out as the most southerly point you can drive to down in Tasmania, but it is Recherche Bay just before Cockle Creek that will really take your fancy as campers and fisher-folk. It was named after one of Bruny D'Entrecasteaux's ships on his scientific exploration visit in 1792 and he considered it to be one of the most attractive locations he had ever been to with the deserted white beaches and turquoise waters. And despite the areas incarnations as a whaling station, a lumber source and occasional mining efforts, nature has returned it to a near pristine condition. The sites are large and grassy, backing onto lush bush with most facing out to the bay. They are well suited to caravans and motor homes of just about any description as you can drive around or manoeuver through. There are 6 or 7 large grassy areas along the Cockle Creek Road, each of them having room for a dozen or so spacious campsites. This is free camping with the harsh restriction being as with the National Park just up the road and over the bridge at Cockle Creek (which requires a Parks Pass), that you can only camp there for one month. Tough deal, but I can live with that. Fires and generators are OK, as are dogs so long as you keep them under control. Caravan access is easy with good roads all the way down from Hobart and only the last 20 kilometres are unsealed. There are several boat ramps nearby and the fishing is pretty good all round.

The bridge over the mouth of the Cockle Creek meeting the sea.

Free Campsites in Tasmania Index

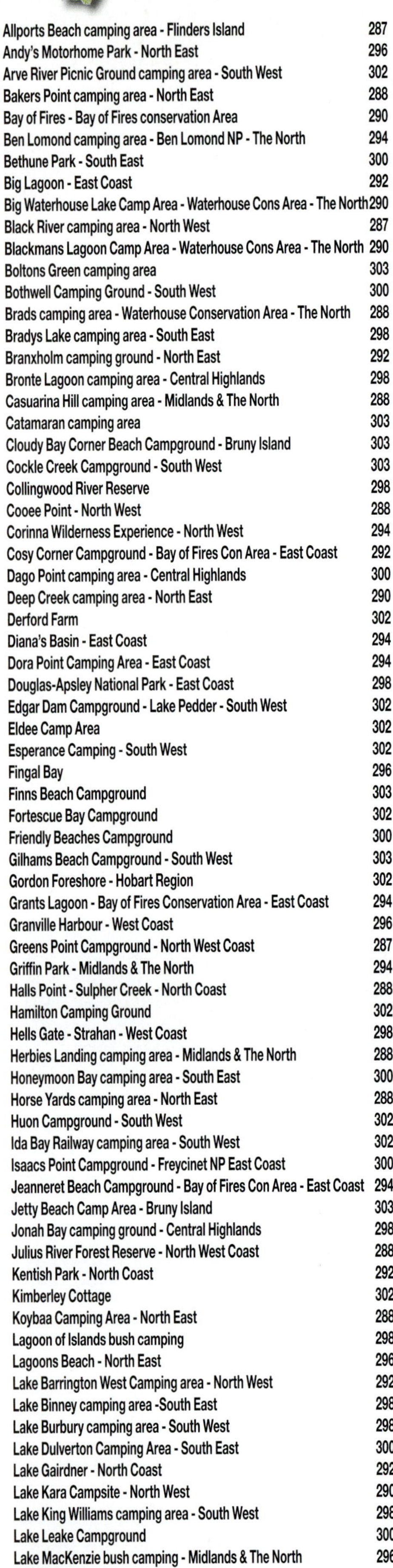